A TREATISE ON
ALGEBRAIC PLANE
CURVES

A TREATISE ON
ALGEBRAIC PLANE
CURVES

By

JULIAN LOWELL COOLIDGE, Ph.D.

DOVER PUBLICATIONS, INC.

NEW YORK

Manufactured in the United States of America

Dover Publications, Inc.
180 Varick Street
New York 14, N. Y.

AI GEOMETRI ITALIANI
MORTI, VIVENTI

PREFACE

FEW people, besides the initiated, realize what an appalling number of books and articles dealing with mathematics are published in each calendar year. A glance at the index of the *Jahrbuch über die Fortschritte der Mathematik* suggests that at least 4,000 contributions to mathematical science are made every 365 days, probably the number is appreciably larger. Any one venturing to add to this incredible collection, especially if he contribute a long work, must justify his temerity. Apart from the obvious consideration that no mathematics should be published which does not come up to a certain standard of clarity and elegance, the writer must show either that his subject-matter is essentially novel, without being trivial, or else that it presents in somewhat new form, matter of permanent value to mathematical science. The present work must lay its claim to recognition primarily on the second score.

There have been times when the study of algebraic plane curves was very much the fashion among mathematicians. One hundred years ago Möbius and Plücker were developing the methods of trilinear coordinates, polar curves, and abridged notation. Fifty years ago there was a perfect rage for algebraic invariants and covariants, their applications to geometry were eagerly sought, the ingenious book of Salmon and the solid tome of Clebsch-Lindemann were widely read. During the same period the theory of analytic functions of a complex variable, especially algebraic functions and their integrals, the brilliant work of such writers as Clebsch and Klein in emphasizing the relations of the theory of functions to curve theory, left a permanent impression on mathematical thought. In Italy the interest in algebraic geometry remained widespread, after the fashion had somewhat passed elsewhere, thanks to the contributions of such men as Bertini, Segre, Castelnuovo, Enriques, and Severi. That interest is alive to-day, yet, as intimated above, the centre of gravity in geometry has shifted quite far into the differential field.

If the subject of algebraic geometry were of transitory importance, we might accept this shift as an accomplished fact. But is it not the case that in judging the importance of mathematical work we must recognize the existence of both variables and constants? Much that is new is of only transitory importance. Are there not, on the other hand, some mathematical subjects that must be considered invariants, matters of abiding interest and importance, which deserve to be always held in honour? Will the contributions of Riemann and Weierstrass to analysis ever become *passé* or negligible? Can mathematical physics ever safely forget Maxwell's equations? In the same way, as long as we use Cartesian geometry, and the attempt to displace it by either synthetic or vector methods has only yielded very partial success, we are going to be interested in Cartesian curves of a more complicated sort than the straight lines and conics which we present to beginners as the last word in erudition. The geometer will be interested in the properties of curves of any degree, his interest will be quickened by finding their relations to algebraic invariants, to analysis situs, to the theory of algebraic functions, and to hyperspace.

It is the object of the volume before us to give an account of the present status of the theory of algebraic plane curves, and their relations to various fields of geometry and analysis. Other works have been written in the past with a more or less similar object in view. Salmon's beautiful *Higher Plane Curves* appears to-day archaic in form, and to some degree, in substance. Enriques's three interesting volumes on the *Teoria geometrica delle equazioni* are charmingly written in a discursive style, but contain a good deal of historical material that does not concern us, and give the impression at times of not being very closely reasoned. The masterly *Vorlesungen über algebraische Geometrie* of Severi-Löffler is a model of excellence, but omits many important parts of the theory of plane curves, and the same is true of the first volume of Severi's *Geometria algebrica*. The comparatively recent English works of Hilton and Ganguli are frankly textbooks, rather than expositions of the complete theory, or original contributions.

The greatest difficulty encountered in preparing this volume has been in the matter of choice—choice of material, choice of method. With regard to the former, if the book were to be kept within anything remotely resembling reasonable bounds, much valuable material had to be excluded. The writer has confined himself almost entirely to the properties of the general curve, departing from the custom of most previous writers who make a detailed study of curves of the third or fourth order. When specialization is made, it has generally been to curves of a particular genus, as rational curves, hyperelliptic curves, etc. It has been rather puzzling to decide just how much attention to give to the theory of invariants. A geometer who is completely ignorant of algebraic invariants is simply illiterate; in the present work the reader has been carried far enough to appreciate the symbolic notation of Aronhold and Clebsch. A student who, after reading what was here presented, found himself unable to understand the invariant theory, let us say in Clebsch-Lindemann, would have a fair grievance against the writer. On the other hand, it is evident that there is comparatively little interest in invariant theory to-day; why cover page after page with extended and artificial calculations which lead to results of comparatively little geometric importance? Another puzzle was how much attention to pay to the uniformization of the general curve, the expression of x and y as automorphic functions of an auxiliary variable. The fact that this can be done is of the very highest theoretic importance, so that it seemed wrong to pass it over in complete silence. On the other hand, a subject which extended Klein and Poincaré to their utmost limit, and which was only perfected by the repeated efforts of subsequent analysts, cannot be completely elucidated in a few lines. The subject has been given a short chapter which is confessedly a sketch with no attempt at complete proof. The writer gladly mentions that in this, as in other matters, he is indebted for help and counsel to his friend and colleague of thirty years' standing, William Fogg Osgood.

No attempt has been made to give a complete bibliography. The reader desirous of such should consult, in the first instance, the article of Berzolari, 'Allgemeine Theorie der algebraischen ebenen Curven', *Enzyklopädie der mathematischen Wissenschaften*, vol. iii. 2, c. 4, and the 'Selected Topics in Algebraic Geometry', *Bulletin of the National Research Council*, No. 68. This latter did not appear till the present work was nearing completion. It proved of the greatest help in preparing the last chapters, and is currently referred to as 'Topics'.

With regard to the choice of method, preference is given, in the first instance, to algebraic procedure. Large portions of the work are written according to the spirit and methods of the Italian geometers, to whom, indeed, the whole is dedicated. It would be quite impossible to describe the extent of the writer's obligation to them. Yet behind the Italians there stands one whose contributions are even greater, Max Nöther.

Besides algebraic methods, there is much use of geometric ones, especially those involving the projective geometry of hyperspace. Transcendental analysis takes a secondary place, but has been treated at least as an honoured guest in the house. It is assumed that the reader will not have heart failure at the mention of a Riemann surface; in studying the fundamentally important topic of linear series of point-groups on a curve, the relation to Abelian integrals, and Abel's theorem is insisted on. The Chasles-Cayley-Brill correspondence formula recurs again and again, but no one has yet been able to prove all the connected theories without the help of Abel's theorem and the use of theta functions. The needed properties of these latter are given without proof. The only distinct methods which have never been used are those of the theory of algebraic numbers. The reader who wishes to study the properties of plane curves from this point of view is referred to the solid work of Hensel and Landsberg, *Theorie der algebraischen Funktionen*. It would be hypocrisy to attempt to give a sound justification for all the choices made. Every writer must reconcile, as best he may, the conflicting claims of consistency and variety, of rigour in detail and elegance in the whole. The present author humbly confesses that, to him, geometry is nothing at all, if not a branch of art, and the underlying force which compels him to treat any particular topic, or to handle it in any particular way, is either that he is ignorant of any other, or else that his aesthetic sense dictates the choice: it pleaseth him so to do.

J. L. C.

CONTENTS

CHAPTER IV

REAL CIRCUITS OF CURVES

CHAPTER V

ELEMENTARY INVARIANT THEORY

CHAPTER IX

COVARIANT CURVES

CHAPTER X

METRICAL PROPERTIES OF CURVES

BOOK II

THE SINGULAR POINTS

CHAPTER I

THE REDUCTION OF SINGULARITIES

CHAPTER II

DEVELOPMENT IN SERIES

CHAPTER III

CLUSTERING SINGULARITIES

CHAPTER IV

ADJOINT CURVES AND PLÜCKER'S EQUATIONS

BOOK III

SYSTEMS OF POINTS ON A CURVE

CHAPTER I

GENERAL THEORY OF LINEAR SERIES

CHAPTER II

ABELIAN INTEGRALS

CHAPTER III

SINGULAR POINTS OF CORRESPONDENCES

CHAPTER IV

MODULI AND LIMITING VALUES

CHAPTER V

CURVES OF SPECIAL TYPE

3. *Hyperelliptic curves*

§ 4. *Polygonal curves*

§ 5. *Φ-curves*

§ 6. *Reducible curves*

CHAPTER VI

NON-LINEAR SERIES OF GROUPS OF POINTS ON A CURVE

§ 1. *General theorems about series*

§ 2. *Series of index* 1

§ 3. *Groups common to a* g_N^r *and a* γ_M^ρ

§ 4. *The defect of equivalence*

CHAPTER VII

HIGHER THEORY OF CORRESPONDENCES

§ 1. *General theorems*

§ 2. *Application of Abelian Integrals*

CHAPTER VIII

PARAMETRIC REPRESENTATION OF THE GENERAL CURVE. A SKETCH

CHAPTER IX

RATIONAL CURVES

CONTENTS

xxi

BOOK IV
SYSTEMS OF CURVES

CHAPTER I
POSTULATION OF LINEAR SYSTEMS BY POINTS

CHAPTER II
THE TRANSFORMATION OF LINEAR SYSTEMS

CHAPTER III

TERNARY APOLARITY

CHAPTER IV

SPECIAL CURVES IN LINEAR SYSTEMS

CHAPTER V

NON-LINEAR SYSTEMS OF CURVES

CHAPTER VI

THE GENERAL CREMONA TRANSFORMATION

CHAPTER VII

TYPES OF CREMONA TRANSFORMATIONS

CHAPTER VIII

GROUPS OF CREMONA TRANSFORMATIONS

A TREATISE ON
ALGEBRAIC PLANE
CURVES

BOOK I

ELEMENTARY THEORY

CHAPTER I

THE FUNDAMENTAL PROPERTIES OF POLYNOMIALS

§ 1. Polynomials in one variable

LET $\quad f(x) \equiv a_0 x^n + a_1 x^{n-1} + a_2 x^{n-2} + \ldots + a_{n-1} x + a_n$

be a polynomial of order n or less in a single complex variable x, which can take all values, including the fictitious value infinity. If there be such a value α that

$$f(\alpha) = 0,$$

then α is called a 'root' of the polynomial. If the polynomial have an infinite root, that is to say, if the function

$$x^n f\left(\frac{1}{x}\right)$$

have a root 0, then $a_0 = 0$ and conversely. When this is not the case, the order of the polynomial is exactly n; we shall assume from now on that this is so. The fundamental theorem of algebra tells us that then

$$f(x) \equiv a_0 (x - \alpha_1)(x - \alpha_2)\ldots(x - \alpha_n) \tag{1}$$

$$f'(x) \equiv a_0 \sum_{i=1}^{i=n} \frac{f(x)}{x - \alpha_i}. \tag{2}$$

We state the facts as follows:

The Fundamental Theorem of Algebra 1] *A polynomial of the nth order in a single variable can be divided into n linear variable factors, and every linear variable factor is a constant multiple of one of these. The polynomial will have at most n roots, and these will all be distinct, unless the polynomial and its derivative share a variable factor.*

A necessary and sufficient condition for a multiple root is written

$$\prod_{i,j=1}^{i,j=n} (\alpha_i - \alpha_j)^2 = 0. \tag{3}$$

This expression is a symmetric function of the roots. It can be written as a rational function of the coefficients by various devices. The classical relations between the roots and coefficients are given by the formulae

$$\sum_{i=1}^{i=n} \alpha_i = (-1)\frac{a_1}{a_0}, \; \frac{1}{2}\sum_{i,j=1}^{i,j=n} \alpha_i\alpha_j = (-1)^2\frac{a_2}{a_0}, \; ..., \prod_i \alpha_i = (-1)^n\frac{a_n}{a_0}. \quad (4)$$

Each of these symmetric functions is rational in the coefficients. The degree of the numerator or denominator in the a's is the degree of the corresponding polynomial looked upon as a function of any chosen individual root, the sum of the subscripts in each term of the numerator is the degree on the left in all the roots together. If we add symmetric polynomials of the same degree, or multiply two of the same or different degrees, we get rational fractions in the a's which have these same properties. From such considerations it is easy to prove*

The Fundamental Theorem of Symmetric Functions 2] *Any symmetric homogeneous polynomial in the roots of a polynomial in one variable is a rational fraction in the coefficients, whose denominator is a_0 raised to a power equal to the degree of the polynomial in any one root. The numerator is homogeneous to the same degree, and the sum of the subscripts in each term is equal to the total degree of the polynomial in all the roots together.*

The degree of the numerator or denominator is called the 'degree' of the symmetric function, the sum of the subscripts in each term its 'weight'. A polynomial like this, where the sum is the same in each term is said to be *isobaric*.

Definition. Any constant multiple, not 0, of the numerator of the fraction in the coefficients which is equal to the left-hand side of (3) is called the 'discriminant' of the polynomial.

Theorem 3] *The discriminant of the general polynomial of order n is of order $2(n-1)$ and weight $n(n-1)$.*

Suppose that we allow the ratios of the coefficients of our polynomial to vary, the roots will vary also, for if two polynomials have the same roots their coefficients are proportional by (4). Let us suppose in particular that each coefficient takes a small increment. We write

$$f(x) \equiv a_0 x^n + a_1 x^{n-1} + ... + a_{n-1}x + a_n$$
$$\phi(x) \equiv (a_0 + \Delta a_0)x^n + (a_1 + \Delta a_1)x^{n-1} + ... +$$
$$+ (a_{n-1} + \Delta a_{n-1})x + (a_n + \Delta a_n).$$

* Cf. Bôcher, p. 243.

Let us reduce the roots of ϕ by the quantity α_1 which is a root of f. This is done by replacing x by $x+\alpha_1$ and expanding by Taylor's theorem:

$$\phi(x+\alpha_1) \equiv \phi(\alpha_1)+x\phi'(\alpha_1)+\frac{x^2}{2}\phi''(\alpha_1)+\dots$$

$$\phi(\alpha_1) \equiv (a_0+\Delta a_0)\alpha_1^n+(a_1+\Delta a_1)\alpha_1^{n-1}+\dots+$$
$$+(a_{n-1}+\Delta a_{n-1})\alpha_1+(a_n+\Delta a_n)$$
$$\equiv \Delta a_0\alpha_1^n+\Delta a_1\alpha_1^{n-1}+\dots+\Delta a_{n-1}\alpha_1+\Delta a_n.$$

The product of the roots of $\phi(x+\alpha_1)$ is $(-1)^n\dfrac{\phi(\alpha_1)}{a_0+\Delta a_0}$ and is infinitesimal since each term of the expanded numerator is infinitesimal, while the denominator is not. Hence the polynomial $\phi(x+\alpha_1)$ must have at least one infinitesimal root, or $\phi(x)$ has one root infinitely near α_1, say $\alpha_1+\Delta\alpha_1$.

$$a_0x^n+a_1x^{n-1}+\dots+a_n$$
$$\equiv (x-\alpha_1)(a_0x^{n-1}+c_1x^{n-2}+c_2x^{n-3}+\dots+c_{n-1})$$
$$(a_0+\Delta a_0)x^n+(a_1+\Delta a_1)x^{n-1}+\dots+(a_n+\Delta a_n)$$
$$\equiv (x-\alpha_1-\Delta\alpha_1)[(a_0+\Delta a_0)x^{n-1}+d_1x^{n-2}+\dots+d_{n-1}].$$

Comparing coefficients

$$a_0=a_0 \qquad a_0+\Delta a_0=a_0+\Delta a_0 \qquad c_1=a_0\alpha_1+a_1$$
$$d_1=(a_0+\Delta a_0)(\alpha_1+\Delta\alpha_1)+(a_1+\Delta a_1)$$
$$d_1=c_1+\alpha_1\Delta a_0+a_0\Delta\alpha_1+\Delta a_0\Delta\alpha_1.$$

Hence d_1 differs infinitesimally from c_1, and we may show in the same way that each d differs infinitesimally from the corresponding c, or f has a second root extremely close to a root of ϕ, and so on.

In this development we have assumed that $a_0\neq0$. Let us now assume

$$a_0=a_1=\dots=a_{p-1}=0 \qquad a_p\neq0.$$

We may assume that a_n is not 0, for if this quantity were 0 we could divide f by such a power of x that the quotient had no vanishing root, and proceed as before. We then write

$$f_1(x)=x^nf\left(\frac{1}{x}\right)\equiv a_nx^n+a_{n-1}x^{n-1}+\dots+a_px^p$$

$$\phi_1(x)\equiv x^n\phi\left(\frac{1}{x}\right)=(a_n+\Delta a_n)x^n+(a_{n-1}+\Delta a_{n-1})x^{n-1}+\dots+$$
$$+(a_p+\Delta a_p)x^p+\Delta a_{p-1}x^{n-1}+\Delta a_1x+\Delta a_0.$$

By what precedes we see that ϕ_1 has exactly p roots close to 0.

Fundamental Continuity Theorem 4] *Given two polynomials of the same order in one variable, where the first p coefficients, but not the first $p+1$ of the first are 0, while the coefficients of the second approach the corresponding coefficients of the first as limits, then the second polynomial will have exactly p roots that increase indefinitely, and exactly k roots of the second will approach each root of multiplicity k of the first as a limit.*

Theorem 5] *If the coefficients of a polynomial vary continuously according to some law, and if for certain values of these coefficients the number of distinct roots is less than the order of the polynomial, then either some roots have become infinite, or else multiple roots have appeared.*

Theorem 6] *If for any values of the coefficients the number of roots is greater than the order of the polynomial, then every coefficient must vanish.*

It is to be understood in these theorems that the constant is included among the coefficients.

We next suppose that we have two polynomials

$$f(x) \equiv a_0 x^n + a_1 x^{n-1} + \ldots + a_{n-1}x + a_n \equiv a_0(x-\alpha_1)(x-\alpha_2)\ldots(x-\alpha_n) \tag{5}$$

$$\phi(x) \equiv b_0 x^m + b_1 x^{m-1} + \ldots + b_{m-1}x + b_m$$
$$\equiv b_0(x-\beta_1)(x-\beta_2)\ldots(x-\beta_m).$$

The necessary and sufficient condition for a common root is

$$\prod_{\substack{i=1 \\ j=1}}^{\substack{i=n \\ j=m}} (\alpha_i - \beta_j) = 0. \tag{6}$$

This function is symmetric in each set of roots and homogeneous in the two together. Any constant multiple not zero, of the numerator of the corresponding rational fraction in its lowest terms is called the 'resultant of the two polynomials'.

Theorem 7] *If two polynomials be given in one variable, their resultant is homogeneous in the coefficients of each to a degree equal to the order of the other polynomial. It is isobaric in the two sets of coefficients together, its weight being the product of the orders of the two polynomials. A necessary and sufficient condition that the two polynomials should have a common root is that the resultant should vanish.*

There are two other ways of writing the resultant, as a function of the roots, namely,

$$\phi(\alpha_1)\phi(\alpha_2)...\phi(\alpha_n)$$
$$f(\beta_1)f(\beta_2)...f(\beta_m).$$

To find it in terms of the coefficients, there is a much better method than that of symmetric functions. Suppose that the common root is α_1,

$$f(x) \equiv (x-\alpha_1)(a_0'x^{n-1}+a_1'x^{n-2}+...+a_n')$$
$$\phi(x) \equiv (x-\alpha_1)(b_0'x^{m-1}+b_1'x^{m-2}+...+b_m')$$
$$f(b_0'x^{m-1}+b_1'x^{m-2}+...+b_{m-1}')-\phi(a_0'x^{n-1}+a_1'x^{n-2}+...+a_{n-1}') \equiv 0.$$
$$(7)$$

Here is a polynomial which is identically 0; hence by 6] each coefficient vanishes. This fact will lead us to $m+n$ linear homogeneous equations in as many variables a', b' which will be compatible when, and only when, the determinant of the coefficients is 0, i.e. when

$$\begin{vmatrix} a_0 & a_1 & . & . & . & . & a_n & 0 & 0 & . & . & . & 0 \\ 0 & a_0 & a_1 & . & . & . & a_{n-1} & a_n & 0 & . & . & . & . \\ . & . & . & . & . & . & . & . & . & . & . & . & . \\ . & . & . & . & . & . & . & . & . & . & . & . & . \\ 0 & 0 & . & . & . & . & . & . & . & . & a_{n-1} & a_n \\ b_0 & b_1 & . & . & . & b_m & 0 & 0 & . & . & . & 0 \\ 0 & b_0 & b_1 & . & . & . & b_m & 0 & . & . & . & 0 \\ . & . & . & . & . & . & . & . & . & . & . & . & . \\ 0 & 0 & . & . & . & . & . & . & . & . & b_{m-1} & b_m \end{vmatrix} = 0. \quad (8)$$

Conversely, if this expression vanish we may find such values for the coefficients a', b' as to satisfy (7) identically, and as there is essentially only one way to divide a polynomial into variable linear factors, the two polynomials must have a common root.

This method of finding the resultant leads us back to the discriminant. Let f be the given polynomial, and let us write

$$\phi \equiv nf - xf'.$$

If f and f', its derivative, have a common root, this is certainly a root of ϕ and so a common root of the two polynomials of degree $n-1$, f' and ϕ. Conversely, if these two have a common root, this is a root of f also, and so this latter has a multiple root by 1].

$$f \equiv a_0 x^n + a_1 x^{n-1} + \ldots + a_{n-1} x + a_n$$
$$f' \equiv n a_0 x^{n-1} + (n-1) a_1 x^{n-2} + \ldots + a_{n-1}$$
$$\phi \equiv a_1 x^{n-1} + 2 a_2 x^{n-2} + \ldots + n a_n.$$

The discriminant will be

$$\begin{vmatrix} n a_0 & (n-1)a_1 & . & . & a_{n-1} & 0 & 0 & . & 0 \\ . & . & . & . & . & . & . & . \\ . & . & . & . & . & . & . & . \\ a_1 & 2 a_2 & . & . & n a_n & 0 & 0 & . & . \\ . & . & . & . & . & . & . & n a_n \end{vmatrix}.$$

The degree is certainly $2(n-1)$. To find the weight we write

$$A_i = (n-i) a_i \qquad B_j = (j+1) a_{j+1}.$$

The result is isobaric in A_i and B_j of weight $(n-1)^2$ in these letters. Since it is homogeneous of degree $(n-1)$ in the B's and each of these has a subscript one less than that of the corresponding a, the total weight in the a's is

$$(n-1)^2 + (n-1) = n(n-1)$$

as stated in 3].

There is still another method of finding the resultant which should not be overlooked. Let us look for the highest common factor of the polynomial and its derivative by the method of division due originally to Euclid. The resultant will be the last remainder in the process. If it vanish, the two polynomials have a common factor which is the last divisor, not identically 0, that appeared in the process. The process of division is long and tedious, but the student should understand the principle. We return to (8) and re-write the left-hand side with the later rows reversed in order:

$$\begin{vmatrix} a_0 & a_1 & . & . & . & a_n & 0 & 0 & . & . & . & . \\ 0 & a_0 & a_1 & . & . & . & . & a_n & 0 & . & . & . \\ . & . & . & . & . & . & . & . & . & . & . \\ 0 & 0 & . & . & . & . & . & . & . & a_{n-1} & a_n \\ 0 & 0 & . & . & . & . & . & . & . & b_{m-1} & b_m \\ . & . & . & . & . & . & . & . & . & . & . \\ 0 & b_0 & b_1 & . & . & b_m & 0 & 0 & . & . & 0 \\ b_0 & b_1 & . & . & . & b_m & 0 & 0 & 0 & . & 0 \end{vmatrix} \equiv R_0 \qquad (9)$$

We mean by the kth sub-resultant of f and ϕ the determinant obtained here by striking off the first and last k rows, also the first and last k columns. We thus get the remarkable theorem which we state without proof.*

Theorem 8] *The degree of the highest common factor of two polynomials in one variable is the dimension of the first sub-resultant which does not vanish.*

There are times when it is best to replace the study of polynomials in one variable by that of homogeneous polynomials in two variables. We have merely to replace such a function as f by

$$f(x,z) = z^n f\left(\frac{x}{z}\right).$$

Each pair of values x and z, not both 0, corresponds to a single finite or infinite value for $\frac{x}{z}$. The variables x and z are homogeneous in the sense that $\frac{x}{z} = \frac{\rho x}{\rho z}$, $\rho \neq 0$.

The theorems which we have developed for polynomials in one variable are carried over with ease. We mean by a root of the homogeneous polynomial a pair of values of x and z, not both 0, which makes the polynomial vanish. Proportional pairs of values are looked upon as essentially the same, so that the homogeneous polynomial of order n has at most n distinct roots.

To find the discriminant, we remember Euler's theorem

$$n f(x,z) = x \frac{\partial f}{\partial x} + z \frac{\partial f}{\partial z}.$$

The discriminant is, thus, the resultant of $\dfrac{\partial f(x,z)}{\partial x}$ and $\dfrac{\partial f(x,z)}{\partial z}$.

There are times when it is troublesome to have the two homogeneous variables. We avoid the complication by the use of a rather bizarre notation whereby we treat the number 1 as if it were a variable. For instance, we may find the discriminant of the polynomial f in one variable by looking for the resultant of the two polynomials of order $(n-1)$: $\dfrac{\partial f}{\partial x}, \dfrac{\partial f}{\partial 1}$. We mean by the latter strange expression the following:

a) The polynomial has been changed to the homogeneous form in x and z as above.

* Cf. Bôcher, pp. 191–7.

b) The homogeneous polynomial has been differentiated partially with respect to *z*.

c) In the resulting polynomial *z* has been made equal to 1.

It is purely a convenient formal process which the student will find quite easy in practice.

§ 2. Polynomials in *N* variables

One of the most frequent phrases used in geometry is to say that a certain statement is true 'in general'. It is time to give an explicit meaning to this convenient but dangerous locution.

Definition. If the truth or falsity of an algebraic statement depend upon the values taken by *N* independent parameters $x_1, x_2, ..., x_N$, which are free to vary in certain continuous well-defined *N*-dimensional regions, then this statement is true 'in general' if a sufficient condition for its truth be given by an inequality

$$\Phi(x_1, x_2, ..., x_n) \neq 0, \tag{10}$$

where Φ is a polynomial which does not vanish identically for values of $x_1, x_2, ..., x_N$ in these regions.

If Φ can never vanish for values of the variables in that region, the theorem is true universally.

Let us take some examples. Consider the straight lines whose equations are

$$a_1 x + b_1 y + c_1 = 0$$
$$a_2 x + b_2 y + c_2 = 0$$

We may say that they have 'in general' a common point, for a sufficient condition therefore is

$$\begin{vmatrix} a_1 & b_1 \\ a_2 & b_2 \end{vmatrix} \neq 0.$$

This condition is sufficient; it is not necessary; for they might be identical, in which case there are plenty of common points, although the determinant vanishes.

If the polynomial Φ do not vanish identically for sets of values in the regions, then to equate it to 0 will impose an extra condition on the variables. We may test whether it vanish identically or not by seeing whether we can find a single set of values for which it does not vanish. If, thus, the truth of a statement depend on an inequality such as (10), and if we can find a single set of values of the variables in the regions for which the inequality is satisfied, then the statement is *true in general*.

We may extend our phrase further. A point in the plane is said to be 'in general position' if its coordinates x and y satisfy an inequality
$$\Phi(x,y) \neq 0.$$

We use the same form of speech when the point is restricted to a particular region, or particular curve; we speak of a general curve of given order, etc.

In practice we approach the matter from the other end. If a necessary condition for the 'falsity' of a certain statement be
$$\Phi(x_1, x_2, ..., x_n) = 0,$$
and if this polynomial do not vanish identically for sets of variables in the region, then the statement is true 'in general'. We mention, once for all, that we accept the logical canon of the excluded middle as valid. We make no attempt at definitions in a system of mathematics where a statement is not compelled to choose between truth and falsity.

Definition. N polynomials $f_1, f_2 ..., f_N$ in as many variables are said to be 'independent' if

$$\begin{vmatrix} \dfrac{\partial f_1}{\partial x_1} & \cdots & \dfrac{\partial f_1}{\partial x_N} \\ \dfrac{\partial f_2}{\partial x_1} & \cdots & \dfrac{\partial f_2}{\partial x_N} \\ \cdot & \cdots & \\ \dfrac{\partial f_N}{\partial x_1} & \cdots & \dfrac{\partial f_N}{\partial x_N} \end{vmatrix} \equiv \frac{\partial(f_1, f_2, ..., f_N)}{\partial(x_1, x_2, ..., x_N)} \neq 0. \qquad (11)$$

We see that N polynomials of a given degree are 'in general independent', for we can easily pick N whose functional determinant is not 0.

Let $f_1, f_2, ..., f_N$ be most general polynomials of degrees $n_1, n_2, ..., n_N$ respectively in the variables $x_1, x_2, ..., x_N$. There will then exist a polynomial $\Phi(z)$ in a single variable z which has the following properties:

a) It is 'in general' of degree $n_1 n_2 ... n_N$.

b) Its roots are 'in general' distinct.

c) They are in one-to-one correspondence with sets of solutions of the equations
$$f_1 = f_2 = ... = f_N = 0.$$

This is the rigorous statement of what we put in more common form as

Bézout's Theorem 9] *N polynomial equations of degrees* n_1, n_2, ..., n_N *in N variables have in general* $n_1 n_2 ... n_N$ *common solutions. When the number is greater than this, it is infinite.*[*]

This theorem may, of course, fail completely in particular circumstances. When the polynomials are not independent there may be an infinite number of sets of solutions, or there may be none at all. The case where $N = 2$ is the one of greatest interest to us. Let us work out a proof in detail. We begin by writing out two general polynomials in x and y of degrees n and m respectively.

$$f(x, y) \equiv a_0 x^n + a_1 x^{n-1} + ... + a_{n-1} x + a_n,$$

$$a_k \equiv a_{k0} y^k + a_{k1} y^{k-1} + ... + a_{kk}$$

$$\phi(x, y) \equiv b_0 x^m + b_1 x^{m-1} + ... + b_{m-1} x + b_m,$$

$$b_l \equiv b_{l0} y^l + b_{l1} y^{l-1} + ... + b_{ll}.$$

The resultant, by theorem 7] has the weight mn in a's and b's, and so, 'in general', is a polynomial of degree mn in y. Each root of this polynomial will 'in general' correspond to a single x which with it will make both f and ϕ vanish.

Theorem 10] *Two algebraic curves in the same plane have, in general, a number of intersections equal to the product of their orders.*

Suppose that we have three curves of orders n_1, n_2, n_3 respectively, their resultant is, by definition, the polynomial whose vanishing is the condition for a common point for the three.[†] Let us replace the third polynomial $f_3(x, y)$ by $f_3(x, y) + r\phi_3(x, y)$. The degree of the resultant, in the coefficients of f_3, will be the degree in r when the substitution has been made, and so is the number of curves of the linear system $f_3 + r\phi_3$, through the intersections of f_1 and f_2, i.e. $n_1 n_2$.

Theorem 11] *The resultant of three polynomials in two variables contains the coefficients of each to a degree equal to the product of the orders of the other two.*

[*] Cf. Enriques-Chisini, vol. ii, pp. 102 ff.
[†] For an elaborate discussion of the method of finding this, see Morley.

It is clear from this that if f_1 and f_2 meet in $(x_1, y_1), (x_2, y_2)$...
the resultant differs by a constant factor from

$$f_3(x_1, y_1)f_3(x_2, y_2)... \equiv \prod f_3(x_i, y_i). \tag{12}$$

Reverting to our general theorem 9] we shall get an infinite
number of common solutions when $\phi(z)$ has too many roots,
i.e. vanishes identically. On the other hand, this polynomial in
z might reduce to a constant and so have, 'in general', no root.
But when the constant is 0 there would be an infinite number.

Theorem 12] *If N polynomial equations in as many variables
have 'in general' no common solutions, then if for particular values
of the coefficients they have one solution, they have an infinite
number.*

An example of this curious state of affairs is worth considering. Consider a rigid motion of space. The coefficients of
collineation may be expressed in terms of six independent parameters by the formulae of Olinde Rodrigues. Let us try to find
a rigid motion which will carry two points AB into two others
$A'B'$. Three conditions are imposed by carrying A to A', three
others by carrying B to B', six parameters, six conditions.
Nevertheless we know that the problem cannot usually be
solved; the polynomial $\phi(z)$ is a constant. In the special case
where the polynomial is 0, the distances AB and $A'B'$ are equal,
and there are an infinite number of rigid motions that will effect
the transformation.

The process of solving the simultaneous equations

$$f(x, y) = 0 \qquad \phi(x, y) = 0$$

is the process of finding the intersections of two curves. If the
polynomials have no common variable factor, it must be possible to find such a set of Cartesian axes $x'y'$ that no two
intersections have the same abscissae. There will, then, be such
a polynomial $R(x)$ that each of its roots gives just one intersection, or one set of solutions in x and y.

In studying polynomials in many variables we often reduce
to homogeneous form, as we did when there was but one. Thus
if the original variables be $x_1, x_2, ..., x_N$, we change $f(x_1, x_2, ..., x_N)$ to

$$\phi(x_0, x_1, ..., x_N) \equiv x_0^n f\left(\frac{x_1}{x_0}, \frac{x_2}{x_0}, ..., \frac{x_N}{x_0}\right)$$

If we do not care to use the homogeneous form, we repeat the curious trick suggested above of differentiating partially with respect to 1; we mean by $\frac{\partial f}{\partial 1}$ the expression $\frac{\partial \phi}{\partial x_0}$, where subsequently we have to place $x_0 = 1$.

In dealing with certain expressions in homogeneous variables, especially certain linear expressions, it is convenient to use the language of projective geometry of hyperspace. We very easily prove*

Theorem 13] *If the coordinates of a system of points in N-space be linearly dependent on those of $k+1$ linearly independent points, the multipliers taking all possible sets of values not all 0 at once, then these points form the total intersection of $N - k$ linearly independent hyperplanes, and conversely, the coordinates of every point in such an intersection can be expressed in this way.*

A *hyperplane*, of course, is the system of points whose coordinates satisfy a single linear equation. Let the reader prove the well-known

Theorem 14] *The sum of the numbers of dimensions of two flat spaces lying in a third is equal to the sum of the number of dimensions of their common space, and of the smallest space that can contain the two. For this purpose a point is counted as a space of 0 dimensions, and non-intersection as a space of -1 dimensions.*

The fact that a $k-1$ parameter algebraic variety in a space of k dimensions is given by equating a single polynomial to 0 has far-reaching consequences. Let us prove that if such a variety lie in a space of $N > k$ dimensions, it can be projected into one lying in k dimensions. Thus, in particular, any curve can be projected into a plane curve.

How many linearly independent spaces of l dimensions are there in a space of N dimensions ? Such a space will be determined by its intersections with $l+1$ linearly independent spaces of $N-l$ dimensions. The number sought is thus $(N-l)(l+1)$. The number through an arbitrary point is $l(N-l)$, and through an arbitrary line is $(l-1)(N-l)$.

Let us next notice that it is not possible in N dimensions that every space of $N-k$ dimensions that meets the variety of $k-1$ dimensions once should of necessity meet it more than once.

* Bôcher, pp. 50–2.

For the lines from a point of the variety to the other points of it depend on $k-1$ parameters, so that if we add $k-1$ to the number of parameters giving the spaces of $N-k$ dimensions through a line we should, if each such space meeting the variety once met it twice, have the number of parameters of the spaces through a point. We should have

$$(N-k-1)[N-(N-k)]+(k-1) = (N-k)[N-(N-k)],$$

and this is not true. We therefore take a fixed space of $N-k-1$ dimensions and through it and through each point of the variety pass a space of $N-k$ dimensions. Such a space will not usually meet the variety again, and will have one intersection with a fixed space of k dimensions, whereon it projects the given variety into another of $k-1$ dimensions. The two are in one-to-one correspondence. If coordinates of points in our N-space are given by $x_0, x_1, ..., x_N$ and those of the fixed k-space by $y_0, y_1, ..., y_k$, the variety in the y-space will be given by a single homogeneous equation

$$f(y_0, y_1, ..., y_k) = 0, \tag{13}$$

each corresponding x will depend rationally on the y's, each y on the x's

$$x_i = \rho \, \psi_i(y_0, y_1, ..., y_k) \qquad i = 0, 1, ..., N. \tag{14}$$

Theorem 15] *The homogeneous coordinates in N-space of the points of a $k-1$ dimensional algebraic variety may be expressed as homogeneous polynomials of the same degree in $k+1$ independent parameters, which parameters are connected by a single homogeneous polynomial equation.*

In practice it is often convenient not to use homogeneous parameters in the one space or the other. Under such circumstances the number of parameters involved is less, but it may be necessary to use rational functions instead of polynomials.*

* Cf. Segre[4], p. 47.

CHAPTER II

ELEMENTARY PROPERTIES OF CURVES

§ 1. Ordinary and singular points

DEFINITION. The totality of points in the plane whose Cartesian coordinates satisfy the equation

$$f(x, y) = 0, \tag{1}$$

where f is a polynomial of the nth order not a constant, shall be called a 'curve of the nth order'. If the polynomial be irreducible, the curve shall be said to be irreducible, otherwise reducible. The curve obtained by equating each irreducible variable factor of f to 0 shall be called a 'factor' of the curve f. If we prefer homogeneous variables we write

$$f(x, y, z) \equiv z^n f\left(\frac{x}{z}, \frac{y}{z}\right) = 0. \tag{2}$$

A linear homogeneous equation in x, y, and z will represent a straight line. There will be no exception to this rule if we agree to call

$$z = 0 \tag{3}$$

the line at infinity. A set of three homogeneous coordinates of which the third is 0, but not both of the first two, shall be called an infinite point.

The two finite points

$$x : y : z = 1 : \pm i : 0$$

are called the circular points at infinity. A finite line through one of them is called an 'isotropic'. It fulfils the condition of being perpendicular to itself, and the distance of two finite points thereon appears as 0. The angle of two intersecting lines, i.e. of two lines with finite intersection, neither of which is isotropic, is known to be $\frac{1}{2i}$ multiplied by a cross ratio which they form with the two isotropics through their intersection.

The most convenient way to handle a straight line in many problems is what is known as the parametric method. If the line connect the two points (x_1, y_1, z_1) and (x_2, y_2, z_2) we may write

$$x = \xi_1 x_1 + \xi_2 x_2$$
$$y = \xi_1 y_1 + \xi_2 y_2 \qquad (4)$$
$$z = \xi_1 z_1 + \xi_2 z_2.$$

Substituting in (2) we get

$$\phi(\xi_1, \xi_2) = 0. \qquad (5)$$

If the discriminant of this homogeneous equation be not 0, and if it be not satisfied identically, the line will give just n different points of intersection, of which at most one is infinite.

Theorem 1] *A curve of order n will, 'in general', intersect a straight line n times. If it have more than that number of intersections with any straight line, it must contain that line as a factor.*

Suppose that for every line through a given point, let us say the origin, the discriminant of equation (5) has a multiple root. Let us suppose that the origin is not a point on the curve. In non-homogeneous form, if we put

$$y = lx \qquad f(x, lx) = 0,$$

then the equation has a multiple root for every value of l. We have

$$f(x, lx) \equiv [\phi(x, lx)]^k \psi(x, lx).$$

If the multiple factor were independent of l, then every line through the origin which is not on the curve would meet the curve in a point with a fixed abscissa, which is absurd unless the curve contain a vertical line. Hence this factor is not independent of l, and we have, replacing l by $\frac{y}{x}$,

$$f(x, y) \equiv [\phi(x, y)]^k \psi(x, y).$$

Theorem 2] *If all lines through a point not on a curve meet a curve of order n in less than n distinct points, the curve is reducible with a multiple factor.*

Let us suppose (x_0, y_0) is a point of our curve so that

$$f(x_0, y_0) = 0,$$

and find where a line through that point meets the curve. We have

$$x = x_0 + \rho \cos \theta \qquad y = y_0 + \rho \sin \theta$$

$$f(x, y) \equiv \rho \left(\cos \theta \frac{\partial f}{\partial x_0} + \sin \theta \frac{\partial f}{\partial y_0} \right) + \frac{r^2}{2} \Big[\qquad \Big] + \ldots = 0. \qquad (6)$$

There will always be one root $\rho = 0$ since every line through the point (x_0, y_0) has one intersection accounted for by that point. There will be a second intersection accounted for in the same way if

$$\left(\cos \theta \, \frac{\partial f}{\partial x_0} + \sin \theta \, \frac{\partial f}{\partial y_0} \right) = 0.$$

There are two cases which must be distinguished carefully.

A) If $\dfrac{\partial f}{\partial x_0}$, $\dfrac{\partial f}{\partial y_0}$ are not both 0, then the straight line

$$(x - x_0) \frac{\partial f}{\partial x_0} + (y - y_0) \frac{\partial f}{\partial y_0} = 0 \qquad (7)$$

has two intersections accounted for, and no other line through the point has the same property. This is the tangent, for its slope is

$$- \frac{\partial f}{\partial x_0} \bigg/ \frac{\partial f}{\partial y_0} = \frac{dy}{dx}.$$

A point of the curve where these two partial derivatives do not vanish is called an 'ordinary' point.

Theorem 3] *At a finite ordinary point of an algebraic curve there is but one tangent, whose equation is given by* (7).

Suppose that

$$\frac{\partial f}{\partial y_0} \neq 0.$$

Then, in the vicinity of the pair of values x_0, y_0, y is a single-valued continuous function of x, with a continuous first derivative

$$\frac{dy}{dx} = - \frac{\dfrac{\partial f}{\partial x}}{\dfrac{\partial f}{\partial y}}.$$

It is therefore an analytic function of $x - x_0$ developable in power series by Taylor's theorem

$$y = y_0 + a_1(x - x_0) + a_2(x - x_0)^2 + \dots \qquad (8)$$

This series will be convergent to the nearest point where $\dfrac{\partial f}{\partial y} = 0$.

Theorem 4] *In the vicinity of an ordinary finite point where the tangent is not vertical, y may be expressed as a convergent power series in terms of $x - x_0$ where x_0 is the abscissa of the point* *in question. Where the tangent is vertical we merely have to interchange the roles of x and y.*

B)
$$\frac{\partial f}{\partial x_0} = \frac{\partial f}{\partial y_0} = 0.$$

If these equations be satisfied for an infinite number of points, the curve is reducible with a multiple factor. We exclude this case. We assume, to be perfectly general, that

$$\frac{\partial^r f}{\partial x_0^p \partial y_0^q} \equiv 0 \qquad p+q = k < r$$

$$\frac{\partial^r f}{\partial x_0^p \partial y_0^q} \not\equiv 0 \qquad p+q = r.$$

$\left(\text{The number of conditions imposed is } \dfrac{r(r+1)}{2}.\right)$

We see from equation (6) further expanded that every line through this point will have r intersections accounted for there, but not, 'in general', more than r. Under these circumstances we say that the curve has a singular point of multiplicity or order r.

Further intersections of the line through (x_0, y_0) will fall in there if

$$\frac{\partial^r f}{\partial y_0^r} \sin{}^r\theta + r \frac{\partial^r f}{\partial x_0 \partial y_0^{r-1}} \sin{}^{r-1}\theta \cos\theta + \ldots + \frac{\partial^r f}{\partial x_0^r} \cos{}^r\theta = 0.$$

This is the equation of the directions of the tangents at the singular point. If they be distinct, the singular point is said to be 'ordinary'. An ordinary double point is called a 'node'.

Theorem 5] *If at a point of an irreducible curve all partial derivatives of orders less than r vanish, but not all those of that order; the curve has a singularity of order r, and a general line through that point has r intersections accounted for there. There are at most and in general r tangents at that point, each with more than r intersections.*

Suppose that we have an ordinary singular point of order r, and that no tangent is vertical, i.e. if λ be the slope of a tangent we have

$$\psi_0(\lambda) \equiv \frac{\partial^r f}{\partial y_0^r} \lambda^r + \frac{\partial^r f}{\partial x_0 \partial y_0^{r-1}} \lambda^{r-1} + \ldots + \frac{\partial^r f}{\partial x_0^r} = 0. \tag{9}$$

This equation has r distinct roots as the singularity was assumed to be ordinary. In the equation of the original curve in terms of $(x-x_0)$, $(y-y_0)$ let us put

$$y = y_0 + \lambda(x-x_0)$$
$$\phi(x,\lambda) \equiv (x-x_0)^r[\psi_0(\lambda) + (x-x_0)\psi_1(\lambda) + ...] = 0.$$

Consider for a moment, not the (x, y) plane, but the (x, λ) plane. The line $x = x_0$ meets the curve just above in r distinct points, at each of which $\dfrac{\partial \phi}{\partial \lambda} \neq 0$. We have, therefore, r different developments

$$y = \lambda_i + \beta_{i2}(x-x_0) + \beta_{i3}(x-x_0)^2 + ...$$

and corresponding to them r developments

$$y = y_0 + \lambda_i(x-x_0) + \beta_{i2}(x-x_0)^2 + \beta_{i3}(x-x_0)^3 + ...$$

Theorem 6] *In the vicinity of an ordinary singular point (x_0, y_0) of multiplicity r, where no tangent is vertical, there are just r different developments for y in terms of $x-x_0$. These developments will give all points of the curve in that immediate vicinity.*

Definition. A point of the second order with a single tangent which has just three coincident intersections with the curve is called a 'cusp'. More generally, a point of multiplicity r with a single tangent that meets the curve only $r+1$ times is called a 'hypercusp'. Suppose that we have a cusp at (x_0, y_0) and that the tangent has a slope λ_1 which is finite. If the equation of the curve be written in terms of $x-x_0$ and $y-y_0$ we shall have

$$f(x,y) \equiv [(y-y_0) - \lambda_1(x-x_0)]^2 + a_3(x-x_0)^3 + b_3(x-x_0)^2(y-y_0) + ...$$
$$= 0$$
$$a_3 \neq 0.$$

Replace $y-y_0$ by $\lambda(x-x_0)$

$$(x-x_0)^2\phi(x,\lambda) \equiv (x-x_0)^2\{(\lambda-\lambda_1)^2 + (x-x_0)(a_3 + b_3\lambda + ...)\} = 0.$$

The point (x_0, λ_1) is an ordinary point of $\phi(x, \lambda) = 0$,

$$(x-x_0) = -\frac{1}{a_3}(\lambda-\lambda_1)^2 + c_3(\lambda-\lambda_1)^3 + ...$$

Let us call this t^2, and revert the series,

$$\lambda-\lambda_1 = \alpha_1 t + \alpha_2 t^2 + ...$$
$$= \alpha_1(x-x_0)^{\frac{1}{2}} + \alpha_2(x-x_0)...$$
$$y-y_0 = \lambda_1(x-x_0) + \alpha_1(x-x_0)^{\frac{3}{2}} + \alpha_2(x-x_0)^2 + ... \qquad (10)$$

Theorem 7] *In the vicinity of a cusp (x_0, y_0) with non-vertical tangent there is an integral power-series development for y in terms of the square root of $x - x_0$.*

The question presents itself naturally: Does a curve of given order 'in general' have a singular point ? If (x_0, y_0) be a singular point, that point is common to the three curves

$$f(x, y) = \frac{\partial f}{\partial x} = \frac{\partial f}{\partial y} = 0.$$

Euler's theorem tells us that

$$x\frac{\partial f}{\partial x} + y\frac{\partial f}{\partial y} + \frac{\partial f}{\partial 1} = nf,$$

so that the point (x_0, y_0) is common to three curves of order $n-1$

$$\frac{\partial f}{\partial x} = \frac{\partial f}{\partial y} = \frac{\partial f}{\partial 1} = 0.$$

Do such curves usually have a common point ? The necessary and sufficient condition for such a point is that the resultant should vanish. Now the resultant will not vanish identically for all curves of any chosen order n, for it does not when the original curve has the equation

$$x^n + y^n + 1 = 0.$$

Hence a definite condition must be imposed on a curve if it is to have a singular point.

Theorem 8] *A curve of given order has not, in general, any singular point.*

The conditions written above for a point of multiplicity r and no more, namely, that all partial derivatives of order less than r should vanish, but not those of order r, can be put into more symmetrical form by differentiating to x, y, and 1 as already explained, and making repeated use of Euler's theorem. The reader will easily prove:

Theorem 9] *A necessary and sufficient condition that a point should have the multiplicity r and no more is that all partial derivates of order $r-1$ with respect to x, y, and 1 should vanish there, but not all of order r.*

Euler's theorem enables us to rewrite the equation of a tangent at an ordinary point in the form

$$\frac{\partial f}{\partial x_0}x + \frac{\partial f}{\partial y_0}y + \frac{\partial f}{\partial 1} = 0. \tag{11}$$

If u and v be coordinates of a straight line in the sense that a general line not through the origin is written

$$ux+vy+1=0,$$

then if this line be the tangent at (x_0, y_0) we shall have

$$\frac{\partial f}{\partial x_0}=u\,\frac{\partial f}{\partial 1} \qquad \frac{\partial f}{\partial y_0}=v\,\frac{\partial f}{\partial 1} \qquad f(x_0, y_0)=0.$$

If we eliminate x_0, y_0 from these three equations we get an equation

$$\psi(u, v)=0.$$

If the curve have no singular point, this gives the necessary and sufficient condition that a line shall be tangent to it. If we write the equation of a straight line in homogeneous form,

$$ux+vy+w=0,$$

the corresponding homogeneous tangential equation will be

$$\phi^m(u, v, w)=0. \tag{12}$$

The quantity m, when the curve has no singular points, is called its 'class' and is the number of tangents through a general point.

If the curve have singular points, the straight lines through them will have coordinates which satisfy the last equation, for

$$\frac{\partial f}{\partial x_0}=\frac{\partial f}{\partial y_0}=\frac{\partial f}{\partial 1}\equiv 0.$$

The polynomial ϕ will be factorable, some factors corresponding to lines through multiple points counted each a certain number of times. We shall determine this number subsequently. It is clear right now that, corresponding to multiple points, a curve may have multiple tangents, that is to say, tangents which count multiply among the tangents to the curve through any one of their points. Let us seek them.

We assume that our curve has only ordinary singular points and cusps. In the vicinity of any point not a cusp, where the tangent is not vertical, y can be expressed as an integral power series in terms of $x-x_0$. When a point of the curve has been picked, we may choose the axes so that the tangent, or a particular tangent, is horizontal, and the point is the origin. We shall get a development

$$y=a_2x^2+a_3x^3+\dots.$$

We may write this in terms of an auxiliary parameter

$$x = t \qquad y = a_2 t^2 + a_3 t^3 + \cdots.$$

The equation of the tangent will be

$$\frac{y - (a_2 t^2 + a_3 t^3 + \cdots)}{x - t} = 2a_2 t + 3a_3 t^2 + \cdots$$

$$(2a_2 t + 3a_3 t^2 + \cdots)x - y = a_2 t^2 + 2a_3 t^3 + \cdots.$$

Let us see whether the x axis is a singular tangent, i.e. whether it counts as several tangents to the curve from each of its points. For what values of t will this tangent go through the point $(x_1, 0)$? We must have

$$t[2a_2 x_1 + (3a_3 x_1 - a_2)t + (4a_4 x_1 - 2a_3)t^2 + \cdots] = 0.$$

If $a_2 \neq 0$ the tangent has ordinary two-point contact; the equation here has but one root $t = 0$, which means that the tangent counts as but one tangent to the curve with contact at the origin, from a general point on the x axis. If the tangent be a singular tangent it must have another point of contact elsewhere.

If $a_2 = 0$, $a_3 \neq 0$ the tangent is an ordinary inflexion, since

$$\frac{d^2 y}{dx^2} = 0 \qquad \frac{d^3 y}{\partial x^3} \neq 0.$$

It counts as two tangents to the curve from an arbitrary point of itself, and three from the point of contact. The reader will have no difficulty in extending the reasoning so as to determine the multiplicity of a tangent with as high contact as desired; the multiplicity is one less than the number of coincidences at the point of contact coming from the series development of the curve.

We must now see whether a cuspidal tangent is multiple. We take the tangent as horizontal and write from (10) with $x_0 = y_0 = 0$, $\lambda_1 = 0$

$$x = t^2 \qquad y = \alpha_1 t^3 + \alpha_2 t^4 + \alpha_3 t^5 + \cdots$$

$$\frac{dy}{dx} = \frac{3}{2}\alpha_1 t + 2\alpha_2 t^2 + \frac{5}{2}\alpha_3 t^3 + \cdots.$$

The equation of the tangent will be

$$\frac{y - (\alpha_1 t^3 + \alpha_2 t^4 + \cdots)}{x - t^2} = \frac{3}{2}\alpha_1 t + 2\alpha_2 t^2 + \frac{5}{2}\alpha_3 t^3 + \cdots.$$

To find the tangent from $(x_1, 0)$ we write

$$t[\tfrac{3}{2}\alpha_1 x_1 + 2\alpha_2 x_1 t + \tfrac{1}{2}(5\alpha_3 x_1 - \alpha_1)t^3 + ...] = 0.$$

There is just one root $t = 0$, unless $x_1 = 0$, in which case there are just three. This indicates that the cuspidal tangent is not a singular tangent. There is a correlation between a cusp and an ordinary inflexion which is worth pointing out at this time.

Cusp.	Inflexional tangent.
Point is double.	Tangent is double.
Tangent is non-singular.	Point is non-singular.
Tangent has three-point contact.	Tangents count as three from point.
Tangent counts as three.	Tangent has three-point contact.

A double tangent with distinct points of contact shall be called a bitangent. A multiple tangent where all points of contact are distinct shall be called an 'ordinary' multiple tangent.

Let us now take a general correlation of the plane

$$\rho u = a_{11}x + a_{12}y + a_{13}$$
$$\rho v = a_{21}x + a_{22}y + a_{23}$$
$$\rho w = a_{31}x + a_{32}y + a_{33}$$
$$|a_{ij}| \neq 0.$$

We establish the following correspondence:

Point.	Line.
Line.	Point.
Point of a curve not a line.	Tangent to a curve.
Ordinary singular point.	Ordinary singular tangent.
Node.	Bitangent.
Cusp.	Inflexional tangent.
Cuspidal tangent.	Inflexion.

We next take up in a particular case the vitally important problem of determining how many intersections two given curves have at a given point. The complete solution of this problem cannot be given before Book II, but we are able at this point to cover a very important case.

The point in question shall be the origin; the two curves can be written

$$f \equiv (y-\lambda_1 x)(y-\lambda_2 x)...(y-\lambda_r x)+\phi = 0$$
$$f' \equiv (y-\lambda_1' x)(y-\lambda_2' x)...(y-\lambda_s' x)+\phi' = 0.$$

We make once for all the assumption that no tangent to one curve there is tangent there to the other also. The tangents to either curve may differ or coalesce as they choose. We write a third curve

$$f'' \equiv (y-\mu_1 x)(y-\mu_2 x)...(y-\mu_s x)+(1-\epsilon)\phi' = 0.$$

How many intersections has this with f at the origin ? In general the μ_i's are distinct and not infinite, also different from the λ's. We have s developments for y in terms of x:

$$y = b_{i1}x+b_{i2}x^2+....$$

Substituting in f since $b_{i1}' \neq \lambda_j$, each will give r intersections, hence in general the number of intersections is rs; in particular cases it might be more, but never less. If for a general value of ϵ, and particular values of $\mu_1, \mu_2,...$, there were more, then there would be more when $\epsilon = 1$. But in this case there are always exactly rs provided $\mu_i \neq \lambda_j$. Hence there are always rs when $\mu_i \neq \lambda_j$.

Fundamental Intersection Theorem 10] *If two curves have a common point, but no tangent to one is tangent to the other there, the number of intersections accounted for by this point is the product of its multiplicities for the two curves.*

§ 2. Determination of a curve by points, Nöther's fundamental theorem

Suppose that we have a general curve of the nth order given by

$$f^n(x,y) = 0,$$

f is supposed to be the general polynomial of degree n. The number of coefficients, including the constant, is

$$1+2+3+...+(n+1) = \frac{(n+1)(n+2)}{2} = \frac{n(n+3)}{2}+1.$$

Theorem 11] *A curve of the nth order is completely and uniquely determined by $\dfrac{n(n+3)}{2}$ independent linear homogeneous conditions imposed upon the coefficients.*

The most obvious way to impose a linear homogeneous condition is to require the curve to contain a chosen point. There are cases where assigning a certain number of points to a curve will not impose independent conditions thereon. The simplest case is where $n = 3$. Two curves of the third order intersect, in general, in 9 points, so that although $\dfrac{3 \times 6}{2} = 9$, there are certainly cases where 9 points do not determine a single cubic curve. On the other hand, if we take 4 points on a line, and 5 others on a non-degenerate conic, it is clear that any cubic through the 9 points must include the line, since it meets it four times. The remainder must be a conic through 5 given points, and this also is uniquely determined. There is thus but one cubic through these 9 points.

If we can show that for a general value of n we can find such a set of $\dfrac{n(n+3)}{2}$ points that there is but one curve of order n through them, then it follows that if an arbitrary set of this number of points be taken, the conditions which they impose upon a curve of order n are not necessarily dependent on one another, or through these points will pass, in general, a single curve of that order. We find the points by the following simple device.* Given an irreducible curve of order n, and n lines $l_1, l_2, ..., l_n$ so situated that each meets the curve in n distinct points, no two lines being concurrent on the curve, or on a third line. Let P be a point on the curve, but not on any one of the lines, then choose two intersections of the curve with l_1, three intersections of the curve with l_2, and so on, so as to include finally n intersections with each of the last two lines. The number of points chosen is

$$1 + 2 + 3 + ... + n + n = \frac{n(n+1)}{2} + n = \frac{n(n+3)}{2}.$$

If more than one curve of order n could pass through all of these points, there would be at least a one-parameter family of such curves. We might find one curve of the family to pass through an $(n+1)$th point of l_n and so include the whole line. The remainder would be a curve of order $n-1$ which meets

---

* Berzolari[2].

l_{n-1} in n points, and so includes the whole of it: the remainder is a curve of order $n-2$ that meets l_{n-2} in $n-1$ points, and so includes it. Continuing in this way, it appears that the curve would have to include all n of the lines, and therefore could contain nothing else. But then the point P would be left out.

Theorem 12] *Through $\dfrac{n(n+3)}{2}$ points in general position will pass one and only one curve of order n.*

Theorem 13] *On any curve of order n which is not reducible with a multiple factor, we may in an infinite number of ways find $\dfrac{n(n+3)}{2}$ points which do not lie on any other curve of order n.*

Consider next two curves which have only ordinary multiple points and cusps. If they have a common ordinary point, or ordinary singularity, with no common tangent there, we know just how many intersections they have. Suppose, however, that there is a common tangent, and that we have for the two the developments

$$y-y_0 = a_1(x-x_0)+a_2(x-x_0)^2+...+a_{k-1}(x-x_0)^{k-1}+a_k(x-x_0)^k$$
$$y-y_0 = a_1(x-x_0)+a_2(x-x_0)^2+...+a_{k-1}(x-x_0)^{k-1}+b_k(x-x_0)^k$$
$$b_k \neq a_k.$$

Subtracting,
$$0 = (x-x_0)^k[(a_k-b_k)+(a_{k+1}-b_{k+1})(x-x_0)+...].$$

We see that k intersections of these two developments occur at this point. We shall express this by saying that the two meet at this point and at $k-1$ other infinitely near points. If we have the development given for one curve, and not the other, so that we have

$$y-y_0 = a_1(x-x_0)+a_2(x-x_0)^2+...;$$
$$\phi(x,y) \equiv \phi(x_0,y_0)+(x-x_0)\frac{\partial\phi}{\partial x_0}+(y-y_0)\frac{\partial\phi}{\partial y_0}+... = 0,$$

then to require a certain number of intersections of one curve with the branch of the other would be accomplished by substituting power series for $y-y_0$ from one of these equations in the other, and then requiring that there be a certain number of roots $x-x_0 = 0$, and these conditions will be linear and homogeneous in terms of the coefficients of the second equation. The same thing will happen if the second equation is written as here, while the first curve has a cusp which we express in the form

$$x-x_0 = t^2 \qquad y-y_0 = a_2t^2 + a_3t^3 + \ldots$$

Given two curves with only ordinary singular points and cusps. If a third curve be required to have multiplicity $r_i + s_i - 1$ or more at each point where the first has multiplicity r_i and the second multiplicity s_i, the conditions imposed on the coefficients of the third curve are linear and homogeneous whether the given points be distinct or grouped in infinitely near sets.

We next proceed to the much more difficult task of studying the independence of such conditions. Let the two curves be ϕ and ψ. One intersection of the two is the origin, where they have the respective multiplicities r_0, s_0, the other intersections are $P_1, P_2 \ldots$, and the respective multiplicities $r_1, s_1; r_2, s_2 \ldots$. Let $l_{11}, l_{12} \ldots$ be a set of lines through P_1, $l_{21}, l_{22} \ldots$ a set through P_2, and so on. The multiplicity of the curve we seek shall be in each case $r_i + s_i - 1$ or more. We write the extremely uncouth equation

$$(y - a_{11}x - a_{12}x^2 - \ldots - a_{1p}x^p)(y - a_{21}x - a_{22}x^2 - \ldots - a_{2q}x^q) \ldots$$
$$(y - a_{k1}x - a_{k2}x^2 - \ldots - a_{kv}x^v)l_{11}^{\alpha_1}l_{12}^{\alpha_2}\ldots l_{21}^{\beta_1}l_{22}^{\beta_2}\ldots = 0$$
$$R = r_0 + s_0 - 1.$$

Here, if all of the exponents of the l's be large enough, the conditions at the points $P_1, P_2 \ldots$ are all fulfilled. We may manipulate the coefficients a_{ij} in such a way that all of the tangency conditions at the origin are fulfilled but the last one. Hence this last condition cannot be a result of the multiplicity conditions at O, or of the other tangency conditions at O, or of any of the conditions at any of the other points. Any identical condition among the conditions cannot include the last tangency condition. This being out of the way, we can manipulate the a_{ij}'s so that the next to the last tangency condition is fulfilled or not, hence this also is independent of the others, and so on. Continuing thus we see that any identical relation that may subsist among the conditions cannot involve the tangency conditions at O. We next write a curve of the form

$$x^\alpha y^\beta l_{11}^{\alpha_1}l_{12}^{\alpha_2}\ldots l_{21}^{\beta_1}l_{22}^{\beta_2}\ldots = 0 \qquad \alpha + \beta = r_0 + s_0 - 2.$$

Here all the conditions are fulfilled at $P_1, P_2 \ldots$ and all of the multiplicity conditions are fulfilled at O except an arbitrary one of the last set. Hence this condition cannot result from the others, or an identical relation could not include any one of the multiplicity conditions of highest order at O. We go through the same reasoning when $\alpha + \beta = r_0 + s_0 - 3$ and see that any identical relation among the conditions could not involve a multiplicity condition of next highest order, and so on. Finally we see an identical condition could not involve the origin at all. But this is any one of the intersections. These requirements are linear in the coefficients. Hence, they cannot introduce additional singularities in unspecified situations, for the conditions involved are not linear. Nor could they introduce undesired singularities at specified places, for we can avoid this by changing the l's.

Theorem 14] *If the order of a curve be sufficiently high, the conditions which require it to have multiplicity at least $r_i + s_i - 1$ at each point where one of the curves has multiplicity r_i and the other multiplicity s_i, neither number being 0, are independent, and additional singularities are not necessarily introduced.*

Let f be a curve of very high order which fulfils this condition with respect to two given curves ϕ and ψ of orders n_1 and n_2 respectively. Its coefficients have been subjected to

$$\sum_i \frac{(r_i + s_i)(r_i + s_i - 1)}{2}$$

independent linear homogeneous conditions, so that the amount of freedom left is

$$\frac{(n+1)(n+2)}{2} - \sum_i \frac{(r_i + s_i)(r_i + s_i - 1)}{2} - 1,$$

Next consider a curve whose equation takes the form

$$\phi \psi' + \psi \phi' = 0,$$

Here ϕ' is a curve of order $n - n_2$ which has at each intersection of ϕ and ψ a multiplicity $r_i - 1$ at least, and we may imagine n so very large that the conditions imposed on ϕ' are independent. In the same way ψ' is a curve of order $n - n_1$ with multiplicities $s_i - 1$ all independent. The curve whose equation we have just written fulfils all of the requirements imposed on f.

We next ask whether this same curve could be written in more than one way. This is the case. We write

$$\phi\psi'+\psi\phi' \equiv \phi\bar{\psi}'+\psi\bar{\phi}'$$

$$\phi(\psi'-\bar{\psi}') \equiv \psi(\bar{\phi}'-\phi')$$

$$\bar{\phi}' \equiv \phi'+\theta\phi \qquad \bar{\psi}' \equiv \psi'-\theta\psi.$$

Here θ is a general polynomial of degree $n-(n_1+n_2)$. The reasoning is reversible, the real freedom of a curve compounded out of ϕ and ψ in this way is the apparent freedom, less the freedom of θ. The real freedom of the compounded curve will be

$$\frac{(n-n_2+1)(n-n_2+2)}{2}-\sum_i\frac{r_i(r_i-1)}{2}+\frac{(n-n_1+1)(n-n_1+2)}{2}-$$

$$-\sum_i\frac{s_i(s_i-1)}{2}-\frac{[n-(n_1+n_2)+1][n-(n_1+n_2)+2]}{2}-1$$

$$=\frac{(n+1)(n+2)}{2}-\sum_i\frac{r_i(r_i-1)}{2}-\sum_i\frac{s_i(s_i-1)}{2}-n_1n_2-1.$$

But
$$n_1n_2 = \sum_i r_i s_i,$$

since either gives the total number of intersections of ϕ and ψ. Hence the amount of freedom is

$$\frac{(n+1)(n+2)}{2}-\sum\frac{(r_i+s_i)(r_i+s_i-1)}{2}-1,$$

and this, as we saw above, is exactly the freedom of f. We have thus shown that if the order of f be sufficiently high, it can be compounded out of ϕ and ψ in exactly this way.

What will happen when the order is less high? It is conceivable that there are some curves of order greater than n_1+n_2 which fulfil the conditions at the intersections of ϕ and ψ but do not take this form. Let f be such a curve of the highest possible order where this compound form is not obligatory. It will be obligatory if we multiply f by a linear expression, i.e. if

$$ax+by+c = 0$$

be a straight line not through any intersection of ϕ and ψ

$$(ax+by+c)f \equiv \phi\psi'+\psi\phi'$$

$$\equiv \phi(\psi'-\theta\psi)+\psi(\phi'+\theta\phi).$$

Here θ is an arbitrary curve of order $n+1-n_1-n_2$ or a constant when that difference is 0. The curve

$$\psi'-\theta\psi=0$$

contains the n_2 intersections of the line with ψ. The total freedom of this curve is $\dfrac{[n-(n_1+n_2)+2][n-(n_1+n_2)+3]}{2}$ and is greater than $n-(n_1+n_2)+1$ when $n\geqslant n_1+n_2$. We make use of this freedom to make our curve $\psi'-\theta\psi=0$ go through other points of the line, or meet it altogether in $n-n_1+2$ points, i.e. include it as a part. We have, then,

$$(ax+by+c)f\equiv\phi(ax+by+c)\psi''+\psi(\phi'-\theta\phi).$$

Clearly $\phi'-\theta\phi$ must be divisible by $ax+by+c$. Dividing this factor out, $\qquad f\equiv\phi\psi''+\psi\phi''.$

Let us suppose, lastly, that the order of f is

$$n=n_1+n_2-l \qquad 1\leqslant l\leqslant n_2\leqslant n_1$$

$$\chi f\equiv\phi\psi''+\psi\phi'',$$

where χ is a polynomial of order l.

We may write this equally well

$$\chi f\equiv\phi(\psi''+\rho\psi)+\psi(\phi''-\rho\phi).$$

Every curve $\phi''-\rho\phi$ passes through all the intersections of x and ϕ, for ϕ and ϕ'' both do so. If, then, we use ρ to make this curve include one more point of χ it must include the latter completely. So will $\psi''+\rho\psi$. As before, we may divide out x and get $\qquad f\equiv\phi\psi'''+\psi\phi'''.$

We may sum up all these results in a statement which is of absolutely vital importance in our whole theory.[*]

Nöther's Fundamental Theorem 15] *If two curves ϕ and ψ have only ordinary points or ordinary singular points and cusps in common, then every curve which has at the least the multiplicity r_i+s_i-1 at every point, distinct or infinitely near, where ϕ has the*

[*] Cf. Nöther[1]. There are many proofs extant of this famous theorem, we have followed Scott[1].

multiplicity r_i and ψ the multiplicity s_i, neither of these latter numbers being 0, can be written

$$f \equiv \phi\psi' + \psi\phi' = 0, \tag{13}$$

where the curves ϕ' and ψ' have at least the multiplicities r_i-1 and s_i-1 respectively.

§ 3. Residuation

Definition. A curve which has at least the multiplicity r_i-1 at each point where a given curve, possessed only of ordinary singular points and cusps, has a multiplicity r_i shall be called an 'adjoint' to the given curve. When the given curve is of order n, an adjoint of order $n-3$ is called a 'special adjoint'. It is not, of course, immediately evident that special adjoints exist.

Definition. Two groups of ordinary points on a curve with only ordinary singular points or cusps are said to be 'residual' when they constitute together the total non-singular intersection with an adjoint curve.

Suppose that two groups of points G_1, G_2 are residual on a curve f. Let ϕ be the adjoint which cuts them. Let G_1 and G_2' be residual groups cut by an adjoint ϕ', while G_2 and G_1' are residual groups lying on an adjoint ψ. The curve $\phi'\psi$ contains both groups G_1, G_2, and at a point where f has multiplicity r_i it has multiplicity $2(r_i-1) = r_i+(r_i-1)-1$. Hence by Nöther's fundamental theorem we have the identity

$$\phi'\psi \equiv \theta f + \psi'\phi. \tag{14}$$

By the same theorem ψ' must be an adjoint, and it clearly contains as its non-singular intersection with f the two groups G_1', G_2'. This gives the

Residue Theorem 16] *If two groups be residual to a third, every group residual to the one is residual to the other also.*[*]

Two such groups are defined as 'co-residual'.

The residue theorem is easily generalized in the following manner.

Definition. Given two groups of ordinary points on a curve with only ordinary singular points or cusps, $P_1, P_2\ldots$ of multiplicities $r_1, r_2\ldots$, they are said to be 'pseudo-residual' with the

* Cf. Brill and Nöther, p. 273.

excesses $\rho_1, \rho_2 \ldots$' where $\rho_i \geqslant -(r_i-1)$ if they constitute the total non-singular intersection with a curve whose multiplicity at P_i, is at least $r_i+(\rho_i-1)$.

Suppose G_1 and G_2 are pseudo-residual with these excesses, G_1 and G_2' pseudo-residual with the excesses σ_i, while G_1' and G_2 are pseudo-residual with the excesses τ_i, and that $\sigma_i+\tau_i \geqslant \rho_i$.

Using our notation for the residue theorem, at P_i ϕ has the multiplicity $r_i+\rho_i-1$, ϕ' the multiplicity $r_i+\sigma_i-1$, and ψ the multiplicity $r_i+\tau_i-1$. Nöther's theorem and equation (15) apply, since

$$r_i+\sigma_i-1+r_i+\tau_i-1 \geqslant r_i+\rho_i-1+r_i-1.$$

It appears that ψ' is a pseudo-residual with the excesses $\sigma_i+\tau_i-\rho_i$.

Gambier's Extension of the Residue Theorem 16]* *If two groups be pseudo-residual to a third, then every group pseudo-residual to the first, with an excess greater than or equal to the excess of the first less the excess of the second, is pseudo-residual to the second with a positive or 0 excess.*

This theorem holds in particular when $\rho_i = \sigma_i = \tau_i = -(r_i-1)$

Theorem 17] *If two groups of ordinary points G_1 and G_2 constitute the total intersection of f with a curve ϕ, while G_1 and G_2' constitute its total intersection with a curve ϕ' and G_2 and G_1' its total intersection with a curve ψ, then G_1' and G_2' constitute its total intersection with a curve ψ'.*

Careless writers sometimes speak of such groups as residual.

Suppose that G_1 and G_2 are pseudo-residual with a positive or 0 excess ρ_i, while G_1 and G_2' are residual. Then if G_1' and G_2 are also pseudo-residual with the excesses ρ_i, G_2 and G_2' are residual. We may phrase this differently by saying that G_1 contains $\rho_1 r_1$ points superposed on P_1, as does G_1', $\rho_2 r_2$ points superposed on P_2, etc. We may then say:

Theorem 18] *The residue theorem holds when the given groups contain the same number of points superposed on the multiple points of the given curve, arising from the same positive excesses of multiplicity.*

In theorem 16] we are at liberty to assume that group G_2' is empty, so that G_1 and G_1' are total intersection groups.

---

* Gambier[1], pp. 220 ff.

Total Intersection Theorem 19] *If one part of the total inter-section group of a curve of order n with a curve of order n_1+n_2 constitute the total intersection with a curve of order n_1, the other part will constitute the total intersection with a curve of order n_2.*

There is an astonishing number of simple corollaries easily deducible from this theorem.

Corollary 1] *If six intersections of two curves of the third order lie on a conic, the other three are collinear, and conversely.*

Corollary 2, Pascal's Theorem] *The necessary and sufficient condition that the vertices of a hexagon should lie on a conic is that the intersections of the opposite sides should be collinear.*

Corollary 3] *If two lines meet a curve of the third order in two sets of points A_1, A_2, A_3; B_1, B_2, B_3, and if the line A_iB_i meet the cubic again in C_i, then the three points C_1, C_2, C_3 are collinear.*

Corollary 4] *The tangents to a curve of the third order at three collinear points meet it again in three collinear points.*

Corollary 5] *A line connecting two points of inflexion of a curve of the third order will pass through a third point of inflexion.*

Definition. A system of curves of given order linearly dependent on two given curves of that order shall be called a 'pencil' of curves. They will clearly pass through all points common to the given curves, and have at each point at least the lesser of the given multiplicities. These points are called centres or base-points of the pencil. Such a system may be written

$$\lambda\phi+\mu\psi = 0.$$

If we take the four curves of the system corresponding to parameter values $(\lambda_1, \mu_1), (\lambda_2, \mu_2), (\lambda_3, \mu_3), (\lambda_4, \mu_4)$, the expression

$$\frac{\begin{vmatrix} \lambda_1 & \mu_1 \\ \lambda_2 & \mu_2 \end{vmatrix} \cdot \begin{vmatrix} \lambda_3 & \mu_3 \\ \lambda_4 & \mu_4 \end{vmatrix}}{\begin{vmatrix} \lambda_1 & \mu_1 \\ \lambda_4 & \mu_4 \end{vmatrix} \cdot \begin{vmatrix} \lambda_3 & \mu_3 \\ \lambda_2 & \mu_2 \end{vmatrix}}$$

shall be defined as a 'cross ratio' of the four curves. It is the cross ratio of 4 tangents at a common isolated simple point. Two pencils of curves are said to be 'projective' if corresponding cross ratios be equal.

Given the two projective pencils

$$\lambda\phi+\mu\psi = 0 \qquad \lambda'\phi'+\mu'\psi' = 0,$$
$$A\lambda\lambda' + B\lambda\mu' + C\mu\lambda' + D\mu\mu' = 0 \qquad AD - BC \neq 0.$$

Assuming the two have no common curve, the locus of the intersections of corresponding curves is

$$A\psi\psi' - B\psi\phi' - C\phi\psi' + D\phi\phi' = 0.$$

This is a curve whose order is the sum of the orders of the curves of the two pencils, and which passes through all points common to all curves of either pencil.

Suppose, conversely, that we have a curve of order $n+n'$ which contains all points common to all curves of order n of a certain pencil, distinct or infinitely near, which means it is linearly dependent on such curves in the sense of Nöther's theorem, and so can be written

$$f \equiv \phi\psi' + \psi\phi'.$$

Then f contains all points common to ϕ' and ψ'. Writing the three equations

$$\lambda\phi + \mu\psi = 0 \qquad \lambda'\phi' + \mu'\psi' = 0 \qquad \lambda\mu' + \mu\lambda' = 0$$

we fall back on f if we eliminate λ/μ and λ'/μ' But these equations give us two projective pencils of curves. This gives

Chasles' Theorem 20] *If two projective pencils of curves of orders n and n' respectively have no common curve, the locus of the intersections of corresponding curves of the two is a curve of order $n+n'$ through all centres of either pencil. Conversely, if a curve of order $n+n'$ contain all centres of a pencil of order n to the multiplicity demanded by Nöther's theorem, it is the locus of the intersections of corresponding curves of this pencil, and of one of order n' projective therewith.**

It is assumed, of course, that the curves mentioned have only ordinary singular points and cusps.

Here are two other obvious corollaries from the Total Intersection theorem 19] and Residue theorem 16]:

Theorem 21] *If tangents be drawn to a curve of order n at the intersections with a straight line, their remaining intersections with the curve will constitute its total intersection with a curve of order $n-2$.*

Theorem 22] *If three curves of the third order pass through seven and no more points, the lines connecting their remaining pairs of intersections meet in pairs on the three curves.*

---

* Chasles[2].

In equation (13) there is no reason why the curve f should be irreducible; in fact we get a more symmetric theorem by supposing it to split into two parts. Changing notation slightly, we then get an identity of the form

$$\phi_1\,\phi_1'+\phi_2\,\phi_2'+\phi_3\,\phi_3' \equiv 0. \tag{15}$$

Suppose that three curves ϕ_1, ϕ_2, ϕ_3 go through a common group of points, which may indeed be empty, but which we call G. The remaining groups of intersections shall be called $g_{23}, g_{31},$ and g_{12}. Let ϕ_1' be an arbitrary curve through the group g_{23}, we see by Nöther's theorem that there will exist curves ϕ_2' and ϕ_3' to complete equation (15). We thus get*

Study's Theorem 23] *Given three curves ϕ_1, ϕ_2, ϕ_3 with the common group of ordinary points G, which may be empty. Let their remaining groups of intersections be $g_{23}, g_{31},$ and g_{12}, also ordinary points. Then if ϕ_1' be any other curve through g_{23}, there exist two other curves ϕ_2', ϕ_3' such that the three combined curves $\phi_i\phi_i'$ are of the same order and linearly dependent, each curve ϕ_k' contains the corresponding group g_{ij} and every intersection of ϕ_i or ϕ_i' with ϕ_j or ϕ_j' lies on ϕ_k or ϕ_k'.*

It is to be noted that the total intersection of ϕ_i and ϕ_j is G on ϕ_k and g_{ij} on ϕ_k'. The total intersection of ϕ_i' and ϕ_j' is G' on ϕ_k' and g_{ij}' on ϕ_k. The total intersection of ϕ_i and ϕ_j' is g_{ik} on ϕ_k and g_{jk}' on ϕ_k'.

Let the orders of the three original curves be n_1, n_2, n_3, while the order of each compound curve is n.

Then G contains ν points,

g_{ij} contains $n_in_j-\nu,$

g_{ij}' contains $n_k(n-n_i-n_j)+\nu,$

G' contains $n^2-n(n_1+n_2+n_3)+(n_2n_3+n_3n_1+n_1n_2)-\nu.$

Let us next start with a curve ϕ_i on which there are two groups G and g_{jk}', each of which is pseudo-residual to g_{ij} and g_{ik}. The pencil of curves

$$\lambda\phi_j\,\phi_j'+\mu\phi_k\,\phi_k'$$

will have nn_i fixed points on ϕ_i; we may choose the constant multiplier so as to include one other point of ϕ_i, i.e. the whole curve, the remainder will be a curve fulfilling the identity (15).

Corollary 1] *On a curve ϕ_i are two groups of ordinary points*

* Study[1].

G and g'_{jk} each pseudo-residual to g_{ij} and g_{ik}. Then the four groups, which ϕ_j and ϕ'_j cut on ϕ_k and ϕ'_k, lie on ϕ_i or ϕ'_i, the three sets of curves $\phi_1\phi'_1$, $\phi_2\phi'_2$, $\phi_3\phi'_3$ being of the same order and linearly dependent.

As an example, let us suppose that ϕ_1 is a straight line, G an empty group, g_{12} and g_{13} intersections with $\phi_2\phi_3$ with two other lines g'_{23} a marked point on the line, ϕ_1, ϕ'_2, and ϕ'_3 circles, then g'_{12} and g'_{13} are marked points on the lines ϕ_3 and ϕ_2 respectively, these lines intersecting again in g_{23}, and G' is the group of circular points at infinity.*

Corollary 2, Miquel's Theorem] *If a point be marked on the line of each side of a triangle, the three circles, each through a vertex and the points marked on the lines through that vertex are concurrent.*

Again, let us take G as the circular points at infinity, g_{23} as empty, ϕ_1 as a circle, g_{12} and g_{13} as the pairs of its intersections with two lines. We get:

Corollary 3] *The common secants of three non-coaxal circles are concurrent.*

Suppose that we have three curves ϕ_1, ϕ_2, ϕ_3, of the same order, which are not linearly dependent. Let G be their common group, P an arbitrary point in the plane not on two of the curves. Let ϕ'_2 be the curve linearly dependent on ϕ_1, ϕ_3 which goes through P, while ϕ'_3 is the curve of the ϕ_1, ϕ_2 system through there. The group G' will contain the point P and any other intersections which ϕ'_2, ϕ'_3 have which are not in G.

Corollary 4] *If three curves of the same order be not linearly dependent, then the three curves through an arbitrary point, each linearly dependent on two of the curves, are, themselves, linearly dependent.*

Strictly speaking we have only proved this in the case where the intersections are ordinary points, the other case will come by continuous change. Or more simply, we notice that if (x_1, y_1) be the point in question, the three curves sought have equations of the type
$$\frac{\phi_i(x,y)}{\phi_i(x_1,y_1)} - \frac{\phi_j(x,y)}{\phi_j(x_1,y_1)} = 0,$$
and these are linearly dependent.

* Miquel[1].

Corollary 5] *If three curves of order n which are not linearly dependent have in common n ordinary points on a curve of order n', their residual groups are on three linearly dependent curves of order $n - n'$.*

We leave to the reader the easy task of proving by induction

Theorem 24] *If $\phi_1, \phi_2, ..., \phi_k$ be k curves, no two with a common multiple point, then every curve through each intersection of two of them can be written*

$$\phi_1 \phi_2 ... \phi_k \sum_i \frac{\psi_i}{\phi_i} = 0. \qquad (16)$$

As a last and most important application of Nöther's theorem, let us find under what circumstances the group common to two curves impose independent conditions on a third. We assume all intersections are ordinary.

If the orders of the given curves be n_1, n_2, their intersections, as we saw in the demonstration of Nöther's theorem, will impose independent conditions on every curve whose order is $\geqslant n_1 + n_2$. It will therefore be sufficient to consider curves or order

$$n = n_1 + n_2 - l.$$

The form of the equation of the curve being that given by Nöther's theorem, the conditions are independent if

$$\frac{(n_1 + n_2 - l)(n_1 + n_2 - l + 3)}{2} - n_1 n_2$$

$$= \frac{(n_2 - l + 1)(n_2 - l + 2)}{2} + \frac{(n_1 - l + 1)(n_1 - l + 2)}{2} - 1$$

$$(l - 1)(l - 2) = 0.$$

Theorem 25] *If two curves have no common singular point, their intersections, distinct or infinitely near, will impose independent conditions on every curve whose order plus two is as great as or greater than the sum of their orders.*

Reverting to the equation above, we see that the number of conditions imposed is

$$n_1 n_2 - \tfrac{1}{2}(l - 1)(l - 2).$$

How can we always pick out this number of points from among the $n_1 n_2$ and be sure that every curve of order $n_1 + n_2 - l$ through them will go through all $n_1 n_2$ points ? Let us suppose $n_1 \geqslant n_2$.

There must be some group of $n_1n_2 - \frac{1}{2}(l-1)(l-2)$ intersections which impose independent conditions on our curve. Let us call this group G, and the residual group G': it contains $\frac{1}{2}(l-1)(l-2)$ points. They lie on every curve of order $n_1 + n_2 - l$ through the group G. The group G' lies among the

$$n_2(n_1 + n_2 - l) - [n_1 n_2 - \tfrac{1}{2}(l-1)(l-2)]$$

intersections of a general curve f of our system with $\psi = 0$ exclusive of G. It turns out to be very important whether the $\dfrac{(l-1)(l-2)}{2}$ points lie on a curve of order $l-3$; we may pass such a curve through all but one of the points since

$$\frac{(l-1)(l-2)}{2} - 1 = \tfrac{1}{2}l(l-3).$$

The n_1n_2 points common to ϕ and ψ cannot all lie on a curve of order $l-3$. Let us pick out $\frac{1}{2}(l-1)(l-2)$ which do not, call the group G', and pass a curve of order $l-3$ through all but any chosen one of those points, that last one being P, the curve being χ, and $Ax + By + C = 0$ an arbitrary line through P. Where will the compound curve

$$\chi(Ax + By + C) = 0$$

meet ψ? Evidently in the group G' and in a pseudo-residual group R of $n_2(l-2) - \frac{1}{2}(l-1)(l-2)$ points, which includes $n_2 - 1$ collinear points, and is co-residual to G. Take any curve of order $n \equiv n_1 + n_2 - l$ through G, let its residual group on ψ be $\overline{G}$, the number of points thereon is $n_2(n_1 + n_2 - l) - n_1 n_2 - \dfrac{(l-1)(l-2)}{2}$.

By the extended residue theorem R and $\overline{G}$ are pseudo-residual, and constitute the total intersection of ψ, whose order is n_2 with a curve of order $n_2 - 2$. But among these are $n_2 - 1$ collinear points, so that their line must form a part of the curve of order $n_2 - 2$, and its remaining intersection with ψ, namely P, must be a point of G'. But P was any point of G'. This gives:[*]

Theorem 26] *If among the n_1n_2 simple intersections of two curves of order n_1 and n_2 respectively, there be taken $\frac{1}{2}(l-1)(l-2)$ which do not lie on a curve of order $l-3$, every curve of order*

---

[*] The developments from here to the end of the chapter are taken from Study[1] and Baccharach.

n_1+n_2-l *through the remaining points will pass through these points also.*

Consider the case where $l = 3$. The group G' will contain only a single point.

Corollary 1] *If two given curves have no multiple point in common, every curve whose order is three less than the sum of their orders, through all but one of their intersections, passes through that last one also.*

Corollary 2] *Every curve of order $n_1 \geqslant n_2$ through*

$$n_1 n_2 - \frac{(n_2-1)(n_2-2)}{2}$$

intersections of two curves of orders n_1 and n_2 will contain the remaining intersections provided that they do not lie on a curve of order n_2-3.

Here is a last simple application of corollary 1]:

Theorem 27] *If among the n^2 simple intersections of two curves of order n, and $n-1$, one half lie on a curve of order $n-2$, the other half do the same.*

CHAPTER III
REAL CURVES
§ 1. Asymptotes

IT is our purpose in the present chapter to study real curves, that is, the totality of real points whose coordinates satisfy a real polynomial equation, assuming, of course, there are an infinite number of such points. The only real solution of $x^2+y^2=0$ is given by the values $x=0$, $y=0$, and we should hesitate to call this a real curve. We can only touch the most significant parts of the topic, leaving the reader to study books on 'Curve Tracing' in case he is desirous of a complete treatment.[*]

Definition. We shall mean by a 'branch' of a curve at a point whose homogeneous coordinates are (x_0, y_0, z_0) the totality of values expressible by three convergent power series

$$\rho x = x_0 + a_1 t + a_2 t^2 + \ldots$$
$$\rho y = y_0 + b_1 t + b_2 t^2 + \ldots$$
$$\rho z = z_0 + c_1 t + c_2 t^2 + \ldots \tag{1}$$

It is assumed that the ratios are not all constants.

In the case of a non-singular point, the canonical form for simplified representation of the branch is

$$x = x_0 + t \qquad y = y_0 + b_1 t + b_2 t^2 + \ldots. \tag{2}$$

If we have an ordinary singularity we have several such developments, the canonical form for a cusp will be

$$x = x_0 + t^2 \qquad y = y_0 + b_2 t^2 + b_3 t^3 + \ldots \qquad b_3 \neq 0. \tag{3}$$

We shall show in Book II that the total vicinity of any sort of point can be represented by a number of such branches.

Suppose that the equation of a curve is real, and that it contains a real non-singular point. We orient the axes in such a way that the tangent at this point is not vertical. Then we may develop y in terms of x as an integral power series, the coefficients are rational functions of those of the given polynomial.

Theorem 1] *If an algebraic curve have a real equation, and a single real non-singular point, it has a real branch.*

* Cf. e.g. Frost or Johnson.

A real branch is one with a real development. We get similarly

Theorem 2] *If an algebraic curve with a real equation have a real ordinary singularity with a real tangential direction, it will contain a real branch.*

We emphasize the statement at the beginning of the present chapter with a definition. A curve whose equation can be made real by multiplying through by a factor, not 0, and which contains a real branch shall be called a 'real' curve. This definition is not universally recognized, some writers omit the requirement of a real branch. This seems to me unwise. As an example, let us consider the curve

$$x^8 + y^8 + x^4 + y^2 = 0.$$

This curve has a real point, the origin, and a real direction for its tangent, namely the x-axis, but there is no real branch, and the origin is the only real point of the curve. We therefore call such a curve 'self-conjugate' imaginary, not real.

In plotting curves there are certain fundamental rules which it is well to recall. The equation of the curve being

$$f(x, y) = 0, \tag{4}$$

the slope of the tangent at (x_0, y_0) is

$$\lambda = \frac{dy_0}{dx_0} = -\frac{\dfrac{\partial f}{\partial x_0}}{\dfrac{\partial f}{\partial y_0}}. \tag{5}$$

The curve will be concave up if

$$\frac{d^2 y_0}{dx_0{}^2} > 0$$

$$\frac{\partial^2 f}{\partial x_0{}^2}\left(\frac{\partial f}{\partial y_0}\right)^2 + \frac{\partial^2 f}{\partial y_0{}^2}\left(\frac{\partial f}{\partial x_0}\right)^2 - 2\frac{\partial^2 f}{\partial x_0 \partial y_0}\frac{\partial f}{\partial x_0}\frac{\partial f}{\partial y_0} < 0. \tag{6}$$

The curvature is

$$\frac{2\dfrac{\partial^2 f}{\partial x_0 \partial y_0}\dfrac{\partial f}{\partial x_0}\dfrac{\partial f}{\partial y_0} - \dfrac{\partial^2 f}{\partial x_0{}^2}\left(\dfrac{\partial f}{\partial y_0}\right)^2 - \dfrac{\partial^2 f}{\partial y_0{}^2}\left(\dfrac{\partial f}{\partial x_0}\right)^2}{\left[\left(\dfrac{\partial f}{\partial x_0}\right)^2 + \left(\dfrac{\partial f}{\partial y_0}\right)^2\right]^{\frac{3}{2}}} = \frac{1}{K}. \tag{7}$$

An important help to plotting the curve is to draw the asymptotes, these being defined as the tangents at its infinite points.* We get these as follows. Write the curve in descending powers of x and y

$$f \equiv f_n(x,y) + f_{n-1}(x,y) + f_{n-2}(x,y) + \ldots = 0. \tag{8}$$

Let the slope of an asymptote be $\dfrac{y_1}{x_1}$, or, in other words, let its point of contact have the homogeneous coordinates $(x_1, y_1, 0)$. As at the finite point (x_0, y_0, z_0) the equation of the tangent is given by (7) of Ch. II which takes the homogeneous form

$$z_0 \left(x \frac{\partial f}{\partial x_0} + y \frac{\partial f}{\partial y_0} \right) - z \left(x_0 \frac{\partial f}{\partial x_0} + y_0 \frac{\partial f}{\partial y_0} \right) = 0.$$

Since $\quad x_0 \dfrac{\partial f}{\partial x_0} + y_0 \dfrac{\partial f}{\partial y_0} + z_0 \dfrac{\partial f}{\partial z_0} \equiv nf(x_0, y_0, z_0) = 0,$

the equation of the tangent takes the simpler form

$$x \frac{\partial f}{\partial x_0} + y \frac{\partial f}{\partial y_0} + z \frac{\partial f}{\partial z_0} = 0.$$

Replacing f and its derivatives from (8) in the homogeneous form

$$f(x,y,z) \equiv f_n(x,y) + z f_{n-1}(x,y) + z^2 f_{n-2}(x,y) + \ldots$$

and then changing (x_0, y_0, z_0) to $(x_1, y_1, 0)$ while $z = 1$ we get

$$x \frac{\partial f_n}{\partial x_1} + y \frac{\partial f_n}{\partial y_1} + f_{n-1}(x_1, y_1) = 0. \tag{9}$$

Suppose that the curve meets the line at infinity in n distinct points so that

$$f_n(x,y) \equiv (xy_1 - yx_1)(xy_2 - yx_2)\ldots(xy_n - yx_n)$$

$$x \frac{\partial f_n}{\partial x_1} + y \frac{\partial f_n}{\partial y_1} \equiv K(xy_1 - yx_1)(x_1 y_2 - y_1 x_2)\ldots(x_1 y_n - y_1 x_n)$$

$$\lim_{x \to x_1, \, y \to y_1} \frac{x \dfrac{\partial f_n}{\partial x_1} + y \dfrac{\partial f_n}{\partial y_1}}{f_n(x,y)} = 1.$$

Consider the homogeneous polynomial of degree $n-1$

$$f_n(x,y) \sum_{i=1}^{i=n} \frac{f_{n-1}(x_i, y_i)}{x \dfrac{\partial f_n}{\partial x_i} + y \dfrac{\partial f_n}{\partial y_i}}.$$

This is identical with $f_{n-1}(x,y)$ for n values $(x_1, y_1), (x_2, y_2), \ldots,$

* Cf. Frost, also Pernot et Moisson, and Stolz.

(x_n, y_n). The two polynomials are identical or

$$\frac{f_{n-1}(x,y)}{f_n(x,y)} \equiv \sum_{i=1}^{i=n} \frac{f_{n-1}(x_i,y_i)}{x\frac{\partial f_n}{\partial x_i} + y\frac{\partial f_n}{\partial y_i}}.$$

We thus get the general rule

Theorem 3] *If the algebraic curve*

$$f(x,y) \equiv f_n(x,y) + f_{n-1}(x,y) + \ldots = 0.$$

meet the line at infinity in distinct non-singular points, and if the fraction $\frac{f_{n-1}(x,y)}{f_n(x,y)}$ be expressed as the sum of partial fractions $\sum_i \frac{c_i}{a_i x + b_i y}$ the equations of the asymptotes are[*]

$$a_i x + b_i y + c_i = 0. \tag{10}$$

When only a single asymptote is desired it is better to go at the matter more simply. If the slope be l_1, and we substitute in the curve, $l_1 x + b$ for y, we have an equation in x whose degree is not n, but $n-1$, for there is one infinite root. There will be just one value b_1 for b, which will reduce this to an equation of order $n-2$, i.e. give two infinite roots; the asymptote is

$$y = l_1 x + b_1$$

The reader is advised to try a few examples.

After the asymptotes have been found and drawn, it will be helpful to find the remaining intersections of the curve with the asymptotes. If the asymptote be tangent at a non-singular point, it is important to find out whether the curve goes to infinity on the same side thereof in both directions, or whether, like the hyperbola, it lies on opposite sides of the asymptote when far out beyond the last intersection. We determine this as follows. Let us choose the axes so that one asymptote at a non-singular point is the x-axis. Let us assume that the highest power in x alone is x^{n-k} so that when $y = 0$, x takes k infinite values, i.e. we have k-point contact. When y is extremely near 0, and x numerically large, the preponderant terms are $ax_n^{-1}y + bx^{n-k} \equiv x^{n-k}(ax^{k-1}y + b)$ and neither of these can vanish, for the curve meets the infinite line but once at the end of the axis by hypothesis. If k be even, x^{k-1} and y both

[*] Cf. Wieleitner, p. 88.

change sign with x and y so that the values of y corresponding to numerically large x's with opposite signs are themselves opposite in sign, i.e. the curve goes to infinity on opposite sides of the asymptote. The reverse is true when k is odd.

Theorem 4] *If an asymptote tangent to a real curve at a non-singular infinite point have even-point contact, the corresponding branch of the curve will go to infinity on opposite sides of the asymptote in the two directions. The reverse is true in the case when there is odd-point contact, the distant parts of the branch are all on one side of the asymptote.*

Suppose that our homogeneous polynomial $f_n(x,y)$ has a linear factor with the multiplicity k, which is not a factor of $f_{n-1}(x,y)$. This will not correspond to a singular point on the infinite line, but to k-point contact therewith. We may choose the axes so that this factor is y, and write

$$y^k \phi_{n-k}(x,y) + f_{n-1}(x,y) + \ldots = 0.$$

We now make a change of variable, writing

$$x = \frac{1}{x'} \qquad y = \frac{y'}{x'}$$

$$y'^k \phi_{n-k}(1,y') + x' f_{n-1}(1,y') + \ldots = 0$$

$$\phi_{n-k}(1,0) \neq 0 \qquad f_{n-1}(1,0) \neq 0.$$

Then by Theorem 4] of Ch. II we may write

$$x' = a_k y'^k + \ldots.$$

Suppose $a_k > 0$. If k be even, x' is positive for all values of y' close to 0. Hence x is large and positive, and y changes sign with y', i.e. all horizontal lines meet the curve far out to the right. When $a_k < 0$ they will all meet it far out to the left. If k be odd x' and y' change sign together, hence y is essentially positive and each y will correspond to two numerically large values of x, one positive and one negative.

Theorem 5] *If a real curve have even-point contact with the line at infinity at an ordinary point, a finite line through that point will have one distant intersection with the curve, if the contact be odd-point, there will be two distant intersections or none.*

We can remember the rule by noting that all vertical lines have one real intersection with the parabola $y = x^2$, but if we take the cubic $y^2 = x^3$ some vertical lines have two real intersections, and some none.

Suppose that a curve has an ordinary singular point of order r at infinity, with r distinct parallel asymptotes running there. These r asymptotes have nr intersections with the curve of which $r(r+1)$ are their intersections with the line at infinity counted $(r+1)$ times. Hence, by the total intersection theorem of the last chapter, we are able to prove*

Theorem 6] *If a curve have r parallel asymptotes running to a point of multiplicity r, their finite intersections with the curve lie on a curve of order $n-r-1$.*

§ 2. Real singular points

In most of the work which we have done so far, in connexion with singular points, we have assumed that we had only to deal with ordinary singularities. We shall postpone to the next book a theoretical discussion of the properties of singular points that are not ordinary ones or cusps, but shall give at this point a discussion of the method of plotting a curve in the vicinity of a singularity of a complicated nature. Much of what we do here will prove of great value later.

Suppose that we have a singular point at the origin. When x and y approach 0, the terms become infinitesimal of different orders. We wish to find a set of terms which are of the same order, lower than the infinitesimal orders of the others. These terms alone will give us a partial representation of the curve in that vicinity. Let the curve be

$$\sum_i A_i x^{\alpha_i} y^{\beta_i} = 0.$$

It is conceivable, and in fact, highly plausible, that the curve can be developed in the vicinity of the origin in a set of series of fractional or integral powers of x, of the form

$$y = y' x^\mu + a_2 x^{2\mu} + \dots$$

For points very near the origin, we may content ourselves with the first term of the series, we want then to find such a value μ that if we put $y = x^\mu$, divide out a suitable power of x and then let x become 0, y' 'will approach a finite value. As an approximation to the curve, we content ourselves with those terms where x has the same power, after this substitution, which is lower than its power in the other terms. How do we find

* Cf. Hyashi.

them ? It is well, since μ is probably a fraction, to make a more elaborate change of variable

$$x = x'^r \qquad y = y' x'^s$$
$$\sum A_i x'^{r\alpha_i + s\beta_i} y'^{\beta_i} = 0. \tag{11}$$

We wish to retain those terms where $r\alpha_i + s\beta_i$ has the lowest value, and momentarily reject the others. How can we give to r and s such values that

$$r\alpha_p + s\beta_p = \ldots = r\alpha_l + s\beta_l = \ldots = r\alpha_q + s\beta_q; \tag{12}$$
$$\alpha_p < \ldots < \alpha_l < \ldots < \alpha_q, \qquad \beta_p > \ldots > \beta_l > \ldots > \beta_q \tag{13}$$

whereas in all the other terms the value is greater ? The true method was discovered by Newton.*

Let us start in the north-east quadrant of a new coordinate plane, and mark every point with the exponents (α, β), i.e. we take the exponents of every term in (x, y) actually appearing, and mark the corresponding point in the (α, β) plane. The line from (α_p, β_p) to (α_q, β_q) has the slope

$$\frac{\beta_q - \beta_p}{\alpha_q - \alpha_p} = -\frac{r}{s}.$$

The points (α_l, β_l) indicated in the inequality above lie on this line, whose equation is

$$r\alpha + s\beta = r\alpha_p + s\beta_p.$$

The terms we wish to reject say α_m, β_m for which

$$r\alpha_m + s\beta_m > r\alpha_p + s\beta_p$$

lie on the other side of this line from the origin. The method of procedure is, then, as follows.

The origin in the (α, β) plane is not a marked point, but there is surely some marked point on the β-axis as otherwise our original equation would be divisible by a power of x. Take the marked point on the β-axis nearest the origin, and call it P_1. Let the half-line which starts from P_1 and goes through the origin rotate positively about P_1 till it passes through one or more marked points; P_2 shall be the most distant of these from P_1. Let the half-line through P_2 away from P_1 rotate positively about P_2 till it passes through at least one other marked point, the most distant being P_3, etc. Continuing thus we get a broken

---

* Cf. Newton, vol. i, p. 357, and also Cramer, p. 54.

line running from a point on the β-axis to one on the α-axis, each segment of which contains two or more marked points. The set of terms in the original equation corresponding to the marked points on each segment will give a partial representation of the curve.

As a check to all this let us look at the infinitesimal orders of the origin in the original curve, and in the various partial curves. We mean by this the order of the infinitesimal f, and of the various functions which give the partial curves. If a line have a north-westerly direction the sum of the coordinates of all points thereon is the same. The infinitesimal order of f is the smallest sum $\alpha_i + \beta_i$, i.e. the sum of the coordinates of the points on the nearest north-west line through a marked point. A similar rule holds for the partial curves.

We have three classes of segments in the (α, β) plane:

a) Those which are steeper than a north-west direction.

b) A single segment, which may, perhaps, not be present at all, which takes the north-west direction.

c) Those which are less steep than a north-west direction.

If a segment from (α_p, β_p) to (α_q, β_q) be steeper than the north-west direction the point thereon which lies on the nearest north-west line to the original is (α_q, β_q) if we follow the inequalities (13). If we divide out the extraneous factor $x^{\alpha_p} y^{\beta_q}$ from each of the terms we retain, the lowest infinitesimal order is $\alpha_q - \alpha_p$. The first of these steep segments starts on the β-axis, hence the sum of the infinitesimal orders from them is

$$\alpha_1 + (\alpha_2 - \alpha_1) + \ldots + (\alpha_l - \alpha_k) = \alpha_l.$$

If we have a north-west segment from (α_l, β_l) to (α_m, β_m), and divide out $\alpha_l \beta_m$ we get, as before, the infinitesimal order $(\alpha_m - \alpha_l)$, so that the sum of the infinitesimal order so far is α_m. The remaining segments are the less steep ones, here the nearest north-west line runs through the marked point furthest to the left, that with the smallest subscripts. The quantity divided out is of the form $x^{\alpha_p} y^{\beta_q}$ and the infinitesimal order is $\beta_p - \beta_q$. The sum of all these will be β_m, and the sum for all segments be $\alpha_m + \beta_m$, the order of f. This is very reassuring as it shows nothing has been lost.

The best way to illustrate the general theory is to work out some special examples:

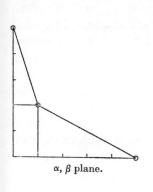

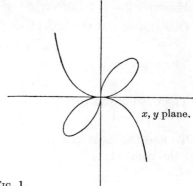

α, β plane.

x, y plane.

Fig. 1.

Example 1. $x^5 - 5xy^2 + 2y^5 = 0.$

The broken line has two segments. The first gives the terms
$$-5xy^2 + 2y^5,$$
and so the simple cubic curve
$$5x = 2y^3.$$

The second gives the terms
$$x^5 - 5xy^2.$$
And so the two parabolas
$$x^2 = \pm\sqrt{5}y.$$

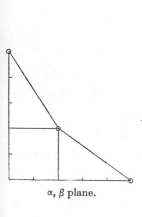

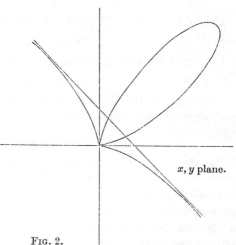

α, β plane.

x, y plane.

Fig. 2.

Example 2. $\qquad x^5-x^2y^2+y^5=0.$

One segment of the broken line gives the cuspidal cubic

$$y^3-x^2=0.$$

The other segment gives the equal cubic

$$x^3-y^2=0.$$

There is but one real asymptote:

$$x+y=\tfrac{1}{3}.$$

To find the most distant part of the loop we put $x=y$, and get the point $(1,1)$.

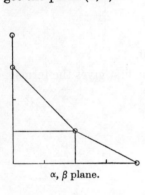

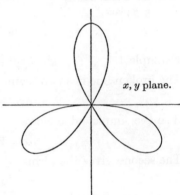

x, y plane.

α, β plane.

Fig. 3.

Example 3. $\qquad x^4+x^2y-y^3+y^4=0.$

The first segment of the broken line gives the two lines

$$x^2-y^2=0.$$

The other segment gives the parabola

$$x^2+y=0.$$

Returning to the theoretical discussion, if there be a north-west segment the partial curve will be given by the homogeneous polynomial

$$a_p y^{\beta_p-\beta_q}+\ldots+a_q x^{\alpha_q-\alpha_p}=0.$$

If the roots of this be distinct we have an ordinary singular point for this partial curve. If the origin be an ordinary singularity for the given curve the broken line consists of a single segment in a north-westerly direction. The partial curves are the various tangents. If the origin be a cusp there is still but one segment to the broken line.

In closing it is well to make one remark about the situation of the real inflexions. We see from (7) that, at such a point

$$\frac{\partial^2 f}{\partial x^2}\left(\frac{\partial f}{\partial y}\right)^2 + \frac{\partial^2 f}{\partial y^2}\left(\frac{\partial f}{\partial x}\right)^2 - 2\,\frac{\partial^2 f}{\partial x\partial y}\left(\frac{\partial f}{\partial x}\right)\left(\frac{\partial f}{\partial y}\right) = 0.$$

This is a homogeneous quadratic form in $\left(\frac{\partial f}{\partial x}\right)$, $\left(\frac{\partial f}{\partial y}\right)$ whose ratio gives minus the slope of the inflexional tangent, hence, at a real inflexion

$$\left(\frac{\partial^2 f}{\partial x^2}\right)\left(\frac{\partial^2 f}{\partial y^2}\right) - \left(\frac{\partial^2 f}{\partial x\partial y}\right)^2 \leqslant 0.$$

If the curve have a real double point at (x, y) its equation can be written

$$0 = (\xi - x)^2 \frac{\partial^2 f}{\partial x^2} + 2(\xi - x)(\eta - y)\,\frac{\partial^2 f}{\partial x\partial y} + (\eta - y)^2\frac{\partial^2 f}{\partial y^2} + \cdots.$$

The tangents are obtained by equating the quadratic terms to 0, the condition for real tangents is that found above for real inflexions. We thus get the pretty theorem*

Theorem 7] *The real inflexions, cusps, and nodes are in that portion of the plane where*

$$\frac{\partial^2 f}{\partial x^2}\cdot\frac{\partial^2 f}{\partial y^2} - \left(\frac{\partial^2 f}{\partial x\partial y}\right)^2 \leqslant 0. \qquad (14)$$

* Cf. Scott[2].

CHAPTER IV

REAL CIRCUITS OF CURVES

§ 1. Topological properties of even and odd circuits

It is the purpose of the present chapter to discuss the topological properties of the various real circuits of a real algebraic
plane curve. We mean by a non-composite circuit a real branch
as previously defined, and its various analytic continuations
taken successively until the first development is reached again.
In common parlance it is the part traced by a continuously
moving real point which eventually comes back to each point
already passed. If a straight line not tangent to a circuit intersect it in an even number of real non-singular points, the same
is true of every line meeting it in distinct non-singular points,
for the intersections can only pass from real to imaginary in
pairs. In this case the circuit is defined as 'even' otherwise
'odd'. A circuit shall be said to be 'simple' if it contain no
point on more than one branch of a curve, no ordinary singularity
for example. We may make a composite circuit out of successive arcs of various curves joined end to end. The distinction
of odd and even will be as before.

Suppose that we have two circuits c_1 and c_2, neither of which
passes through the origin. We shall assume that they are not
tangent to one another, and that c_1 cuts the line at infinity in
distinct points. Then we may take such a large circle about the
origin as centre that each point of c_1 outside thereof is as near
to the nearest asymptote as we please. Thus every outside
curve cutting c_1 at an angle greater than a very small limit ϵ will
cut the near asymptote also, and vice versa.

Let us next fix our attention on c_2. This is an algebraic curve
not through the origin, there will be a finite number of normals
through the origin and, hence, a nearest point. If we make the
transformation
$$x' = rx \qquad y' = ry$$
we may change c_2 to a similar and similarly placed circuit c_3
completely outside the large circle. We may choose r so that
c_3 is not tangent to c_1, and in fact so that every intersection
with an asymptote is at an angle $> \epsilon$. Then the number of inter-

sections of c_3 and c_1 is the number of intersections of c_3 and the asymptotes. Moreover, c_2 and c_3 are even or odd together.

If c_1 and c_2 be both odd c_1 has an odd number of asymptotes, and each will meet c_3 an odd number of times. The number of intersections of c_1 and c_3 is thus odd. If c_3 shrink gradually back to c_2, we shall lose or gain real intersections in pairs, and this will not affect the even or odd question. The case where one or both of our circuits is even is handled in the same way.

Theorem 1] *Two circuits will have no intersections or an even number of intersections unless both are odd, in which case the number of intersections is odd also.*

Theorem 2] *A non-singular curve of odd order has one odd circuit, a non-singular curve of even order has no odd circuit.*

We saw in theorem 4] of the last chapter that a curve which has even-point contact with its asymptote goes to infinity on opposite sides of the asymptote, although at a finite point, a curve with even-point contact does not cross its tangent. Exactly the reverse situation holds for a curve with odd-point contact. We may then say that in passing through infinity the upper and lower neighbourhoods of a line are interchanged.

Suppose that we have a simple even circuit which meets the line at infinity in only two points. Let a sphere be tangent to the plane at its south pole. We may project the plane on the southern hemisphere by lines radiating from the centre, the relation is one to one except that points of the line at infinity are projected into pairs of diametrically opposite points of the equator. We have two arches on the southern hemisphere which do not intersect one another, one connects two points of the equator, the other the two opposite points. We have then, three simply connected regions on the hemisphere. The first is bounded by two curves and two arcs of the equator, each of the others is bounded by one curve and one arc. We may find a continuous path from a point on one equatorial boundary of the first region to the opposite point on the other equatorial boundary arc which does not meet either curve, but a continuous curve from a point on the equatorial boundary of the second region to the opposite point of the third meets both curves and vice versa. Now if we project back upon the plane, region I of the sphere becomes a simply connected region of the plane called region I, which has the property that we may connect two of its points by an odd circuit which does not intersect the given even circuit. Regions II and III of the hemisphere become region II of the plane which has the property that an odd circuit connecting two of its points meets the given circuit an even number of times. Region I is called the 'outside' region, II the 'inside' region. The reader will see which is which in the case where the given even circuit is a hyperbola.

Suppose, next, that it has been shown that a simple even circuit that meets the line at infinity in $2(n-1)$ points divides the plane into an outside and an inside region of exactly this sort, there being odd circuits in the outside which do not meet the curve, but none such which contain points of the inside region. Consider a simple even circuit that meets the line at infinity $2n$ times. Consider two successive intersections with the line at infinity, and project the whole circuit on the southern hemisphere as before. If we take a point A on the curve just before the first crossing with the equator and a point B just after the second crossing and connect them by a simple arc that does not cross the equator, we get a circuit which will project back into a simple even circuit that crosses the line at infinity $2(n-1)$ times. Take an odd circuit that does not meet this new even circuit. If it meets the discarded part of the original circuit it will do so an even number of times, for this discarded part and the new arc AB make an even circuit. Any part of our new odd circuit which is inside the original even circuit can be replaced by a path which follows the arc AB very closely, and so cuts the line at infinity at most twice. We have thus constructed a new odd composite circuit which does not intersect our original even circuit at all. Our new circuit has an outside region, it also has an inside:

Theorem 3] *A simple even circuit divides the plane into two parts, an inside and an outside. Every odd circuit through a point of the inside meets the even circuit in at least two points, certain odd circuits in the outside region do not meet it at all, and so lie completely without.*

Suppose we connect two points, A and B, of an odd circuit by a continuous path which is either finite, or meets the infinite line an even number of times. If we go from A to B one way along the curve we cross the line at infinity an even number of times if we cross it at all. If we go the other way there are an odd number of crossings. If we take the first of these, and the path AB, we get an even circuit. A continuous path from an inside to an outside point will meet the boundary an odd number of times. If we try the same experiment with an even circuit it may be that going from A to B each way we meet the line at infinity an odd number of times, in which case we either get two smaller even circuits, or none at all.

Theorem 4] *A continuous path connecting two points of an odd circuit, which meets the line at infinity, if at all, in an even number of points, will, with one arc of the original circuit, divide the plane into two such parts that a continuous path from a point of the one to one of the other, necessarily meets the boundary an odd number of times. In the case of an even circuit this may, or may not, be the case.* *

As a justification for our last statement let us note that a continuous arc connecting two points on the same half of a hyperbola will, with the corresponding finite arc, divide the plane in two, but a continuous path connecting two points on different branches will not do so if we allow passage through infinity. An arc of an ellipse and a finite arc connecting two of its points will divide the plane, this will not be the case if we connect the points by an arc passing simply through infinity as does a straight line. A continuous arc connecting two points of an even circuit, and dividing the plane with one arc of that circuit shall be said to be 'of the first sort' with regard to the circuit. When it does not divide the plane with either arc it shall be said to be 'of the second sort'.

Let us take two points A_1, B_1 on an even circuit. Connect them by a continuous arc not meeting the circuit elsewhere. It will determine a composite circuit with each arc of the original. If an odd circuit meet one of these smaller circuits an odd number of times it will do so with the other smaller circuit, and the same will be true if the number of intersections be even, including zero as an even number.

Theorem 5] *If a continuous arc be of the second sort with regard to an even circuit, it will form therewith two odd circuits, otherwise two even ones.*

Let the reader show by similar reasoning:

Theorem 6] *If an arc connecting two points of an even circuit divide the plane with one arc of the circuit connecting its extremities, it will do so with the other. If the given circuit be odd, only one of the two arcs on it will divide the plane with the new arc.*

Suppose that A_1B_1 and A_2B_2 are two arcs of the second sort with regard to an even circuit, but with no common point. If the pairs of extremities did not separate one another on the circuit there would be one arc A_1B_1 of the circuit that shared no point with one arc A_2B_2. Then the two arcs connecting A_1, B_1 would make an odd circuit, as would two connecting A_2, B_2, yet these circuits had no point in common, which is contrary to 2].

Theorem 7] *If two arcs be of the second sort with regard to an even circuit their pairs of extremities separate one another on the circuit.*

Theorem 8] *If the intersections of two circuits follow in the same order on the two, then if one circuit be even, at most one arc of the other is of the second sort with regard thereto.*

Suppose that we have two circuits with $k > 2$ intersections following in the same order on them, and that no arc of one is of the second sort with regard to the other. We shall see later that this can be accomplished with ease. Let the successive intersections be $A_1, A_2 \ldots$. Let A_i, A_j be a successive pair. Pick out that arc of the first circuit connecting them which contains no other intersections. This will divide the plane with one arc A_iA_j of the second circuit unless it be of the second sort with regard thereto, a case we may consider excluded by 8]. If the second circuit be even, the chosen arc A_iA_j of the first will divide the plane with either arc A_iA_j of the second by 6]. If the second circuit be odd we must choose the arc of the second rightly; which shall we choose? The only case to consider is that where both circuits are odd, for if either be even we may choose either arc of the other. But if both be odd and we choose that arc of one which contains no other intersection, and that arc of the other contains all the other intersections, then this supposedly even circuit would be cut by the circuit composed of the other two arcs an odd number of times, an absurdity.

We have thus established that if neither curve present an arc of the second sort with regard to the other, the k successive intersections will determine k successive pairs of arcs containing no other intersections, each pair dividing the plane. Let the equations of the curves on which the circuits lie be

$$f_1 = 0 \qquad f_2 = 0.$$

Let us write $\qquad f \equiv f_1 f_2 + \epsilon\phi = 0,$

where ϵ is infinitesimal. The curve f is infinitely near the original curves and meets them only where they meet ϕ or at infinity. If we take for ϕ a curve which meets neither circuit in a real point, and ϵ so that f contains a point inside one of the even circuits, it will contain a point inside each of the k just described and have, in fact, k even circuits infinitely near the others. These circuits, shall be said to be obtained from the others by the method of 'small variations'.*

Suppose that we have two circuits which lie infinitely near to one another, i.e. they are corresponding parts of two curves whose equations differ infinitesimally. A curve meeting one in real points will meet the other in the same number of them. Their intersections, if they have any, must follow in the same order on the two curves, and both must be even or odd together. Moreover, one could not make an arc of the second sort with regard to the other, for an odd circuit lying outside of one, and hence, outside of the other, would fail to meet both, which is not possible if one have an arc of the second sort with regard to the other by 5].

Theorem 9] *If two infinitely near circuits intersect in a number of points, these will follow in the same order on the two, and we may obtain k even circuits from them by the method of small variations.*

Let us see what is the maximum number of circuits obtained by this method. We shall proceed to prove

Theorem 10] *If two curves f_1, f_2 have N simple circuits, and k intersections, the maximum number of circuits obtained from them by the method of small variations is $N + k - 2$, and this number is only attained when all the intersections lie on one pair of circuits arranged in the same order.*

If there be s circuits each intersecting none on the other curve, these will be replaced by an equal number of like circuits.

---

* Cf. Brusotti[1] for this definition.

The number obtained by small variations will thus be $\leqslant k+s$. Our given circuits cannot all be non-intersecting, we must sacrifice at least two to get our s intersections, $s \leqslant N-2$. A combination of these two inequalities gives the theorem.

These relations lead us to the specific question of considering the maximum number of circuits allowable for a curve of assigned sort. We begin by proving:

Theorem 11] *A real irreducible non-singular curve of order n cannot have more than $\frac{1}{2}(n-1)(n-2)+1$ real circuits. When n is even, all of these are even, when n is odd, all but one are even.*

The latter part of our theorem is contained in 3] and need not detain us. Suppose that n is even, so that all of the circuits are even, and that there are $\frac{1}{2}(n-1)(n-2)+2$ of these. Pick out a point on each of these, and require a curve of order $n-2$ which, if non-singular, will also be composed of even circuits, to go through each of the given points, and through $n-4$ others. This is not asking too much, for the number of conditions imposed is $\frac{1}{2}(n-2)(n+1)$ while the amount of freedom for the new curve is $\frac{1}{2}(n-2)(n+1)$. But now the number of intersections of the two curves is

$$(n-1)(n-2)+4+(n-4) = n(n-2)+2$$

and this is too many.

Suppose, secondly, that n is odd. We place one point of our curve of order $n-2$ on each of the even circuits and $n-3$ on the odd circuit there must be one more intersection with each circuit, and this again leads to a contradiction.

We may generalize this theorem to one of much greater generality. Suppose that we have a curve of even order n, with singular points of orders $s_1, s_2, \ldots$ and

$$\tfrac{1}{2}[(n-1)(n-2)-\sum s_i(s_i-1)]+2$$

circuits, of which ν are odd. Let us construct an adjoint curve of order $n-2$ passing through a point on each of the even circuits. The amount of freedom left for this curve is at least

$$\tfrac{1}{2}(n-2)(n+1)-\tfrac{1}{2}[(n-1)(n-2)-\sum s_i(s_i-1)]-2-\tfrac{1}{2}\sum s_i(s_i-1)+\nu$$
$$= n+\nu-4.$$

Since n is even, the number of odd circuits ν is even, as is the number $n+\nu-4$.

Let us require our adjoint to go through $n+\nu-4$ more points on an even circuit. The number of intersections accounted for is

$$(n-1)(n-2)-\sum s_i(s_i-1)+4+\sum s_i(s_i-1)-2\nu+n+\nu-4$$
$$= n(n-2)-\nu+2.$$

We must lastly consider a singular point of an odd circuit. Let its total multiplicity be s_i, its multiplicity for the circuit t_i. Then $\sum t_i(s_i-t_i)$ is an odd number, for it represents the total number of intersections of our odd circuits with certain even circuits, and an odd number $\nu-1$ of odd circuits. It appears then that $\sum s_i t_i$ is odd when $\sum t_i^2$ is even or vice versa, or $\sum t_i s_i$ is even or odd when $\sum t_i$ is odd or even, or, lastly, that $\sum t_i(s_i-1)$ is odd. But this represents the sum of the singular intersections of an odd circuit with an adjoint of even order, and as the total sum of real intersections must be even, there must be at least one non-singular intersection not yet accounted for. This holds for each of the ν odd circuits. The number of intersections with the adjoint is at least $n(n-2)+2$, which is absurd. A similar method may be followed when n is odd. We get finally:

Harnack's First Theorem 12]* *A real irreducible curve of order n cannot have more than $\frac{1}{2}(n-1)(n-2)-\sum s_i(s_i-1)+1$ circuits.*

§ 2. Generation of curves by small variations

We have, so far, established an upper limit for the number of circuits, without showing that there exist curves with this maximum number. That must be our next great task.†

Definition. An arc of a curve of order n shall be called a 'base arc' if it contain $n\nu$ points, the total intersection with a curve of order ν.

Definition. A curve of order n shall be called a 'generating curve' when

  $a)$ it is non-singular and has $\frac{1}{2}(n-1)(n-2)+1$ real circuits;

  $b)$ it has two base arcs with no common points.

It is not certain yet whether there exist generating curves of high degree, though there is no difficulty in finding them in simple cases. When $n=2$ the ellipse is a good example, when $n=3$ we take the bipartite cubic consisting of an oval and an

* Cf. Harnack, p. 192.
† For the next developments cf. Brusotti².

odd circuit. A line connecting two points of the odd circuit will meet that circuit again, and give a base arc.

Suppose, next, that we have a generating curve E_n of order n, and another curve C_r of order r called an 'aggregate curve' with the maximum number of circuits. Let us assume further:

a) That all of the intersections of the two are real and distinct, lying on one circuit e of E_n and one circuit c of C_r.

b) That E_n contains a base arc b_1 containing all its intersections with a curve of order ν_1, a number which divides both n and r, this base arc lying on one of the arcs determined on e by c. If one of these arcs be of the second sort, that shall be the one on which b_1 lies.

c) That E_n shall contain a second base arc b_2 which contains all its intersections in proper order with a curve of order ν_2, which number divides both n and $2r$.

Since b_1 contains the total intersection with a curve of order ν_1 it will contain the total intersection with a curve of order $(n+r)$ made up of $\dfrac{n+r}{\nu_1}$ infinitely close curves of order ν_1. Call this curve $\theta_{\nu+r}$ and write

$$C_{n+r} \equiv C_r E_n + \delta\theta_{n+r},$$

where δ is supposed to be infinitesimal. This curve lies infinitely close to C_r and E_n, meeting the latter only in $n(n+r)$ points of one arc b_1, which will follow in the same order on the two, with no arcs of the second sort by 9]. It will have one circuit near to each of the other circuits of E_n and C_r and nr even circuits obtained from e and c by small variation. The total number of circuits will thus be

$$\frac{(n-1)(n-2)}{2} + \frac{(r-1)(r-2)}{2} + nr = \frac{(n+r-1)(n+r-2)}{2} + 1,$$

and this is the maximum possible for a curve of the order $n+r$. It is to be noted that this new curve C_{n+r} could be taken as a new aggregate curve to E_n. We now pass to b_2 and take a curve ψ_{2n+r} of order $2n+r$ having all its intersections real and lying on one arc of b_2 and write as before

$$C_{2n+r} = C_{n+r} E_n + \delta\psi_{2n+r}.$$

The intersections of this curve and E_n are real, $n(2n+r)$ in number, following in the same order on the two and lying on b_2. The number of circuits is obtained from the previous formula, changing r to $n+r$

$$\frac{(2n+r-1)(2n+r-2)}{2}+1.$$

A few moments' consideration will show that we can step up indefinitely in this way, using first b_1 and then b_2, thus getting a curve of order
$$kn+r,$$
where k is a positive integer, with the maximum permissible number of circuits.

There are various remarks which should be made at this point. Whenever we are about ready to stop, so that we do not care where our last curve may intersect E_n, we may replace our curve ψ or θ by a curve consisting in whole or in part of such factors as $(x^2+y^2+1)^m$. We next see that if we can find separate aggregate curves of order 1, 2,..., $n-1$ we can find a curve of any degree greater than n with the maximum number of circuits. In fact we may do this in an extraordinary number of different ways. We proceed to illustrate a few (see figs. 4 and 5).*

A) Take $n=1$. The generating curve is a straight line, the curves and sets of lines meeting it in the one or the other of two well-separated segments.

B) $n=2$. We start with a conic, and the two arcs determined thereon by two lines which intersect outside. If we be content to seek curves of even order we take as C_2 another ellipse, θ_4 as four lines meeting E_2 in pairs of points of one arc determined by C_2, and proceed as above.

The case of the cubic is easily handled in the same way. We thus get

Theorem 13] *It is possible in a great many ways to construct by small variations a non-singular curve of any order with the maximum number of permissible circuits.*

It is now necessary to see if we can find curves with the maximum number of circuits compatible with a certain number of singular points.

* Cf. Harnack, p. 197, also Ragsdale, pp. 381 ff. The two figures (4 and 5) are taken from the latter source. The author takes this opportunity to thank the editors of the *American Journal of Mathematics* for their courtesy in permitting him to copy them.

We saw in 12] that if the number of double points be $n-k-2$ the maximum possible number of circuits possible is

$$\frac{(n-1)(n-2)}{2} - (n-k-2) = \frac{(n-2)(n-3)}{2} + k.$$

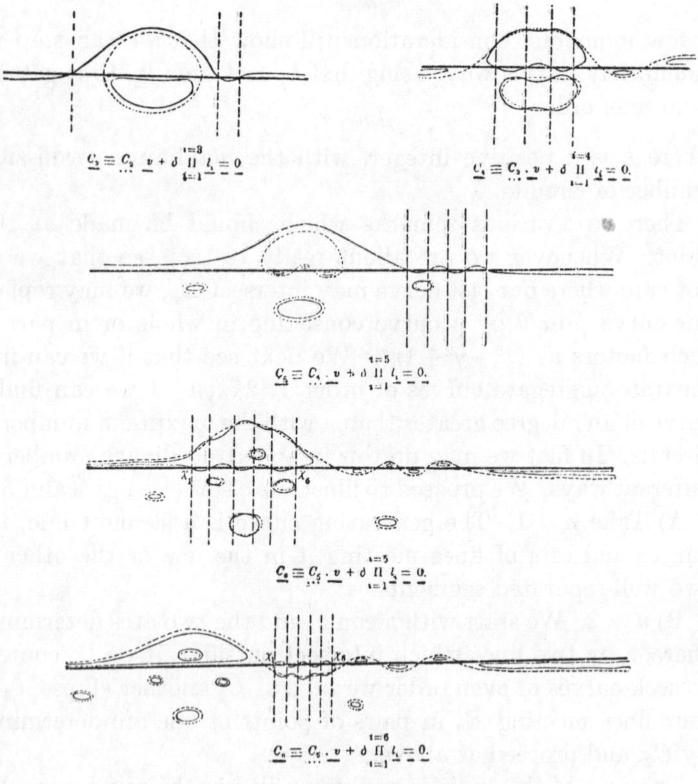

$$C_3 \equiv C_2 \cdot v + \delta \prod_{i=1}^{i=3} l_i = 0$$

$$C_4 \equiv C_3 \cdot v + \delta \prod_{i=1}^{i=4} l_i = 0.$$

$$C_5 \equiv C_4 \cdot v + \delta \prod_{i=1}^{i=5} l_i = 0.$$

$$C_6 \equiv C_5 \cdot v + \delta \prod_{i=1}^{i=5} l_i = 0.$$

$$C_6 \equiv C_5 \cdot v + \delta \prod_{i=1}^{i=6} l_i = 0.$$

FIG. 4.

Let us assume that for every value of the order up to and including n, and for every value of k up to and including $n-2$ it has been shown that there exists a curve with this maximum number of circuits. Let us also assume that a line can be found cutting one circuit in n distinct points which follow in the same order on the line and on the circuit, the curve being E_n and the line l_1. These conditions can certainly be fulfilled for n taking any one of the values 1, 2, or 3. Let ϕ_n be another curve of the same order as E_n and with the same double points, and meeting

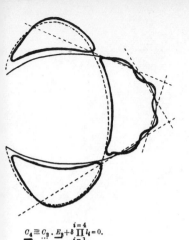

$$\underline{C_4} \equiv C_2 \cdot \underline{E_2} + \delta \prod_{i=1}^{i=4} l_i = 0.$$

$$\underline{C_4} \equiv C_2 \cdot \underline{E_2} + \delta \prod_{i=1}^{i=4} l_i = 0.$$

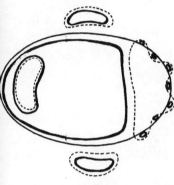

$$\underline{C_6} \equiv C_4 \cdot \underline{E_2} + \delta \prod_{i=1}^{i=6} l_i = 0.$$

C_6 from C_4 by 1st mode of generation.

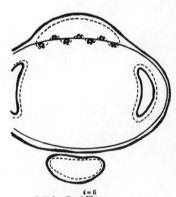

$$\underline{C_6} \equiv C_4 \cdot \underline{E_2} + \delta \prod_{i=1}^{i=6} l_i = 0.$$

C_6 from C_4 by 2nd mode of generation.

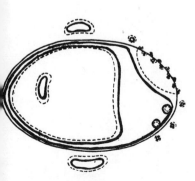

$$\underline{C_8} \equiv C_6 \cdot \underline{E_2} + \delta \prod_{i=1}^{i=8} l_i = 0.$$

C_8 from C_6,
C_6 from C_4 by 1st mode of generation.

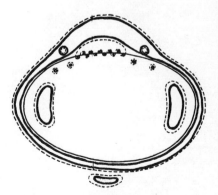

$$\underline{C_8} \equiv C_6 \cdot \underline{E_2} + \delta \prod_{i=1}^{i=8} l_i = 0.$$

C_8 from C_6,
C_6 from C_4 by 2nd mode of generation.

Fig. 5.

it also at P, one intersection with l_1, while the remaining inter-sections of l_1 and ϕ_n shall be on a segment PQ, where Q is a neighbouring intersection of l_1 and E_n. If l_1 have an arc of the second sort with regard to E_n we must choose this for PQ. The number of conditions imposed on ϕ_n, since a double point imposes 3, is

$$3(n-k-2)+n = 4n-3k-6.$$

Now since

$$n^2-5n+12 > 0$$

$$n(n+3) > 8n-12$$

$$n\frac{(n+3)}{2} > 4n-6,$$

so that we have not, really, asked too much of ϕ_n. Lastly, let l_2 be another line through P. We write

$$E_{n+1} = l_1 E_n + \epsilon l_2 \phi_n.$$

The curve E_{n+1} will have a double point at each of the $n-k-2$ double points of E_n, also an additional one at P. It has a circuit near each of the $\dfrac{(n-2)(n-3)}{2}+k-1$ circuits of E_n away from that cut by l_1, $n-2$ circuits near E_n and l_1 by small variation, and a circuit with a double point at P.

The number of double points of E is

$$n+1-k-2.$$

The number of circuits is

$$\frac{(n-2)(n-3)}{2}+k-1+(n-2)+1 = \frac{(n-1)(n-2)}{2}+k$$

$$= \frac{[(n+1)-2][(n+1)-3]}{2}+k.$$

This holds for all values of k up to $n=2$. For $k=n-1$ we get a number compatible with the order n. Lastly it is clear we can step up, for the line l_1 meets E in $n+1$ successive points on one circuit.

Harnack's Second Theorem 14] *There exists a curve of each order with the maximum number of circuits compatible with that order and with a certain number of double points, provided that number is not permissible for a curve of lower order.* *

* Harnack, p. 193.

§ 4. Nesting circuits

In our discussion of the circuits on a curve we have, so far, paid no attention to their relative positions. We shall promptly see that there are very definite rules governing this matter.

Definition. Two even circuits shall be said to 'nest' if one be inside the other. A set of even circuits shall be said to 'nest' if they can be so arranged in order that each is inside the preceding one. It is clear that a line which intersects the innermost circuit of a nest will meet each circuit twice. We thus get some simple theorems due to Hilbert.* His theorems read somewhat differently from ours as he does not include the outermost circuit as forming a part of the nest.

Theorem 15] *If the order of a curve be n, an upper bound for the number of circuits in any one nest is $\dfrac{n}{2}$ and this number cannot be attained if there be any circuits other than those in this nest.*

Theorem 16] *The upper bound for the total number of even circuits in any two nests is $\dfrac{n}{2}$, when n is even, and $\dfrac{n-1}{2}$ when n is odd.*

Theorem 17] *When n is odd an upper bound for the number of circuits in one nest is $\dfrac{n-1}{2}$. If there be this number there can be no other nest.*

It is often a far cry from determining an upper bound for any number of objects, to showing that this bound is ever reached in practice. Fortunately in the present case it is possible to do so.†

We start with $n = 4$, noticing that in fig. 5 we have an example of a curve of the fourth order with four circuits, one of which meets the ellipse in 8 points arranged in the same order on the two. Neither has an arc of the second sort with regard to the other, but one arc of this circuit and one arc of the ellipse determine a region containing other circuits of the quartic.

Suppose, in general, we have our ellipse, the generating curve E_2, and an aggregate curve C_n with the following properties:

---

* Cf. Hilbert, pp. 116 ff.
† Hulburt[1], pp. 197 ff.

1) It has the maximum number of circuits $\dfrac{(n-1)(n-2)}{2}+1$ and a nest of $\dfrac{n-2}{2}$.

2) One circuit meets the ellipse in $2n$ points arranged in the same order on the two.

3) One of the regions determined by arcs of C_n and E_2 connecting two points contains some circuits of the nest, or is contained in some.

Let us take $n+2$ lines meeting E_2 in pairs of points on some other arc besides that last mentioned. We write

$$C_{n+2} \equiv C_n E_2 + \delta \Pi l_i = 0.$$

What can we say about C_{n+2}?

1) Its order is $n+2$.

2) It lies very close to C_n and E_2.

3) It meets E_2 in $2(n+2)$ points in the same order on the two.

4) It has a nest of $\dfrac{n}{2}$ circuits close to the nest of C_n and the arc of $C_n E_2$ mentioned.

5) A composite circuit made of arcs of C_n and E_2 includes circuits of the nest or is included therein.

6) It has the maximum number of circuits for a curve of order $n+1$, namely

$$n\frac{(n-1)}{2}.$$

7) It may be used to step up further.

It appears from this that we can get a curve of any even order with no singular points, with the maximum number of circuits, and the maximum number of nesting circuits compatible with the total number. Moreover, in deducing this curve we might have replaced our ellipse by a pair of intersecting lines whose intersection was outside the first aggregate ellipse C_2. The curve C_4 would have four circuits, two within the ellipse, one without the ellipse, but between it and segments of the lines running to their intersection, one starting in the opposite angular opening, meeting each of the lines four times and running around to the ellipse through infinity. The essential arrangement is just as before, and we may step up indefinitely. But now we have a curve of even order n intersecting a line n times. If we make a small variation of this curve and l we get a curve with these properties:

1) Its order is $n+1$.

2) It has a nest of $\dfrac{n}{2}$ curves.

3) It has a circuit near each of the circuits of C_n which does not meet the l, $n-1$ even circuits near l and the crinkly circuit of C_n, and one odd circuit near the two.

These, however, are the maximum numbers for an odd circuit.

Hilbert's Theorem 18] *For every order n there exists a non-singular curve with the maximum number of circuits, and the maximum number for any one nest.*[*]

When $n = 6$ the maximum number of circuits is 11, the maximum in any nest is 2, and there exist such sextic curves. It is a curious fact that if a sextic have eleven circuits, at least one pair must nest.[†]

It is now time to look for curves with the maximum number of circuits and double points together. A double point may be classed as a circuit of zero extent.

The new circuits were created in our system of small variations by an arc of C_n and one of E_2 which had $2n$ successive intersections. Now if instead of taking our lines l_1, l_2, etc., all meeting some other arc of E_2, we take some of them to form a succession of segments connecting successive intersections of $C_n E_2$; such intersections, being double points both for $C_n E_2$ and for pairs of lines l_i, l_i, will be double points for C_{n+2}, which will have certain new double points in place of as many new circuits away from the nest. This gives

Hulburt's Theorem 19] *There exist curves of every order n with the maximum number of nesting circuits compatible with their order and other circuits, and the maximum number of circuits and double points in any combination which is impossible for a curve of lower order.*[‡]

---

[*] Hilbert,[2] p. 122, for the case n even.
[†] Cf. Wright.   [‡] Hulburt[2].

§ 3. Apparent order and index of circuits

We shall mean by the 'apparent order' of a circuit the maximum number of different real intersections with any real line. This number can never exceed the order of the curve, and may fall far below it. We shall mean by the 'index' of a circuit the minimum number of real points on any real line not tangent or passing through a singular point. This number will frequently be 0, it cannot exceed $n-2$, for if a tangent be slightly displaced away from the curve it will lose two real intersections. It is the purpose of the present section to look for curves of certain types with the greatest possible index. Are there any curves of index $n-2$?

Let us begin with a curve of order n and an ordinary singularity of order $n-1$. There is no difficulty in writing the equation of such a curve. We merely have to put down

$$l_1 l_2 l_3 ... l_n + m_1 m_2 ... m_{n-1} = 0, \tag{1}$$

where the l's and m's are homogeneous polynomials of the first order in x and y. Let us assume that all the l's and all the m's are distinct, and that the m's, equated to 0, bisect all but two of the successive angular openings about the origin determined by the l's. These latter lines are parallel to the asymptotes, and none of them can meet the curve at any point except the origin and at infinity. There is, thus, an infinite arc of the curve in each of $2(n-1)$ angular openings of the l's, those which contain the halves of the m's. The curve crosses each of the l's at infinity and so, by Ch. III 5] it goes to infinity on the same side of the l in each of the opposite angular openings. In one of the angular openings where there is no m there will be a loop of our curve, the opposite opening will be empty. A straight line, not through the origin will cross $n-1$ angular openings, and enter two opposite angular openings. If it cross an angular opening with an arc of the curve running from the origin to infinity it must cross the curve. If it enter without crossing an angular opening with a part of a hyperbola it will cut that part of the curve once. A line with the minimum number of real intersections will be one that crosses the empty angular opening and enters, without crossing, two containing arcs that run from the origin to infinity.

Theorem 20] *There exist curves of order n consisting of a single circuit of apparent order n and index n—2.*

The curves of index $n-2$ have been elaborately studied by Nagy.* Some of the methods employed are not entirely convincing on the score of rigour, and extended discussion would lead us too far afield.

* See Nagy[1], Nagy[2], and Nagy[3], the first being the most interesting.

CHAPTER V

ELEMENTARY INVARIANT THEORY

§ 1. Trilinear coordinates

ONE great advantage in using homogeneous coordinates, $x : y : z$, instead of ordinary Cartesian ones, x and y, is the way that parallel lines can be handled as lines intersecting on the fictitious line at infinity, also the symmetrical way in which the three variables can be handled. Both of these advantages are retained in a more general system of coordinates which we shall now explain.

What is the most general system of coordinates x_1, x_2, x_3 which are

 a) homogeneous;

 b) such that x, y, and z are functions of x_1, x_2, and x_3 with continuous first partial derivatives;

 c) such as to give to every straight line a homogeneous linear equation?

We write

$$x \equiv x(x_1, x_2, x_3) \qquad y \equiv y(x_1, x_2, x_3) \qquad z \equiv z(x_1, x_2, x_3)$$
$$ux + vy + wz \equiv k(u_1 x_1 + u_2 x_2 + u_3 x_3).$$

Since our coordinates are homogeneous we may replace kx_1, kx_2, kx_3 by x_1, x_2, x_3, getting

$$ux + vy + wz \equiv u_1 x_1 + u_2 x_2 + u_3 x_3.$$

Differentiating partially to x_i

$$u \frac{\partial x}{\partial x_i} + v \frac{\partial y}{\partial x_i} + w \frac{\partial z}{\partial x_i} = u_i.$$

As u, v, and w are perfectly independent variables each partial derivative is a constant. The functions involved are linear and homogeneous:

$$\sigma x = A_{11} x_1 + A_{12} x_2 + A_{13} x_3$$
$$\sigma y = A_{21} x_1 + A_{22} x_2 + A_{23} x_3$$
$$\sigma z = A_{31} x_1 + A_{32} x_2 + A_{33} x_3.$$

If the determinant $|A_{ij}|$ were 0, these equations would be linearly dependent, which is not the case. Hence we may solve them getting

$$\rho x_1 = a_{11}x + a_{12}y + a_{13}z$$
$$\rho x_2 = a_{21}x + a_{22}y + a_{23}z \qquad |a_{ij}| \neq 0. \qquad (1)$$
$$\rho x_3 = a_{31}x + a_{32}y + a_{33}z$$

Such a system of coordinates are called 'trilinear'. Let the reader prove:

Theorem 1] *The trilinear coordinates of a point are proportional to constant multiples of the distances of that point from three non-concurrent lines, when all of those lines are finite.*

The Cartesian coordinates, in homogeneous form, are a special case of trilinear coordinates, but do not come under this theorem, since one line is at infinity. When the three lines are chosen we may use such multiples of the distances that any chosen point, not on one of the lines, is the 'unit' point, i.e. that one with three equal coordinates. The commonest way is to take the centre of the inscribed circle as the unit point, then the co-ordinates of a point are proportional to its distances from the sides of the triangle, with proper algebraic signs attached. If a_1, a_2, a_3 be the lengths of the sides of the triangle, the equation of the infinite line is

$$a_1x_1 + a_2x_2 + a_3x_3 = 0.$$

If, on the other hand, we take the centre of gravity as the unit point, since the three triangles whose vertices are in each case this point and two vertices of the given triangle have equal areas, the coordinates of a point are proportional to the areas of the triangles it makes with two vertices of the given triangle. The equation of the line at infinity is

$$x_1 + x_2 + x_3 = 0.$$

These are sometimes called the 'Barycentric Coordinates' of Möbius.*

We shall also have occasion once or twice to use oblique Cartesian coordinates, where a point is located by its distances from two lines which make an oblique angle, the distance from each axis being measured, not directly, but in a direction

---

* Cf. Möbius.

parallel to the other axis. Oblique axes may be put in **homo-**geneous form if desired. They are to-day much less taught **and** considered than they were two generations ago.

As a matter of notation the points whose coordinates are $(1, 0, 0)$, $(0, 1, 0)$, and $(0, 0, 1)$ shall be called the points O_1, O_2, O_3 respectively.

Theorem 2] *Any four coplanar points, no three of which are collinear, may be taken as the unit point and the points O_1, O_2, O_3 of a trilinear coordinate system. The coordinates of every point are then completely determined except for the factor of homogeneity.*

Theorem 3] *Every set of numbers, not all 0, will correspond to the coordinates of a perfectly definite finite or infinite point in any trilinear system.*

Let
$$\rho x_i = a_{i1}x + a_{i2}y + a_{i3}z$$
$$\rho y_i = a_{i1}x' + a_{i2}y' + a_{i3}z'.$$

Then $\rho(\lambda x_i + \mu y_i) = a_{i1}(\lambda x + \mu x') + a_{i2}(\lambda y + \mu y') + a_{i3}(\lambda z + \mu z').$

Theorem 4] *If the homogeneous Cartesian coordinates of three points be linearly dependent, then the trilinear coordinates of those same points are linearly dependent, and the multipliers are the same in the two cases.*

Suppose that we take four collinear points with the coordinates

$$\lambda_1(x) + \mu_1(y), \qquad \lambda_2(x) + \mu_2(y), \qquad \lambda_3(x) + \mu_3(y), \qquad \lambda_4(x) + \mu_4(y).$$

Assuming that their line is not vertical, the projections of these points on the x-axis will have the non-homogeneous coordinates

$$\frac{\lambda_1 x + \mu_1 x'}{\lambda_1 + \mu_1}, \qquad \frac{\lambda_2 x + \mu_2 x'}{\lambda_2 + \mu_2}, \qquad \frac{\lambda_3 x + \mu_3 x'}{\lambda_3 + \mu_3}, \qquad \frac{\lambda_4 x + \mu_4 x'}{\lambda_4 + \mu_4}.$$

The cross ratios of the original points and their projections are the same, the cross ratios of the projections are found immediately from their distances, which are the differences of their abscissae, and take the form

$$\frac{\begin{vmatrix} \lambda_1 & \mu_1 \\ \lambda_2 & \mu_2 \end{vmatrix} \cdot \begin{vmatrix} \lambda_3 & \mu_3 \\ \lambda_4 & \mu_4 \end{vmatrix}}{\begin{vmatrix} \lambda_1 & \mu_1 \\ \lambda_4 & \mu_4 \end{vmatrix} \cdot \begin{vmatrix} \lambda_3 & \mu_3 \\ \lambda_2 & \mu_2 \end{vmatrix}}.$$

Theorem 5] *A cross ratio of the four points* $\lambda_1(x)+\mu_1(y)$, $\lambda_2(x)+\mu_2(y)$, $\lambda_3(x)+\mu_3(y)$, $\lambda_4(x)+\mu_4(y)$ *may be written in the form*

$$\frac{\begin{vmatrix} \lambda_1 & \mu_1 \\ \lambda_2 & \mu_2 \end{vmatrix} \cdot \begin{vmatrix} \lambda_3 & \mu_3 \\ \lambda_4 & \mu_4 \end{vmatrix}}{\begin{vmatrix} \lambda_1 & \mu_1 \\ \lambda_4 & \mu_4 \end{vmatrix} \cdot \begin{vmatrix} \lambda_2 & \mu_2 \\ \lambda_3 & \mu_3 \end{vmatrix}}. \tag{2}$$

Theorem 6] *A cross ratio of* (x), (y) *as one pair and* $\lambda(x)+\mu(y)$, $\lambda'(x)+\mu'(y)$ *as the other pair may be written*

$$\frac{\lambda\mu'}{\lambda'\mu}.$$

Theorem 7] *The points* $\lambda(x)+\mu(y)$ *and* $\lambda'(x)+\mu'(y)$ *divide the points* (x), (y) *harmonically if and only if*

$$\lambda\mu'+\lambda'\mu = 0. \tag{3}$$

A point (x) will be on a line (u) when, and only when,

$$(ux) \equiv u_1x_1+u_2x_2+u_3x_3 = 0. \tag{4}$$

The coefficients are called the 'tangential coordinates' of the line, and are homogeneous.

Theorem 8] *The tangential coordinates of a line are proportional to constant multiples of its distances from the points* O_1, O_2, O_3.

Of course this ceases to hold when any one of these points is at infinity.

Theorem 9] *A linear homogeneous equation of the first order in tangential coordinates characterizes the lines through a point. The trilinear coordinates of the point are proportional to the coefficients in the equation.*

Suppose that (x) lies on the line (u) and (y) on the line (v)

$$(ux) = (vy) = 0.$$

Then the point $\lambda(uy)(x)-\mu(vx)(y)$ lies on the line $\lambda(u)+\mu(v)$. Our previous expression for cross ratios will be unaltered if we replace $\lambda_i : \mu_i$ by $(uy)\lambda_i : -(vx)\mu_i$.

Theorem 10] *A cross ratio of four concurrent lines* $\lambda_1(u)+\mu_1(v)$, $\lambda_2(u)+\mu_2(v)$, $\lambda_3(u)+\mu_3(v)$, $\lambda_4(u)+\mu_4(v)$ *may be written*

$$\frac{\begin{vmatrix} \lambda_1 & \mu_1 \\ \lambda_2 & \mu_2 \end{vmatrix} \cdot \begin{vmatrix} \lambda_3 & \mu_3 \\ \lambda_4 & \mu_4 \end{vmatrix}}{\begin{vmatrix} \lambda_1 & \mu_1 \\ \lambda_4 & \mu_4 \end{vmatrix} \cdot \begin{vmatrix} \lambda_3 & \mu_3 \\ \lambda_2 & \mu_2 \end{vmatrix}}. \tag{5}$$

It is evident that theorems 6] and 7] hold equally in tangential coordinates.

As every system of trilinear coordinates is linear and homogeneous in $x:y:z$, so is every system linear and homogeneous in every other system. The relation between two such systems may be written in the standard form

$$\begin{aligned}
\rho x_1 &= a_{11}x_1' + a_{12}x_2' + a_{13}x_3' \\
\rho x_2 &= a_{21}x_1' + a_{22}x_2' + a_{23}x_3' \quad |a_{ij}| \neq 0. \\
\rho x_3 &= a_{31}x_1' + a_{32}x_2' + a_{33}x_3'
\end{aligned} \tag{6}$$

Solving these equations, we get the inverse relations

$$\begin{aligned}
\sigma x_1' &= A_{11}x_1 + A_{21}x_2 + A_{31}x_3 \\
\sigma x_2' &= A_{12}x_1 + A_{22}x_2 + A_{32}x_3 \quad A_{ij} = \frac{\partial |a_{ij}|}{\partial a_{ij}}. \\
\sigma x_3' &= A_{13}x_1 + A_{23}x_2 + A_{33}x_3
\end{aligned} \tag{7}$$

If we multiply equations 7) through by u_1', u_2', u_3' respectively we get the contragredient relation

$$\begin{aligned}
\lambda u_1 &= A_{11}u_1' + A_{12}u_2' + A_{13}u_3' \\
\lambda u_2 &= A_{21}u_1' + A_{22}u_2' + A_{23}u_3' \\
\lambda u_3 &= A_{31}u_1' + A_{32}u_2' + A_{33}u_3'.
\end{aligned} \tag{8}$$

The inverse is obtained by solving these equations:

$$\begin{aligned}
\mu u_1' &= a_{11}u_1 + a_{21}u_2 + a_{31}u_3 \\
\mu u_2' &= a_{12}u_1 + a_{22}u_2 + a_{32}u_3 \\
\mu u_3' &= a_{13}u_1 + a_{23}u_2 + a_{33}u_3.
\end{aligned} \tag{9}$$

The equations are compactly written in the notation of the modern differential geometry, where the repetition of a superior or inferior index means a summation

$$\rho x_i = a_{i\alpha}x_\alpha' \qquad \sigma x_i' = A_{\alpha i}x_i \qquad \lambda u_i = A_{i\alpha}u_\alpha' \qquad \mu u_i' = a_{\alpha i}u_\alpha$$

It is clear that exactly similar equations will hold in a projective space of any number of dimensions as discussed in our first chapter.

§ 2. Invariants and covariants, first principles

Our equations (6) to (9) give us the most general method of changing coordinates so that a straight line shall have a linear homogeneous equation of the first order. There is, however, a seemingly different interpretation that can be put upon them. Instead of imagining that each point in the plane stays in

place, and the coordinate apparatus is changed in a certain
way, we may assume no change in that apparatus, but that each
point is replaced by another according to a definite scheme.
Thus our equations may be looked upon as giving the most
general transformation of the plane which depends on functions
with continuous first derivatives, where a point goes to a point,
and the points of a line to the points of a line. The two interpretations are, essentially, the same thing. The coordinates of a
point give its relations to the points O_1, O_2, O_3, and the unit
point. The equations state that that relation is altered in a
definite way, it is immaterial whether we look upon the general
point, or the four particular points, as staying fixed.

Theorem 11] *The most general transformation of the plane
depending on functions of the homogeneous Cartesian coordinates
with continuous first derivatives which carry a point to a point,
and the points of a line to the points of a line, is a homogeneous
linear transformation of non-vanishing determinant.*

In making a further study of these linear transformations or
'collineations' as they are called, it is well to generalize to
a projective space of N dimensions in the fashion indicated in
Chapter II. A point has $n+1$ homogeneous coordinates

$$x_1 : x_2 : \ldots : x_{N+1},$$

and every such system, not all 0, corresponds to a point.
A linear equation

$$\sum_{i=1}^{i=N+1} u_i x_i \equiv (ux) = 0 \qquad (10)$$

gives a hyperplane.

Theorem 12] *The most general transformation that depends on
functions having continuous first partial derivatives, and carries
points of a hyperplane into points of a hyperplane, is linear and
homogeneous, with non vanishing determinant.*

We may write our four equations (6) to (9) once more:

$$\rho x_i = \sum_j a_{ij} x'_j \qquad \sigma x'_i = \sum_j A_{ji} x_i$$

$$\lambda u_i = \sum_j A_{ij} u'_j \qquad \mu u'_i = \sum_j a_{ij} u_i, \qquad (11)$$

or, in tensor notation,

$$\rho x_i = a_{i\alpha} x'_\alpha \qquad \sigma x'_i = A_{\alpha i} x_i \qquad \lambda u_i = A_{i\alpha} u'_\alpha \qquad \mu u'_i = a_{\alpha i} u_i. \qquad (12)$$

Suppose that we have a set of k homogeneous polynomials

$$f_1(x_1, x_2, ..., x_{N+1}), \ f_2(x_1, x_2, ..., x_{N+1}), ..., f_k(x_1, x_2, ..., x_{N+1})$$

which are subjected to the transformations (11). Suppose there is a homogeneous polynomial C, involving the coefficients of the f's and the coordinates (x) perhaps those of several points, and which has the property that when the coordinates (x) are subjected to the transformation (11) we have identically

$$C' \equiv R(a_{11}, ..., a_{N+1, N+1})C,$$

where C' is the same expression in the new coordinates and variables that C is in the old ones, while R is a homogeneous polynomial depending on the coefficient of the transformation alone, then this polynomial C is called a 'covariant' of the given forms under the given transformation. If the variables (x) do not appear, it is called an 'invariant'. It is clear that the definition of invariant can be widened to other kinds of functions, and that all constants are invariants, but we assume that we are not speaking of such. If the (x)'s be replaced by u's the expression is called a 'contravariant'. The order in the variables (x), assuming that only one such set is involved, is called the 'order' of the covariant; its order in the coefficients is called its 'degree'. This is one of the cases, like the theory of differential equations, where the words 'order' and 'degree' have different meanings.

The first essential matter is to determine the nature of the multiplier R. Fortunately this is not difficult. If we follow a transformation by its inverse, everything must come back into place, hence

$$R(a_{11}, ..., a_{N+1, N+1})R\left(\frac{A_{11}}{|a_{ij}|}, ..., \frac{A_{N+1, N+1}}{|a_{ij}|}\right) = 1.$$

Now the general determinant is unfactorable, hence

$$R(a_{11}, ..., a_{N+1, N+1})R(A_{11}, ..., A_{N+1, N+1}) = |a_{ij}|^\sigma$$

$$R(a_{11}, ..., a_{N+1, N+1}) = |a_{ij}|^w.$$

The exponent w is defined as the 'weight' of the covariant. When we are dealing with a single form $f(x_1, x_2, ..., x_{N+1})$ of order n there is a simple relation connecting these characteristic numbers. The order of C being ν and its degree δ we have

$$C^\nu(x_1', x_2', ..., x_{N+1}') \equiv |a_{ij}|^w C^\nu(x_1, x_2, ..., x_{N+1}).$$

The coefficients of f' are of degree n in the variables a_{ij}. The degree in these variables on the left is $n\delta$, on the right $(N+1)w+\nu$.

Theorem 13] *The degree of a covariant of a single polynomial, multiplied by the order of the polynomial, is equal to the order plus the product of the weight and the number of variables.*

Theorem 14] *A plane curve of even order cannot have an invariant of odd weight.*

There are certain standard methods of grinding out invariants and covariants that deserve passing notice. Let us rewrite our last equation

$$C^\nu(b_1', c_1', ..., x_1', x_2', ..., x_{N+1}') \equiv |a_{ij}|^w C^\nu(b, c, ..., x_1, x_2, ..., x_{N+1}).$$

If we replace each of our original polynomials by a linear combination of itself and another general one of the same order, we should do the same for the transformed polynomials, as linearly dependent polynomials are transformed into linearly dependent ones. We thus get:

$$C^\nu(\lambda b' + \mu \bar{b}_1', \lambda c' + \mu \bar{c}_1', ..., x_1', x_2', ..., x_{N+1}')$$
$$\equiv |a_{ij}|^w C^\nu(\lambda b + \mu \bar{b}, \lambda c + \mu \bar{c}, ..., x_1', x_2', ..., x_{N+1}').$$

Expanding by Taylor's theorem:

$$\sum \bar{b}' \frac{\partial C^\nu}{\partial b'} \equiv \sum \bar{b} \frac{\partial C^\nu}{\partial b}.$$

We may look upon this as a device for passing from a covariant of k forms to a set of covariants of $2k$ forms, or we may do what appears, at first sight, as a rather senseless proceeding, i. e. look on $\bar{b}$ as meaning the same thing as b, $\bar{c}$ meaning the same thing as c, so that we have the original covariant in slightly modified shape. Repeating a number of times we get:

$$C^\nu(b'^{(1)}, b'^{(2)}, ..., c'^{(1)}, c'^{(2)}, ..., x_1', x_2', ..., x_{N+1}')$$
$$\equiv |a_{ij}|^w C^\nu(b^{(1)}, b^{(2)}, ..., c^{(1)}, c^{(2)}, ..., x_1, x_2, ..., x_{N+1}).$$

Here is a covariant with a great many redundant letters in it, but if the process be continued sufficiently we can get down to an expression of the first degree in any one of the equivalent sets of coefficients b, c, etc. The process by which it is found is called the 'Aronhold' process.

Theorem 15] *If the Aronhold process be applied a sufficient number of times to any covariant, there will result a new covariant,* *involving various sets of equivalent coefficients, but of the first degree in any one set.*

Closely akin to the Aronhold process is the so-called 'polar process', in fact the Aronhold process is the polar process applied not to the forms but to the covariant looked upon as a polynomial in the coefficients of the forms. Given

$$f(x_1, x_2,...,x_{N+1}) \equiv f'(x_1', x_2',...,x_{N+1}')$$

$$f(\lambda x_1+\mu y_1, \lambda x_2+\mu y_2,...,\lambda x_{N+1}+\mu y_{N+1})$$

$$\equiv f'(\lambda x_1'+\mu y_1', \lambda x_2'+\mu y_2',...,\lambda x_{N+1}'+\mu y_{N+1}')$$

$$\left(y\,\frac{\partial f}{\partial x}\right) \equiv \left(y'\,\frac{\partial f'}{\partial x'}\right); \qquad \sum_{ij} y_i y_j \frac{\partial^2 f}{\partial x_i \partial x_j} \equiv \sum y_i' y_j' \frac{\partial^2 f}{\partial x_i' \partial x_j'}.$$

The operator $\qquad \dfrac{1}{n}\left(y\,\dfrac{\partial f}{\partial x}\right) \equiv \dfrac{1}{n}\sum_i y_i \dfrac{\partial f}{\partial x_i}$

is called the 'polar operator'. It changes a covariant in one set of variables into one involving two sets, or even more, if it be applied several times. When only two sets are used, we have the successive polar forms

$$\frac{1}{n}\left(y\,\frac{\partial f}{\partial x}\right) \equiv \frac{1}{n}\sum_i y_i \frac{\partial f}{\partial x_i} \equiv \frac{1}{n} y_\alpha \frac{\partial f}{\partial x_\alpha}$$

$$\frac{1}{n(n-1)}\left(y\,\frac{\partial f}{\partial x}\right)^2 \equiv \frac{1}{n(n-1)}\sum_{ij} y_i y_j \frac{\partial^2 f}{\partial x_i \partial x_j} \equiv \frac{1}{n(n-1)} y_\alpha y_\beta \frac{\partial^2 f}{\partial x_\alpha \partial x_\beta}.$$

As an example, let us consider the quadratic form

$$\sum_{ij} b_{ij} x_i x_j \qquad b_{ij}=b_{ji} \qquad |b_{ij}| \neq 0.$$

Polarizing once, we get

$$\sum_{ij} b_{ij} x_i y_j.$$

Transforming the variables (x) but not the variables (y) by (11),

$$\sum_{ij} \bar{b}_{ij} x_i' y_j \qquad \bar{b}_{ij} \equiv \sum_k a_{ki} b_{kj} \qquad |\bar{b}_{ij}| = |a_{ij}|.|b_{ij}|.$$

Transforming (y) by the same process we have

$$\sum_{ij} b_{ij}' x_i' y_j' \, b_{ij} \equiv \sum_k a_{jk} \bar{b}_{ik} \qquad |b_{ij}'| = |\bar{b}_{ij}|.|a_{ij}|$$

$$|b_{ij}'| = |a_{ij}|^2.|b_{ij}|. \tag{13}$$

Theorem 16] *The discriminant of a general quadratic form is an invariant of weight 2.*

If we apply the Aronhold process to this invariant we get

$$\sum_{ij} c_{ij} B_{ij} \equiv c_{\alpha\beta} B_{\alpha\beta} \qquad B_{ij} = \frac{\partial |b_{ij}|}{\partial b_{ij}}.$$

Suppose, in particular, that we have two binary quadratic forms

$$b_{11}x_1^2 + (b_{12}+b_{21})x_1x_2 + b_{22}x_2^2 \qquad c_{11}x_1^2 + (c_{12}+c_{21})x_1x_2 + c_{22}x_2^2.$$

We find at once three invariants

$$b_{11}b_{22} - b_{12}^2 \qquad c_{11}c_{22} - c_{12}^2 \qquad b_{11}c_{22} + b_{22}c_{11} - 2b_{12}c_{12}.$$

We shall subsequently learn the meaning of the vanishing of each of these. Returning to the case of $N+1$ variables, the second polar form is

$$\tfrac{1}{2} \sum y_i y_j \frac{\partial^2 f}{\partial x_i \partial x_j}.$$

The discriminant of this quadratic form in (y) is

$$K \begin{vmatrix} \dfrac{\partial^2 f}{\partial x_1^2} & \dfrac{\partial^2 f}{\partial x_1 \partial x_2} & \cdot & \cdot & \dfrac{\partial^2 f}{\partial x_1 \partial x_{N+1}} \\ \cdot & \cdot & \cdots & \cdot & \cdot \\ \dfrac{\partial^2 f}{\partial x_{N+1} \partial x_1} & \dfrac{\partial^2 f}{\partial x_{N+1} \partial x_2} & \cdot & \cdot & \dfrac{\partial^2 f}{\partial x_{N+1}^2} \end{vmatrix},$$

where K is a constant to be determined later. We are not free to say that this expression is a covariant, because the (x)'s are transformed by the same transformation as the (y)'s. Such is the case, however, as we learn by studying a new operator. Suppose that we take $N+1$ functions of as many sets of variables. Such variables are supposed to be 'cogredient', meaning that they are all affected by the same linear transformation, they represent different points in the same projective space of N dimensions. We create a new function

$$F \equiv f_1^{n_1}(x_1, x_2, \ldots, x_{N+1}) f_2^{n_2}(y_1, y_2, \ldots, y_{N+1}) f_3^{n_3}(\ldots)\ldots.$$

The superscripts $n_1, n_2, \ldots$ indicate the orders of the polynomial. The 'Cayley operator' is defined by

$$\Omega F \equiv \frac{1}{n_1 n_2 \ldots} \begin{vmatrix} \dfrac{\partial}{\partial x_1} & \dfrac{\partial}{\partial x_2} & \cdot & \cdot & \dfrac{\partial}{\partial x_{N+1}} \\ \dfrac{\partial}{\partial y_1} & \dfrac{\partial}{\partial y_2} & \cdot & \cdot & \dfrac{\partial}{\partial y_{N+1}} \\ \cdot & \cdot & \cdot & \cdot & \cdot & \cdot \end{vmatrix} F. \qquad (14)$$

It must be understood that the determinant expands into symbolic products, not $\dfrac{\partial F}{\partial x_i}\dfrac{\partial F}{\partial y_j}\ldots$ but $\dfrac{\partial^{N+1}F}{\partial x_i\partial y_j\ldots}$. Also it can be applied to any polynomial which is homogeneous in the separate sets of variables (x), (y),..., not merely a factorable one like F. We see at once

$$\begin{vmatrix} \dfrac{\partial}{\partial x'_1} & \dfrac{\partial}{\partial x'_2} & \cdot & \cdot & \dfrac{\partial}{\partial x'_{N+1}} \\ \dfrac{\partial}{\partial y_1} & \dfrac{\partial}{\partial y'_2} & \cdot & \cdot & \dfrac{\partial}{\partial y'_{N+1}} \\ \cdot & \cdot & & & \end{vmatrix} F' \equiv |a_{ij}| \cdot \begin{vmatrix} \dfrac{\partial}{\partial x_1} & \dfrac{\partial}{\partial x_2} & \cdot & \cdot & \dfrac{\partial}{\partial x_{N+1}} \\ \dfrac{\partial}{\partial y_1} & \dfrac{\partial}{\partial y_2} & \cdot & \cdot & \dfrac{\partial}{\partial y_{N+1}} \\ \cdot & \cdot & \cdot & \cdot & \cdot \end{vmatrix} F.$$

If in the F first written all the factors f_1, f_2,..., be identical and of order n we have

$$\Omega\, f(x)f(y)\ldots = \frac{1}{n^{N+1}} \begin{vmatrix} \dfrac{\partial f}{\partial x_1} & \dfrac{\partial f}{\partial x_2} & \cdot & \cdot & \dfrac{\partial f}{\partial x_{N+1}} \\ \dfrac{\partial f}{\partial y_1} & \dfrac{\partial f}{\partial y_2} & \cdot & \cdot & \dfrac{\partial f}{\partial y_{N+1}} \\ \cdot & \cdot & \cdot & \cdot & \cdot \end{vmatrix}.$$

If, at this point, we put $(x) \equiv (y) \equiv \ldots$ we get

$$\frac{1}{n^{N+1}} \begin{vmatrix} \dfrac{\partial f}{\partial x_1} & \dfrac{\partial f}{\partial x_2} & \cdot & \cdot & \dfrac{\partial f}{\partial x_{N+1}} \\ \dfrac{\partial f}{\partial x_1} & \dfrac{\partial f}{\partial x_2} & \cdot & \cdot & \dfrac{\partial f}{\partial x_{N+1}} \\ \cdot & \cdot & \cdot & \cdot & \cdot \end{vmatrix} \equiv 0.$$

But if we apply the Aronhold operator *twice* and then put $(x) = (y) =$ etc., we get the so-called 'Hessian covariant'

$$H(x_1, x_2,\ldots, x_{N+1}) = K \begin{vmatrix} \dfrac{\partial^2 f}{\partial x_1^2} & \dfrac{\partial^2 f}{\partial x_1\partial x_2} & \cdot & \cdot & \dfrac{\partial^2 f}{\partial x_1\partial x_{N+1}} \\ \dfrac{\partial^2 f}{\partial x_2\partial x_1} & \dfrac{\partial^2 f}{\partial x_2^2} & \cdot & \cdot & \dfrac{\partial^2 f}{\partial x_2\partial x_{N+1}} \\ \cdot & \cdot & \cdot & \cdot & \cdot \end{vmatrix}. \quad \textbf{(15)}$$

If the Cayley operator be applied once to $N+1$ linear forms there will result the $N+1$ row determinant of their coefficients; if it be applied twice to a quadratic form we get a constant multiple of the discriminant.

§ 3. The symbolic notation

Suppose that we take the most general polynomial of order n in our $N+1$ homogeneous variables. We may write this with certain apparently useless numerical coefficients in the form

$$\sum_{pqr} \frac{n!}{p!\,q!\,r!}\, a_{pqr}\dots x_1^p x_2^q x_3^r \dots \quad p+q+r\dots = n.$$

Let us compare this with the nth power of the linear form

$$(a_1 x_1 + a_2 x_2 + a_3 x_3 + \dots + a_{N+1} x_{N+1})^n.$$

It will be seen at once that we pass from the one to the other by replacing a_{pqr} by $a_1^p a_2^q a_3^r$. The number of independent variable coefficients is much less in the second case, but as the same powers of all the a's do not appear in any two *the coefficients a_{pqr} are not linearly dependent* when the original polynomial is a power of a linear one. The coefficients in this latter case are connected by a number of algebraic relations, *none of which are linear*. They take the form

$$p_1 + p_2 = p_1' + p_2' \qquad q_1 + q_2 = q_1' + q_2' \qquad r_1 + r_2 = r_1' + r_2'\dots$$

$$(a_1^{p_1} a_2^{q_1} a_3^{r_1})(a_1^{p_2} a_2^{q_2} a_3^{r_2}) = (a_1^{p_1'} a_2^{q_1'} a_3^{r_1'})(a_1^{p_2'} a_2^{q_2'} a_3^{r_2'})$$

$$a_{p_1 q_1 r_1} a_{p_2 q_2 r_2} = a_{p_1' q_1' r_1'} a_{p_2' q_2' r_2'}.$$

The condition that $f(x_1, x_2, \dots, x_{N+1})$ should be a power of a linear form will only involve *non-linear* relations among its coefficients.

Suppose now, that we have a relation involving the covariants and invariants of a system of forms. We may apply the Aronhold process so often that the relation becomes linear in each type of coefficients, even though different types may stand for the same thing. Then whatever *linear* relations hold when the original forms were powers of linear forms in $x_1, x_2, \dots, x_{N+1}$ will hold universally, for these linear relations cannot be altered by the truth or falsity of irreducible non-linear relations. If, thus, we replace our original forms by perfect powers of linear ones, and introduce a sufficient number of equivalent symbols so that no 'actual' coefficient appears above the first degree, or no coefficient of a linear form to a degree above the order to which that form was raised to replace a given form, then whatever identical relations exist in the new notation are true in the old also.

Fundamental Principle of the Clebsch-Aronhold Symbolic Notation] *If each of a number of forms be replaced by a power of a linear form in the same number of variables equal to the order of the given form, and if a sufficient number of equivalent symbols be introduced by the Aronhold process so that no actual coefficient appears except to the first degree, then every identical relation holding for the new specialized forms holds for the general ones.* *

This means in practice that we replace a form

$$\sum_{pqr} \frac{n!}{p!\,q!\,r!\dots}\, a_{pqr}\dots x_1^p x_2^q x_3^r \dots \equiv \sum_{pqr} \frac{n!}{p!\,q!\,r!\dots}\, a'_{pqr}\dots x_1^p x_2^q x_3^r \dots \equiv \dots$$

by

$$(a_1 x_1 + a_2 x_2 + \dots + a_{N+1} x_{N+1})^n \equiv (a'_1 x_1 + a'_2 x_2 + \dots + a'_{N+1} x_{N+1})^n,$$

and this, again, we write symbolically

$$a_x^n \equiv a'^{\,n}_x \equiv a''^{\,n}_x \equiv \dots$$

where the symbols a are meaningless except in products of n together, in which case they mean the actual coefficients with corresponding subscripts.

If we are dealing with the contragredient variables, that is to say, the hyperplane coefficients (u) we write

$$u_\alpha^m \equiv u_{\alpha'}^m \equiv u_{\alpha''}^m.$$

As an example of the compactness of this notation we note that the rth polar of a_x^n is

$$a_y^r a_x^{n-r} \qquad\qquad (16)$$

If we apply the Cayley operator to $a_x^n a'^{\,n}_y a''^{\,n}_z \dots$ we get

$$\frac{1}{n^{N+1}} \, |aa'a''\dots|\, a_x^{n-1} a'^{\,n-1}_y a''^{\,n-1}_z \dots| \, .$$

The Hessian of $a_x^n \equiv a'^{\,n}_x \equiv a''^{\,n}_x \dots$ is written

$$H \equiv |aa'a''\dots|^2 a_x^{n-2} a'^{\,n-2}_x a''^{\,n-2}_x \dots \qquad\qquad (17)$$

The following are the usual types thus found:

$$a_x^n, \quad u_\alpha^m, \quad |abc\dots|^k, \quad |\alpha\beta\gamma\dots|^l, \quad |abc\dots uvw\dots|^r, \quad |\alpha\beta\gamma\dots xyz\dots|.$$

---

* Clebsch[1], pp. 1 ff. For an excellent discussion in English of the whole invariant theory from this point of view, see Grace and Young.

It may be proved that when we are dealing with polynomial covariants in (x) there are no terms of other form than $|abc...|a_x^l b_x^m....$ The demonstration is too long to reproduce here.*

There is one identical relation from which many others may be deduced

$$\begin{vmatrix} a_1 & a_2 & . & . & a_{N+1} & a_x \\ b_1 & b_2 & . & . & b_{N+1} & b_x \\ c_1 & c_2 & . & . & c_{N+1} & c_x \\ . & . & . & . & . & . \\ N_1 & N_2 & . & . & N_{N+1} & N_x \\ p_1 & p_2 & . & . & p_{N+1} & p_x \end{vmatrix} \equiv 0.$$

Developing this we have

$$|bcd...Np|a_x - |acd...Np|b_x + |abd...Np|c_x + ... + \\ + (-1)^N|abcd...p|N_x \equiv 0. \qquad (18)$$

§ 4. Binary domain

Suppose that we are dealing with the binary domain, the projective geometry on a straight line, so that $N = 1$. Let us use Greek letters for our point coordinates, to distinguish from the trilinear coordinates (x) which are our principal affair. There are no contragredient variables (u). There are but two types of symbolic expression in the Clebsch-Aronhold notation,

$$|ab|, \quad a_\xi.$$

If we put $\qquad d_2 = \xi_1 \qquad d_1 z = -\xi_2 \qquad a_\xi = |ad|,$

our identity (18) takes several forms:

$$|ab|c_\xi + |bc|a_\xi + |ca|b_\xi \equiv 0 \qquad (19)$$

$$|ab|.|cd| + |bc|.|ad| + |ca|.|bd| = 0 \qquad (20)$$

$$|ab|.|\xi\eta| \equiv a_\xi b_\eta - a_\eta b_\xi. \qquad (21)$$

By shifting $a_\xi|bc|$ to the other side in (19) and squaring we get

$$a_\xi^2|bc|^2 = b_\xi^2|ca|^2 + c_\xi^2|ab|^2 - 2|ab|.|ac|b_\xi c_\xi \qquad (22)$$

$$|ab|^2|\xi\eta|^2 = a_\xi^2 b_\eta^2 + b_\xi^2 a_\eta^2 - 2a_\xi b_\xi a_\eta b_\eta \qquad (23)$$

$$2|ab|.|ac|b_\xi c_\xi = b_\xi^2|ac|^2 + c_\xi^2|ab|^2 - a_\xi^2|bc|^2.$$

---

* It is more common to write a determinant $(abc...)$ but our form is really better. For a proof in the binary case, see Grace and Young, pp. 25 ff.

Squaring and transposing

$$|bc|^4 a_\xi^4 + |ca|^4 b_\xi^4 + |ab|^4 c_\xi^4 - 2|ca|^2|ab|^2 b_\xi^2 c_\xi^2 -$$
$$- 2|bc|^2|ab|^2 c_\xi^2 a_\xi^2 - 2|bc|^2|ca|^2 a_\xi^2 b_\xi^2 = 0. \quad (24)$$

Let us find the simplest invariants and covariants of the simplest binary forms. If we have a set of linear forms

$$a_\xi, \quad b_\xi, \quad c_\xi,$$

we have invariants of the type

$$|bc|, \quad |ca|, \quad |ab|.$$

As a matter of fact there are no others. For when three linear forms are given, the roots of all others are expressible as cross ratios which the roots of the new forms make with the points which are the roots of the three original ones. The reader will easily see that cross ratios of the type (2) are expressed by means of just such two-row determinants as these.

If we have a single quadratic form

$$a_\xi^2 \equiv a_\xi'^2 \equiv a_\xi''^2,$$

the roots will fall together when, and only when, there is a point (namely this root) whose harmonic conjugate with regard to the roots of the form is indeterminate. Now if (η) lie on the first polar of (ξ) so that
$$a_\eta a_\xi = 0,$$

it is easy to show that (ξ) and (η) are harmonically separated by the roots of our quadratic form. The condition for equal roots is that we can find (η) so that

$$a_\eta a_1 = a_\eta a_2 = 0.$$

In other words

$$a_1^2 \eta_1 + a_1 a_2 \eta_2 = 0 \qquad a_1' a_2' \eta_1 + a_2'^2 \eta_2 = 0 \qquad a_1 a_2' |aa'| = 0$$
$$a_2 a_1' |aa'|^2 = 0 \qquad |aa'|^2 = 0. \qquad (25)$$

This method of finding the discriminant may be generalized at once to the former case of $N+1$ variables which we treated in the preceding section. If a 'hyperquadric' have a symbolic equation
$$a_x^2 \equiv a_x'^2 \equiv a_x''^2 \ldots = 0,$$

there is a point (7) whose polar hyperplane is indeterminate when, and only when,

$$a_\eta a_\xi \equiv 0$$

$$a_1 a_y = 0 \qquad a_2' a_y = 0 \qquad a_3'' a_y = 0 \ldots$$

$$a_1 a_2' a_3'' \ldots |aa'a'' \ldots| = 0$$

Permuting the equivalent symbols a, a', a'', etc., in all possible ways, and combining we get

$$|aa'a'' \ldots|^2 = 0. \tag{26}$$

Let the reader show that the left-hand side of this differs only by a constant factor from the discriminant given in (12). It is to be noted that the roles of the letters a have been changed.

Theorem 17] *In N-dimensional space, the necessary and sufficient condition that there should be a point whose polar hyperplane with regard to a given hyperquadric should be indeterminate is that the discriminant should vanish.*

We return to the binary domain, and take the case of two quadratic forms

$$a_\xi^2 \equiv a'_\xi{}^2 = 0, \qquad b_\xi^2 \equiv b'_\xi{}^2 = 0.$$

Their Jacobian is $\qquad |ab| a_\xi b_\xi,$

and this is, from its very definition, a covariant. We have also the simultaneous invariant

$$|ab|^2,$$

which we found in non-symbolic form in a previous section. Let (η), (ζ), the roots of the second form, be harmonically separated by those of the first form.

$$b_\eta^2 = b_\zeta^2 = a_\eta a_\zeta = 0$$

$$a_\eta^2 b_\zeta^2 + a_\zeta^2 b_\eta^2 - 2a_\eta a_\zeta b_\eta b_\zeta = 0$$

$$\begin{vmatrix} a_\eta & a_\zeta \\ b_\eta & b_\zeta \end{vmatrix}^2 = 0.$$

Then, by (21) $\qquad |\eta\zeta|^2 . |ab|^2 = 0.$

If $(\eta) \neq (\zeta)$, $\qquad |\eta\zeta| \neq 0.$

Hence $\qquad |ab|^2 = 0. \tag{27}$

The vanishing of this simultaneous invariant means, then, that the roots of the two forms, if distinct, separate one another harmonically. Next consider the Jacobian of the two forms

$$j_\xi^2 \equiv |ab|a_\xi b_\xi$$
$$|ja'|^2 \equiv |ab|.|aa'|.|ba'|$$
$$\equiv -|a'b|.|a'a|.|ba|.$$

But a and a' mean exactly the same thing, and these two expressions ought to be equal. If, therefore, one equals the negative of the other, both are equal to 0. Similarly $|jb'|^2 = 0$.

Theorem 18] *If two binary quadratic forms have distinct roots, the roots of their Jacobian divide each of the given pairs harmonically. The Jacobian will vanish identically when, and only when, the two forms have the same roots.*

If the two roots of the Jacobian fall together they will pinch in with them one root of each of the forms, so that the two have a common root. Conversely, if they have a common root, that must be a double root for the Jacobian.

Theorem 19] *The discriminant of the Jacobian of two binary quadratic forms differs by a constant factor from the resultant of the two forms.*

We calculate this invariant as follows. We wish $|jj'|^2$ where

$$j_\xi^2 \equiv |ab|a_\xi b_\xi \qquad j'_\xi{}^2 \equiv |a'b'|a'_\xi b'_\xi$$
$$j'_\xi j'_\eta \equiv \tfrac{1}{2}|a'b'|.[a'_\xi b'_\xi + b'_\xi a'_\eta]$$
$$jj'|^2 \equiv |ab|.|aj'|.|bj'|$$
$$\equiv \tfrac{1}{2}|ab|.|a'b'|.[|aa'|.|bb'| + |ab'|.|ba'|]. \quad \textbf{(28)}$$

The study of the covariants of pairs of binary forms is fundamental in the differential theory of surfaces. If we have three quadratic forms

$$a_\xi^2, \qquad b_\xi^2, \qquad c_\xi^2,$$

the Jacobian of the first two divides the roots of the last harmonically in

$$|ab|.|bc|.|ca| = 0. \quad \textbf{(29)}$$

This then, is the condition that their roots be pairs of an involution.

Consider, next, the binary cubic

$$a_\xi^3 \equiv a'_\xi{}^3 \equiv a''_\xi{}^3 \equiv a'''_\xi{}^3 \ldots.$$

Let us look for an invariant. The most obvious one is $|aa'|^3$. This, however, is identically equal to 0, as we see by permuting the equivalent symbols a and a'. In fact we have a general principle that any invariant or covariant which changes sign when equivalent symbols are permuted must be exactly 0. After a little experiment we get another invariant

$$|aa'|^2 . |a''a'''|^2 . |aa'''| . |a'a''| .$$

Let us show that this is, except for a constant factor, the discriminant of the Hessian

$$h_\xi^2 \equiv h'_\xi{}^2 \equiv |aa'|^2 a_\xi a'_\xi .$$

We wish to find $|hh'|^2$, and note that we can get this at once from the Hessian itself by replacing $h'_1 : h'_2$ by $\xi_2 : -\xi_1$.

$$|hh'|^2 \equiv |aa'|^2 . |ah'| . |a'h'| \qquad |a''a'''|^2 a'_\xi a''_\xi \equiv h_\xi'^2$$

$$\tfrac{1}{2}|a''a'''|^2 [a''_\xi a'''_\eta + a''_\eta a'''_\xi] \equiv h'_\xi h'_\eta$$

$$|hh'|^2 \equiv \tfrac{1}{2}|aa'|^2 . |a'a'''|^2 [|aa''| . |a'a'''| + |aa'''| . |a'a''|]$$

$$\equiv |aa'|^2 . |a''a'''|^2 . |aa'''| . |a'a''| . \quad \textbf{(30)}$$

To find the significance of the vanishing of this, let us assume that the three roots of the original cubic are not all equal (when they are the Hessian vanishes identically). We may make a linear transformation so that two roots become $(1, 0)$ and $(0, 1)$. Our form then is

$$a_\xi^3 \equiv \xi_1 \xi_2 |\xi\eta| , \qquad |hh'|^2 = -b\eta_1\eta_2 .$$

This vanishes when, and only when, the cubic has $(1, 0)$ or $(0, 1)$ as a double root.

Theorem 20] *The discriminant of a general binary cubic form differs by a constant factor from that of its Hessian and can be written in the form* (30).

A binary cubic form could not have another polynomial invariant not a constant, or a power of this one. For if it had two, I_1 of weight w_1 and I_2 of w_2, the expression

$$J \equiv \frac{I_1^{w_2}}{I_2^{w_1}},$$

not a constant, would be an 'absolute invariant', i.e. one whose value would remain entirely unaltered by a linear transformation of the binary domain. Two binary cubic forms for which this took different values could not be carried into one another by such a linear transformation. But it is well known that we can find a linear transformation to carry any three distinct collinear points into any other three.

As a last example of binary methods, let us consider the quartic

$$a_\xi^4 \equiv a_\xi'^4 \equiv a_\xi''^4 \equiv a_\xi'''^4.$$

Two invariants will be found immediately:

$$I \equiv |aa'|^4 \qquad J \equiv |aa'|^2.|a'a''|^2.|a''a|^2. \tag{31}$$

Let us find their value in non-symbolic notation:

$$a_\xi^4 \equiv (a_1\xi_1 + a_2\xi_2)^4 \equiv a_0\xi_1^4 + 4a_1\xi_1^3\xi_2 + 6a_2\xi_1^2\xi_2^2 + 4a_3\xi_1\xi_2^3 + a_4\xi_2^4$$

$$I = (a_1a_2' - a_2a_1')^4 = 2(a_0a_4 - 4a_1a_3 - 6a_2^2). \tag{32}$$

$$J = (a_1a_2' - a_2a_1')^2(a_1'a_2'' - a_2'a_1'')^2(a_1''a_2 - a_2''a_1)^2 = 6\begin{vmatrix} a_0 & a_1 & a_2 \\ a_1 & a_2 & a_3 \\ a_2 & a_3 & a_4 \end{vmatrix}. \tag{33}$$

Suppose that we have three distinct roots $(0, 1)$, $(1, 0)$, $(1, 1)$ and that the fourth is $(r, 1)$, so that r is a cross ratio of the four roots. Our form can be written

$$\xi_1\xi_2(\xi_1 - \xi_2)(\xi_1 - r\xi_2)$$

$$a_0 = a_4 = 0 \qquad a_1 = \tfrac{1}{4} \qquad a_2 = -\frac{r+1}{6} \qquad a_3 = \frac{r}{4},$$

$$I = \frac{(r+1)^2}{6} - \frac{r}{2} = \frac{r^2 - r + 1}{6},$$

$$J = 6\left[-\frac{r(r+1)}{48} + \frac{(r+1)^3}{246}\right] = \frac{(r+1)(2r-1)(r-2)}{72}.$$

Theorem 21] *If a binary quartic form have three distinct roots, the invariant J vanishes when the roots form a harmonic set, and the invariant I when they form an equi-harmonic set, i.e. their cross ratios are the imaginary cube roots of -1*

$$I^3 - 6J^2 = \frac{r^2(r-1)^2}{8}.$$

This expression will vanish if $r = 0$ or $r = 1$, two of the possible cases where the fourth root equals one of the original ones. The numerators of I and J will be unaltered if we replace r by $\frac{1}{r}$, so that $I^3 - 6J^2$ will vanish if $\frac{1}{r} = 0$, and this is the other possible case where the last root equals one of the first three.

Theorem 22] *The discriminant of the binary quartic will differ by a constant factor from* $\quad I^3 - 6J^3$.

§ 5. Ternary forms

The theory of ternary forms, which we should like to use at every turn in studying the projective properties of plane curves, is, unfortunately, ever so much more complicated than that of binary forms. We shall therefore treat it but slightly, largely to give the reader some familiarity with the symbolic expressions which will be convenient in our subsequent work. The types of covariant expressions are

$$a_x^n \qquad u_\alpha^m \qquad (a\alpha)^r \qquad |abc|^s \qquad |\alpha\beta\gamma|^t$$
$$|\alpha\beta x|^p \qquad |abw|^q \qquad (ux).$$

The only identity often used is (18), and one obtained therefrom by squaring. Let us exhibit a very interesting liaison between binary and ternary invariant theory due to Clebsch.* Suppose that we have a curve of order n given by equations

$$a_x^n \equiv a'^n_x = 0.$$

Let us find where the line from (y) to (z) meets this curve. We write

$$x_i = \xi_1 y_i + \xi_2 z_i$$
$$a_x^n \equiv A_\xi^n \equiv [a_y \xi_1 + a_z \xi_2]^n.$$

Suppose, next, that we have some invariant of this binary form

$$|AA'|^p . |A'A''|^q ...$$

$$|AA'| \equiv \begin{vmatrix} a_y & a_z \\ a'_y & a'_z \end{vmatrix} \equiv |aa'u|$$

where $\qquad u_i = y_j z_k - y_k z_j.$

An invariant of degree d and weight w in the binary domain will involve w determinant factors, and d sets of equivalent symbols A, and will give as many factors and sets of symbols in the ternary domain, and so a contravariant (i.e. covariant in the variables u) of degree d and order w. If we equate the invariant to 0 we get an envelope of all lines cutting our curve in sets of points for which the invariant vanishes.

* Clebsch¹, p. 28.

Let us consider some simple special cases. Take a single conic

$$a_x^2 \equiv a_x'^2 = 0. \tag{34}$$

A line (u) will be tangent thereto if the corresponding binary quadratic form have a double root. We thus get the tangential equation of the conic from (25)

$$|aa'u|^2 = 0. \tag{35}$$

The conic will degenerate, and become two lines if there be a point whose polar line is illusory. The condition for this is found from (26)

$$|aa'a''|^2 = 0. \tag{36}$$

If we have two conics

$$a_x^2 = 0, \qquad b_x^2 = 0,$$

the envelope of lines meeting them in two harmonically separating pairs is found from (27)

$$|abu|^2 = 0. \tag{37}$$

In the same way the locus of points whence the tangents to the two conics

$$u_\alpha^2 \equiv u_\beta^2 = 0 \tag{38}$$

form a harmonic set is

$$|\alpha\beta x|^2 = 0. \tag{39}$$

If these conics be the same as those above

$$u_\alpha^2 \equiv |aa'u|^2 \qquad u_\beta^2 \equiv |bb'u|^2$$

$$\alpha_i = \begin{vmatrix} a_j & a_k \\ a_j' & a_k \end{vmatrix} \qquad \beta_i = \begin{vmatrix} b_j & b_k \\ b_j' & b_k' \end{vmatrix}$$

$$|\alpha\beta x| = \sum \begin{vmatrix} a_j & a_k \\ a_j' & a_k' \end{vmatrix} \cdot \begin{vmatrix} \beta_j & \beta_k \\ x_j' & x_k' \end{vmatrix} = \begin{vmatrix} a_\beta & a_x \\ a_\beta' & a_x' \end{vmatrix} = \begin{vmatrix} |abb'| & a_x \\ |a'bb'| & a_x' \end{vmatrix}.$$

Hence our equation is

$$|abb'|^2 a_x'^2 + |a'bb'|^2 a_x^2 - 2|abb'| \cdot |a'bb'| a_x a_x' = 0.$$

Or, since a and a' are the same,

$$|a'bb'|^2 a_x^2 - |abb'| \cdot |a'bb'| a_x a_x' = 0. \tag{40}$$

If we have a cubic curve with no singular point, a line which meets it in two coincident points must be tangent. If, thus, the equation of the cubic be

$$a_x^3 \equiv a_x'^3 \equiv a_x''^3 \equiv a_x'''^3 = 0, \tag{41}$$

the tangential equation is found from (30)

$$|aa'u|^2 \cdot |a''a'''u|^2 \cdot |aa''u| \cdot |a'a'''u| = 0. \tag{42}$$

In the same way, if we have a non-singular quartic

$$a_x^{(1)4} \equiv a_x^{(2)4} \equiv a_x^{(3)4} \equiv a_x^{(4)4} \equiv a_x^{(5)4} \equiv a_x^{(6)4} = 0, \qquad (43)$$

the envelope of lines meeting it in a harmonic set is

$$|a^{(1)}a^{(2)}u|^4 = 0; \qquad (44)$$

the tangential equation is

$$|a^{(1)}a^{(2)}u|^4 . \; |a^{(3)}a^{(4)}u|^4 . \; |a^{(5)}a^{(6)}u|^4 -$$

$$-6|a^{(1)}a^{(2)}u|^2 . |a^{(2)}a^{(3)}u|^2 . |a^{(3)}a^{(2)}u|^2 . |a^{(4)}a^{(5)}u|^2 . |a^{(5)}a^{(6)}u|^2 . |a^{(6)}a^{(4)}u|^2$$

$$= 0. \quad (45)$$

There is one more connexion between binary and ternary forms which must be mentioned. Let us rewrite our previous equations of passage

$$x_i = \xi_1 y_i + \xi_2 z_i \qquad a_x \equiv A_\xi \equiv a_y \xi_1 + a_z \xi_2.$$

If (z) be on the rth polar of (y) with regard to $a_x^n = 0$

$$a_y^r a_z^{n-r} = 0.$$

Now in the binary domain (y) has the coordinates $(1, 0)$ and its rth polar with regard to A_ξ^n is

$$A_1^r A_z^{n-r} \equiv a_y^r a_z^{n-r}.$$

Theorem 23] *The rth polar of a point with regard to a curve is the locus of its rth polars with regard to binary forms giving groups of points cut from the given curve on lines through the given point.*

CHAPTER VI

PROJECTIVE THEORY OF SINGULAR POINTS

§ 1. Polar curves and singular points

Suppose that we have given a curve of the nth order

$$f(x'_1, x'_2, x'_3) \equiv a^n_x = 0. \tag{1}$$

We find its intersections with the line from (y) to (x) by writing

$$x'_i = \xi_1 y_i + \xi_2 x_i. \tag{2}$$

Substituting in the given equation

$$\xi^n_1 f(y_1, y_2, y_3) + \xi^{n-1}_1 \xi_2 \left(\frac{\partial f}{\partial y} x \right) + \tfrac{1}{2} \xi^{n-2}_1 \xi^2_2 \sum_{i,j} x_i x_j \frac{\partial^2 f}{\partial y_i \partial y_j} + \ldots +$$

$$+ \xi_1 \xi^{n-1}_2 \left(y \frac{\partial f}{\partial x} \right) + \xi^n_2 f(x_1, x_2, x_3) = 0. \tag{3^1}$$

In the tensor notation this becomes

$$\xi^n_1 f(y_1, y_2, y_3) + \xi^{n-1}_1 \xi_2 \frac{\partial f}{\partial y_\alpha} x_\alpha + \tfrac{1}{2} \xi^{n-2}_1 \xi^2_2 \frac{\partial^2 f}{\partial y_\alpha \partial y_\beta} x_\alpha x_\beta + \ldots +$$

$$+ \xi_1 \xi^{n-1}_2 \frac{\partial f}{\partial x_\alpha} y_\alpha + \xi^n_2 f(x_1, x_2, x_3) = 0. \tag{3^2}$$

In the Clebsch-Aronhold symbolic notation we have the still simpler form

$$\xi^n_1 a^n_y + \xi^{n-1}_1 \xi_2 a^{n-1}_y a_x + \frac{n(n-1)}{2} \xi^{n-2}_1 \xi^2_2 a^{n-2}_y a^2_x + \ldots +$$

$$+ n \xi_1 \xi^{n-1}_2 a_y a^{n-1}_x + \xi^n_2 a^n_x = 0. \tag{3^3}$$

We shall call this Joachimsthal's equation.[*]

The various terms equated to 0 give the various polar

---

[*] Cf. Sálmon[1]. I cannot find out the reason for the ascription to Joachimsthal.

curves of (y). They are covariants. Some are particularly important:

$$\left(y \frac{\partial f}{\partial x}\right) \equiv y_\alpha \frac{\partial f}{\partial x_\alpha} \equiv n a_y a_x^{n-1} = 0 \qquad \text{First polar}$$

$$\sum_{ij} y_i y_j \frac{\partial^2 f}{\partial x_i \partial x_j} \equiv y_\alpha y_\beta \frac{\partial^2 f}{\partial x_\alpha \partial x_\beta} \equiv n(n-1) a_y^2 a_x^{n-2} = 0$$

Second polar   (4)

$$\sum_{ij} x_i x_j \frac{\partial^2 f}{\partial y_i \partial y_j} \equiv x_\alpha x_\beta \frac{\partial^2 f}{\partial y_\alpha \partial y_\beta} \equiv n(n-1) a_x^2 a_y^{n-2} = 0$$

Conic polar

$$\left(\frac{\partial f}{\partial y} x\right) \equiv \frac{\partial f}{\partial y_\alpha} x_\alpha \equiv n a_y^{n-1} a_x = 0 \qquad \text{Line polar}$$

The symmetry of the terms at equal distances from the ends, which is especially evident in the symbolic form, gives us

Theorem 1] *If (x) lie on the sth polar of (y) with regard to a curve of order n, then (y) lies on the $(n-s)$th polar of (x) with regard to the same curve.*

Theorem 2] *If the sth polar form of (y) vanish identically, then (y) lies on the $(n-s)$th polar of every point in the plane.*

An examination of the short symbolic form $a_y^t a_z^s a_x^{n-t-s}$ gives

Theorem 3] *The tth polar of (y) with regard to the sth polar of (z) is the sth polar of (z) with regard to the rth polar of (y).*

Since $a_y^n \equiv a_y^s a_y^{n-s}$ we have

Theorem 4] *A necessary and sufficient condition that a point should lie on any one of its polar curves is that it should lie on the original curve.*

Theorem 5] *The sth polar of a point with regard to its tth polar, is its $(s+t)$th polar with regard to the original curve.*

Theorem 6] *The first polars of the points of a line are linearly dependent on two of their number. Their intersections are composed of all points with no line polars, and all that have the given line as a line polar.*

Let us look more closely at the possibility that one polar or another is illusory. Suppose this is the case with the $(n-s)$th

$$a_y^{n-s} a_x^s \equiv 0 \qquad a_y^{n-s} a_1^\lambda a_2^\mu a_3^\nu \equiv 0 \qquad \lambda + \mu + \nu = s$$

$$a_1 y_1 a_y^{n-s} a_1^{\lambda-1} a_2^\mu a_3^\nu + a_2 y_2 a_y^{n-s} a_1^\lambda a_2^{\mu-1} a_3^\nu + a_3 y_3 a_y^{n-s} a_1^\lambda a_2^\mu a_3^{\nu-1} = 0$$

$$a_y^{n-s+1} a_x^{s-1} \equiv 0$$

Theorem 7] *If the $(n-s)$th polar of a point with regard to a curve of order n be illusory, that point lies on the sth, and every previous polar of every point in the plane.*

Let us return to our Joachimsthal equation (3). This will have $s+1$ roots $\xi_2 = 0$ for all values of (x) when

$$a_y^{n-s}a_x^s \equiv 0 \qquad a_y^{n-s+1}a_x^{s-1} \equiv 0 \qquad a_y^{n-1}a_x \equiv 0 \qquad a_y^n = 0.$$

Theorem 8] *The necessary and sufficient condition that a point should have exactly the multiplicity $s+1$ for a curve of order n is that its $(n-s)$th polar should be illusory, but no previous polar.*

Theorem 9] *If a point have the multiplicity $s+1$ with regard to a given curve it will have at least, and in general, the multiplicity $s+1-t$ with regard to a tth polar.*

Suppose (y) has the multiplicity $s+1$. Joachimsthal's equation will have on $s+1$ roots $\xi_2 = 0$ if

$$a_y^{n-s-1}a_x^{s+1} = 0.$$

Theorem 10] *If a curve have a point of multiplicity $s+1$ its $(n-s-1)$th polar consists in the tangents at that point, each counted but once when the singularity is an ordinary one. This point will have the same multiplicity and same tangents for all the previous polars.*

Theorem 11] *The line polar of a double point is illusory. The conic polar of a node is the two tangents, that of a cusp is the cuspidal tangent counted twice.*

Theorem 12] *The line polar of a non-singular point is the tangent, and this line touches all the polars of that point.*

It is evident that there is a polar theory in tangential coordinates exactly corresponding to that in point coordinates. If we have the envelope
$$u_\alpha^m = 0,$$

the successive polars of a line (v) are

$$v_\alpha u_\alpha^{m-1} = 0 \qquad v_\alpha^2 u_\alpha^{m-2} = 0 \qquad v_\alpha^{m-1}u_\alpha = 0.$$

The last of these shall be called its 'point polar'. The point polar of the line at infinity shall be called the 'tangential centre'. If the equation of a typical line be written

$$ux+vy+w = 0,$$

and an envelope be given which is homogeneous of degree m in u, v, w, then the homogeneous Cartesian coordinates of the tangential centre are proportional to the coefficients of uw^{m-1}, vw^{m-1}, and w^m. The tangential centre of a set of finite points is their centre of gravity.

Returning to point coordinates, suppose that we have a singular point (y) of multiplicity r

$$a_y^{n-r+1} a_x^{r-1} \equiv 0.$$

The sth polar of (z) with regard to this is

$$a_z^s a_x^{n-s} = 0.$$

The tangents to the original curve at (y) are

$$a_y^{n-r} a_x^r = 0.$$

The equation $a_y^{n-r} a_z^s a_x^{r-s} = 0$

will give us the tangents to the sth polar of (z) and the sth polar of (z) with regard to the tangents at (y) to the original curve.

Theorem 13] *If a curve have a singularity of order r, the tangents thereat to the sth polar of a point not on one of the tangents there to the original curve are identical with the sth polar of that point with regard to the tangents to the original curve.*

Theorem 14] *If a curve have a node, the tangent thereat to the first polar of a point, not on one of the nodal tangents, is harmonically separated by those tangents from the line from the node to the chosen point.*

§ 2. The effect of singular points

In the binary domain, the first polar form of the point $(1, 0)$ is the partial derivative with respect to the first variable. A binary form and one partial derivative cannot have a common root, which is not also a root of the other partial derivative, and therefore is multiple for the given form. We thus see from 13] that if a curve have an ordinary singularity, the first polar of a point not on one of the tangents there will have a multiplicity of one less at that point, and share no tangent there with the original curve. Thus, if the point have multiplicity r for the original curve, the number of intersections with a general first polar is, by Ch. II, theorem 10], $r(r-1)$.

Theorem 15] *If a curve have an ordinary singular point of order r, the number of intersections with a general first polar absorbed there is $r(r-1)$.*

Suppose, next, that our curve has a cusp. Let us give this the trilinear coordinates $(0, 0, 1)$ and to the cuspidal tangent the equation $x_2 = 0$. To a point in general position we can assign the coordinates $(0, 1, 0)$. The equation of the curve may be written

$$f(x_1, x_2, x_3) \equiv x_2^2 x_3^{n-2} + a_1 x_1^3 x_3^{n-3} + \ldots \qquad (a_1 \neq 0).$$

The first polar of $(0, 1, 0)$ is

$$\frac{1}{n} \frac{\partial f}{\partial x_2} = \frac{2}{n} x_2 x_3^{n-2} + \ldots$$

Let us change to non-homogeneous coordinates, writing

$$\frac{x_1}{x_3} = x \qquad \frac{x_2}{x_3} = 0.$$

The two curves are

$$0 = y^2 + a_1 x^3 + \ldots$$
$$0 = y + px^2 + 2qxy + sy^2 + \ldots$$

We can express the first curve parametrically as in Ch. II

$$x = t^2, \qquad y = \sqrt{-a_1}\, t^3 + \ldots$$

If we substitute in the second equation we see there are exactly three roots $t = 0$.

Theorem 16] *The first polar of a point not on a cuspidal tangent has exactly three intersections with a given curve at a cusp.*

The last two theorems are of vital importance, as they enable us to determine an important number connected with a curve, when the latter has only ordinary singular points and cusps.

Definition. The number of tangents to a curve from a general point is defined as the 'class' of the curve. It is the order of the polar reciprocal. If a point P lie on the tangent at Q, then Q, by theorems 1] and 12] is one of the non-singular intersections with the first polar of P, and conversely. If, thus, our curve have ordinary singular points of orders $r_1, r_2, \ldots$, and κ cusps, the class m is given by r.

Theorem 17] *If a curve of order n have only ordinary singular points of orders $r_1, r_2, \ldots$ and κ cusps, its class is*

$$m = n(n-1) - \sum r_i(r_i - 1) - \kappa. \qquad \textbf{(5)}$$

If the branches of a curve through an ordinary singular point of order r were pulled apart a short distance, so that each two intersected, the number of nodes created in this way should be $\frac{r(r-1)}{2}$ and the reduction in the class as before. From this point of view we may look upon each ordinary singular point as a group of virtual nodes, if δ be the total number of nodes, virtual or actual, we have another form for the last formula

$$m = n(n-1) - 2\delta - 3\kappa. \tag{6}$$

We get by the principle of duality explained at the end of the first section of Chapter II

$$n = m(m-1) - 2\tau - 3\iota. \tag{7}$$

Here τ means the number of bitangents, actual or virtual.

These two equations lead us to a very pretty paradox. We know that a curve will not 'in general' have a double point. Hence, 'in general', $m = n(n-1)$.

By similar reasoning 'in general'

$$n = m\,(m-1)$$
$$n^2(n-2) = 0$$
$$n = 2.$$

Hence, 'in general', a curve is a conic !

The explanation is as follows. What do we mean by a curve 'in general' ? If we mean a polynomial in point coordinates about which we do not make the explicit assumption that the discriminant vanishes, then such a curve has no singular points. But if we mean by a curve 'in general' the point locus corresponding to the general polynomial in tangential coordinates about which we do not assume that the discriminant vanishes, then this is quite a different sort of general curve.

Let us next look at the inflexions of a given curve. We return to the Joachimsthal equation (3). If (y) be an inflexion, and (x) on the inflexional tangent, there are three roots $\xi_2 = 0$ when there are two. Hence the conic polar

$$a_y^{n-2}a_x^2$$

includes the line polar $a_y^{n-1}a_x = 0$

as a factor. The conic polar must then, be a pair of lines, so that its discriminant vanishes thus getting by (26) and (36) of the last chapter

$$|aa'a''|^2 a_y^{n-2} a_y'^{n-2} a_y''^{n-2} = 0.$$

This means that (y) lies on the Hessian curve

$$|aa'a''| a_x^{n-2} a_x'^{n-2} a_x''^{n-2} = 0. \tag{8}$$

The left-hand side is the Hessian covariant that we found in (15) of the last chapter.

Suppose, conversely, that (y) is a non-singular intersection of the curve and its Hessian. The conic polar is a pair of lines, and one of them is tangent to the original curve. Hence if the line from (y) to (x) have two intersections with the curve at (y) it has three, or (y) is an inflexion.

Theorem 18] *The non-singular inflexions of a curve are its non-singular intersections with the Hessian.*

It is worth noticing that a curve can have an ordinary singular point which absorbs inflexions into itself. Such is the case with a lemniscate or figure 8.

It will be well to deduce a very different proof for 18] so as to connect it more closely with the usual idea of an inflexion. Since the Hessian is a covariant, we can write it in Cartesian coordinates, if we allow differentiation with respect to 1 as explained in the first chapter. Its equation then is

$$\begin{vmatrix} \dfrac{\partial^2 f}{\partial x^2} & \dfrac{\partial^2 f}{\partial x \partial y} & \dfrac{\partial^2 f}{\partial x \partial 1} \\[2mm] \dfrac{\partial^2 f}{\partial y \partial x} & \dfrac{\partial^2 f}{\partial y^2} & \dfrac{\partial^2 f}{\partial y \partial 1} \\[2mm] \dfrac{\partial^2 f}{\partial 1 \partial x} & \dfrac{\partial^2 f}{\partial 1 \partial y} & \dfrac{\partial^2 f}{\partial 1^2} \end{vmatrix} = 0.$$

Applying Euler's theorem to the columns and rows, this becomes

$$\begin{vmatrix} \dfrac{\partial^2 f}{\partial x^2} & \dfrac{\partial^2 f}{\partial x \partial y} & \dfrac{\partial f}{\partial x} \\[2mm] \dfrac{\partial^2 f}{\partial x \partial y} & \dfrac{\partial^2 f}{\partial y^2} & \dfrac{\partial f}{\partial y} \\[2mm] (n-1)\dfrac{\partial f}{\partial x} & (n-1)\dfrac{\partial f}{\partial y} & nf \end{vmatrix} = 0.$$

Expanding, and disregarding the term with a factor f, as this is immaterial when we seek the intersections with $f = 0$, we get

$$\frac{\partial^2 f}{\partial x^2}\left(\frac{\partial f}{\partial y}\right)^2 + \frac{\partial^2 f}{\partial y^2}\left(\frac{\partial f}{\partial x}\right)^2 - 2\frac{\partial^2 f}{\partial x \partial y}\frac{\partial f}{\partial x}\frac{\partial f}{\partial y} = 0.$$

On the other hand, at an inflexion, since there is no curvature

$$\frac{d}{dx}\left(\frac{dy}{dx}\right) = 0; \qquad \frac{dy}{dx} = -\frac{\dfrac{\partial f}{\partial x}}{\dfrac{\partial f}{\partial y}}$$

$$\frac{d}{dx}\left(\frac{\partial f}{\partial x}\right) = \frac{\partial^2 f}{\partial x^2} + \frac{\partial^2 f}{\partial x \partial y}\left(\frac{dy}{dx}\right) = \frac{\dfrac{\partial^2 f}{\partial x^2}\dfrac{\partial f}{\partial y} - \dfrac{\partial^2 f}{\partial x \partial y}\dfrac{\partial f}{\partial x}}{\dfrac{\partial f}{\partial y}}$$

$$\frac{d}{dx}\left(\frac{\partial f}{\partial y}\right) = \frac{\partial^2 f}{\partial x \partial y} + \frac{\partial^2 f}{\partial y^2}\left(\frac{dy}{dx}\right) = \frac{\dfrac{\partial^2 f}{\partial x \partial y}\dfrac{\partial f}{\partial y} - \dfrac{\partial^2 f}{\partial y^2}\dfrac{\partial f}{\partial x}}{\dfrac{\partial f}{\partial y}}$$

$$\frac{d}{dx}\left(\frac{dy}{dx}\right) = -\frac{\dfrac{\partial^2 f}{\partial x^2}\left(\dfrac{\partial f}{\partial y}\right)^2 + \dfrac{\partial^2 f}{\partial y^2}\left(\dfrac{\partial f}{\partial x}\right)^2 - 2\dfrac{\partial^2 f}{\partial x \partial y}\dfrac{\partial f}{\partial x}\dfrac{\partial f}{\partial y}}{\left(\dfrac{\partial f}{\partial y}\right)^3}$$

We must now face the serious task of ascertaining how the Hessian behaves at a singular point. Let us imagine that this point is at the origin, and put $x = \xi_1$, $y = \xi_2$, then arrange the given polynomial in terms of ascending powers of (ξ). We thus get a set of homogeneous binary forms of increasing order, so that our equation becomes

$$0 = a_\xi^r + b_\xi^{r+1} + \dots.$$

The tangents at the origin are given by

$$a_\xi^r = 0.$$

The Hessian of this binary form is

$$|aa'|^2 a_\xi^{r-2} a_\xi'^{\,r-2} = 0.$$

The lowest terms of the ternary Hessian are

$$\begin{vmatrix} r(r-1)a_1^2 & r(r-1)a_1a_2 & (n-r)ra_1a_2 \\ r(r-1)a_2'a_1' & r(r-1)a_2'^2 & (n-r)ra_2'a_2' \\ (n-r)ra_1''a_\xi'' & (n-r)ra_2''a_\xi'' & (n-r)(n-r-1)a_\xi''^2 \end{vmatrix} a_\xi^{r-2}a_\xi'^{r-2}a_\xi''^{r-2}.$$

The cofactor of $(n-r)(n-r-1)a_\xi''^2$ is

$$r^2(r-1)^2 \begin{vmatrix} a_1^2 & a_1a_2 \\ a_1'a_2' & a_2'^2 \end{vmatrix} = \frac{r^2(r-1)^2}{2}|aa'|^2.$$

The remainder of the determinant is

$$Ka_1a_2'[\,|a'a''|a_\xi - |aa''|a_\xi'\,] = \tfrac{1}{2}K|aa'|^2a_\xi'';$$

by (19) of the last chapter. The lowest terms of the Hessian are

$$L|aa'|^2a_\xi^{r-2}a_\xi'^{r-2}a_\xi''^r.$$

Theorem 19] *If a curve have an ordinary singular point, the tangents to the Hessian at that point are the tangents to the original curve, and the Hessian of the binary form giving those tangents.*

If the two curves had different tangents at that point the number of intersections would be

$$r(3r-4).$$

They must, however, owing to the tangency, have at least one more intersection on each branch. If there were automatically still more intersections at that point, which we may suppose to be the origin, there would be more when the degree of the given curve was only $r+1$. Since the tangents are given by an irreducible curve, if one branch of the curve had a higher contact with the Hessian, so would each branch and the number of intersections at the origin would be $3r^2-2r$ and the number away from there $2r-3$. But if we take the simple curve

$$a_\xi^r + A\xi_1^{r+1} = 0$$

the Hessian will have the form

$$|aa'|^2a_\xi^{r-2}a_\xi'^{r-2}a_\xi''^r + B\xi_1^r|aa'|a_\xi^{r-2}a_\xi'^{r-2}a_\xi''^r = 0$$

and it is not hard to show that the different branches do not have higher contacts with the Hessian than desired.

Theorem 20] *If a curve have an ordinary singular point of order r, the number of intersections with the Hessian that are absorbed there is $3r(r-1)$.*

When the point is a node, the number is 6, and this shows that an ordinary singular point absorbs just as many intersections with the Hessian as if it were divided into virtual nodes as before.

There remains the case of a cusp. We write our curve

$$0 = -y^2 + ax^3 + 3bx^2y + 3cxy^2 + dy^3 + \dots.$$

This may be written as before

$$x = \frac{1}{a}t^2 + \dots \qquad y = \frac{1}{a}t^3 + \dots.$$

A short calculation gives the lowest terms in the Hessian

$$0 = ty^2(ax + by) + \dots.$$

Substituting we get 8 roots $t = 0$.

Theorem 21] *A curve will meet its Hessian 8 times at a cusp.*

If ι be the number of inflexions, δ and τ the nodes and bitangent, actual or virtual respectively, we get from 20 and 21

$$\iota = 3n(n-2) - 3\sum r_i(r_i - 1) - 2\kappa \tag{9}$$

$$\iota = 3n(n-2) - 6\delta - 8\kappa \tag{10}$$

$$\kappa = 3m(m-2) - 6\tau - 8\iota. \tag{11}$$

CHAPTER VII

PLÜCKER'S EQUATIONS AND KLEIN'S EQUATION

§ 1. Forms of Plücker's equations

In the last chapter we developed certain fundamental equations connecting the number of point and line singularities of curve whose worst singularities are ordinary point and line ones, cusps and inflexions. These are called Plücker's equations.* Their importance cannot be overestimated.

Let the order of a curve be n.

Let the class be m.

Let the number of actual or virtual nodes be δ.

Let the number of actual or virtual bitangents be τ.

Let the number of cusps be κ.

Let the number of inflexions be ι.

The equations of the last chapter are, then,

$$m = n(n-1)-2\delta-3\kappa \quad \textbf{(1)} \qquad n = m(m-1)-2\tau-3\iota \quad \textbf{(1')}$$

$$\iota = 3n(n-2)-6\delta-8\kappa \quad \textbf{(2)} \qquad \kappa = 3m(m-2)-6\tau-8\iota \quad \textbf{(2')}$$

Adding (1) and (1') and transposing, we get

$$n^2-2n+m^2-2m-2(\delta+\tau)-3(\iota+\kappa) = 0.$$

Adding (2) and (2'), transposing and dividing by 3, we get the same result. This shows that only three of the equations are linearly independent. It is well, in practice, to keep the equations in symmetrical pairs, or to reduce to forms which are symmetrical in point and line characteristics. The six numbers and a seventh to be deduced presently are called the 'Plücker characteristics' of the curve. It should be noted that they do not by any means classify a curve completely under the projective group of transformations. There are irreducible curves of the fifth order with six nodes, as we shall see later. Such curves have the same Plücker characteristics as those composed of a conic and a cubic, but are, obviously, very different. If we restrict ourselves to irreducible curves, then the Plücker characteristics give a good classification, as it can be proved that the totality of curves of a given order which are irreducible and

---

* For an historical account, see Berzolari[1], p. 343.

have a given number of nodes form a single irreducible continuum in higher space.*

Let us return to our equations. We get from (2) and (2')

$$3n^2 - 6n - 6(\delta + \kappa) - \kappa = 3m^2 - 6m - 6(\tau + \iota) - \iota.$$

From (1) and (1')

$$n^2 - 2(\delta + \kappa) - \kappa = m^2 - 2(\tau + \iota) - \iota.$$

Subtracting and dividing by 2,

$$n^2 - 3n - 2(\delta + \kappa) = m^2 - 3m - 2(\tau + \iota)$$

$$\frac{(n-1)(n-2)}{2} - (\delta + \kappa) = \frac{(m-1)(m-2)}{2} - (\tau + \iota) \equiv p. \quad (3)$$

This last characteristic, p, is called the 'genus' and is for many purposes the most important of all. We shall see, much later in our work, that whereas the other characteristics are invariant under all linear transformations of the plane, p has the fundamental property of being unaltered by every transformation of the curve which is one to one and algebraic. We have already seen in Ch. IV, theorem 12, that it is one less than the maximum number of real circuits possible for the given curve, when all the singular points are supposed real. From (1) and (1')

$$2(\tau - \delta) = m^2 - n^2 - 3(\iota - \kappa),$$

$$6(\tau - \delta) = 3(m^2 - n^2) - 9(\iota - \kappa).$$

From (1) and (1'), (2) and (2') eliminating $\delta + \tau$,

$$\iota - \kappa = 3(m - n), \quad (4)$$

$$2(\tau - \delta) = (m - n)(m + n - 9). \quad (5)$$

If $m = n$,   then $\iota = \kappa$, $\tau = \delta$.

If $\iota = \kappa$,   then $m = n$, $\tau = \delta$.

If $\tau = \delta$,   either $m = n$, $\iota = \kappa$,

  or $m + n = 9$.

We have the following cases under the last hypothesis:

$n = 3$	$m = 6$	$\delta = \kappa = \tau = 0$	$\iota = 6$,	
$n = 4$	$m = 5$	$\delta = 2$ $\tau = 2$	$\kappa = 1$	$\iota = 4$,
$n = 5$	$m = 4$	$\delta = 2$ $\tau = 2$	$\kappa = 4$	$\iota = 1$,
$n = 6$	$m = 3$	$\delta = \tau = \iota = 0$	$\kappa = 6$.	

* Cf. Severi-Löffler, Appendix.

We thus get a pretty theorem due to Bioche.*

Theorem 1] *If two complementary Plücker characteristics be equal, then each characteristic is equal to its complement, except in four cases where the sum of the order and class is* 9.

Let us seek an expression for τ in terms of the point characteristics alone. We easily find from (5)

$$2\tau = (n^2 - 2n - 2\delta - 3\kappa)(n^2 - 2\delta - 3\kappa - 9) + 2\delta.$$

Let us now make an apparently arbitrary change of notation.

$$x' = x(x-1) - 2y - 3z \qquad x = x'(x'-1) - 2y' - 3z',$$
$$2y' = (x^2 - 2x - 2y - 3z)(x^2 - 2y - 3z - 9) + 2y$$
$$2y = (x'^2 - 2x' - 2y' - 3z')(x'^2 - 2y' - 3z' - 9) + 2y',$$
$$z' = 3x(x-2) - 6y - 8z \qquad z = 3x'(x'-2) - 6y' - 8z'$$

If we introduce homogeneous space coordinates $x:y:z:t$ we get

$$\rho x' = t^2[x(x-t) - 2yt - 3zt],$$
$$\rho y' = \tfrac{1}{2}(x^2 - 2xt - 2yt - 3zt)(x^2 - 2yt - 3zt - 9t^2) + yt^3,$$
$$\rho z' = t^2[3x(x-2t) - 6yt - 8zt],$$
$$\rho t' = t^4.$$
$$\rho' x = t'^2[x'(x'-t') - 2y't' - 3z't'],$$
$$\rho' y = \tfrac{1}{2}[x'^2 - 2x't' - 2y't' - 3z't'][x'^2 - 2y't' - 3z't' - 9t'^2] + y't'^3.$$
$$\rho' z = t'^2[3x'(x'-2t') - 6y't' - 8z't'],$$
$$\rho' t = t'^4.$$

We have here, if we interpret $x:y:z:t$ as homogeneous Cartesian coordinates in projective space of three dimensions, a transformation which is involutory, i.e. the same as its inverse, algebraic, and one to one. A plane is transformed into a surface of the fourth order linearly dependent on four such surfaces. There is thus a three-parameter family of these surfaces. There is a two-parameter sub-system of reducible surfaces which correspond to planes parallel to the y-axis, namely,

$$t^2\{\lambda(x^2 - xt - 2yt - 3zt) + \mu(3x^2 - 6xt - 6yt - 8zt) + \nu t^2\} = 0.$$

If we take $\lambda + 3\mu = 0$ we get

$$t^3[\mu(-3x+z) + \nu t] = 0,$$

and this is the plane at infinity counted three times and a pencil

* Bioche, p. 68.

of parallel planes. They correspond to curves the number of whose cusps exceeds three times their orders by some constant. The quadric

$$3x(x-2t)-6yt-8zt = 0,$$

which corresponds to curves with no inflexions, is a cone with its vertex at $(0, 4, -3, 0)$, a cylinder parallel to the plane $x = 0$.*

§ 2. Existence conditions

If a curve exist with only the sort of point and line singularities that we have considered, its Plücker characteristics satisfy our equations (1), (1'), (2), and (2'). An important question, to which, so far, no complete answer has been found, is the following. Given a system of positive integers or 0's n, m, δ, κ, τ, ι where $mn \neq 0$ which satisfy Plücker's equations, is there always a curve having these numbers as Plücker characteristics? We shall prove shortly that this is not always the case; unfortunately all we can do is to prove the non-existence of curves to fit *some* sets of characteristics, without surely knowing which.

Suppose that we have three linearly independent polynomials of degree n in an auxiliary variable X,

$$\rho x_1 = f_1(X) \qquad \rho x_2 = f_2(X) \qquad \rho x_3 = f_3(X).$$

Let us further suppose that a single point (x) of the plane curve so determined will not, usually, correspond to two distinct values of X. What will be the order of the plane curve? If we write

$$(ux) \equiv u_1 f_1(X) + u_2 f_2(X) + u_3 f_3(X) = 0,$$

we get n different roots X and so n points of the plane curve, its order is n. We shall call such a curve a 'rational' one. In non-homogeneous coordinates we should express x and y as rational functions of the auxiliary parameter.

Has our rational curve any nodes? In order to have a node, we must have

$$\frac{f_1(X)}{f_1(Y)} = \frac{f_2(X)}{f_2(Y)} = \frac{f_3(X)}{f_3(Y)},$$

$$f_1(X)f_2(Y) - f_2(X)f_1(Y) = 0, \qquad f_1(X)f_3(Y) - f_3(X)f_1(Y) = 0.$$

Each of these polynomials is divisible by $(X-Y)$. The quotient will, in each case, give us a curve of order $2(n-1)$

* Cf. Kantor[1], pp. 769 ff.

with a point of order $n-1$ at the end of each axis. The number of finite intersections will be

$$4(n-1)^2 - 2(n-1)^2 = 2(n-1)^2.$$

From these we must deduct the sets of intersections of the lines $f_1(X) = 0, f_1(Y) = 0, X \neq Y$, which are $n^2 - n$ in number, leaving $(n-1)(n-2)$.

These points appear in pairs, symmetrical with regard to the line $X = Y$. Each pair will correspond to a node. The number of nodes will thus, 'in general', be $\dfrac{(n-1)(n-2)}{2}$. The curve will not, usually, have any cusp. If it had a cusp corresponding to the parameter value X_0, each line through that point would meet the curve twice there, which involves

$$\frac{f_1'(X_0)}{f_1(X_0)} = \frac{f_2'(X_0)}{f_2(X_0)} = \frac{f_3'(X_0)}{f_3(X_0)}.$$

These equations have not, in general, any common solution, as we can see in a special case, and apply the reasoning explained in the first chapter. As a matter of fact, we shall see in a subsequent chapter that when such curves have cusps, the number of nodes is reduced accordingly.

Theorem 2] *A rational curve of order n has, 'in general', $\dfrac{(n-1)(n-2)}{2}$ nodes.*

Suppose, conversely, that we have a curve of order n with multiple points of orders r_1, r_2 which are ordinary or cusps, and where

$$\sum \frac{r_i(r_i-1)}{2} = \frac{(n-1)(n-2)}{2} \qquad (p=0).$$

Let us try to construct an adjoint curve of order $n-2$ which passes through $n-3$ ordinary points of the curve. The number of conditions imposed is not greater than

$$\sum \frac{r_i(r_i-1)}{2} + (n-3) = \frac{(n-2)(n+1)}{2} - 1,$$

so that we have at least one degree of freedom. If the given curve be irreducible and so do not include this adjoint as a part of itself, there is exactly one variable intersection. The number of degrees of freedom could not exceed the number of variable intersections, for if there were more freedom we could fix too many arbitrary points, and make the given curve 'swallow' the adjoint, which is not possible when the former is irreducible. Moreover, the conditions imposed on the adjoints are all linear, hence these form a system of the form

$$\phi + X\psi = 0.$$

Combining this with the equation of the given curve, only one intersection will depend on X, so that x and y will be rational functions of X; we have a rational curve.

Theorem 3] *A curve of genus 0 is always rational.*

Let us next notice that a polynomial of order n in one variable depends upon $n+1$ coefficients, including the constants. The three polynomials $f(X)$ together, allowing for homogeneity, depend on $3(n+1)-1$ parameters. Moreover, each such curve is carried into itself by the three-parameter system of transformations

$$X = \frac{\alpha X' + \beta}{\gamma X' + \delta},$$

so that the number of degrees of freedom cannot exceed $3n-1$.

Now let us look at the matter otherwise. If we require a curve to have a multiplicity two or more at a particular point, we impose three conditions. If we require it to have one double point, and then require that double point to be at a particular spot, we impose one plus two conditions. Hence but one condition is imposed by requiring it to have a double point. The number of conditions imposed by $\frac{(n-1)(n-2)}{2}$ double points will, thus, not exceed $\frac{(n-1)(n-2)}{2}$, and the amount of freedom of a rational curve will not be less than $3n-1$. Comparing these two calculations, we see that the amount of freedom must be exactly this, and each double point must have imposed one condition. This gives

Lefschetz's Theorem 4] *Each double point assigned to an irreducible curve whose genus is not negative imposes exactly one condition.**

Suppose that we have a continuous system of curves of given

* Lefschetz, pp. 23 ff.

order and genus, the general curve being irreducible with a certain number of cusps. Suppose that a particular curve is reducible, we may find an irreducible curve infinitely near to this. The Riemann surface of the irreducible curve hangs together in one piece: we may find a single path away from all branch points going from any one point of the surface to any other. In the case of the reducible curve this is not possible. Take a path of the irreducible curve which connects two points which pass continuously into two points of different factors of the reducible curve. This path by a slight deformation goes into a path through a critical point. Now if the branch points of the irreducible curve were at finite distances from one another, we could take a path from any point to any other which remained at a finite distance from each branch and critical point, and so by a slight deformation could not go into a path through a critical point. Hence, in the irreducible curve two branch points must be infinitely near. Hence, in the passage to the limit two branch points must coalesce. Now whether these come from vertical tangents, or cusps, when two come together we get a limiting case of either a new singularity or a more complicated singularity. This gives an interesting theorem, which I believe is due to Bertini, though I cannot verify the fact.

Theorem 5] *If a continuous system of algebraic curves of assigned order be given, and if the general curve be irreducible of given genus and given number of cusps, then if a particular curve of the system become reducible, it will have more, or more complicated, singularities than the general curve.**

As an example of this, we see that if we have a system of rational quintic curves with six double points, a particular curve cannot become a conic and a cubic; it might become a rational quartic and a line.

Let us next look at the cuspidal conditions. Let us start with a curve of order n, a rational curve, with an ordinary singularity of multiplicity $n-1$ at the origin O. Let A be another point of the curve. We pass a non-degenerate quadric surface through O and A, not tangent to the plane of the curve, and call V an

---

* Cf. Severi-Löffler, p. 319. There is a long algebraic discussion of this and kindred questions.

intersection of a generator through O with one through A. If we project the plane curve on the quadric from V we get a space curve of order n, for it will meet VA once, and VO $n-1$ times. This space curve is rationally connected with the plane curve, and so rational. We project it back into a plane curve of order n from a point not on the quadric, not on a tangent to the space curve, nor on a line connecting two points of that curve with coplanar tangents. We get a rational plane curve of order n with no singularity but a node, or one with just one cusp, if the new centre of projection be on one tangent. Just one condition is hereby imposed. We may thus find a rational curve of any order with no cusp, or just one cusp; hence, by the principle of duality, or by polar reciprocation in a conic, we may find a plane curve of any class with no inflexion or with just one inflexion. If a curve of genus 0 have no inflexion its order is

$$n = m(m-1) - 2\frac{(m-1)(m-2)}{2} = 2(m-1).$$

If it have just one inflexion, the order becomes

$$n = 2m - 3.$$

We may thus have a rational curve of any even order with no inflexion, or any odd order with just one.

Suppose next that we had a curve of any chosen order and positive genus with a certain number of double points. Suppose that some of these were automatically compelled to be cusps. The same would hold if that curve had additional double points, enough to have genus 0. But in the latter case we are not compelled to have any cusps, or we may have just one. Hence, in the original case we may have no cusps, or just one. The same will hold for the inflexions of a curve of given class.

Suppose that a curve of class m have no inflexions. Since $\tau \geqslant 0$,

$$(m-1)(m-2) - 2p \geqslant 0,$$
$$2(m-1) \geqslant 1 + \sqrt{8p+1}.$$

If m be compatible with the genus p, this relation must hold; conversely, Plücker's characteristics can be found with $\iota = 0$ and m and p connected by this relation. But

$$n + \iota = 2(m-1) + 2p \qquad (\iota = 0).$$

Hence $n \geqslant 2p + 1 + \sqrt{8p+1}$,   (6) and n can have any value for p given, and $\iota = 0$ that satisfies this relation. In the same way we have, when $\iota = 1$,

$$n > 2p + \sqrt{8p+9}. \tag{6'}$$

We have, moreover, from equations (2) and (2'),

$$\iota = 3[(n-2)+2p] - 2\kappa$$

$$\kappa = \tfrac{3}{2}[(n-2)+2p] - \tfrac{1}{2}\iota,$$

so that when n and p are given, the maximum number of cusps is obtained when ι is 0 or 1. If, then, n and p be connected by the suitable relation (2) or (2'), there will actually exist a curve of that order and positive genus with the maximum permissible number of cusps.

Will there exist curves of this order and genus with a lesser number of cusps ? Let us start with assigned values for n and p, compatible with (6) or (6'), and assume that all the double points, or all but one, are nodes. Such curves, we have seen, exist. The number of free parameters, by Lefschetz's theorem, is exactly

$$\frac{n(n+3)}{2} - \delta = 3n + (p-1), \quad \text{or} \quad \frac{n(n+3)}{2} - \delta - 2 = 3n + p - 2.$$

Suppose next that we require one double point (x_0, y_0) to become a cusp, by writing

$$\frac{\partial^2 f}{\partial x_0^2} \frac{\partial^2 f}{\partial y_0^2} - \left(\frac{\partial^2 f}{\partial x_0 \partial y_0} \right)^2 = 0,$$

then a second, and so on until we reach the requisite maximum number of cusps. None of these cuspidal conditions could automatically introduce new nodes, for if one did, we should depress the genus, which need not happen, for we have seen that a curve does exist of just this order and genus with the maximum number of cusps. It might conceivably happen, however, that at some stage when we wished to change one node to a cusp, we automatically changed several at once, then when all the cusps were reached, we should have more freedom than we should expect, i.e. the freedom would be greater than

$$\frac{n(n+3)}{2} - (\delta + 2\kappa) = 3n + (p-1) - \kappa.$$

But, by (4), $\iota - \kappa = 3(m-n)$,

$$3n + (p-1) - \kappa = 3m + (p-1) - \iota,$$

and we have just seen, by Lefschetz's theorem, that when $\iota = 0$ or $\iota = 1$ the right-hand side represents the exact freedom. That being so, the cuspidal conditions must have been independent, and the cusps come in one at a time.

Theorem 6] *Given the order n of a curve, and the genus p, subject to the restriction that when n is even $n \geqslant 2p+1+\sqrt{8p+1}$ and when odd $n \geqslant 2p+\sqrt{8p+q}$, then there will exist irreducible curves of this order and genus with any desired number of cusps up to the maximum permissible, and each node will deduct one from the total freedom of the curve, each cusp two.*[*]

We shall, towards the end of the present work, find a means by the theory of linear series of point-groups on a curve, to extend this theorem to a certain extent, though no one can say to-day in every case just what are the necessary and sufficient conditions that an apparently proper set of solutions of Plücker's equations should correspond to actual curves. The fact that there exist sets which do not so correspond is easily established in the following fashion. Here is, apparently, a perfectly good set of solutions:

$$n = m = 14 \qquad \delta = \tau = 0 \qquad \kappa = \iota = 56 \qquad p = 22.$$

If this curve does not exist, our statement is justified. If it does, it must have at least eight degrees of freedom, for the collineation group in the plane which carries such a curve into another such depends on eight parameters, and the curve is not carried into itself by any one-parameter group of collineations. For if it were, there would be an infinite number of collineations leaving all the cusps in place, hence an infinite number leaving in place every line through each cusp, which is absurd. On the other hand, a curve of order 14 with 56 double points has $\dfrac{14 \times 17}{2} - 56 = 63$ degrees of freedom. If the cusps came in one at a time, the amount of freedom of the present curve would be $63 - 56 = 7$.

* Cf. Coolidge[3], p. 452.

We leave to the reader the easy task of proving in the same way

For every value of n above 13 there exist solutions of Plücker's equations which do not correspond to any curve.

It is evident that there must be many further restrictions when we allow singular points of order above two. A triple point is equivalent to three nodes in determining the other Plücker characteristics, but whereas an irreducible curve of the fifth order can perfectly well have six nodes, it cannot have two triple points; the line connecting them would meet it too often.

§ 3. Klein's equation

Plücker's equations are reached by purely algebraic means, and do not involve any question as to the reality of the curves or the singularities. It is evident that in dealing with real curves an important question is, what real point and line singularities are permissible? Are there any equations connecting the number of these?

As a preliminary investigation, let us see what is the effect of sliding a real curve an infinitesimal pure-imaginary distance in a real direction, x. Let the equation of the curve, whose only real singularities are nodes, cusps, bitangents, and inflexions, be

$$f(x, y) = 0. \tag{7}$$

The equation in the new position will be

$$f(x + \epsilon i, y) = 0. \tag{8}$$

Has this new curve any real points? They lie also on

$$f(x - \epsilon i, y) = 0,$$

and so on the following two real curves:

$$\phi(x, y) \equiv \tfrac{1}{2}[f(x+\epsilon i, y) + f(x-\epsilon i, y)] \equiv f(x, y) - \frac{\epsilon^2}{2}\frac{\partial^2 f}{\partial x^2} + \ldots = 0,$$

$$\psi(x, y) \equiv \frac{1}{2\epsilon i}[f(x+\epsilon i, y) - f(x-\epsilon i, y)] \equiv \frac{\partial f}{\partial x} - \frac{\epsilon^3}{6}\frac{\partial^3 f}{\partial x^3} + \ldots = 0. \tag{9}$$

They are, therefore, extremely near to points on the original curve where the tangent takes the direction of sliding, or which are singular.

At this point we must stop and make one or two remarks

about a question of procedure. In the present investigation we shall feel free to use the somewhat archaic apparatus of oblique Cartesian coordinates, where a point is located by its distance from each of two intersecting but not necessarily mutually perpendicular lines, measured in a direction parallel to the other line. Projective properties of curves receive the same statement in these coordinates and in rectangular ones, as well as relations to the line at infinity which do not involve distances or angles. We shall use the usual (x, y) notation for these. We shall also feel free to change coordinates of this sort as often as the fancy take us. We seek those cases where the curve (8) has a real point near the origin, that being suitably located on (7). Lastly, we see that if all real points near the origin on f lie close also to points of a simpler curve f', we may substitute for ϕ and ψ corresponding simpler curves ϕ' and ψ' and count their real intersections near by.

Suppose, first, that our curve has a horizontal tangent at the origin end of the x-axis

$$f \equiv y + ax^2 + \ldots \qquad f' \equiv y + ax^2,$$
$$\phi' \equiv y + a(x^2 - \epsilon^2) \qquad \psi' \equiv 2ax,$$

there is clearly one intersection of ϕ' and ψ', and so of ϕ and ψ, near the origin.

Suppose, secondly, there is a node at the origin. We choose our oblique axes so as to divide the nodal tangents harmonically, getting

$$f \equiv y^2 + ax^2 + \ldots \qquad f' \equiv y^2 + ax^2,$$
$$\phi' \equiv y^2 + a(x^2 - \epsilon^2) \qquad \psi' \equiv 2ax.$$

When $a < 0$, i.e. when the node has real tangents, there are no real intersections near the origin, but when $a > 0$, i.e. when the tangents a reconjugate imaginary and we have a so-called 'conjugate point', we have two real intersections close to $(0, \pm \epsilon \sqrt{a})$.

Suppose, thirdly, we have a cusp whose cuspidal tangent does not lie in the direction of sliding,

$$f \equiv x^2 + ay^3 + \ldots \qquad f' \equiv x^2 + ay^3,$$
$$\phi' \equiv -\epsilon^2 + x^2 + ay^3 \qquad \psi' \equiv 2x;$$

we have one intersection close to $\left(0, \sqrt[3]{\dfrac{\epsilon^2}{a}}\right)$.

Let δ_1' be the number of real nodes with real tangents, δ_2' that of real conjugate points as described above, τ_1' that of real bitangents with real contact, τ_2' that of real conjugate bitangents, i.e. with contact at pairs of conjugate imaginary paths of points, κ' the number of real cusps, and ι' that of real inflexions; then, if N be the number of finite points with real horizontal tangents, the number of points sought is

$$N + 2\delta_2' + \kappa'.$$

We return to our curve (8) and see how many real tangents it has. To begin with we have N real horizontal tangents found above. Let us show that there are no other real non-singular tangents.

Let the equation of a non-horizontal line be

$$x = uy + v.$$

The sliding of the plane will have the effect of changing v to $v - \epsilon i$, and this will change the tangential equation of the curve from $\Phi(u, v) = 0$ to $\Phi(u, v - \epsilon i) = 0$. The new curve, by our previous reasoning, has only real non-singular tangents where $\dfrac{\partial \Phi}{\partial v} = 0$, i.e. at infinite points, and has only real singular tangents which come from the real inflexional or conjugate tangents of the original curve. The number of real tangents of (8) is

$$N + 2\tau_2' + \iota'.$$

The difference between the number of real points and real tangents to (8) is $\quad 2(\delta_2' - \tau_2') + \kappa' - \iota'.$

It is our next task, and a difficult one, to show that this number can be calculated in terms of our Plücker characteristics. Let us project the curve (8) vertically on the plane $z = i$, the Cartesian coordinates in space not necessarily being rectangular. We shall also project the curve $f(x - \epsilon i, y) = 0$ on the plane $z = -i$. We have two conjugate imaginary plane curves in two conjugate imaginary planes. If we connect a real infinite point with them we get two conjugate imaginary cylinders, whose intersections are either real lines or pairs of conjugate imaginary ones. The common tangent planes to the two are either real, or conjugate imaginary in pairs. When the projecting point is the end of the z-axis, the difference between the number of real lines and real planes is $2(\delta_2'-\tau_2')+\kappa'-\iota'$; let us show that it has this value in every case, and then calculate it in other terms when the infinite point is skilfully chosen.

The real lines of the cylinder are the generators through its infinite vertex which belong to the two (real)-parameter system of lines connecting conjugate imaginary points in the two conjugate imaginary planes $z = i$ and $z = -i$. This number will only change when two lines of the family fall together, i.e. when the infinite point crosses the infinite trace of the developable determined by conjugate imaginary points in the two planes whose tangents are coplanar, and so parallel. The real planes through a point P tangent to the two curves are tangent to this developable, and their number will only change when P crosses the surface, or crosses a singular tangent plane to the developable. As a matter of fact, in this case the number will not alter. We see it in this way. Consider the dual problem, when the developable becomes a space curve. If a moving plane which passes across a double point of this space curve lose or gain two real intersections, the double point must be a cusp. But if for one particular way of crossing no real intersections are lost or gained, then this is not a cusp, and two are never lost. In the same way, if there be one way for an infinite point P to cross a singular tangent plane without changing the number of real tangent planes through it, the same will hold for all passages. We have merely to assume that no singular tangent plane is horizontal, which must be the case, considering how the surface is generated, and let P move along the infinite line common to the planes $z = $ const. The number of real planes here is always m, the class of the curve; we have merely to draw from P, which lies in the plane of both curves, tangents to one, and the conjugate imaginary tangents to the other.

It remains to be seen how the number of real lines and planes changes as the infinite point moves across the developable. We take a generator of the developable, which connects conjugate imaginary points in the planes $z = i$, $z = -i$, with parallel tangents, as the z-axis, the x-axis shall take the direction of these tangents, while the point P shall subsequently move slightly in the y direction. Projecting the conjugate imaginary curves from the end of the z-axis on the (x, y) plane, we get the curves

$$y = (p_2 + q_2 i)x^2 + \dots \qquad y = (p_2 - q_2 i)x^2 + \dots .$$

If P move a small distance in the y direction, we get

$$y + \delta i = (p_2 + q_2 i)x^2 + \dots \qquad y - \delta i = (p_2 - q_2 i)x^2 + \dots .$$

Any real intersections of these curves will be common to

$$y = p_2 x^2 + \dots \qquad \delta = q_2 x^2 + \dots .$$

These will have two real intersections near the origin if $\delta q_2 > 0$.

Now for tangent planes through P or tangent lines to the complex projected curves. The equation of the tangent at (x_0, y_0) to $y_0 + \delta i = (p_2 + q_2 i)x_0^2 + \dots$ is

$$\frac{y + \delta i - (p_2 + q_2 i)x_0^2 - \dots}{x - x_0} = 2(p_2 + q_2 i)x_0 + \dots$$

$$y + \delta i = [2(p_2 + q_2 i)x_0 + \dots]x - [(p_2 + q_2 i)x_0^2 + \dots].$$

Calling this $y + \delta i = ux + v,$

$$u = 2(p_2 + q_2 i)x_0 + \dots \qquad v = -(p_2 + q_2 i)x_0^2 - \dots$$

$$v = -\frac{1}{4(p_2 + q_2 i)}u^2 + \dots .$$

For a real line, u and $v - \delta i$ are real.

Hence $$0 = -\delta + \frac{q_2}{4(p_2^2 + q_2^2)}u^2 + \dots,$$

and there will be two roots close to O if $\delta q_2 > 0$. This shows that if P cross the developable so as to lose two real lines, it will lose two real planes at the same time, and conversely, which is another way of saying that

$$2(\delta_2' - \tau_2') + \kappa' - \iota'$$

is a constant. But when P is on the infinite line common to the planes $z = i$, $z = -i$, the line at infinity counted n times, where n is the order of the curve, gives the real lines, and the m tangents to one curve, and the conjugate imaginary tangents to the other, give the real planes. We thus get

$$2(\delta_2' - \tau_2') + \kappa' - \iota' = n - m,$$

and so, finally, $$n + 2\tau_2' + \iota' = m + 2\delta_2' + \kappa'. \qquad (10)$$

This is called Klein's equation.

Klein's Theorem 7] *If a real curve have no singularities but nodes and cusps, bitangents and inflexions, the order, plus twice the number of conjugate tangents plus the number of real inflexions, is equal to the class, plus twice the number of real conjugate points plus the number of real cusps.**

Certain very simple corollaries flow from this. If our curve have no cusps, or real conjugate points, we have from (4) and (10)

$$m-n = \iota' + 2\tau_2'$$
$$3(m-n) = 3\iota' + 6\tau_2'$$
$$3(m-n) = \iota.$$

Theorem 8] *If a real curve have no cusps, and no real conjugate points, not more than one-third of the inflexions can be real.*

Suppose that there are i'' pairs of conjugate imaginary inflexions, and κ'' pairs of conjugate imaginary cusps, and suppose that $\delta_2' = \tau_2'$.

$$3(m-n) = \iota - \kappa = 3(\iota' - \kappa')$$
$$\iota = \iota' + 2\iota'' \qquad \kappa = \kappa' + 2\kappa''$$
$$\iota'' - \kappa'' = \iota' - \kappa'$$
$$\iota'' - \iota' = \kappa'' - \kappa'.$$

Theorem 9] *If a real curve have the same number of real conjugate points and real conjugate tangents, and no singularities but cusps and nodes, inflexions and bitangents, then the difference between the number of pairs of conjugate imaginary cusps and the number of real cusps is equal to the same difference for inflexions.*

As a final topic for the present chapter, let us see whether there be any other equations, independent of those already shown, which always connect the real Plücker characteristics. We make a large list of these:

$n =$ The order of the curve.	$m =$ Class of curve.
$n' =$ The apparent order.	$m' =$ Apparent class.
$c' =$ The number of real circuits.	$c' =$ Number of real circuits.
$\delta =$ Number of nodes.	$\tau =$,, of bitangents.
$\kappa =$,, of cusps.	$\iota =$,, of inflexions.

* Cf. Klein[1]. The proof is taken from Juel, the only rigorous proof yet published.

$\delta_1' =$ Number of real nodes with real tangents.

$\tau_1' =$ Number of real bitangents with real points of contact.

$\delta_2' =$ Number of real conjugate points.

$\tau_2' =$ Number of real conjugate tangents.

$\kappa' =$ Number of real cusps.

$\iota' =$ Number of real inflexions.

Suppose that some polynomial involving some or all of these characteristics is identically 0 for every curve. We may assume it to be self-dual, for, if not, the dual polynomial will vanish, and the sum will be self-dual. Let us use Plücker's equations to eliminate m, τ, and ι, and Klein's to eliminate τ_2', and thus get

$$F(n, n', m', c', \delta, \kappa, \iota', \kappa', \delta_1', \tau_1', \delta_2') \equiv 0. \qquad (11)$$

Let us assume that the highest power to which any one argument appears is N. We proceed to show that each of the arguments in turn may be given more than N values, without altering the values of such of the other arguments as may still be in the equation; hence we show that one argument after another is not there, and so, finally, there is no polynomial at all.

The equation of the curve we are going to study shall take the bizarre form

$$f(x, y)\phi(x, y) + \epsilon 1^3(x - a)^3 \psi(x, y) = 0. \qquad (12)$$

The curious factor 1^3 is introduced to indicate that the degree of ψ is at least 6 less than that of $f\phi$, hence the form of the curve at infinity is determined by the first part. ϕ and ψ are supposed to be real definite forms, i.e. real polynomials whose signs are the same for all values of the variables. ϵ is supposed to be a real infinitesimal, so that in appearance the curve differs as little as we please from the real curve f, whose form we shall prescribe with minute care. As a preliminary we shall prove a proposition which will be of utmost importance to us at various times in the present work.

Bertini's Theorem 10] *The general curve of a system linearly dependent on a certain number of given irreducible curves will not* **have a singular point which is not fixed for all the curves of the system.**[*]

* Bertini[4].

This theorem is certainly true if we can prove it for a set linearly dependent on two given curves. Write this set

$$R(x,y)+z\,S(x,y) = 0.$$

This may be interpreted as a surface of order $n+1$ in three-dimensional space, the end of the z-axis being a multiple point of order n since every line through it has but one finite intersection with the surface. If for every value of z there were a moving singularity, then either every horizontal plane would have to be tangent to the surface, or there would be a curve of singular points. If every point on a line lies on a surface, all the tangent planes pass through that line, so, dually, if every horizontal plane were tangent to a surface, the point of contact would lie in the infinite line in these planes, a case we may exclude at once. But if the surface had a curve of singular points, a vertical line through a point of that curve would meet the surface too often or be swallowed therein. If there were an infinite number of these lines the surface would be a vertical cylinder, and z would not appear. But if there were a finite number, the singular points would correspond to fixed values for x and y.

The immediate consequence which we draw from this vitally important theorem is that the singular points of our curve (12) are known for the general ϵ.

We shall assume that the compound curve $f\phi$ has no singular points which are singular for ψ, so that the only singularities we need bother about are those which lie on the line

$$x-a = 0, \tag{13}$$

or on the line at infinity.

It remains to describe the curve

$$f = 0.$$

This shall consist in

A) Pairs of conjugate imaginary straight lines which meet either on (13) or on the line at infinity.

B) Quartic ovals of the three following types:

1) Convex ovals. We get such curves from equations like

$$\left(\frac{x^2}{a^2}+\frac{y^2}{b^2}-1\right)(x^2+y^2+1)+\delta = 0,$$

where δ is a real infinitesimal. This curve looks exactly like an ellipse and has no real inflexions. Some of these shall intersect in pairs on (13).

2) Lima-bean ovals. These have each a real bitangent and a pair of real inflexions. We get such a curve by a small change in the equation of a cardioid.

3) Crescent loops. Each of these has a real cusp at each horn, and one real inflexion near each horn. We construct such a curve in the following fashion. Start with the curve

$$(xy+x+y)^2-xy+\delta' = 0,$$

where δ' is a real infinitesimal. We have a real cusp at the end of each axis, but no other real singularity. The line $x+y = \delta'-\frac{1}{4}$ is a conjugate tangent. By Plücker's equation (5),

$$2(\tau-\delta) = (m-n)(m+n-q) = 2,$$
$$\delta = 0 \qquad \tau = 1.$$

Our conjugate tangent is the only double tangent, and so, by Klein's equation, there are two real inflexions. By projecting to infinity a line near the conjugate tangent we get a similar curve in the finite part of the plane, and we may make this as small as we please.

Let us see now on what will each of the arguments in (11) depend.

c'. This is the total number of real circuits. It can be altered at will by replacing stray ovals, not in the nest nor intersecting in pairs, by self-conjugate imaginary ovals such as $x^4+y^4+1 = 0$. Hence c' can be given more than N values, and so cannot appear in the equation.

δ_1'. This depends on the number of circuits that intersect in pairs on (13) and can be altered at will by pulling such circuits about. Hence it cannot occur in the equation. τ_1' can be altered by nesting and un-nesting, and so cannot come in.

n', the apparent order, i.e. the maximum number of real intersections with any line. This may be made to depend on the number of real intersections with (13) and may be changed at will, for instance, by transferring conjugate points from (13) to the line at infinity. Hence n' does not enter. m' can be altered by replacing convex ovals by imaginary loops.

κ'. This depends on the number of crescent circuits. If a crescent circuit be replaced by a Lima-bean, taking care not to alter relations to the line (13), and if the lost real cusps be replaced by pairs of conjugate imaginary ones on the line at infinity, no argument has been changed but κ', and this was changed at will. Hence κ' and the symmetrical ι' can be altered by replacing Lima-beans by convex ovals.

δ_2'. This depends on the number of pairs of conjugate imaginary lines meeting on (13) or on the line at infinity. We alter it by replacing two pairs of conjugate imaginary parallel lines by a pair of ellipses which are similar, and similarly placed, so that they have the same imaginary infinite points.

The only arguments which remain are n, δ, and κ, and we have seen that within the range of certain inequalities these are independent numbers.

Theorem 11] *There are no identical polynomial equations connecting the Plücker characteristics and the real characteristics enumerated above, which are not deducible from the equations of Plücker and Klein.**

A study of the upper limits for the numbers of real singularities of various sorts has been made by Hollcroft;† there is, however, no rigorous proof that the curves so described really exist.

* Cf. Coolidge².   † Cf. Hollcroft.

CHAPTER VIII

THE GENUS

§ 1. Definition of genus, Riemann's theorem

WE have already had occasion once or twice to speak of the genus of a curve; it is given by the equations

$$\frac{(n-1)(n-2)}{2} - \sum \frac{r_i(r_i-1)}{2} = \frac{(m-1)(m-2)}{2} - \sum \frac{\rho_i(\rho_i-1)}{2} = p. \tag{1}$$

In terms of nodes and bitangents, actual or virtual, this is

$$\frac{(n-1)(n-2)}{2} - (\delta+\kappa) = \frac{(m-1)(m-2)}{2} - (\tau+\iota) = p. \tag{2}$$

It is to be understood in these definitions that the curve has no singular points but ordinary ones and cusps, with a like restriction on singular tangents. A curve, no matter what its singularities, has a definite genus, as we shall see in Book II, but we are not yet prepared to give the definition.

We saw in Lefschetz's theorem 4] of the last chapter that the genus of an irreducible curve can have any value from $\frac{(n-1)(n-2)}{2}$ down to 0. We postulated in certain subsequent theorems that the genus of the curve in question was not negative. As a matter of fact we cannot have an irreducible curve of negative genus. We have only to consider the system of adjoints of order $n-1$ which exist, since first polar curves are that.

The amount of freedom of such a system is

$$\geqslant \frac{(n+2)(n-1)}{2} - \sum \frac{r_i(r_i-1)}{2} = p+2(n-1).$$

The number of free intersections with the given curve is

$$\leqslant n(n-1) - \sum r_i(r_i-1) = 2p+2(n-1).$$

But we have already seen that the freedom cannot exceed the number of free intersections.

Theorem 1] *If a curve have no singular points but ordinary ones and cusps, its genus can never be negative.*

Theorem 2] *The genus of a curve is the amount that the number of nodes, actual or virtual, and cusps, falls short of the maximum possible for an irreducible curve of that order.*

It is for this reason that the genus was habitually called the 'deficiency' by the earlier English-speaking writers.

Suppose that the plane in which a curve lies is so oriented that no singular tangent is vertical, or has an infinite point of contact, and no singular point lies at infinity, a condition easily obtainable by a linear transformation. Then y is an n-valued algebraic function of x or a single-valued function on a certain definite n-leaved Riemann surface. The branch points of this surface arise from those values of x where two values of y on one branch fall together, and these are either the points of contact of vertical tangents, or else the cusps. Their number is thus

$$m + \kappa = 2n + 2(p-1),$$

$$m + \kappa - 2n = 2(p-1).$$

Now the left-hand side of this last equation is the connectivity of the surface, and is unaltered by any continuous one-to-one transformation. Hence the genus is unaltered. We thus get

Riemann's Theorem 3] *If two algebraic plane curves with only ordinary singular points and cusps be so related that the coordinates of a point on either are rational functions of a corresponding point on the other, then the two curves have the same genus.**

Here is a shorter statement. Two algebraic curves in any number of dimensions which are related in the way here described are said to be 'birationally related': each is said to be obtained from the other by a 'birational transformation' of the other. Any transformation that is algebraic and one-to-one is birational. We thus get

Riemann's Theorem 3'] *The genus of a curve is unaltered by a birational transformation.*

If the reader reflect upon this theorem he must be struck by its great generality and importance. The only proof we have given so far is entirely transcendental, based on the connectivity of Riemann surfaces. That will not do; we must give an algebraic proof. This we proceed to do, though indirectly; the proof comes incidentally out of a fundamentally important formula which must be developed for its own sake.

* Riemann, pp. 127 ff. A list of various forms of proof will be found in Clebsch-Lindemann, pp. 681 ff.

§ 2. The Chasles-Cayley-Brill correspondence formula

Suppose that we have a fixed curve, with only the sort of singularities we have so far allowed, and a linear system of curves. The variable groups of points which the curves of the system cut on the fixed curve, which we shall call the 'base curve', shall be called a 'linear series of point-groups'. We shall consider only non-singular points as belonging to such groups. It may be that all of the variable groups contain a certain number of fixed, non-singular points. *These we are at liberty to count as forming parts of the groups or to exclude at will.*

A linear system of curves may be built up by pencils of curves each connecting a fixed new curve with the curves of some previously recognized linear system, and the same holds, of course, for linear systems of point-groups. Consider the pencil

$$t\psi_0(x,y)+\psi_1(x,y) = 0,$$

which we may also write

$$t = -\frac{\psi_1(x,y)}{\psi_0(x,y)}.$$

The groups of the corresponding linear series are groups of points on the base curve where the rational function $-\dfrac{\psi_1(x,y)}{\psi_0(x,y)}$ takes constant values. Conversely, if we have a rational function of x and y, we may adjoin the factor 1, representing the line at infinity, to the numerator or denominator in such a way that we imagine them of the same order. Then the variable groups of points where this function takes assigned values are the groups of a one-parameter linear series.

Suppose, now, we make a rational transformation of our curve

$$x = \frac{\theta_1(x',y')}{\theta_0(x',y')} \qquad y = \frac{\theta_2(x',y')}{\theta_0(x',y')}.$$

A rational function goes into a rational function, hence a group where a rational function takes assigned values goes into another such group, and so a one-parameter linear system goes into a one-parameter system. Finally, any linear system is built out of one-parameter ones, which gives

Theorem 4] *If a base curve be rationally transformed, a linear system of point-groups will go over into a linear system.*

Let the reader notice that in this theorem we have said 'rationally', not the more restrictive 'birationally', and we have made no reference to singular points.

Let the groups g_1, g_2 of a linear system on a base curve f which has only ordinary singular point and cusps, be cut by the curves ψ_1 and ψ_2 of a linear system. Let the group g_1 also lie on an adjoint curve ϕ_1. We have, by Nöther's Fundamental Theorem 15] of Ch. II,

$$\phi_1 \psi_2 \equiv \theta f + \phi_2 \psi_1.$$

The curve ϕ_2 is thus an adjoint cutting the group g_2. Any group residual to g_1 is residual to g_2 also.

Linear Group Theorem 5] *Any linear system of point-groups on a curve with only ordinary singularities may be cut by adjoint curves.*

There are two advantages in using adjoint curves for this purpose. One is that we may make use of the residue theorem of Ch. II. The other is that, as we shall see later, we are able to count the number of degrees of freedom exactly.

Definition. Two groups of the same linear series are said to be 'equivalent'. We write this

$$g_1 \equiv g_2.$$

If $g_1 \equiv g_2$; then $g_2 \equiv g_1$.

If $g_1 \equiv g_3$, $g_2 \equiv g_3$; then $g_1 \equiv g_2$.

This last is a simple result of the residue theorem; we leave the proof to the reader.

Definition. The number of points in each group of a series is called its 'order.' The number of parameters on which it depends is called its 'dimension'. A series of order N and dimension r is called a g_N^r.

Definition. A linear series is said to be 'complete' if it be not contained in any other series of the same order and larger dimension.

Theorem 6] *If a group of points be residual to one group of a complete series, it is residual to every group of it.*

This is an immediate consequence of the residue theorem.

Consider the totality of adjoints of a given order on which no restriction is placed except that they go through a certain umber, perhaps zero, of points on the base curve. These points will be residual to every group of the complete series which includes the series cut by these adjoints. But the complete eries will be cut by adjoint curves, and they must be of such n order as to meet the base curve as often as do the given djoints; hence, they are nothing but the given adjoints, and he given series is complete. Conversely, by the last theorem, f we have a complete series, and pass an adjoint through one roup, that complete series will be cut by the totality of adjoints f that order through the residual group cut by the first one.

Theorem 7] *The totality of adjoints of a given order on which o restriction is placed except that they pass through a certain umber, perhaps zero, of fixed points on the base curve, will cut complete series on that curve, and every complete series can be ut in that way.*

Theorem 8] *A linear series is contained in but one complete eries.*

Definition. We mean by 'the sum of two linear series' the omplete series which contains the totality of groups composed f a group of the first and a group of the second. If, for instance, he given series be cut by the curves

$$\lambda_0 \phi_0 + \lambda_1 \phi_1 + \ldots + \lambda_r \phi_r = 0,$$
$$\mu_0 \theta_0 + \mu_1 \theta_1 + \ldots + \mu_s \theta_s = 0,$$

heir sum will be the complete series containing every group ut by

$$\sum_{ij} \nu_{ij} \phi_i \theta_j = 0.$$

n the same way we may define a positive integral multiple of series as the complete series whose groups include those com- osed of any selection of that number of groups of the given eries.

If $\qquad g_1 \equiv g_1' \qquad g_2 \equiv g_2',$

hen $\qquad g_1 + g_2 \equiv g_1' + g_2'.$

Let $\qquad g_1 \equiv g_1' \qquad g_1 + g_2 \equiv g_1' + g_2'.$

To prove $\qquad g_2 \equiv g_2',$

uppose $\qquad g_2 \equiv \bar{g}_2,$

hen $\qquad g_1 + g_2 \equiv g_1' + g_2' \equiv g_1' + \bar{g}_2.$

Let all these groups be residual to γ.

Then g_2' and $\bar{g}_2'$ are residual to $g_1' + \gamma$.

Hence $$g_2 \equiv \bar{g}_2 \equiv g_2'. \qquad \text{Q.E.D}$$

If g_3 include g_1, we mean by $g_3 - g_1$ the remainder of the group, and our last statement amounts to saying

If $g_1 \equiv g_1'$, $g_3 \equiv g_3'$; then $g_3 - g_1 \equiv g_3' - g_1'$.

We thus see that our symbols for addition, subtraction, and equivalence obey the rules for addition, subtraction, and equality in elementary arithmetic.

Suppose that on a base curve we have two variable points (x) and (y), $$f(x_1, x_2, x_3) = 0 \qquad f(y_1, y_2, y_3) = 0.$$

Let them be connected by a series of equations

$$\psi_1(x_1, x_2, x_3, y_1, y_2, y_3) = 0, \qquad \psi_2(x_1, x_2, x_3, y_1, y_2, y_3) = 0, \dots,$$
$$\psi_p(x_1, x_2, x_3, y_1, y_2, y_3) = 0.$$

Suppose further to each point (x), which we shall also call the point P, there corresponds in this way exactly ν' variable points (y) or P', no one of which is, in general, identical with P, and that to each P' there correspond ν variable points P. We shall say that we have a ν-to-ν' correspondence, the numbers ν and ν' being called the 'indices' of the correspondence. Suppose lastly that there is a positive, negative or zero integer γ with these properties:

a) When $\gamma \geqslant 0$, if P corresponds to P_1', $P_2', \dots, P_{\nu'}'$ and Q to Q_1', $Q_2', \dots, Q_{\nu'}'$, then

$$P_1' + P_2' + \dots + P_{\nu'}' + \gamma P \equiv Q_1' + Q_2' + \dots + Q_{\nu'}' + \gamma Q.$$

b) When $\gamma < 0$, if P correspond to P_1', $P_2', \dots, P_{\nu}'$ and Q to Q_1', $Q_2', \dots, Q_{\nu}'$, then

$$P_1' + P_2' + \dots + P_{\nu'}' - \gamma Q \equiv Q_1' + Q_2' + \dots + Q_{\nu'}' - \gamma P,$$

then γ is called the 'value' of the correspondence.

Could a correspondence have two different 'values'?

$$P_1' + P_2' + \dots + P_{\nu}' + \gamma_1 P \equiv Q_1' + Q_2' + \dots + Q_{\nu}' + \gamma_1 Q,$$
$$P_1' + P_2' + \dots + P_{\nu}' + \gamma_2 P \equiv Q_1' + Q_2' + \dots + Q_{\nu}' + \gamma_2 Q,$$
$$(\gamma_1 - \gamma_2) P \equiv (\gamma_1 - \gamma_2) Q.$$

If $$\gamma_1 - \gamma_2 \neq 0,$$

we have a one-parameter linear system of curves tangent to the base curve, but the condition for contact is not linear, so that such a system is only possible when $\gamma_1 - \gamma_2 = 1$ or $P \equiv Q$.

Our base curve will, then, have a g_1^1. Let this be given by

$$\phi_0 + X\phi_1 = 0.$$

Only one intersection of such a curve and the base curve will depend on X, so that x and y will be rational functions of this parameter, which is a rational function of them; the curve is rational and so has genus 0 by 2] of the last chapter.

Theorem 9] *A correspondence cannot have more than one value on any curve whose genus is greater than zero.*

Theorem 10] *The indices and value of a correspondence are unaltered by a birational transformation.*

Correspondences on curves of genus zero are easily studied. Since the coordinates of points on such a curve are rational functions of one parameter, say X, which is a rational function of them, the curve may be birationally transformed into the X-axis. The correspondence will be given by equations

$$\psi_0(X, X') = \psi_1(X, X') = \ldots = \psi_k(X, X') = 0.$$

These curves in the (X, X') plane must all have a common factor, hence our whole correspondence must be given by a single equation: $F(X, X') = 0.$

Definition. If in one correspondence a point P corresponds to points P_1', P_2',..., $P_{\nu'}'$ and in a second to P_1'', P_2'',..., $P_{\nu''}''$ the correspondence where it corresponds either to P_i' or to P_j'' is their 'sum'. We get at once from the arithmetic of point-groups developed at the beginning of this section:

Theorem 11] *The value of the sum of two correspondences is the sum of their values.*

Suppose that in one correspondence P corresponds to P_1', P_2',..., $P_{\nu_1'}'$, and in a second P_i' corresponds to P_{i1}'', P_{i2}'',..., $P_{i\nu_2''}''$, then the correspondence where P corresponds to P_{ij}'' (except when the latter is identical with P) is called the 'product' of the two. Let the indices and value of the first correspondence be ν_1, ν_1', γ_1, and of the second be ν_2', ν_2'', γ_2.

$$P_1' + P_2' + \ldots + P_{\nu_1'}' + \gamma_1 P \equiv Q_1' + Q_2' + \ldots + Q_{\nu_1'}' + \gamma_1 Q,$$

$$P_{i1}'' + P_{i2}'' + \ldots + P_{i\nu_2''}'' + \gamma_2 P_i' \equiv Q_{i1}'' + Q_{i2}'' + \ldots + Q_{i\nu_2''}'' + \gamma_2 Q_i'.$$

Adding all these latter relations we get

$$\gamma_2 \sum_i P'_i + \sum_{i,j} P''_{ij} \equiv \gamma_2 \sum_i Q'_i + \sum_{i,j} Q''_{ij}.$$

But $$\gamma_2[\sum P'_i + \gamma_1 P] \equiv \gamma_2[\sum Q'_i + \gamma_1 Q].$$

Hence $$\sum_{i,j} P''_{ij} - \gamma_1\gamma_2 P \equiv \sum_{i,j} Q''_{ij} - \gamma_1\gamma_2 Q.$$

Theorem 12] *The value of the product of two correspondence. is the negative of the product of their values.*

It is the existence of this unexpected negative that clears up all our difficulties. If we have a g_N^1 on our base curve, to each point P will correspond $N-1$ points P' and conversely, i.e. we have a correspondence of indices $N-1$, and of value 1. By adding and multiplying such correspondences, we get

Theorem 13] *There exist correspondences of positive, negative or 0 values.*

The correspondences of value 0 are those which we must look at next. To each point (y) will correspond a group of points $(x$ cut by a curve of the linear series

$$\lambda_0 \phi_0 + \lambda_1 \phi_1 + ... + \lambda_r \phi_r = 0.$$

The coefficients λ_i are single-valued algebraic functions of $(y$ when $f(y_1, y_2, y_3) = 0$, so that under these circumstances they are rational, and we may write

$$\phi(x_1, x_2, x_3, y_1, y_2, y_3) = 0, \qquad (3$$

$$\phi(x, y, x', y') = 0. \qquad (3'$$

This polynomial will not vanish identically when we put $(x) = (y)$, nor contain f as a factor, for the correspondence has the value 0, so that (x) is not, in general, a point of the group corresponding to (x). From this we see incidentally that the inverse correspondence has also the value 0. The matter with which we are especially concerned is to find the coincidences i.e. the self-corresponding points. These are among the intersections of the curves

$$f(x_1, x_2, x_3) = 0 \qquad \phi(x_1, x_2, x_3, x_1, x_2, x_3) = 0, \qquad (4$$

$$f(x, y) = 0 \qquad \phi(x, y, x, y) = 0. \qquad (4'$$

Suppose there is a coincidence at an ordinary singular point.

Let us take this as the origin, and make an ordinary circular inversion:

$$x = \frac{x'}{x'^2 + y'^2} \qquad y = \frac{y'}{x'^2 + y'^2}.$$

What can we say about the new base curve ? If the first curve have a singular point of order r at the origin, the new curve is of order $2n-r$, with a singularity of order n at the origin, and one of order $n-r$ at each circular point at infinity, otherwise its singular points correspond to those of the original curve. Hence, as we see by a short calculation, it has the same genus p. We shall have on it a v-to-v' correspondence of value 0. The branches at the origin will be dissipated into different points on the infinite line. A coincidence at the origin which came from two points on different branches will be dissipated, one that came from two points approaching on the same branch will become a coincidence at a non-singular point. No new coincidences need be introduced at the origin or circular points at infinity. If we make such a transformation a number of times, we may be sure finally of having no coincidences arising from points approaching on different branches; the indices, value, and genus of f are unchanged.

Now look at coincidences coming from points which approach on the same branch. We may write this

$$x = a_1 t + a_2 t^2 + \dots \qquad y = b_1 t + b_2 t^2 + \dots$$
$$x' = a_1 t' + a_2 t'^2 + \dots \qquad y' = b_1 t' + b_2 t'^2 + \dots .$$

We get from (3') $\qquad \phi(t, t') = 0.$

If this be divisible by t^ρ and $t'^{\rho'}$, then for the general (x, y) in (3') the curve in (x', y') has ρ' intersections with f at the origin, and for the general (x', y') the curve (3') has ρ intersections with f there. If we divide $t^\rho t'^{\rho'}$ out of $\phi(t, t')$, the number of coincidences at $t = t' = 0$ will be the intersections there of the curves

$$\phi(t, t') = 0 \qquad t - t' = 0,$$

and so is the excess of intersections at $(0, 0)$ of

$$f(x', y') = 0 \qquad \phi(x', y', x', y') = 0$$

over the intersections there of

$$f(x', y') = 0 \qquad \phi(x, y, x', y') = 0$$

for the general (x, y), and of

$$f(x, y) = 0 \qquad \phi(x, y, x, y) = 0$$

over those of

$$f(x, y) = 0 \qquad \phi(x, y, x', y') = 0$$

for the general (x', y').

Let the order of f be n. Let (3') be of order N in (x, y) and N' in (x', y'). Then for a general (x, y) the curves

$$f(x', y') = \phi(x, y, x', y') = 0$$

have $N'n - \nu'$ fixed intersections, and for a general (x', y') the curves $f(x, y) = \phi(x, y, x', y')$ have $Nn - \nu$ fixed intersections. The number of coincidences is obtained by taking these from the total intersections of the curves f and (4) and so is

$$n(N + N') - [N'n - \nu'] - [Nn - \nu] = \nu + \nu'.$$

We have here the number of coincidences of a correspondence of value 0. The coincidences in the other cases are obtained from this formula as follows.

Suppose that we have a correspondence of negative value γ. Let us take $-\gamma$ points in general position and draw radiating lines through them, each set cutting the base curve in a g_r^n giving rise to a correspondence of indices $n - 1$, $n - 1$, and value 1. The coincidences of these latter are the points of contact of the tangents from the points whence the lines radiate, and the cusps, the number of coincidences in each such case, is

$$m + \kappa = 2n + 2(p - 1).$$

When we add these $-\gamma$ correspondences to the original one, we get a correspondence whose indices are $\nu - \gamma(n - 1)$, $\nu' - \gamma(n - 1)$ and whose value is 0. The number of its coincidences is

$$\nu + \nu' - 2\gamma(n - 1).$$

If we take from this the $2p + 2(n - 1)$ coincidences of each of the added correspondences, we have left the coincidences we seek, in number

$$\nu + \nu' + 2p\gamma.$$

Suppose, lastly, we have a correspondence with positive value γ. If we add a correspondence of indices $\bar{\nu}$, $\bar{\nu}'$ and value $-\gamma$, we get one of indices $\nu + \bar{\nu}$, $\nu' + \bar{\nu}'$, and of value 0. The coincidences are in number $\nu + \bar{\nu} + \nu' + \bar{\nu}'$. Deducting the $\bar{\nu} + \bar{\nu}' + 2p(-\gamma)$ undesired coincidences of the correspondence added we have left

$$\nu + \nu' + 2p\gamma.$$

This very long and involved discussion leads us at last to

Theorem 14] *The number of coincidences of a (v, v') correspondence of value γ on a curve of genus p is given by the Chasles-Cayley-Brill formula**

$$v+v'+2p\gamma. \qquad (5)$$

Theorem 15] *A correspondence and its inverse have the same values.*

It is clear that the number of coincidences of a correspondence is invariant for a birational transformation of the curve. We thus get from 7]

Riemann's Theorem 3'] *The genus of a curve is unaltered by a birational transformation.*

The formula (5) is certainly one of the sharpest tools available for attacking problems in the theory of algebraic plane curves, but for that reason the unwary reader is in the greatest danger of cutting his fingers therewith. This we shall endeavour to show by a series of examples.

Suppose that we wished to apply the formula to find how often a certain line meets a given circle. We might reason as follows. A point lies on a circle when it lies on a tangent and on the corresponding normal. Let P be a point of the line. Through it we may draw two tangents to the circle, the normals at the points of contact will meet the line in the two points P' which correspond to P. Conversely, if P' be given, the normal through it is the line to the centre, the tangents at the two points where it meets the circle give the corresponding points P. We have thus a 2-to-2 correspondence on a curve of deficiency 0, and four coincidences; the line meets the circle four times!

The difficulty here is not very deep-seated. If a point lie on a curve it is on both the tangent and the normal, but this necessary condition is not sufficient, for the tangent and normal might coincide in case the tangent passed through one of the circular points at infinity. In the present case we have a proper 2-to-2 correspondence with four coincidences, but two of these are the intersections with the minimal lines through the centre.

---

* For the history of this formula see Segre[1]. The literature dealing with it is very extensive. Chasles only treated the case where $p = 0$. Cayley surmised the true formula, but the first proof was given by Brill[1]. The proof here given is taken from Severi[1]. Further references will be found in 'Topics', Ch. 7.

Here is another example of the same rather trivial sort. How many circles with a given centre touch a given line ? These circles determine a 1-to-1 correspondence on the line with two coincidences, yet there is surely only one circle, that which touches at the foot of the perpendicular from the given point.

The explanation here is even simpler. The circles in question cut an involution of points equidistant in pairs from the foot of that perpendicular. One coincidence is the foot of the perpendicular, the other at infinity, in which case the circle is the line at infinity counted twice. We must always take account of infinite coincidences.

Here is a much more subtle example. Let us find the order of the curve traced by the points of contact of tangents to a set of concentric circles from a chosen finite point. Let P be a point of a line not through the given point. There will be one circle passing through it and belonging to the given concentric system, and the two tangents to it from the given point will meet the given line in the desired points P'. Conversely, if P' be given, one circle of the system will touch the line from P' to the given point, and this will cut the line in the two desired points P. We have thus a 2-to-2 correspondence on the given line, with four coincidences, yet the locus we seek is the circle whose diameter is bounded by the given point and the centre of the given circles.

This does not fall under either of the preceding cases. There are no coincidences which we do not want, and there are none at infinity. What is the matter ? Let us put the thing through algebraically. The fixed point shall be the origin, the centre of the circles (x_0, y_0), the given line $y = 1$. The line from $(x, 1)$ to the origin has the equation

$$\xi - x\eta = 0.$$

The distance from (x_0, y_0) to this line is $\dfrac{x_0 - x y_0}{\sqrt{1 + x^2}}$.

The circle with (x_0, y_0) as centre tangent to the given line has the equation

$$(1 + x^2)[(x' - x_0)^2 + (y' - y_0)^2] = (x_0 - x y_0)^2.$$

Putting $y' = 1$, we get the equation of our 2-to-2 correspondence:

$$x'^2(1 + x^2) - 2x_0(1 + x^2)x' + x^2[1 + x_0 - 2y_0] + 2x_0 y_0 x + (1 - y_0)^2 = 0.$$

To get the coincidences we replace x' by x, getting

$$x^4 - 2x_0x^3 + [x_0^2 + 2(1-y_0)]x^2 - 2x_0(1-y_0)x + (1-y_0)^2 = 0,$$
$$[x^2 - x_0x + (1-y_0)]^2 = 0.$$

The trouble here is that the quartic equation is reducible, and merely the square of a quadratic equation, so that there are but two coincidences. How could we have foreseen geometrically that this was going to happen ? How can we tell just how many coincidences should be counted at a particular point ? The answer is due to Zeuthen.*

Let us assume, for simplicity, that no coincidences occur at a cusp, and that the tangent at a coincidence which we take as origin is not vertical. We may then develop y in terms of x and y' in terms of x', so that our correspondence on this branch is given by an equation $\phi(x, x') = 0.$

Writing $x' = (x'-x)+x$, we may put this equation also in the form $$\psi(x, x'-x) = 0. \tag{6}$$

When $x'-x = 0$, how many roots in x are given by $x = 0$? Let the lowest term in x alone here be x^s. Then s will be the number of roots. But it is also the infinitesimal order of the product of the roots of (6) looked upon as an equation in $x'-x$, when x is an infinitesimal of the first order.

Zeuthen's Rule, Theorem 16] *The sum of the number of coincidences at a non-cuspidal point C is the sum of the orders of the infinitesimal distances from a near-by point P to the corresponding points, when the distance PC is taken as the principal infinitesimal.*

When the coincidence comes at a cusp the situation is a little more complicated. We shall see in a subsequent chapter that it will be the sum of the orders of the infinitesimal distances PP' when $\sqrt{PC}$ is taken as a principal infinitesimal.

Here are some important applications of the Chasles-Cayley-Brill formula to the theory of linear series. Suppose that we have a g_N^1 and a $g_{N'}^1$ on a base curve of genus p, how many pairs of points can we find that belong to a group of each ? A g_N^1 produces a correspondence of indices $N-1$, $N-1$, and value 1;

* Zeuthen[2], pp. 186 ff.

the pairs of points we see are coincidences in the products of our two correspondences. The indices of the product are $(N-1)(N'-1)$, $(N-1)(N'-1)$, and the value -1; hence the number of coincidences is $2(N-1)(N'-1)-2p$.

Theorem 17] *Given a g_N^1 and a $g_{N'}^1$ on a curve of deficiency p, the number of pairs of points which belong to a group of each is*

$$(N-1)(N'-1)-p. \tag{7}$$

The reader will remember that such a statement gives the number of pairs 'in general', or the degree of the equation on which their determination depends.

If s points of a correspondence come together, all infinitesimal distances being of the same order, by Zeuthen's rule that counts as $s-1$ coincidences. Thus the coincidences of a g_N^1 are given by the formula $\sum (s_i-1) = 2(N+p-1)$.   **(8)**

Suppose that a g_N^1 and a $g_{N'}^1$ are such that a group of s points $A, B, ..., S$ belong to one group of each. How many coincidences do they count for ? When P is close to A it has a mate in the first correspondence close to B, C,...., and when P' is close to B, C,...or S, it has a mate P in the second correspondence close to A. The number of coincidences in the product correspondence at A is $s-1$, so that the number at A, B,... or S is $s(s-1)$: $\sum s_i(s_i-1) = 2[(N-1)(N'-1)-p]$.   **(9)**

If we have a correspondence with indices ν_1, ν_1', and value γ_1, and a second with indices ν_2, ν_2', and value γ_2, the number of points with the same mate in both correspondences is

$$\nu_1\nu_2'+\nu_2\nu_1'-2p\gamma_1\gamma_2. \tag{10}$$

Here is another important application. Given a g_N^r on a curve of genus p. In how many places will $r+1$ points of the same group fall together ? We reach the answer by mathematical induction. When $r=1$ the number is, as we know, $2[N+(p-1]$. Suppose that we have demonstrated that when the dimension of the series is $r-1$ the number of coincidences is

$$r[N'+(r-1)(p-1].$$

for all values of N'. Consider a g_N^r. If P be given, there is residual thereto a g_{N-1}^{r-1} with $r[N-1+(r-1)(p-1)]$ coincidences P'. When P' is given, there will be one group of our g_N^r with

r points there, and the remainder will be $N-r$ points P. The value of this inverse correspondence, and so of the original, is r; hence the number of coincidences is

$$r[N-1+(r-1)(p-1)]+N-r+2pr = (r+1)[N+r(p-1)].$$

In certain cases we have to make important reductions from this owing to the presence of certain special points. Suppose there is a point A_i which has this series of properties:

∞^{r-1} adjoints cutting the series meet the curve $\nu_{i1}+1$ times there.

∞^{r-2} adjoints cutting the series meet the curve $\nu_{i2}+2$ times there etc.

∞^1 adjoints cutting the series meet the curve $\nu_{ir-1}+r-1$ times there.

One adjoint cutting the series meets the curve $\nu_{ir}+r$ times there.

To what extent will this enter into the number found above?

For a g_N^1, this will be ν_{i1}. Suppose that we have demonstrated that for a $g_{N'}^{r-1}$ the reduction must be $\nu_{i1}+\nu_{i2}+...+\nu_{ir-1}$. Consider a g_N^r. If P be given, we have residual thereto a g_{N-1}^{r-1}; the number of groups of r coincident points is

$$r[N-1+(r-1)(p-\nu)]- \sum_i [\nu_{i1}+\nu_{i2}+...+\nu_{ir-1}]$$

after deduction has been made for the undesired coincidences. When P' is given there correspond $N-r$ points as before, in a correspondence of value r. The number of coincidences is thus $(r+1)[N+r(p-1)]- \sum_i (\nu_{i1}+\nu_{i2}+...+\nu_{ir-1})$, but we must discard ν_{ir} coincidences at A_i.*

Theorem 18] *Given a g_N^r and certain points $A_1, A_2,..., A_l$ such that ∞^{r-j} adjoints cutting groups of the series meet the base curve $\nu_{ij}+j$ times at A_i, then the number of places other than the A's where a group has $r+1$ coincident points is*

$$(r+1)[N+r(p-1)]- \sum_{i,j} \nu_{ij}. \qquad (11)$$

If the group have $r+s$ coincident points, this will count for $s-1$ places.

An application of this theorem is to finding Plücker's equations. The lines through an arbitrary point meet the curve in

* Cf. Segre[1], pp. 86–8.

a g_n^1 whose coincidences come from the nodes and cusps. We get an equation and its dual, namely,

$$m+\kappa = 2(n+p-1) \qquad n+\iota = 2(m+p-1).$$

The totality of lines in the plane cut the curve in a g_n^2. When will three points of a branch lie in a line ? Either the line is an inflexional or a cuspidal tangent. In the case of a cusp there are ∞^1 lines that meet the curve twice there, one line that meets it thrice, so that $\nu_{i1} = \nu_{i2} = 1$:

$$\iota = 3[n+2(p-1)]-2\kappa,$$

$$\kappa = 3[m+2(p-1)]-2\iota.$$

Lastly, by Riemann's theorem,

$$\frac{(n-1)(n-2)}{2} -\delta-\kappa = \frac{(m-1)(m-2)}{2} -\tau-\iota = p.$$

All other Plücker equations are easily deduced from these.

§ 3. Correspondences on different curves

Suppose that we have a 1-to-$\bar{\nu}$ correspondence between the points of a curve f of genus p and a curve $\bar{f}$ of genus $\bar{p}$. If (x, y) be the coordinates of a point on the first curve, $(\bar{x}, \bar{y})$ of a corresponding point on the second, since the former variables are, by hypothesis, single-valued algebraic functions of the second, we have

$$x = \frac{f_1(\bar{x},\bar{y})}{f_3(\bar{x},\bar{y})} \qquad y = \frac{f_2(\bar{x},\bar{y})}{f_3(\bar{x},\bar{y})}.$$

A one-parameter linear system of curves

$$\phi_1(x,y)+\lambda\phi_2(x,y) = 0$$

will correspond to a one-parameter linear system

$$\psi_1(\bar{x},\bar{y})+\lambda\psi_2(\bar{x},\bar{y}) = 0,$$

so that a g_N^1 will correspond to a $g_{N\bar{\nu}}^1$. A coincidence on the curve $\bar{f}$ will arise either from a coincidence of f or from the fact that two of the points on $\bar{f}$ which correspond to the same point on f fall together. A point on one curve of such a nature that two corresponding points on the same branch of the other fall together is called a 'branch' point of the first (for that correspondence). If the number of branch points on the first curve (there are none on the second) be β, a comparison of the coincidences on the two curves gives

$$2(N\bar{\nu}+\bar{p}-1) = \bar{\nu}[2N+2(p-1)]+\beta$$
$$\beta+2\bar{\nu}(p-1) = 2(\bar{p}-1). \tag{12}$$

Suppose, in particular, $p = \bar{p} > 1$,

$$\beta = 2(p-1)(1-\bar{\nu}). \tag{13}$$

The left-hand side is positive or 0, the first two factors on the right are positive, the third is negative or 0. This gives

Weber's Theorem 19] *If two curves of the same genus which is greater than one be in rational correspondence, that correspondence is birational.*[*]

Theorem 20] *If a curve of genus greater than one be rationally transformed into itself, the transformation is birational.*

Suppose next in (12) that $\bar{p} = 0$, the right-hand side is essentially negative and the equation can only be satisfied if $\beta = 1$, $p = 0$.

Theorem 21] *If a curve of genus 0 be rationally transformed, the correspondence is birational, and the new curve has genus 0.*

Suppose that we have given x and y rational functions of a parameter t, but are not sure that t is a rational function of those coordinates. Then the (x, y) curve is a rational transform of a curve of genus 0, and so it has genus 0 and is rational in some other parameter which is rational in them. This gives

Lüroth's Theorem 22] *If x and y be rational functions of a parameter, neither constants, the curve so defined has genus 0 and x and y may be expressed rationally in terms of a parameter which is rational in them.*[†]

Suppose, lastly, that we have a ν-to-ν' correspondence between two curves of genera p and p' respectively, which curves we may assume to lie in the same plane. The lines connecting corresponding points will envelop a curve of genus $\bar{p}$ in ν'-to-1 correspondence with the first curve, ν-to-1 correspondence with the second. We thus get

$$\beta+2\nu'(p-1) = 2(\bar{p}-1)$$
$$\beta'+2\nu(p'-1) = 2(\bar{p}-1)$$
$$\beta+2\nu'(p-1) = \beta'+2\nu(p'-1), \tag{14}$$

[*] Weber[1].   [†] Lüroth[1], p. 163.

an elegant formula due to Zeuthen.* It is to be remarked that the correspondence must be supposed to be irreducible, as otherwise the intervening curve might become reducible and our equation (13) would not apply.

It is to be noted also that in certain cases special care is necessary in assigning values to these constants. If we have corresponding branches

$$x = a_0 + a_1 X + a_2 X^2 + \dots \qquad x' = a_0' + a_1' Y + a_2' Y^2 + \dots$$
$$y = b_0 + b_1 X + b_2 X^2 + \dots \qquad y' = b_0' + b_1' Y + b_2' Y^2 + \dots,$$

the correspondence will be given by the curve

$$F(X, Y) = 0,$$

which we may call the correspondence curve. The branch points will come from $\dfrac{\partial F}{\partial X} = 0$ or $\dfrac{\partial F}{\partial Y} = 0$, i.e. points where the tangents are horizontal or vertical, but also from the singular points of F which yield branch points that correspond to branch points.†

* Zeuthen[1], p. 152.
† For an elaborate discussion of this, see Severi[5], pp. 211 ff.

CHAPTER IX

COVARIANT CURVES

§ 1. Polar curves

IN studying the general theory of invariants and covariants we saw that there are certain polynomials which preserve their form under the most general linear transformation of the variables. A fundamental principle of projective geometry is expressed in the following form:

Every geometric theorem which results from the vanishing of an invariant, or the identical vanishing of a covariant, is unaltered by a general linear transformation of the variables, whose determinant is not zero.

The converse of this theorem seems also to be true; it seems to be the case that every projectively unaltered theorem is expressed either by the vanishing of an invariant, or the identical vanishing of a covariant. I have never seen a demonstration, however, and it seems likely that it would be difficult to give an absolutely satisfactory definition of a projectively unaltered theorem. Is the theorem, 'All men are mortal', projectively unaltered, and, if so, how is it mathematically expressed ? Let us leave these general speculations and come to something concrete.

Definition. A system of curves of a given order linearly dependent on two such curves which are not the same is called a 'pencil'. They all pass through all points common to the original two called centres of the pencil; conversely, we get from Nöther's Fundamental Theorem 15] of Ch. II:

Theorem 1] *If two curves of the same order intersect only in ordinary points, distinct or infinitely near, the system of all curves of that order through those points is the pencil determined by the first two.*

More generally, if two irreducible curves of the same order have the same multiplicity at each intersection, then every curve of their pencil has at least that multiplicity there. It can have no higher multiplicity there, as otherwise it would intersect them too often. This statement holds only when all the common points are distinct. If we have a pencil of curves tangent to one another at a given point, one curve of the pencil will have a double point there; we have only to consider a pencil of curves tangent to the y-axis at the origin. No curve of the pencil will have an equation with a constant term nor a term in y to the first power; hence one of the curves will lack the term in x to the first power, and so have a singular point there. If two irreducible curves of the same order intersect only in distinct points and have the same order of multiplicity at each of them, then if any other irreducible curve of that order have just those multiplicities it must be identical with a curve of the pencil through another one of its points.

Theorem 2] *If two curves of the same order be not reducible with a common factor, and intersect in distinct points having the same multiplicity at each, then every irreducible curve of their order which has that multiplicity at each of their common points is a curve of their pencil.*

Let us next turn our attention to polar curves. They are covariants of the curve to which they are polar, and we have given them a satisfactory algebraic definition. Let us show that we can give them a projectively invariant geometric definition.

Suppose that we have an r-parameter linear system of curves

$$f \equiv \lambda_0 f_0 + \lambda_1 f_1 + \ldots + \lambda_r f_r = 0, \tag{1}$$

and seek the points where tangents from the origin have r-point contact with curves of the system. We get from Joachimsthal's equation (3^3) of Ch. VI that f and its first r derivatives with respect to 1 are 0. Eliminating the λ's,

$$\begin{vmatrix} f_0 & f_1 & \cdot & \cdot & \cdot & f_r \\ \dfrac{\partial f_0}{\partial 1} & \dfrac{\partial f_1}{\partial 1} & \cdot & \cdot & \cdot & \dfrac{\partial f_r}{\partial 1} \\ \cdot & \cdot & \cdot & \cdot & \cdot & \cdot \\ \dfrac{\partial^r f_0}{\partial 1^r} & \dfrac{\partial^r f_1}{\partial 1^r} & \cdot & \cdot & \cdot & \dfrac{\partial^r f_r}{\partial 1^r} \end{vmatrix} = 0. \tag{2}$$

The degree of this equation is

$$n + (n-1) + \ldots + (n-r) = \frac{(2n-r)(r+1)}{2}.$$

Let us write further

$$f_i = a_{i0} + (a_{i1}x + b_{i1}y) + (a_{i2}x^2 + 2b_{i2}xy + c_{i2}y^2) + \dots$$

$$\frac{\partial f_i}{\partial 1} = na_{i0} + (n-1)(a_{i1}x + b_{i1}y) + (n-2)(a_{i2}x^2 + 2b_{i2}xy + c_{i2}y^2)\dots +$$

$$\frac{\partial^2 f_i}{\partial 1^2} = n(n-1)a_{i0} + (n-1)(n-2)(a_{i1}x + b_{i1}y) + \dots.$$

We may find such multipliers $\rho_0, \rho_1, \rho_2, \dots, \rho$ that

$$\rho_0 + n\rho_1 + n(n-1)\rho_2 + \dots = 0$$

$$\rho_0 + (n-1)\rho_1 + (n-1)(n-2)\rho_2 + \dots = 0$$

$$\rho_0 + (n-2)\rho_1 + (n-2)(n-3)\rho_2 + \dots = 0$$

$$\cdot \quad \cdot \quad \cdot \quad \cdot \quad \cdot \quad \cdot \quad \cdot \quad \cdot \quad \cdot \quad \cdot \quad \cdot \quad = 0.$$

Multiplying the various rows of the determinant (2) by the corresponding ρ's and adding to the first row, we see that we have at the head of each column a polynomial with no term in x or y of order less than $r+1$, so that this polynomial equated to 0 gives a curve with a point of that multiplicity, at least, at the origin. Let us note, finally, that if a point have the multiplicity $r+1$ or greater for a curve of the system it will lie on the curve (2).

Theorem 3] *The locus of points of multiplicity $r+1$ for curves of an r-parameter linear system and the locus of points where a curve of the system has $(r+1)$-point contact with a tangent passing through a fixed point, not common to all curves of the system, is a curve of order $\dfrac{(2n-r)(r+1)}{2}$ with a multiplicity $r+1$ at the given point.*[*]

Suppose that each f_s, where $s < r$, consists in a system of $n-s$ lines through the origin, and the line at infinity (which may be altered to any line by a linear transformation) counted s times, while f_r is a curve of the nth order cutting the line at infinity in n distinct points, the corresponding asymptotes having 2-point contact, and not passing through the origin. In (2) every term below the principal diagonal will drop out. This diagonal will give the rth polar of the origin with regard to f_r and a system of lines through the origin.

---

[*] For this theorem and the next, see Guccia[1], pp. 266 and 271.

Theorem 4] *The rth polar of a point with regard to a curve of the nth order is a part of the locus described in theorem 3]. The linear system of curves is composed of the given curve, and sets of n—s lines through the given point and a certain line counted s times, where s takes successively the values 0, 1,...,(r—1). The remainder of the locus is a set of lines through the given point.*

When $r = 1$ we see that the first polar is the locus of points of contact of tangents from the given point, and of double points of the curves of a pencil made up from the given curve and a set of n lines through the given point.

The coordinates of a point enter linearly into the equation of its first polar. This gives:

Theorem 5] *The first polars of the points of a line generate a pencil of curves; the non-singular points common to the curves of this pencil are the only ones that have the given line as line-polar.*

Definition. The system of curves linearly dependent on three given linearly independent curves of the same order is called a 'linear net'. The system of all first polar curves with regard to a given curve is a linear net. Let us inquire when, conversely, a linear net is composed of first polars. Let the net be

$$\lambda_0 \theta_1 + \lambda_1 \theta_2 + \lambda_2 \theta_3 = 0.$$

Then the multipliers λ must be single-valued algebraic functions of (y), the point whose polar is in question, and since (y) enters linearly into the equations of the first polar, it must enter linearly here.

$$y_1 \psi_1 + y_2 \psi_2 + y_3 \psi_3 \equiv \left(y \frac{\partial f}{\partial x} \right).$$

Polarizing to (z) and comparing the two sides,

$$y_1 \left(z \frac{\partial \psi_1}{\partial x} \right) + y_2 \left(z \frac{\partial \psi_2}{\partial x} \right) + y_3 \left(z \frac{\partial \psi_3}{\partial x} \right) \equiv \tfrac{1}{2} \sum y_i z_j \frac{\partial^2 f}{\partial x_i \partial x_j}.$$

Conversely, if this left side $= z_1 \left(y \frac{\partial \psi_1}{\partial x} \right) + z_2 \left(y \frac{\partial \psi_2}{\partial x} \right) + z_3 \left(y \frac{\partial \psi_3}{\partial x} \right),$

$$\frac{\partial \psi_i}{\partial x_j} = \frac{\partial \psi_j}{\partial x_i}; \text{ hence } \psi_i = \frac{\partial f}{\partial x_i}.$$

Theorem 6] *A necessary and sufficient condition that a linear net of curves should be a set of first polars is that the coordinates of an auxiliary point should enter linearly, and that the first polar of a point (z) with regard to the curve corresponding to (y) should always be identical with the first polar of* (*y*) *with regard to the curve corresponding to* (*z*).

A curve is the locus of all points which lie on their own first polars with regard to it. A system of curves having the properties described in 6] is a system of first polars, and we may say that a curve is constructed from its first polar system in the sense that it is the locus of the points which lie on the curves which correspond to them.

Theorem 7] *The order of an irreducible curve is the number which exceeds by unity the number of successive polar systems necessary to construct it.*

We note that the class of a curve may be defined in the same way from the polar reciprocal curve with regard to a chosen conic. For *p* we have

$$p = \frac{m}{2} + \frac{\kappa}{2} - (n-1).$$

We shall show in a subsequent chapter that it is always possible to transform a real curve birationally into one with no cusps. If this have the order *n'* and the class *m'*, since the genus is unaltered we have

$$p = \frac{m'}{2} - (n'-1).$$

It thus appears that the genus of a curve is the maximum value for the difference between one-half the class and a number one less than the order of any curve birationally transformable into the given curve. We are enabled in this way to give a definition for the order, class, and genus, and so for the other Plücker characteristics in terms of strictly real quantities.[*]

Let us look at the singular points of the first polars. We find at once

Theorem 8] *If the first polar of* (*z*) *have a double point at* (*y*), *the conic polar of* (*y*) *has a double point at* (*z*).

This may be generalized to the form

Theorem 9] *If the rth polar of* (*z*) *have a point of multiplicity s at* (*y*), *then the n—*(*r+s—*1)*th polar of* (*y*) *has a point of multiplicity s at* (*z*).

Let us see if we can find out when the first polar of (*z*) has a cusp at (y). It must certainly have a double point there whose tangents are given by

$$a_z a_y^{n-3} a_x^2 = 0 \qquad a_z a_y^{n-2} a_x \equiv 0.$$

Putting $\chi_i = \xi_1 t_i + \xi_2 s_i$, the intersections with the line (t) to (s) which we may call (u), and suppose to be any line, are given by

$$a_z a_y^{n-3}[a_t^2 \xi_1^2 + 2a_t a_s \xi_1 \xi_2 + a_s^2 \xi_2^2] = 0.$$

If the double point be a cusp, the two roots fall together, and we have

$$a_z a_z' a_y^{n-3} a_y'^{n-3} |aa'u|^2 = 0.$$

This will be divisible by $(uy)^2$. The vanishing of the other factor will give the desired condition.

At the other end of the scale from the first polar is the line polar. This is completely determined by two of its points. Let (y) be the point whose line polar interests us. The intersection of this polar with any line through (y) is obtained by polarizing the binary form which gives the intersections of that line with the curve, as we saw in Ch. V. 23], so that the line polar will be obtained by polarizing with regard to the intersections with two such lines. Let these two lines meet our curve in $P_1, P_2, ..., P_n$ and $Q_1, Q_2, ..., Q_n$ respectively. Matching these P's and Q's one to one in any convenient way we get n lines $P_i Q_i$. The line polar of (y) with regard to these is its line polar with regard to the original curve. If we single out one of these lines, say (v), the equation of all n may be written

$$(vx)b_x^{n-1} = 0.$$

The line polar of (y) with regard to them will be

$$b_y^{n-1}(vx) + (n-1)(vy)b_y^{n-2}b_x = 0.$$

The second term equated to 0 gives the line polar of (y) with regard to the other lines than (v). The line polar we seek will pass through the intersection of this and the line singled out. **The line through this intersection to the point (y) has the equation** $\qquad b_y^{n-1}(vx) - (vy)b_y^{n-2}b_x.$

The cross-ratio of these four concurrent lines is $-(n-1)$.

Theorem 10] *The line polar with regard to n lines of a point not on any one of them is obtained by finding its line polar with regard to $n-1$ of them, and finding a line through the intersection of this and the nth line which makes, with these and the line from* *that intersection to the given point when taken in proper order, a cross-ratio of* $-(n-1)$.

Theorem 11] *The line polar with regard to a curve of order* n *of a point not on that curve is its line polar with regard to lines connecting in pairs the intersections of the curve with two transversals through the given point, no such intersection lying on two connectors.*[*]

Suppose that we have m pairs of lines

$$[(u^{(1)}x)(v^{(1)}x)][(u^{(2)}x)(v^{(2)}x)]...[(u^{(m)}x)(v^{(m)}x)] = 0.$$

The line polar of (y) will be

$$\sum_i \frac{(u^{(i)}x)(v^{(i)}y) + (u^{(i)}y)(v^{(i)}x)}{(u^{(i)}y)(v^{(i)}y)} = 0.$$

The line polar of (y) with regard to the ith pair is

$$(u^{(i)}y)(v^{(i)}x) + (v^{(i)}y)(u^{(i)}x) = 0.$$

The system of these m lines is

$$\prod_i [(u^{(i)}y)(v^{(i)}x) + (v^{(i)}y)(u^{(i)}x)] = 0.$$

The line polar of (y) with regard to this system is the expression above.

Theorem 12] *The line polar of a point with regard to* m *pairs of lines is its line polar with regard to those lines which are its line polars with regard to the separate pairs.*

Suppose that we have a curve of order n,

$$a_x^n = 0.$$

This shall be required to meet the line $x_3 = 0$ in n distinct points, the tangents there having the equations $(cx) = 0$, $(dx) = 0$.... By Nöther's fundamental theorem

$$a_x^n \equiv (cx)(dx)... + x_3^2 b_x^{n-2}.$$

We see that the coefficients of x_3^0 and x_3^1 are the same in the equations of the original curve and of the n tangents. A corresponding theorem will hold for envelopes expressed in line coordinates.

Suppose, next, that we have a set of envelopes

$$u_\alpha^m = 0 \qquad u_\beta^q = 0...,$$

* For this theorem and the preceding see Schwarz, pp. 42 ff.

one of which may be, if desired, the original curve. Let (v) **and** (w) meet in (x):

$$x_i = \begin{vmatrix} v_j & v_k \\ w_j & w_k \end{vmatrix}$$

$$u_i = \xi_1 v_i + \xi_2 w_i.$$

The tangents to the various envelopes through (x) are given by

$$[v_\alpha \xi_1 + w_\alpha \xi_2]^m = 0 \qquad [v_\beta \xi_1 + w_\beta \xi_2]^q \dots$$

Let (x) be such a point that one of the invariants of these binary forms vanishes, i.e. such a point that there exists among the tangents thence to the various envelopes a projectively invariant condition given by the vanishing of an invariant. Since

$$\begin{vmatrix} v_\alpha & v_\beta \\ w_\alpha & w_\beta \end{vmatrix} \equiv |x\alpha\beta|,$$

the coordinates of the point (x) fulfil an equation of the type

$$|x\alpha\beta|^\mu . \; |x\beta\gamma|^\nu \dots \equiv k_x^N = 0.$$

If we replace the envelope $u_\alpha^m = 0$ by the points of contact of tangents from $(0, 0, 1)$, which we may take to stand for any point, the coefficients of u_3^0 and u_3^1 will be unaltered, as was the case above for a_x^n. On the other hand the line polar of $(0, 0, 1)$ with regard to $k_x^N = 0$ is $k_3^{N-1} k_x = 0$, which involves only the coefficients of k_3^N, $k_1 k_3^{N-1}$, $k_2 k_3^{N-1}$ in the equation of the locus, and when this is written in terms of the coefficients α, β, $\gamma \dots$ the subscript 3 appears but once with these Greek letters, i.e. the expression would have been the same had we replaced $u_\beta^m u_\gamma^q \dots$ by the points of contact of tangents from $(0, 0, 1)$. This gives a curious theorem due to Laguerre.[*]

Theorem 13] *If a curve be the locus of points such that there exists among the sets of tangents thence to a number of envelopes, a projectively invariant relation expressed by the vanishing of an invariant, then the line polar of an arbitrary point with regard to this locus is unaltered if we replace any number of the given envelopes by the points of contact of the tangents thereto from the given point.*

If a point lie on a common tangent to two curves, the resultant of the binary forms giving the sets of tangents thereto from the point is 0.

* Laguerre[1], p. 410.

Theorem 14] *The line polar of a point with regard to the common tangents to two envelopes is identical with its line polar with regard to the lines connecting the points of contact of its tangents with one envelope to the points of contact of its tangents with the other.*

A curve is the locus of points whence two tangents to it fall together:

Theorem 15] *The line polar of a point with regard to a curve is identical with its line polar with regard to the lines connecting two by two the points of contact of tangents from the given point.*

Theorem 16] *The line polar of a point with regard to the tangents to a curve from a second point is identical with its line polar with regard to the lines from the second point to the points of contact of tangents from the first.*

It is worth noting in conclusion what sorts of envelopes are generated by polars with regard to a given curve, when a point moves in a specified manner. Let us start with a curve, and the rth polar of a point (y):

$$a_x^n = 0 \qquad a_y^r a_x^{n-r}$$

What sort of a curve will this polar envelop when (y) traces a curve of order n' ?

$$b_y^{n'} = 0,$$

which we shall assume has δ' nodes, actual or virtual, and κ' cusps. The coordinates of (y) shall be functions of a single parameter t, as will those of (x), the point of contact of the polar and its envelope. If we substitute in the equation of the rth polar for both (x) and (y), we get an identity in t. Differentiating this, we have

$$r a_y^{r-1} a_{y'} a_x^{n-r} + (n-r) a_y^r a_x^{n-r-1} a_{x'} = 0.$$

Since (x') lies on the tangent to the rth polar of (y) at (x),

$$a_y^r a_x^{n-r-1} a_{x'} = 0.$$

Hence $\qquad a_y^{r-1} a_{y'} a_x^{n-r} = 0,$

and (y') lies on the tangent at (y) to the $(n-r)$th polar of (x), or the $(n-r)$th polar of (x) touches the locus of (y) at (y).

To find the order of the envelope of the rth polar of (y) we must find how many points on a given line l have their $(n-r)$th polars tangent to the locus of y, a curve of order n' with Plücker characteristics given above.

Let P be a point of this latter curve. Its rth polar cuts l in $(n-r)$ points each having an $(n-r)$th polar through P and meeting the curve of P in $n'r-1$ other points P'. The relation of P and P' is symmetrical; we have a correspondence of indices $(n-r)$ $(n'r-1)$, and value $n-r$. The coincidences will come from points on the curve where $(n-r)$th polars are tangent, and from the cusps. As we have not at present the time to calculate whether these will yield multiple coincidences or not, we shall limit ourselves to the simple case where $\kappa'=0$. Then we get by Chasles-Cayley-Brill of the last chapter:*

Theorem 17] *If a point trace a curve of order n, with only ordinary singular points, the envelope of its rth polar with regard to a curve of order n will be a curve of order $(n-r)[2n'r+2(p'-1)]$.*

Suppose, in particular, that we are interested in the line polar. The order will be
$$2[n'(n-1)+p'-1].$$

The class is found by determining the number of line polars through a given point, and this again is the number of intersections of the (y) curve with a general first polar. Lastly, a line tangent to the envelope will have a good many poles, but, in general, only one on the (y) curve; the two are birationally related and have the same genus.

Theorem 18] *If a point trace a curve of order n' and genus p' with no cusps, the envelope of its line polars with regard to a curve of the nth order, when each tangent to this envelope corresponds, in general, to but one point of the original locus, is a curve of order $2[n'(n-1)+p'-1]$, class $n'(n-1)$, and genus p'.*

If a line envelop a curve of class $n'(n-1)$, it will have $n'(n-1)^2$ positions tangent to a curve of class $(n-1)$. If a point trace a curve of order n', the remaining poles of its line polar with regard to a curve of order n trace a locus whose order can be found as follows.

The line l being given, the line polar of a point thereon is also the line polar of a point on a curve of order n' if the given line polar be tangent to a certain curve of class $n'(n-1)$ and to another of class $(n-1)$, but the point itself is not an intersection of the line l and the curve of order n'. The order of the curve we seek is, therefore, $n'[(n-1)^2-1]$.

* Cf. Cremona², p. 81.

Theorem 19] *If a point trace a curve of order n' not passing through any singular point of a curve of order n, the remaining poles of its line polar with regard to the curve of order n will trace a curve of order $n'[n^2-2n]$.*

Let the reader prove by means of Chasles-Cayley-Brill:

Theorem 20] *If a point trace a curve of order n' which passes through no singular point of a curve of order n, and if in no case its rth polar and its sth polar are reducible with a common factor, then the locus of the intersections of those two polars is a curve of order $n'[n(r+s)-2rs]$.*

§ 2. The simplest linear systems

The simplest linear system of curves is the pencil already defined. Consider the pencil

$$\xi_1 a_x^n + \xi_2 b_x^n = 0.$$

Differentiating to x_i,

$$\xi_1 a_x^{n-1} a_i + \xi_2 b_x^{n-1} b_i = 0.$$

There are three of these equations. We get the degree of the resultant by theorem 11] of the first chapter.

Theorem 21] *If the curves of a pencil have no common singular point, then at most, and in general, $3(n-1)^2$ of these curves will have singular points.*

A line (u) has usually $(n-1)^2$ poles with regard to each curve of the pencil. What can we say about the locus of these poles? Identifying (u) with the line polar of a point (x'), we have

$$\xi_1 a_{x'}^{n-1} a_x + \xi_2 b_{x'}^{n-1} b_x + \rho(ux) \equiv 0.$$

Eliminating ξ_1, ξ_2, and ρ, we get

$$|abu| a_x^{n-1} b_{x'}^{n-1} = 0.$$

Theorem 22] *The locus of the poles of a line not through one of the points common to the curves of order n of a pencil is a curve of order $2(n-1)$.*

When $n=2$, we get the familiar 11-point conic of projective geometry.

We get immediately from Chasles-Cayley-Brill:

Theorem 23] *If a line do not pass through a centre of a pencil of curves of order n, and if no curve of the pencil be reducible with a multiple factor, then $2(n-1)$ curves of the pencil touch the line.*

Suppose that we have two pencils

$$\xi_1 a_x^n + \xi_2 b_x^n = 0 \qquad \eta_1 c_x^{n'} + \eta_2 d_x^{n'} = 0.$$

The curves through (y) are

$$b_y^n a_x^n - a_y^n b_x^n = 0 \qquad d_y^{n'} c_x^{n'} - c_y^{n'} d_x^{n'} = 0;$$

their tangents are

$$a_y^{n-1} b_y^{n-1}[a_y b_x - b_y a_x] = 0 \qquad c_y^{n'-1} d_y^{n'-1}[c_y d_x - d_y c_x] = 0.$$

The curves are tangent to one another if their tangents meet an arbitrary line (v) in the same points:

$$a_y^{n-1} b_y^{n-1} c_y^{n'-1} d_y^{n'-1}[a_y c_y |vbd| - a_y d_y |vbc| - b_y c_y |vad| + b_y d_y |vac|]$$
$$= 0.$$

Now, by Ch. V (18),

$$c_y[a_y|vbd| - b_y|vad|] \equiv c_y[(vy)|abd| - d_y|vab|],$$
$$d_y[a_y|vbc| - b_y|vac|] \equiv d_y[(vy)|abc| - c_y|vab|].$$

Subtracting and substituting we cast out the extraneous factor (vy), getting

$$a_y^{n-1} b_y^{n-1} c_y^{n'-1} d_y^{n'-1}[c_y|abd| - d_y|abc|] = 0. \qquad (3)$$

Theorem 24] *If two pencils of curves of order n and n' respectively have no common centre, and neither contain a reducible curve with a multiple factor, the locus of points where curves of the two pencils touch is of order $2(n+n')-3$. It will pass through the centres of both pencils and all singular points.*[*]

Let us next take the linear net, say

$$X_1 a_x^n + X_2 b_x^n + X_3 c_x^n = 0. \qquad (4)$$

If three linearly independent curves of the system have a common point, that will be a point of every curve of the system, and if it be multiple for all three, it will in every case have at least the lowest of the three multiplicities. The line polar of (y) with regard to the general curve (4) is a linear combination of the three line polars

$$a_y^{n-1} a_x = 0 \qquad b_y^{n-1} b_x = 0 \qquad c_y^{n-1} c_x = 0.$$

If these three be linearly independent, i.e. if

$$|abc| a_y^{n-1} b_y^{n-1} c_y^{n-1} \neq 0,$$

[*] Cremona[2], p. 69.

this may be any line in the plane. If they be linearly dependent, but not identical, they form a pencil of lines. The centre of this pencil could not be the point (y) itself, unless every curve of the net went through (y). When it is not (y), then all the curves of the pencil through (y) touch the line thence to the centre of this pencil, except one which has a singular point there. The condition for all this is that (y) lie on the Jacobian of the net, whose equation is

$$|abc|a_x^{n-1}b_x^{n-1}c_x^{n-1} = 0. \tag{5}$$

Theorem 25] *The Jacobian of a linear net of curves of order n is a curve of order $3(n-1)$. It passes through all points common to all curves of the net. It is the locus of points where curves of the net touch one another, and of singular points of the curves.*

We might naturally expect that, as all the curves of the net but one through a point of the Jacobian touch one another, they would also touch the Jacobian. This is not the case. Let the origin be a point of the Jacobian, the coordinates being homogeneous Cartesian. Then, with the aid of Euler's theorem,

$$\frac{1}{n}J \equiv \begin{vmatrix} \dfrac{\partial f_1}{\partial x} & \dfrac{\partial f_1}{\partial y} & f_1 \\[2mm] \dfrac{\partial f_2}{\partial x} & \dfrac{\partial f_2}{\partial y} & f_2 \\[2mm] \dfrac{\partial f_3}{\partial x} & \dfrac{\partial f_3}{\partial y} & f_3 \end{vmatrix} = 0.$$

Let
$$f_1 \equiv a_2 x^2 + 2b_2 xy + c_2 y^2 + \ldots$$
$$f_2 \equiv a_1' x + a_2' x^2 + 2b_2' xy + c_2' y^2 + \ldots$$
$$f_3 \equiv a_0'' + a_1'' x + b_1'' y + a_2'' x^2 + 2b_2'' xy + c_2'' y^2 + \ldots$$

The lowest terms in $\dfrac{1}{n}J$ are

$$0 = 2a_0'' a_1'(b_2 x + c_2 y) + \ldots$$

The tangent to the Jacobian is thus harmonically separated from the line $x = 0$ by the tangents to the curve with a double point there.

Theorem 26] *The tangent to the Jacobian is harmonically separated from the common tangent to the curves of the net through that point of the Jacobian, by the tangents to that curve of the net which has a double point there.*

Let us see if we can determine under what circumstances the Jacobian will have a double point.[*]

If $a_0'' = 0$, the origin is common to all curves of the system.

If $a_0'' \neq 0$, we must have $a_1'b_2 = a_1'c_2 = 0$; then, if $a_1' \neq 0$, either one curve of the system has a cusp with the common tangent of all the other curves as cuspidal tangent, or else it has a higher singularity, or when $a_1' = 0$, all curves of the system through the origin have a double point there.

Theorem 27] *A point will be at least a double point for the Jacobian if:*

a) *it be common to all curves of the system;*

b) *it be a cusp, and all curves through there touch the cuspidal tangent, or else it be a singularity of higher order;*

c) *it be at least double for all curves of the net through it.*

If (y) be a point of the Jacobian, its line polars are concurrent in a point (z) given by the equations

$$a_y^{n-1}a_z = b_y^{n-1}b_z = c_y^{n-1}c_z = 0.$$

If we eliminate (z), we get the fact that (y) is on the Jacobian; if we eliminate (y), we get (z) on a curve of order $3(n-1)^2$, called the Steinerian.

Theorem 28] *The locus of points whose first polars with regard to the curves of a linear net have a common point, which is also the locus of points of concurrence of line polars of points of the Jacobian, is a curve of order $3(n-1)^2$. It passes through all points common to all curves of the system.*

The Jacobian and Steinerian are in birational correspondence, and so have the same genus. A third curve of this genus is the Cayleyan, the envelope of lines connecting corresponding points on the two. If corresponding points on the Jacobian and Steinerian be connected with a fixed point, we have a correspondence among the lines through this point with indices $3(n-1)$, $3(n-1)^2$.

Theorem 29] *The Cayleyan of a net of curves of order n has the same genus as the Jacobian and Steinerian, and, in general, the class $3n(n-1)$.*

---

[*] Cf. Gerbaldi, pp. 22 ff.

§ 3. Fundamental covariant curves

The most interesting linear nets are those composed of first polars. But how do we know that the first polars of all points with regard to a given curve do always form a net? If they were linearly dependent we should have

$$r_1 \frac{\partial f}{\partial x_1} + r_2 \frac{\partial f}{\partial x_2} + r_3 \frac{\partial f}{\partial x_3} \equiv 0.$$

This means that the first polar of (r) goes everywhere or that all line polars go through (r). If all the tangents to a curve go through the origin,

$$\frac{dy}{dx} = \frac{y}{x} \qquad \frac{dy}{y} = \frac{dx}{x} \qquad \log y = \log x + \log \rho \qquad y = \rho x,$$

and the curve is a line through the origin. Conversely, if a curve consists in a set of concurrent lines through the origin, $\frac{\partial f}{\partial 1} \equiv 0$, and our identical relation is satisfied.

Theorem 30] *The necessary and sufficient condition that a curve should be a set of concurrent lines is that the three partial derivatives should be linearly dependent. In this case, and in this case only, the system of first polars do not form a net.*

If the original curve be $a_x^n = 0,$

three linearly independent first polars are

$$a_x^{n-1} a_1 = a_x^{n-1} a_2 = a_x^{n-1} a_3 = 0,$$

and the Jacobian is

$$|aa'a''|^2 a_x^{n-2} a_x'^{\,n-2} a_x''^{\,n-2}.$$

Theorem 31] *The Jacobian of the system of first polars with regard to a curve which is not a system of concurrent straight lines is the Hessian covariant. It is the locus of points which are singular for first polars, and of points whose conic polars are reducible.*

Theorem 32] *The Steinerian covariant of a curve of order n is of order $3(n-2)^2$. It is the locus of double points of conic polars, and of points whose first polars have singularities, variable in position.*

If (y) be a point on the Hessian, we find the corresponding point on the Steinerian in the following way. Let (r) be an arbitrary point on the line polar of (y). The intersection of this line polar with the tangent at (y) to the first polar of (r) will be (z). As (y) traces the Hessian and (z) the Steinerian, both are functions of an arbitrary parameter t,

$$\frac{d}{dt}[a_y^{n-2}a_z a_1] = 0 \qquad \frac{d}{dt}[a_y^{n-2}a_z a_2] = 0 \qquad \frac{d}{dt}[a_y^{n-2}a_z a_3] = 0.$$

Multiplying through by y_1, y_2, y_3 and adding, we get

$$(n-2)a_y^{n-2}a_{y'}a_z + a_y^{n-1}a_{z'} = 0.$$

But $a_y^{n-2}a_z a_{y'} = 0$. Hence $a_y^{n-1}a_{z'} = 0$.

This shows that the point (z'), which surely lies on the tangent to the Steinerian, is on the line polar of the corresponding point of the Hessian.

Theorem 33] *The tangent to the Steinerian at a non-singular point is the line polar of the corresponding point of the Hessian.*

If two first polars touch, the corresponding line has coincident poles.

Theorem 34] *The Steinerian is the envelope of lines with two coincident poles.*

Let us note in passing that when the original curve is a cubic, the Hessian and Steinerian are identical. We revert to the previous equations

$$(n-2)a_y^{n-3}a_{y'}a_z a_i + a_y^{n-2}a_{z'}a_i = 0.$$

Multiplying through by z_i and summing,

$$(n-2)a_y^{n-3}a_z^2 a_{y'} + a_y^{n-2}a_z a_{z'} = 0.$$

But $a_y^{n-2}a_z a_{z'} = 0.$

Hence $a_y^{n-3}a_z^2 a_{y'} = 0.$

The first polar of (z) has a double point at (y), the equation of the tangents is $a_z a_y^{n-3}a_x^2 = 0.$

The equation just above shows that (y') is on the polar of (z) with regard to these two tangents.

Theorem 35] *The tangent at a non-singular point of the Hessian is the tangent to the second polar of the corresponding point of the Steinerian, and is harmonically separated from the corresponding tangent to the Cayleyan by the two tangents to the first polar of that point of the Steinerian.*[*]

[*] Cf. Clebsch-Lindemann, p. 370.

We saw in Ch. VI that if the original curve have a singular point, that point is singular for the Hessian also. It is natural to ask whether the Hessian usually has a singular point apart from those of the original curve. We can prove that this is not the case by a very elegant method due to Valentiner.*

Let us write our Hessian

$$|aa'a''|^2 a_x^{n-2} a_x'^{n-2} a_x''^{n-2} = 0.$$

Assuming that the point O_3 is not on the given curve, it will be singular for the Hessian if and only if

$$|aa'a''|^2 a_3^{n-2} a_3'^{n-2} a_3''^{n-3} a_i = 0 \qquad i = 1, 2, 3.$$

How many conditions will these equations usually impose on the curve ? Three if the Hessian usually have no double point, otherwise two or less. But if there were only two conditions in general, there would be only two in the case of a cubic curve, for the only coefficients involved are those of x_1 and x_2 in the original equation to a degree 3 or less, so that the condition will be the same if the curve consists of a cubic curve and the line $x_3 = 0$ counted $n-3$ times. But the Hessian of a cubic is also a cubic, usually non-singular, as we see if we write the original curve in the form

$$x_1^3 + x_2^3 + x_3^3 + 3k x_1 x_2 x_3 = 0.$$

Hence, for the general cubic, or the general n-ic, three conditions are imposed by requiring the Hessian to have a singularity at O_3, or the Hessian has not usually any singularity.

Theorem 36] *The Hessian has not, in general, any singular point which is not a singularity of the original curve.*

This does not mean that there are not cases where such singularities do occur. The Hessian is the Jacobian of the first polars, so that we can use theorem 27]. If all first polars go through a point, that point can have no line polar, and so must be singular for the given curve. Let the point in which we are interested be $(0, 0, 1)$, and let its line polar be $x_3 = 0$. If we put $x_1 = \xi_1$, $x_2 = \xi_2$, our curve can be written

$$0 = x_3^n + a_\xi^2 x_3^{n-2} + b_\xi^3 x_3^{n-3} + \dots.$$

---

* Valentiner[1]. I am sorry to say I have not been able to see the original article, only an account of it.

The first polar of the general point (η_1, η_2, η_3), is

$$0 = 2a_\eta a_\xi x_3^{n-2} + 3b_\eta b_\xi^2 x_3^{n-3} + \ldots + \eta_3[nx_3^{n-1} + (n-2)a_\xi^2 x_3^{n-4} + \ldots].$$

This will pass through $(0, 0, 1)$ when and only when $\eta_3 = 0$. The equation of the tangent there is

$$a_\eta a_\xi = 0.$$

This will be independent of $\eta_1 : \eta_2$, so that all first polars have the same tangent there (a point of the Hessian) if

$$|aa'|^2 = 0.$$

Our curve can therefore be written

$$0 = x_3^n + a\xi_2^2 x_3^{n-2} + b_\xi^3 x_3^{n-3} + \ldots,$$

and the first polar of $(\eta_1, \eta_2, 0)$ is

$$0 = 2a\eta_2 \xi_2 x_3^{n-2} + 3b_\eta b_\xi^2 x_3^{n-3} + \ldots.$$

If $a = 0$, all first polars through O_3 have a double point there, and the original curve has a triple or higher singularity. If $a \neq 0$, we shall have a cusp for the first polar of $(\eta_1, \eta_2, 0)$ with $\xi_2 = 0$ as cuspidal tangent if

$$\eta_2 = b_1^3 = b_1^2 b_2 = 0 \qquad b_1 b_2^2 \neq 0.$$

The cubic polar of O_3 is now

$$A(3b_1 b_2^2 \xi_1 + b_2^3 \xi_2)\xi_2^2 + B\xi_2^2 x_3 + Cx_3^3 = 0.$$

This has a cusp at $(1, 0, 0)$ with $x_2 = 0$ as tangent. Still assuming $a \neq 0$, we have a triple point O_3 if

$$\eta_2 = b_1^3 = b_1^2 b_2 = b_1 b_2^2 = 0,$$

and the cubic polar of O_3 has a triple point at O_1.

Theorem 37] *The Hessian will have a singular point at a point P not singular for the original curve, if, when Q is the intersection of the common tangent to all first polars through P, with the line polar of this point: a) the cubic polar of P has a cusp at Q with QP as cuspidal tangent; or b) the cubic polar of P has a singularity of order 3 or more at Q; or c) the conic polar of P is its line polar counted twice.* [*]

Suppose that our original curve has no singularities but nodes and cusps, and that the conditions of the last theorem are none of them fulfilled. At each node the Hessian will have a node. At each cusp it will have a triple point whose effect on the

* For a much longer and more detailed discussion see Del Pezzo, pp. 203 ff.

other Plücker characteristics is not at once apparent. The calculations leading to 21] of Ch. VI showed that when the original curve can be written

$$0 = -y^2 + (ax^3 + 3bx^2y + 3cxy^2 + y^3) + \dots,$$

and the Hessian

$$0 = y^2(ax + by) + \dots,$$

the first polar of $(0, 1, 0)$ (which we may take to stand for any point) is

$$0 = y(2ax + 3by) + \dots.$$

This curve has a node with two branches:

$$y = a_2x^2 + a_3x^3 + \dots \qquad y = -\frac{2a}{3b}x + b_2x^2 + \dots.$$

The first of these will meet the Hessian four times at the origin, the second but three times. This shows that from the point of view of the class and genus this singular point of the Hessian counts as two nodes and a cusp.

Theorem 38] *If a curve of order n have no singularities but δ nodes and κ cusps, and do not fulfil any of the conditions of theorem 37], the Plücker characteristics of its Hessian are given by the equations*

$$n_1 = 3(n-2) \qquad \delta_1 = \delta \qquad \kappa_1 = 2\delta + \kappa$$
$$p_1 - 1 = 3(p-1) + 3(n-3)^2 + 2\kappa. \tag{6}$$

If the Hessian include the original curve as a part of itself, every point must have curvature 0, and the curve consists of a set of straight lines.

Theorem 39] *The necessary and sufficient condition that the Hessian of a curve with no multiple factor should include the curve as a factor of itself or vanish identically is that the curve should consist only of straight lines.*

When will the Hessian vanish identically? The curve must consist only of a set of straight lines. We begin in the binary domain. If a homogeneous polynomial of degree n have two distinct roots, it can be written

$$x_1x_2[c_0x_1^{n-2} + c_1x_1^{n-3}x_2 + \dots + c_{n-2}x_2^{n-2}].$$

If the Hessian vanish identically, we have

$$c_0 = c_1 = \dots = c_{n-2} = 0,$$

which is absurd. The vanishing of the Hessian is the N.S. condition that all roots should be identical. Suppose now we have

$$|aa'a''|^2 a_x^{n-2} a_x'^{\,n-2} a_x''^{\,n-2} \equiv 0;$$

this is the Jacobian of

$$a_x^{n-1} a_1 \equiv p_x^{n-1} = 0 \qquad a_x^{n-1} a_2 \equiv q_x^{n-1} = 0 \qquad a_x^{n-1} a_3 \equiv r_x^{n-1} = 0$$

$$|pqr| p_x^{n-2} q_x^{n-2} r_x^{n-2} \equiv 0.$$

If (u) be any line

$$|pqr|(u_x) \equiv |qru| p_x + |rpu| q_x + |pqu| r_x$$

$$|qru| q_x^{n-2} r_x^{n-2} p_x^{n-1} + |rpu| r_x^{n-2} p_x^{n-2} q_x^{n-1} + |pqu| p_x^{n-2} q_x^{n-2} r_x^{n-1} \equiv 0.$$

Now
$$|qru| q_x^{n-2} r_x^{n-2} = 0$$

is the locus of points whose line polars with regard to q_x^{n-1} and r_x^{n-1} are concurrent on (u). If (u) go through no intersection of q_x^{n-1}, r_x^{n-1}, these intersections cannot lie on the curve we have last found. Hence they must lie on p_x^{n-1}, and so our three curves of order $n-1$ are linearly dependent:

$$y_1 p_x^{n-1} + y_2 q_x^{n-1} + y_3 r_x^{n-1} \equiv a_x^{n-1} a_y \equiv 0.$$

There is thus a point (y) whose first polar is non-existent; it must have the multiplicity n, or the curve consists in n concurrent straight lines. This condition is also easily seen to be sufficient.

Theorem 40] *The necessary and sufficient condition that the Hessian covariant of a curve should vanish identically is that the curve should consist entirely of concurrent straight lines.* [*]

A very special case is where the curve consists of a straight line counted n times. Here a line connecting two points of the plane will meet the curve in n coincident points:

$$x_i = \xi_1 y_i + \xi_2 z_i$$
$$a_x^n \equiv |a_y \xi_1 + a_z \xi_2|^n \equiv c_\xi^n = 0.$$

But we have just seen that we must have $|cc'|^2 c_\xi^{n-1} c_\xi'^{\,n-2} \equiv 0$.

Hence, $\quad |aa'u|^2 a_x^{n-2} a_x'^{\,n-2} \equiv 0$ if $(ux) = 0$.

Theorem 41] *The N.S. condition that a curve $a_x^n = 0$ should consist in a line counted n times, is*

$$|aa'u|^2 a_x^{n-2} \equiv 0 \qquad \text{if } (ux) = 0. \tag{7}$$

---

[*] Cf. Hesse, p. 117. The proof here given is from Clebsch-Lindemann, p. 598 note.

Let us next look at the Steinerian. We already know its order and genus; if we can find its class, the other characteristics will come easily enough. The Steinerian is the envelope of the line polars of points of the Hessian, so its class will be the number of non-singular intersections with a general first polar. At a node the Hessian has the same tangents as the original curve, so that it will meet a general first polar twice; at a cusp it has essentially a cusp and a simple branch; the cusp will meet a first polar three times, as we can verify from the equation of the Hessian given recently, and the branch once, so that the total deduction is 4.

Theorem 42] *If a curve of order n have no singularities but nodes and cusps, and do not fulfil any of the conditions of theorem 6], the Plücker characteristics of its Steinerian are**

$$n_2 = 3(n-2)^2 \qquad m_2 = 3(n-1)(n-2) - 2\delta - 4\kappa$$

$$p_2 - 1 = p_1 - 1 = 3(p-1) + 3(n-3)^2 + 2\kappa \qquad (8)$$

The characteristics of the Cayleyan are more difficult to find. We shall limit ourselves to the case of a non-singular curve. We know the class and genus already; we are going to show that it has no inflexional tangents. Suppose that there were one, we take it as the y-axis, the point of contact being the origin. Let the distance to the corresponding point of the Hessian be $\phi(x_3)$:

$$y_3 = a_3 x_3^3 + a_4 x_3^4 + \dots ,$$

then the coordinates of this point are

$$x_1 = x_3 + \phi \cos \theta \qquad y_1 = y_3 + \phi \sin \theta$$

$$\tan \theta = \frac{dy_3}{dx_3} = 3a_3 x_3^2 + 4a_4 x_3^3 + \dots$$

$$x_1 = b_0 + b_1 x_3 + \dots \qquad y_1 = 3a_3 x_3^2 + c_4 x_3^4 + \dots .$$

Since the Hessian has no singular point, the y-axis would be a common tangent to the Hessian and Cayleyan, whereas we know by 35] that the two are harmonically separated by the tangents to the first polar, having a double point there. The polar would have to have a cusp there, and this would involve a singularity for the Hessian.

* Cf. Wölfling, p. 43.

Theorem 43] *If a non-singular curve of order n fulfil none of the conditions of theorem 37], the Plücker characteristics of the Cayleyan are*

$$m_3 = 3(n-1)(n-2) = 6p \qquad p_3 = \tfrac{1}{2}(3n-7)(3n-8) \qquad \iota_3 = 0. \quad \textbf{(9)}$$

§ 4. Covariants of two curves or envelopes

Let us return to theorem 24] in the simple case where $n' = 1$. We seek the locus of points of contact of tangents from a given point, not a centre of a pencil of curves, to the curves of that pencil. The point being (y), we write

$$\lambda a_x^n + \mu b_x^n = 0 \qquad \lambda a_x^{n-1} a_y + \mu b_x^{n-1} b_y = 0$$
$$a_y a_x^{n-1} b_x^n - b_y a_x^n b_x^{n-1} = 0. \quad \textbf{(10)}$$

This goes through the point (y), the tangent there being the same as that to the curve of the pencil through that point, namely,

$$a_y^{n-1} b_y^{n-1} [a_y b_x - b_y a_x] = 0.$$

This will not be a singular point for our locus. Let us change notation and write our curves

$$0 = a_0 + a_{10}x + a_{01}y + a_{20}x^2 + 2a_{11}xy + a_{02}y^2 + \cdots \equiv f$$
$$0 = b_0 + b_{10}x + b_{01}y + b_{20}x^2 + 2b_{11}xy + b_{02}y^2 + \cdots \equiv \phi$$
$$f \left[x_1 \frac{\partial \phi}{\partial x} + y_1 \frac{\partial \phi}{\partial y} + \frac{\partial \phi}{\partial 1} \right] - \phi \left[x_1 \frac{\partial f}{\partial x} + y_1 \frac{\partial f}{\partial y} + \frac{\partial f}{\partial 1} \right] = 0.$$

The conditions for a double point at the origin will not involve the coefficients of any term above the second degree, and will be the same for the general case, and for the case where the curves are conics. In this latter case three conditions are imposed. Hence, in general, three conditions are imposed and, following the corresponding reasoning in the case of the Hessian, we see that, in general, there is no singular point to our locus.

Theorem 44] *If a pencil of curves of order n have no fixed singular point, the locus of points of contact of tangents to them from a general point is, 'in general', a non-singular curve of order $2n-1$ and class $2(n-1)(2n-1)$.*

When will an inflexional tangent to a curve of the pencil go through a given point (y) ? An inflexional tangent will touch the first polar of every point on itself, so that the inflexional tangents through (y) must be among the $2(n-1)(2n-1)$ tangents from there to the new curve. We must deduct the tangent at (y) counted twice. We need make no deduction for lines to the singular points of curves of the pencil, for such lines are not singular tangents, while inflexional tangents are singular, but we must deduct the n^2 lines to centres of the pencil.

Theorem 45] *The inflexional tangents to the curves of a pencil with no fixed singular points will, 'in general', envelop a curve of class $3n(n-2)$.*

It is curious that this should be the same as the number of inflexional tangents possessed by a general curve of the pencil.[*]

In equation (10) (y) appears to the first degree only; if, then, (y) trace a line, the corresponding curves (10) will describe a pencil. The centres are the n^2 centres of the original pencil, the $2(n-1)$ points where curves of the original pencil touch the given line, and the double points of curves of the given pencil which we know from 21] are $3(n-1)^2$ in number. As a check,

$$n^2+2(n-1)+3(n-1)^2 = (2n-1)^2.$$

Suppose that we have a curve f of order n, and suppose that the origin is in general position with regard thereto, which means, in the present case,

a) it is not on the curve;

b) it is not on the Hessian;

c) it is not on a singular tangent;

d) it is not on a tangent at a singular point.

The origin will have the same first polar with regard to the given curve, and to a curve ϕ of order n if and only if $\dfrac{\partial f}{\partial 1} \equiv k\dfrac{\partial \phi}{\partial 1}$

$$\phi \equiv kf+\pi(x,y),$$

where π is a homogeneous polynomial of degree n in x and y. Geometrically this means that ϕ is a general curve of a pencil formed by the given curve and any set of n lines through the given point. Consider a line through the origin which does not go to a singular point of this pencil. How many curves of the pencil touch that line? By Chasles-Cayley-Brill there should be $2(n-1)$, but the origin itself will count as $n-1$ coincidences, by Zeuthen's rule, theorem 16] of Ch. VIII. There are, thus, but $n-1$ curves of the pencil which touch the line, each having

[*] Cf. Bouwmann, p. 259.

$n-2$ other intersections with the line. The locus of these latter intersections, as the line rotates about O, shall be called a 'satellite' of O with regard to the given curve. The satellite will not be altered if we replace f by any curve of the pencil $kf+\pi = 0$. It would seem to depend on the choice of the lines $\pi(x,y) = 0$, but that is not the case. For instance, let us find where the satellite cuts $y = 0$, which we may take as a general line through the origin. We have an equation

$$k\psi^n(x)+x^n = 0,$$

and this is independent of the slopes of the lines of $\pi(x,y)$. Hence we may speak of 'the satellite' instead of 'a satellite'. We know by Bertini's theorem 10] of Ch. VII that the curves of the pencil do not have variable singular points. The lines through the origin have no singular point but that one which is not singular for the other curves, hence the general curve has no singular point, or we may say f has none. The satellite will not go through O.

Theorem 46] *If from a point which does not lie on a curve of order n, nor on its Hessian, nor on a singular tangent or tangent at a singular point, tangents be drawn to the curve, their remaining intersections with the curve, besides the contacts, will lie on a satellite curve of order $(n-1)(n-2)$, which will be unaltered if the original curve be replaced by any curve of a pencil determined by the first curve and any set of n lines through the given point.*

If the point (x, y) of the satellite be known, when π has been chosen, the point of contact (x', y') and the curve of that pencil are determined. Thus x' and y' are rational functions of x and y,

$$x' = \frac{\psi(x,y)}{\chi(x,y)} \qquad y' = \frac{y\,\psi(x,y)}{x\,\chi(x,y)}.$$

Now let us see how (x', y') behaves near the x-axis, which we may take as an arbitrary line through the origin.

Let
$$x = a_0+a_1t+a_2t^2+\dots$$
$$y = b_1t+b_2t^2+\dots$$
$$x' = \frac{\psi(a_0,0)}{\chi(a_0,0)}+\left[\frac{\partial\left(\dfrac{\psi}{\chi}\right)}{\partial x}a_1+\frac{\partial\left(\dfrac{\psi}{\chi}\right)}{\partial y}b_1\right]t+\dots$$
$$y' = \frac{b_1}{a_0}\frac{\psi(a_0,0)}{\chi(a_0,0)}\,t+\dots.$$

As t varies, (x',y') moves along the *fixed* first polar curve $\frac{\partial f}{\partial 1} = 0$. If the satellite had a cusp, we should have $a_1 = b_1 = 0$, and the first polar would have a cusp not on the curve, and this we shall assume is not the case. *A fortiori* it could not have a more complicated type of singularity.

The first polar of the origin will touch the x-axis when, and only when, it touches the satellite, but in that case it will touch the satellite $(n-2)$ times corresponding to the one contact with the polar. This gives us the Plücker characteristics of the satellite

$$n_4 = (n-1)(n-2) \qquad m_4 = (n-1)(n-2)^2 \qquad \kappa_4 = 0$$
$$2(p_4-1) = m_4 + \kappa_4 - 2n_4 = (n-1)(n-2)(n-4).$$

As a check* on this we note that between the first polar and the satellite we have a 1-to-$(n-2)$ correspondence with no branch point, as we just saw; hence, since the first polar will usually be non-singular, we have

$$p' = \frac{(n-2)(n-3)}{2}.$$

Applying Zeuthen's rule of Ch. VIII (12),

$$2(p_4-1) = [(n-2)(n-3)-2](n-2) = (n-1)(n-2)(n-4).$$

Theorem 47] *If a point be not on a curve of order n, nor on a singular tangent, nor on the Hessian, nor on a tangent at a singular point, and if its first polar have no singularity not on the curve, the Plücker characteristics of the satellite are*

$$n_4 = (n-1)(n-2) \qquad m_4 = (n-1)(n-2)^2 \qquad \kappa_4 = 0$$
$$2(p_4-1) = (n-1)(n-2)(n-4). \qquad \textbf{(11)}$$

Let us close this chapter with the study of a rather more complicated covariant of a curve and an envelope. Let the envelope f' have the leading Plücker characteristics n', m', and p', while the curve has characteristics n, m, p. Let a variable tangent to the envelope meet the curve in n moving points. The tangents at these intersect in $\frac{n(n-1)}{2}$ other points, whose

---

* The only article I have seen dealing with satellite curves is that of Kohn. His methods are entirely synthetic, and open to grave question on the score of rigour. His Plücker characteristics do not agree with these for he apparently evolves certain cusps out of his inner consciousness. Moreover, this check will not work when applied to his figures.

locus we wish to study. We shall assume that f and f' have no common singular point or tangent, and that a singular tangent to the envelope, or tangent at a singular point, never passes through a singular point of the curve.

To find the order of our locus, let P be a variable point on a straight line 'in general position'. Through it we may draw m tangents to f, through each point of contact will pass m' tangents to f', each meeting f in $(n-1)$ other points whose tangents meet our line in points P'. The relation between P and P' is a symmetrical one, the number of coincidences is $2mm'(n-1)$.

From what will these coincidences come ?

a) Intersections with the locus we are interested in.

b) Intersections with common tangents to the curve and envelope.

c) Intersections with the cuspidal tangents to f each counted m' times.

The desired coincidences count double, for close to each will be a point on two tangents to f, whose points of contact lie on two tangents to f', each meeting f in a point whose tangent passes near the given point on the original line. The order of our locus is therefore

$$n_5 = mm'(n-1) - \frac{m'}{2}(m+\kappa) = m'[(m-1)(n-1)-p].$$

We next look for the genus. There is between this curve and f' a $\frac{n(n-1)}{2}$-to-1 correspondence. The branch points on f' are the points of contact with common tangents with f, or tangents from the cusps of the latter, each counted $(n-2)$ times, once for each other intersection with f. We thus get from (12) of Ch. VIII.

$$2(p_5-1) = \frac{n(n-1)}{2}[2(p'-1)] + m'(m+\kappa)(n-2),$$

$$p_5 - 1 = \frac{n(n-1)}{2}(p'-1) + m'(n-2)[n+p-1].$$

How could a cusp arise ? Consider two branches of f,

$$y = a_0 + a_1 x + a_2 x^2 + \dots \qquad \bar{y} = b_0 + b_1 \bar{x} + b_2 \bar{x}^2 + \dots.$$

The equations of their tangents are

$$\frac{Y-(a_0+a_1x+a_2x^2+...)}{X-x}=a_1+2a_2x+...$$

$$(a_1+2a_2x+...)X-Y=-a_0+a_2x^2+...,$$

$$(b_1+2b_2\bar{x}+...)X-Y=-b_0+b_2\bar{x}^2+....$$

Solving simultaneously, we have

$$X=-\frac{a_0-b_0}{a_1-b_1}+\frac{(a_0-b_0)}{a_1-b_1}(2a_2x-2b_2\bar{x})+...$$

$$Y=\frac{a_1b_0-a_0b_1}{a_1-b_1}+\frac{(a_0-b_0)}{a_1-b_1}[2b_1a_2x-2a_1b_2\bar{x}]+....$$

A) The y-axis is a common tangent to f and f'. Developing x' and y' on f' in terms of a single parameter t, we get x and $\bar{x}$ single-valued in t also.

$$x=p_1t+p_2t^2+...\qquad \bar{x}=q_1t+q_2t^2+....$$

Hence (X, Y) traces a simple branch, no cusp.

B) The y-axis is a bi-tangent. Then there are two different developments, giving two different branches for (X, Y).

C) The y-axis is an inflexional tangent. For x and $\bar{x}$ close to O we get two values of t:

$$x=p_2t^2+p_3t^3+...\qquad \bar{x}=q_2t^2+q_3t^3+....$$

The (X, Y) curve has a cusp.

D) The curve f has a node $a_0=b_0$, and the (X, Y) curve has a cusp.

E) The curve f has a cusp:

$$x=s^2\qquad y=a_2s^2+a_3s^3+....$$

Let the tangent to f' be

$$tx+y=(b_1t+b_2t^2+...)$$

$$ts^2+(a_2s^2+a_3s^3+...)=(b_1t+b_2t^2+...)$$

$$t=\frac{a_2}{b_1}s^2+q_3s^3+...$$

Let $\qquad\qquad t=t'^2.$

Then $\qquad\qquad s=\sqrt{\frac{b_1}{a_2}}t'+r_2t'^2+....$

If we change t' to $-t'$ we get the second value of s corresponding to t.

The tangent to f has the equation

$$\frac{y-a_2 s^2-a_3 s^3-\cdots}{x-s^2}=a_2+\tfrac{3}{2}a_3 s,$$

$$\left(a_2+\tfrac{3}{2}a_3\sqrt{\frac{b_1}{a_2}}\,t'+\cdots\right)X-Y=\frac{a_3}{2}\left(\frac{b_1}{a_2}\right)^{\frac{3}{2}}t'^3+r_4 t'^4\cdots.$$

The other tangent corresponding to $-t'$ is

$$\left(a_2-\tfrac{3}{2}a_3\sqrt{\frac{b_1}{a_2}}\,t'+\cdots\right)X-Y=-\frac{a_3}{2}\left(\frac{b_1}{a_2}\right)^{\frac{3}{2}}t'^3+r_4 t'^4$$

$$X=A_1 t'^2+A_2 t'^4+\cdots \qquad Y=B_1 t'^2+B_2 t'^4+\cdots$$

$$X=A_1 t+A_2 t^2+\cdots \qquad Y=B_1 t+B_2 t^2+\cdots,$$

and there is no cusp. The number of cusps is thus

$$\kappa_5=\iota'\frac{n(n-1)}{2}+m'\delta.$$

Theorem 48] *If an envelope have the Plücker characteristics* n', m', p' *and a curve have the characteristics* n, m, p, δ, κ, ι, *and if a singular tangent of the envelope meets the curve in distinct points, the intersections of tangents to the curve at points where it meets tangents to the envelope will trace a curve with the characteristics*[*]

$$n_5=m'[(m-1)(n-1)-p],$$

$$p_5=\frac{n(n-1)}{2}(p'-1)+m'(n+p-1)(n-2)+1, \qquad (12)$$

$$\kappa_5=\iota'\frac{n(n-1)}{2}+m'\delta.$$

Corollary] *When the envelope is a point in general position, the characteristics are*

$$n_5=(m-1)(n-1)-p \qquad p_5=\frac{n(n-3)}{2}+(p-1)(n-2)$$

$$\kappa_5=\delta. \qquad (13)$$

[*] First found by Sisam. Zeuthen[3] discussed the case in the corollary, giving a wrong answer by overlooking the cusps that come from nodes.

CHAPTER X

METRICAL PROPERTIES OF CURVES

§ 1. Centres of gravity

THE great majority of the properties of curves which we have developed so far have been projective properties, i.e. those which are unaltered by a projective transformation of the plane. In some cases we have limited ourselves to real projective transformations, when we were studying real curves or real circuits. In Books III and IV we are going to study properties which are unaltered under the much wider groups of birational transformations of the whole plane, or of the curve alone. We have already seen that the genus has this sort of invariance. It is our present task, however, not to widen the group, but to narrow it, studying those properties which have to do with distances and angles, and so are invariant under the group of motions, but not under the projective group in general.*

We must begin with certain algebraic theorems of very general nature concerning elimination. Suppose that we have two equations of degree n and n' respectively in x and y, and wish to eliminate y between them. We first introduce a third variable z to make them homogeneous, as explained in Ch. I, and arrange in ascending powers of this variable:

$$\phi_n(x,y)+\phi_{n-1}(x,y)z+\phi_{n-2}(x,y)z^2+...+\phi_0(x,y)z^n = 0,$$
$$\psi_{n'}(x,y)+\psi_{n'-1}(x,y)z+\psi_{n'-2}(x,y)z^2+...+\psi_0(x,y)z^{n'} = 0.$$

Eliminating y by Bézout's method of Ch. I (8), we get

$$a_0x^{nn'}+a_1x^{nn'-1}z+a_2x^{nn'-2}z^2+...+a_{nn'}z^{nn'} = 0.$$

The subscript, in each case, will be identical with the exponent of z. Moreover, as this resultant has been reached by a series of additions, subtractions, and multiplications, no one of which can depress any exponent of z, if the coefficients be perfectly general, the term involving z^k in the resultant cannot come from higher powers of z in the two polynomials, and the subscripts of ϕ and ψ involved must be at least $n-k$ and $n'-k$. This gives

Theorem 1] *If two polynomials with general coefficients be given, of degrees n and n' respectively, the terms of degree $nn'-k$*

---

* For an enumeration of Euclidean invariants see Weisner.

in the resultant, when one variable has been eliminated, will only involve coefficients in the original polynomials which are of degrees $n-k$ *and* $n'-k$ *or greater respectively.**

The most interesting application is to find the centres of gravity of the total intersection group of two curves. The abscissae of such points are given by the sums of the roots of the corresponding equations divided by nn', and so will only involve the coefficients of the two highest terms in the x equation. These, by 1], involve only the two highest terms in the given equations and so are unaltered when either curve is replaced by its asymptotes.

Waring's Theorem 2] *If each of two curves meet the line at infinity in distinct, non-singular points, and if all their intersections be finite, then if to each common point there be attached a weight equal to the number of intersections absorbed therein, the centre of gravity of these points is the centre of gravity of the intersections of the asymptotes.*†

Theorem 3] *If a curve meet the line at infinity in distinct, non-singular points, no one of which is circular, the centre of gravity of the intersections with a circle depends on the position of its centre, but not on its radius.*

There is a point which plays a special role in centre of gravity theorems, namely, the tangential centre already defined in Ch. VI in what follows 12]. The line polar of a set of finite points is their centre of gravity, i.e. the point polar of the infinite line. Let us write the equations

$$f(x,y) = 0,$$

$$x_1 \frac{\partial f}{\partial x} + y_1 \frac{\partial f}{\partial y} = 0.$$

If we eliminate y we shall get an equation whose roots are the abscissae of the points whose tangents pass through the infinite point $(x_1, y_1, 0)$ as well as the nodes counted twice and the cusps three times. We saw in 15] of the last chapter that the line polar of a point with regard to a curve is its line polar with regard to the lines connecting two by two the points of contact of tangents from that point, so by duality the tangential

---

* Cf. Fouret[1], p. 259.

† Cf. Waring. I have not been able to see this article, only Terquem, p. 182.

centre is the centre of gravity of the intersections of the asymptotes two by two. On the other hand, if we look at the equations
above, we see that if we replace f by the terms of two highest
orders, i.e. the asymptotes, we get the same centre of gravity.
The tangents to the asymptotes are the lines to their intersections counted doubly.

Theorem 4] *If a curve meet the line at infinity in distinct,
non-singular points, its tangential centre is the centre of gravity
of the points of contact of tangents in any non-asymptotic direction
plus the actual or virtual nodes each counted twice and the cusps
each counted three times, or of the points of intersection of the
asymptotes each counted twice.*

Let (x_1, y_1), (x_2, y_2),...,(x_m, y_m) be the points of contact of tangents making an angle θ with the horizontal. Then, since their
centre of gravity is fixed,

$$\sum \frac{dx_i}{d\theta} = \sum \frac{dy_i}{d\theta} = 0 \qquad \frac{dx_i}{ds_i} = \cos\theta \qquad \frac{dy_i}{ds_i} = \sin\theta$$

$$\sum \frac{dx_i}{ds_i}\frac{ds_i}{d\theta} = 0 \qquad \sum \frac{dx_i}{ds_i}\frac{ds_i}{d\theta} = 0$$

$$\frac{ds_i}{d\theta} = \rho_i = \text{radius of curvature.}$$

Let (ξ_i, η_i) be the corresponding centre of curvature

$$\xi_i = x_i - \rho_i \sin\theta \qquad \eta_i = y_i + \rho_i \cos\theta$$

$$\sum \xi_i = \sum x_i - \sum \frac{dy_i}{ds_i}\frac{ds_i}{d\theta} = \sum x_i \qquad \sum \eta_i = \sum y_i.$$

Theorem 5] *If a curve meet the infinite line in distinct non-
singular points, its tangential centre is the centre of gravity of the
centres of curvature corresponding to tangents in a given direction,
plus the nodes counted twice and the cusps three times.*

The relation between the point equation and the tangential
equation of a curve gives another property of the tangential
centre. Let the curve be $f(x, y) = 0.$

To find the tangential centre we write

$$\frac{\partial f}{\partial x} : u = \frac{\partial f}{\partial y} : v = \frac{\partial f}{\partial 1} : w.$$

Let the points common to these polar curves be (x_1, y_1),
(x_2, y_2),.... There are two ways of finding the tangential equation:

1) We eliminate x and y between these and the equation of the curve.

2) We eliminate x and y between these and $(ux+vy+w)=0$.

In the one case we have the condition that the point whose line polar we have is on the curve, in the second case that it is on that polar. We get from Ch. I (12)

$$\Pi f(x_i, y_i) = \Theta \cdot \phi(u, v, w)$$

$$\Pi(ux_i + vy_i + w) = \phi(u, v, w).$$

Taking the logarithmic derivatives with respect to u, after the equations are made homogeneous, we get

$$\sum \frac{\left(\dfrac{\partial f}{\partial x_i}\dfrac{\partial x_i}{\partial u} + \dfrac{\partial f}{\partial y_i}\dfrac{\partial y_i}{\partial u} + \dfrac{\partial f}{\partial z_i}\dfrac{\partial z_i}{\partial u} \right)}{f(x_i, y_i, z_i)} = \frac{1}{\phi}\frac{\partial \phi}{\partial u},$$

$$\sum \frac{x_i}{ux_i + vy_i + wz_i} + \sum \frac{u\dfrac{\partial x_i}{\partial u} + v\dfrac{\partial y_i}{\partial u} + w\dfrac{\partial z_i}{\partial u}}{ux_i + vy_i + wz_i} = \frac{1}{\phi}\frac{\partial \phi}{\partial u}.$$

But
$$u:v:w = \frac{\partial f}{\partial x_i} : \frac{\partial f}{\partial y_i} : \frac{\partial f}{\partial z_i}.$$

Hence
$$\sum \frac{x_i}{ux_i + vy_i + wz_i} = \lambda \frac{\partial \phi}{\partial u}. \tag{1}$$

Here the right-hand side is the first coordinate of the point polar of the line (u, v, w) with regard to the curve, the left-hand side is the first coordinate of the same line with regard to the points (x_1, y_1), (x_2, y_2),..., i.e. with regard to those points that have the line as line polar.

Theorem 6] *If a line be not tangent to a curve, its point polar with regard to that curve is its point polar with regard to the points which have that line as line polar and with regard to the singular points counted as in the last theorems.*

Definition. A point whose line polar is the line at infinity shall be called a 'centre' for a given curve.

Theorem 7] *If a curve meet the line at infinity in distinct, non-singular points, its tangential centre is the centre of gravity of its centres and of its nodes counted twice and cusps counted three times.*[*]

There is a theorem which is, in a sense, dual to Waring's **and**

[*] Cf. Roberts[1], pp. 25 ff.

which we may deduce therefrom by a roundabout process. Consider the intersections of

$$f(x, y) = 0 \qquad \phi(x, y) + \lambda \frac{\partial \phi}{\partial y} = 0.$$

These shall be the points (x_1, y_1), (x_2, y_2), ... Let the equation of the asymptotes of f be $f_1(x, y) = 0$, and let their intersections with the other curve be $(\bar{x}_1, \bar{y}_1)$, $(\bar{x}_2, \bar{y}_2)$,....

Waring's theorem gives

$$\sum x_i = \sum \bar{x}_i \qquad \sum y_i = \sum \bar{y}_i.$$

The coordinates x_i, y_i, $\bar{x}_i$, $\bar{y}_i$ are all functions of λ, and if we substitute these values in the equations of the various curves, we get expressions in which are identically 0:

$$\frac{\partial f}{\partial x_i} \frac{dx_i}{d\lambda} + \frac{\partial f}{\partial y_i} \frac{dy_i}{d\lambda} = 0$$

$$\left(\frac{\partial \phi}{\partial x_i} + \lambda \frac{\partial^2 \phi}{\partial x_i \partial y_i}\right) \frac{dx_i}{d\lambda} + \left(\frac{\partial \phi}{\partial y_i} + \lambda \frac{\partial^2 \phi}{\partial y_i^2}\right) \frac{dy_i}{d\lambda} + \frac{\partial \phi}{\partial y_i} = 0$$

$$\frac{dx_i}{d\lambda} = \frac{\dfrac{\partial \phi}{\partial y_i} \dfrac{\partial f}{\partial y_i}}{\dfrac{\partial(f, \phi)}{\partial(x_i, y_i)} + \lambda \dfrac{\partial\left(f, \dfrac{\partial \phi}{\partial y_i}\right)}{\partial(x_i, y_i)}} \qquad \frac{d\bar{x}_i}{d\lambda} = \frac{\dfrac{\partial \phi}{\partial y_i} \dfrac{\partial f_1}{\partial y_i}}{\dfrac{\partial(f_1, \phi)}{\partial(x_i, y_i)} + \lambda \dfrac{\partial\left(f_1, \dfrac{\partial \phi}{\partial y_i}\right)}{\partial(x_i, y_i)}}.$$

Putting $\lambda = 0$ and remembering

$$\sum \frac{dx_i}{d\lambda} = \sum \frac{d\bar{x}_i}{d\lambda}$$

$$\sum \frac{\dfrac{\partial f}{\partial x_i} \dfrac{\partial \phi}{\partial x_i}}{\dfrac{\partial(f, \phi)}{\partial(x_i, y_i)}} = \sum \frac{\dfrac{\partial f_1}{\partial x_i} \dfrac{\partial \phi}{\partial x_i}}{\dfrac{\partial(f, \phi)}{\partial(x_i, y_i)}}.$$

Similarly

$$\sum \frac{\dfrac{\partial f}{\partial y_i} \dfrac{\partial \phi}{\partial y_i}}{\dfrac{\partial(f, \phi)}{\partial(x_i, y_i)}} = \sum \frac{\dfrac{\partial f_1}{\partial y_i} \dfrac{\partial \phi}{\partial y_i}}{\dfrac{\partial(f_1, \phi)}{\partial(x_i, y_i)}}.$$

Hence

$$\sum \frac{\dfrac{\partial f}{\partial x_i} \dfrac{\partial \phi}{\partial x_i} + \dfrac{\partial f}{\partial y_i} \dfrac{\partial \phi}{\partial y_i}}{\dfrac{\partial(f, \phi)}{\partial(x_i, y_i)}} = \sum \frac{\dfrac{\partial f_1}{\partial x_i} \dfrac{\partial \phi}{\partial x_i} + \dfrac{\partial f_1}{\partial y_i} \dfrac{\partial \phi}{\partial y_i}}{\dfrac{\partial(f, \phi)}{\partial(x_i, y_i)}}.$$

The summation on the left covers all intersections of f and ϕ, that on the right all intersections of f_1 and ϕ, it being assumed that all are finite in each case. But these expressions are the cotangents of the angles of intersection, when neither has a tangent which is a minimal line.

Theorem 8] *If each of two given curves meet the line at infinity in distinct, non-singular points, and if no asymptote of one be parallel to an asymptote of the other, and if neither touch a minimal line at a point common to the two, then the sum of the cotangents of the angles which they make at their intersections is the sum of the cotangents of the angles the one makes with the asymptotes of the other.**

Theorem 9] *If two curves be given which fulfil the conditions of theorem* 8], *the sum of the cotangents of their angles is the sum of the cotangents of the angles of their asymptotes.*

Theorem 10] *If a curve fulfil the conditions of theorem* 8], *the sum of the cotangents of the angles which a line makes therewith is unaltered when the line moves parallel to itself.*

Suppose that one of the curves is a circle. If we replace it by its asymptotes, these are minimal lines. The cotangent of the angle which a minimal line makes with a non-minimal one is i or $-i$, according to which circular point the line goes through. This yields a really striking theorem:

Theorem 11] *If a curve fulfil the conditions of theorem* 8], *the sum of the cotangents of the angles which it makes with any circle which is not tangent and does not meet it at a point of contact with a minimal tangent is* 0.

Let us find the polar reciprocal of this last theorem, reciprocating with regard to the given circle. The angle between the curve and circle is equal to the angle subtended at the centre of the latter by the corresponding tangential segment of the circle and the polar reciprocal curve. The cotangent of this angle is, thus, the radius of the circle divided by the length of the common tangential segment. If we count the radius of the circle, when real, as positive, this segment will be counted positive when progress thereon from the point of contact with the circle to that with the curve corresponds to a positive rotation about the centre of the circle. The original curve was

* Cf. Humbert[1], pp. 352 ff.

restricted so as not to pass through a circular point at infinity; the transformed curve must not touch an asymptote of the circle.

Theorem 12] *If a curve do not pass through the centre of a circle, nor touch one of its asymptotes, the sum of the reciprocals of their common tangential segments, when properly oriented, is* 0.*

The sceptical reader will be inclined to doubt the accuracy of theorems 10], 11], 12]. Suppose that we have contact between two curves, what then ? The angles are 0 and have infinite cotangents, the reciprocals of the common tangential segments become infinite also. The difficulty is removed in both cases by considering the penultimate positions. The curves will have two angles close to 0 and π, the sum of the cotangents will approach a finite limit. In the same way the reciprocals of two common tangential segments will approach infinity positively and negatively together, and their sum go towards a definite limit also.

§ 2. Foci

Definition. A point of intersection of tangents to a curve from the two circular points at infinity, the points of contact being both finite, is called a 'focus' of the curve. As the circular inverse of a minimal line is a minimal line, we see that the inverse of a focus is also a focus. If the curve pass through the circular points we might be tempted to call the intersections of the tangents there foci also. That would not be wise; the inverse points would not have the same property with regard to the inverse curve. Thus, the tangents to a circle at the circular points at infinity intersect at the centre, but the inverse of the centre of a circle is not, usually, the centre of the inverse circle. If a real curve of class m have multiplicity r at each circular point, the total number of foci is $(m-2r)^2$, of which $(m-2r)$ are real.

Definition. A set of foci of a curve, of which one lies on each minimal tangent, but no two are on the same minimal tangent, are called 'associated foci'. The real foci of a real curve are the most obvious example. A set of associated foci will be carried by inversion into another associated set.

* Cf. Genese, p. 308.

How shall we find the coordinates of the foci ? Let the equation of the curve be
$$f(x, y) = 0.$$

Then, if (x', y') be a focus, the curve is tangent to the two lines
$$(y-y') = i(x-x') \qquad (y-y') = -i(x-x').$$

These will yield two equations:
$$P(x', y') \pm i Q(x', y') = 0; \qquad P(x', y') = 0 \qquad Q(x', y') = 0.$$

In finding them we must change i into $-i$ only where it comes in through the equation of the tangent line, not where it may be involved in the coefficients of the given curve.

The problem takes a more satisfactory form when the equation of the curve is given in tangential coordinates.
$$\phi(u, v, w) = 0. \tag{2}$$
The minimal line
$$y-y' = \pm i(x-x')$$
is tangent to the curve if
$$\phi(\pm i, -1, y' \mp ix') = 0, \tag{3}$$
$$H(x', y') = 0 \qquad K(x', y') = 0.$$

As an example, take the ellipse
$$\frac{x^2}{a^2} + \frac{y^2}{b^2} - 1 = 0$$
$$a^2 u^2 + b^2 v^2 - w^2 = 0$$
$$-a^2 + b^2 = (y' \pm ix')^2 \qquad (x' \pm iy')^2 = a^2 - b^2$$
$$x'^2 - y'^2 = a^2 - b^2 \qquad x'y' = 0.$$

It is to be noted, for future use, that even as Nöther's theorem gives us the form for the equation of a curve through the intersections of two curves, so will its dual give us the tangential equation of a curve touching the common tangents to two curves. If, thus, (x_1, y_1), (x_2, y_2),... be the coordinates of the foci of a curve, then the tangential equation of a curve with these and no other foci will be
$$\prod_i (ux_i + vy_i + w) + (u^2 + v^2)\psi^{m-2}(u, v, w) = 0. \tag{4}$$

There is a good deal of advantage, in studying foci, especially real foci, in using minimal coordinates, i.e.
$$z = x + iy \qquad z' = x - iy.$$

Then (3) takes the form

$$\phi(-1, -i, z) = 0.$$

Let this polynomial be expanded to

$$a_0 z^m + a_1 z^{m-1} + \ldots + a_m = 0.$$

The sum of the roots gives m times the first coordinate of the centre of gravity of the foci, and this is the root of the equation

$$\frac{d^{m-1}\phi}{dz^{m-1}} = 0.$$

On the other hand, if the tangential centre have the co-ordinates (ξ, η),

$$\frac{\partial^{m-1}}{\partial w^{m-1}} \phi(u, v, w) \equiv u\xi + v\eta + w = 0$$

$$\frac{d^{m-1}}{dz^{m-1}} \phi(-1, -i, x+iy) \equiv -\xi - i\eta + (x+iy) = 0$$

$$\xi + i\eta = x + iy.$$

This gives a pretty theorem due, apparently, to Siebeck:*

Theorem 13] *If a curve with real equation do not touch the line at infinity, nor pass through a circular point, the tangential centre is the centre of gravity of the real foci.*

We saw in 4] that the tangential centre was the centre of gravity of the points of contact of tangents through an infinite point. When we have lines through a finite point the theorem has to be modified. Let the radius vector from (x, y) on a curve to a fixed point (x', y') make an angle $-\theta$ with the tangent

$$\cos\theta\left[(x-x')\frac{\partial f}{\partial x} + (y-y')\frac{\partial f}{\partial y}\right] + \sin\theta\left[(x-x')\frac{\partial f}{\partial y} - (y-y')\frac{\partial f}{\partial x}\right] = 0.$$

A node will be a solution of this equation counting twice, a cusp counting thrice. When $\theta \not\equiv 0 \pmod{\pi}$, the highest terms are of degree n and come from the highest terms of f.

Theorem 14] *If a curve meet the line at infinity in distinct, non-singular points and do not pass through a circular point, the centre of gravity of those points where the tangents make a chosen angle, not congruent to $0 \pmod{\pi}$, with the radii vectores from a fixed finite point, plus the nodes counted twice and the cusps three times, is the centre of gravity of the corresponding points on the asymptotes plus their intersections each counted twice.*

* Siebeck, p. 175.

Let us see how many of these points there are when the order of the curve is n and the class m. Through the given point take a line l; this will meet the curve in n points, each with its tangent, so that through the given point will pass n lines making the required angles with their tangents. Conversely, if a line be given through our point, there are m tangents making therewith the given angle, and so n lines to the points of contact. We have among our lines a correspondence, with indices n and m, with $n+m$ coincidences, all desirable.

Theorem 15] *Through a point not on a curve of order n and class m, and not on a minimal tangent, will pass, at most and in general, $n+m$ lines meeting it at an assigned angle, not congruent to $0 \pmod{\pi}$.*

When the angle is congruent to $0 \pmod{\pi}$, n of these lines become parallel to the asymptotes, the others are the tangents from the point.

The position of the centre of gravity mentioned in 14] will usually vary with the point chosen. If, however, the asymptotes be minimal lines, every line making an assigned angle with them is parallel to them, in other words, if a line approach a minimal direction as a limit, every line making an assigned angle with it will approach that same limiting direction. The points on the asymptotes whose centres of gravity we seek will tend to pass out of the picture, leaving only the intersections. At the same time the number of points on the curve where the tangents make a fixed angle with the radii vectores will come down to m, for, in the Chasles-Cayley-Brill correspondence formula just used, there will be n undesired coincidences in the minimal directions. We thus get from 4] and the limiting case of 14]:

Theorem 16] *If all of the asymptotes of a curve be distinct, but go through the circular points at infinity, and if the curve be not tangent to the infinite line, the centre of gravity of the points where it meets the radii vectores from an arbitrary point at a given angle, plus the nodes each counted twice and the cusps each counted thrice, is the tangential centre.*

§ 3. Products of distances

The present section, like the first in this chapter, must start with an algebraic lemma or, rather, with three of them.

Lemma 1] *If the polynomial*

$$a_0 x^n + a_1 x^{n-1} + \ldots + a_{n-1} x + a_n$$

be divisible by $1 + x^2$, *then*

$$a_0 - a_2 + a_4 - \ldots = 0 \qquad a_1 - a_3 + a_5 - \ldots = 0.$$

The proof is immediate, and left to the reader.

Lemma 2] *If the polynomial written above be the sum of two others of its degree, then the expressions* $a_0 - a_2 + a_4 \ldots$ *and* $a_1 - a_3 + a_5 \ldots$ *are the sums of the corresponding expressions in the two other polynomials.*

Lemma 3] *In finding the expressions* $a_0 - a_2 + a_4 \ldots$ *and* $a_1 - a_3 + a_5 \ldots$ *we may disregard any part of a polynomial that is divisible by* $1 + x^2$.

Suppose that we have a curve which does not go through a circular point at infinity. Let us find its intersections with a circle of radius r passing through the point (x_0, y_0) and then the product of their distances from (x_0, y_0) divided by $(2r)^n$. It is well to use minimal coordinates:

$$f(x,y) \equiv A_0 y^n + A_1 y^{n-1} x + \ldots + A_{n-1} y x^{n-1} + A_n x^n +$$
$$+ b_0 y^{n-1} + \ldots + k = 0 \quad (5)$$

$$z = x + iy \qquad \bar{z} = x - iy \qquad x = \frac{z + \bar{z}}{2} \qquad y = \frac{z - \bar{z}}{2i}$$

$$f(x,y) \equiv F(z, \bar{z}) \equiv F(z_0, \bar{z}_0) + (z - z_0) \frac{\partial F}{\partial z_0} + (\bar{z} - \bar{z}_0) \frac{\partial F}{\partial \bar{z}_0} + \ldots. \quad (6)$$

Let the circle through (x_0, y_0) have the equation

$$P(z - z_0)(\bar{z} - \bar{z}_0) + q(z - z_0) + \bar{q}(\bar{z} - \bar{z}_0) = 0 \qquad r = \frac{\sqrt{q\bar{q}}}{P}$$

$$\bar{z} - \bar{z}_0 = - \frac{q(z - z_0)}{P(z - z_0) + \bar{q}}.$$

Substituting, we get

$$F(z_0, \bar{z}_0) + (z - z_0) \frac{\partial F}{\partial z_0} - \frac{q(z - z_0)}{P(z - z_0) + \bar{q}} \frac{\partial F}{\partial \bar{z}_0} + \ldots = 0.$$

Clearing of fractions:

$$F(z_0, \bar{z}_0) \bar{q}^n + \ldots + P^n \frac{\partial^n F}{\partial z_0^n} (z - z_0)^{2n} = 0.$$

For the product of the roots we have

$$\Pi(z_i - z_0) = (-1)^n \frac{F(z_0, \bar{z}_0)\bar{q}^n}{P^n \dfrac{\partial^n F}{\partial z_0^n}}.$$

The product of the distances from (x_0, y_0) to these intersections is

$$\sqrt{\Pi(z_i - z_0)\Pi(\bar{z}_i - \bar{z}_0)} = \frac{F(z_0, \bar{z}_0)}{P^n} \sqrt{\frac{q^n \bar{q}^n}{\dfrac{\partial^n F}{\partial z_0} \dfrac{\partial^n \bar{F}}{\partial \bar{z}_0}}}$$

$$= \frac{(2r)^n f(x_0, y_0)}{\sqrt{(A_0 - A_2 + A_4 - \ldots)^2 + (A_1 - A_3 + A_5 - \ldots)^2}}.$$

Theorem 17] *If a curve of order n passing through no circular point at infinity have the equation*

$$f(x,y) \equiv A_0 x^n + A_1 x^{n-1}y + \ldots + A_n y^n + b_0 x^{n-1} + b_1 x^{n-2}y + \ldots + k = 0$$

the product of the distances from a point (x_0, y_0) to the intersections with a circle through it divided by the nth power of the diameter is

$$\frac{f(x_0, y_0)}{\sqrt{(A_0 - A_2 + A_4 - \ldots)^2 + (A_1 - A_3 + A_5 - \ldots)^2}}. \tag{7}$$

Definition. The expression (7) is called the 'power' of the given point with regard to the given curve.[*]

Let us seek the product of the distances from a point to the $m+n$ points on a curve where the tangents make assigned angles with the radii vectores. The desired angle being θ, we have three equations:

$$f(x, y) = 0,$$

$$\sin\theta\left[(x-x_0)\frac{\partial f}{\partial y} - (y-y_0)\frac{\partial f}{\partial x}\right] - \left[(x-x_0)\frac{\partial f}{\partial x} + (y-y_0)\frac{\partial f}{\partial y}\right]\cos\theta = 0,$$

$$(x-x_0)^2 + (y-y_0)^2 - p^2 = 0.$$

We must eliminate x and y and seek the product of the roots of the resulting equation in p. This product will vanish in two cases only: the point lies on the curve, or the line from there to one of the $m+n$ points is minimal. But a minimal line and a non-minimal tangent cannot make an assigned angle; the pro-

---

[*] This concept is due to Laguerre,[2] p. 20. He uses the radius of the circle instead of the diameter, and gives no proof.

duct would only vanish if the point (x_0, y_0) lay on a minimal tangent. The left side of the equation of the minimal tangents is the product of the squares of the distances from an arbitrary point to a complete set of foci. Hence the product of the squares of the distances to these $m+n$ points which is of degree $2(m+n)$ in (x_0, y_0) vanishes with the square of the power of (x_0, y_0) and with the product of the squares of the distances to a complete set of foci. The product will become infinite only if one point go to infinity. When $\theta = 0$, n of the points go off to the ends of the axes, but the limit of the distance multiplied by $\sin \theta$ remains finite; hence the product of the distances becomes infinite with $\sin^n \theta$. There remains a constant factor, which we find to be unity by taking the case where $\theta = 0$ and the curve is n lines.

Theorem 18] *If a curve meet the infinite line in distinct non-singular and non-circular points, the product of the distances from a general point to those points of the curve, where the tangent makes an assigned angle, not 0, with the radius vector, is the power of the point with regard to the curve, multiplied by the product of its distances from a complete set of foci, and divided by the sine of the given angle raised to a power equal to the order of the curve.*

When $\theta = 0$, as before, n of the points go off to the ends of the asymptotes.

Theorem 19] *If a curve meet the line at infinity in distinct non-singular and non-circular points, the product of the tangential segments from a point to the curve is equal to the power of the point, multiplied by the distances to a complete set of foci, and divided by the product of the distances to the asymptotes.*

Theorem 20] *If a curve be related to the line at infinity as in the last example, the product of the normal distances from a general point thereto is equal to the power of the point with regard to the curve, multiplied by the product of the distances to a complete set of foci.*

Theorem 21] *If a curve be related to the line at infinity as in these examples, the product of the distances to the points where the tangent makes an assigned angle, not 0, with the radius vector, is the product of the normal distances divided by the nth power of the sine of the angle.*

* Laguerre,[2] p. 21, for this and the two following . No proofs are given.

§ 4. Sums of angles

This section, like the preceding one, must begin with an easy general theorem. We begin with the easy trigonometric proposition that, if we have given angles $\theta_1, \theta_2, ..., \theta_n$,

$$\tan \sum \theta_i = \frac{\sum \tan \theta_i - \sum \tan \theta_i \tan \theta_j \tan \theta_k + ...}{1 - \sum \tan \theta_i \tan \theta_j + ...}$$

If these tangents be roots of the equation

$$A_0 \tan^n\theta + A_1 \tan^{n-1}\theta + ... + A_n = 0.$$

Then

$$\tan \sum \theta_i = -\frac{A_1 - A_3 + A_5 - ...}{A_0 - A_2 + A_4 - ...}.$$

We thus get from lemma 3]:

Theorem 22] *If the tangents of a system of angles be the roots of a polynomial in* $\tan \theta$, *in finding the tangent of the sum of these angles we may omit all parts of the polynomial with the factor* $1 + \tan^2\theta$.

We next seek the tangents of the half-angles made with the x-axis by radii vectores from the origin to the intersections with a circle of radius r and centre at O. We introduce polar coordinates:

$$x = r \cos \theta = r\frac{1-t^2}{1+t^2} = -r + \frac{2r}{1+t^2}; \qquad y = r \sin \theta = \frac{2rt}{1+t^2};$$

$$t = \tan \frac{\theta}{2}.$$

Substituting in the equation of the curve, we get

$$\alpha_0 t^{2n} + \alpha_1 t^{2n-1} + ... + \alpha_{2n}$$
$$\equiv (1+t^2)\phi(t) + (2r)^n[A_0 t^n + A_1 t^{n-1} + ... + A_n].$$

At this point we must walk most circumspectly. When n is even, the α's with even subscripts go with the A's with even subscripts, and we have

$$-\frac{\alpha_1 - \alpha_3 + \alpha_5 - ...}{\alpha_0 - \alpha_2 + \alpha_4 - ...} = \pm\frac{A_1 - A_3 + A_5 - ...}{A_0 - A_2 + A_4 - ...}.$$

When, however, n is odd, we have even subscripts in one case going with odd in the other, so that

$$-\frac{\alpha_1 - \alpha_3 + \alpha_5 - ...}{\alpha_0 - \alpha_2 + \alpha_4 - ...} = \mp\frac{A_0 - A_2 + A_4 - ...}{A_1 - A_3 + A_5 - ...},$$

which means that the tangent of the sum of the angles is equal to plus or minus the cotangent of the sum of the half-angles.

Theorem 23] *If a curve have the relation to the line at infinity required in recent theorems, and if it be of even order, one-half the sum of the angles which a fixed direction makes with the radii to the intersections with any circle will differ by an even multiple of $\frac{\pi}{2}$ from the sum of the angles which this direction makes with the asymptotes.*

Theorem 24] *When the order is odd, the difference is an odd multiple of $\frac{\pi}{2}$.*

Suppose that we have two curves, and that we know a complete set of foci of one. We write them

$$\phi_1 \equiv \Pi_1(ux_i + vy_i + w) + (u^2 + v^2)\psi_1 = 0 \qquad \chi = 0.$$

Let us find the sum of the angles which the x-axis makes with their common tangent. Eliminating w, let the resultant be

$$A_0 u^{mm'} + A_1 u^{mm'-1}v + \dots + A_{mm'}v^{mm'}.$$

We then seek the expression

$$-\frac{A_1 - A_3 + A_5 - \dots}{A_0 - A_2 + A_4 - \dots}.$$

This will be unaltered if we replace the first curve by its foci of this set.

Theorem 25] *If two curves have the relation to the line at infinity frequently mentioned in recent theorems, the sum of the angles which an arbitrary direction makes with their common tangents is the sum of the angles which it makes with the tangents to one from a complete set of foci of the other.*

Theorem 26] *The sum of the angles which an arbitrary line makes with the common tangents to two curves situated as above is the sum of the angles with the lines connecting a complete set of foci of one with a complete set of the other.**

In these theorems a common multiple tangent must, of course, be properly weighted.

We may extend these theorems a bit as follows. Given two

* Cf. Humbert[3], p. 359.

curves of which one has a complete set of foci included among the foci of the other,

$$\phi_1 \equiv \Pi_1(ux_i+vy_i+w)+(u^2+v^2)\psi_1 = 0,$$

$$\phi_2 \equiv \Pi_1(ux_i+vy_i+w)\Pi_2(ux_i+vy_i+w)+(u^2+v^2)\psi_2 = 0.$$

Let us find the sum of the angles which the x-axis makes with the common tangents of ϕ_1 and a curve $\lambda\phi_2+\mu\chi = 0$.

We must eliminate w between

$$\phi_1 = 0 \qquad \lambda\phi_2+\mu\chi = 0,$$

or between

$$\phi_1 = 0 \qquad \lambda(u^2+v^2)[\psi_2-\Pi_2\psi_1]+\mu\chi = 0,$$

or finally between

$$\phi_1 = 0 \qquad \chi = 0.$$

Theorem 27] *Given three curves with this relation to infinity, of which the first has a complete set of foci included in a complete set of the second. Then the sum of the angles which an arbitrary direction makes with the common tangents of the first, and a curve linearly dependent in line coordinates on the second and the third, is independent of the curve chosen in that system.*

A point, looked upon as an envelope, is its own focus; this gives:

Theorem 28] *The sum of the angles which a fixed direction makes with the tangents to any curve in a system limited as above, and linearly dependent in tangential coordinates on two given curves, from a focus of one curve of the system, is constant, and equal to the sum of the angles which the direction makes with lines from this focus, to a complete set of foci of any curve not including this particular point.*

Theorem 29] *Given a set of curves of a given class linearly dependent on two in tangential coordinates, the general curve being related to infinity as above, the locus of a continuously moving complete set of foci of these curves has the property that, if a finite point thereof be connected with any one set of foci, the sum of the angles these lines make with a given direction is constant.*

This theorem may be generalized as follows, remembering 25] and 27]:

Theorem 30] *If a complete set of foci of a curve be a complete set for a curve of a system linearly dependent on two in tangential coordinates, the original curve and the general curve of the system* *being related to infinity as above, then the sum of the angles with a fixed direction made by the common tangents of the first curve, and a general curve of the system, is constant.**

There are angle-sum theorems connected with asymptotes as well as with foci. Suppose that two curves, related to infinity as above, have the same intersections with a given circle. We write their equations

$$f(x,y) = 0 \qquad f(x,y) + [x^2 + y^2 + px + qy + s]\psi(x,y) = 0.$$

The terms of highest degree give the direction of the asymptotes; these will differ in the two cases, by a polynomial having $(x^2 + y^2)$ as a factor:

Theorem 31] *If two curves of the same order, subject to the restrictions at infinity usual in the present chapter, meet a circle in the same points, the sum of the angles which a given direction makes with their asymptotes is the same.*

The only function of the circle in this theorem is to pass through the circular points at infinity, and thus have the factor $x^2 + y^2$ in the terms of highest degree. Any other curve through the circular points will do that:

Theorem 32] *If two curves of the same order, subject to the present restrictions at infinity, meet a curve through the circular points in the same non-singular points, the sum of the angles which an arbitrary direction makes with their asymptotes is the same.*†

Let us try to transform 27], when the first two curves have a common complete set of foci, by polar reciprocation in a circle. Two curves with the same foci have the same minimal tangents, and so go into two curves having the same intersections with two minimal lines through a point O. The angle which a common tangent makes with a given direction, goes into the angle at O made by a line to a fixed point and to a point of intersection:

Theorem 33] *If two curves of the same order, neither of which passes through a point O, nor has a singular tangent through there, have the same distinct intersections with the minimal lines through that point, then the sum of the angles with a fixed line through O made by lines to the intersections of the first curve and a third*

---

* Cf. Michel, p. 173.   † Cf. Humbert[2], p. 261.

*general curve, having the same restrictions with regard to O, is equal
to the corresponding sum for the second and third curves.**

It is very easy to generalize this theorem by means of a linear
transformation, if we remember Laguerre's theorem that the
angle between two lines is a constant multiple of the logarithm of
the cross ratio they make with the minimal lines through their
intersection. An angle sum is, thus, the logarithm of the product
of a number of cross ratios. If, then, we transform three concurrent lines projectively into oblique x and y axes, and the line
$x - y = 0$, we have for the cross ratio of the three with a line
from O to the point (x, y)

$$\frac{x}{y} = \frac{\text{Dist from } P \text{ to } OY}{\text{Dist from } P \text{ to } OX} = \frac{\sin POY}{\sin POX}.$$

Theorem 34] *Given two curves of the same order, neither of
which passes through a given point O, nor has a multiple tangent
through there, but which have the same intersections with two non-
minimal lines through there, then, if they be brought to intersect
a third curve, the product of the ratios of the distances from the
intersections of curves 1 and 3 to the two lines is the same as the
corresponding product for the curves 2 and 3.†*

This theorem takes a still better form when the two lines are
mutually perpendicular; the ratio of the sines is then the reciprocal of the slope of the line OP.

Theorem 35] *Given two curves of the same order, neither of
which passes through a given point O, nor has a singular tangent
through there, but which meet vertical and horizontal lines through
O in the same non-singular points, then, if they be brought to
intersect a third curve with the same restriction as to O, the product
of the slopes of the lines from O to the intersection of curves 1 and
3 is equal to the corresponding product for the curves 2 and 3.*

We have not yet finished with the foci of a curve; their properties are numerous and varied. We saw in Ch. IX, theorem
12], that the line polar of a point with regard to m pairs of
lines is its line polar with regard to its m polars with regard to

* Cf. Fouret², p. 45. Cuny devotes a whole short volume to the particular
case where one of the curves is a set of lines. He says in his preface that his
book was largely composed under war conditions, in an observation post,
while faithful Poilus were on watch, &c. This explains his ignorance of the
work of his predecessors.

† Fouret², p. 42.

the various pairs. The polar of a point with regard to a pair of minimal lines is the line through their intersection perpendicular to the line connecting that with the given point. The minimal tangents to a given curve are the common tangents to that and the circular points. We thus get from IX 14] and 12]:

Theorem 36] *The line polar with regard to the lines through a complete set of foci of a curve fulfilling the conditions often mentioned in this chapter, perpendicular to the lines from these foci to the given point, is its line polar with regard to the normals to the given curve at the points of contact of tangents from the given point.*

Let us find the loci of foci of certain simple sets of curves. First take a pencil of curves of order n with finite centres, the general curve being of class m. If we draw tangents to these various curves from the two circular points, and find the order of the locus of their intersections, by finding how many of its points lie on a given line, a simple application of the Chasles-Cayley-Brill formula gives $4mn$ as the answer. From this, however, we must subtract undesired coincidences. $2(n-1)$ curves of the pencil touch the line at infinity, and there will be $2(n-1)$ infinite coincidences. A linear transformation will show that each of these counts only once. The order is, really,

$$4m(n-1)-2(n-1)=2(2m-1)(n-1).$$

As a check, let us see how often the curve meets the line at infinity. When a curve of the pencil touches the line at infinity, one tangent from each circular point becomes the infinite line, the other $m-1$ become tangents at that circular point to the locus sought; this latter has, therefore, a multiplicity of $2(m-1)(n-1)$ at each circular point; it also passes simply through each point of contact of a curve of the pencil with the infinite line:

$$4(m-1)(n-1)+2(n-1)=2(2m-1)(n-1).$$

With regard to m, we note by Bertini's theorem 10] of Ch. VII, if there be n^2 common points $m=n(n-1)$.

Theorem 37] *If a pencil of curves of order n be given, the general curve being of class m, and if there be no infinite centre to the pencil and no curve touch the infinite line at a circular point, the locus of their foci is a curve of order $2(2m-1)(n-1)$ with the multiplicity $2(m-1)(n-1)$ at each circular point.*

Let us next take a set of curves linearly dependent in tangential coordinates on two curves with the relation to the line at infinity usual in this chapter. This locus is an old friend. By Chasles-Cayley-Brill, this is a curve of order $2m-1$, for we have an m-to-m correspondence on a general line, with one undesired infinite coincidence. One curve of the system touches the infinite line. There are $m-1$ other tangents to this from each circular point, hence each circular point has the multiplicity $m-1$; the curve also meets the infinite line at the point of contact with one curve of the system. If $A_1, A_2, \ldots$ and $B_1, B_2, \ldots$ be two complete sets of foci thereon, and P a general point of the curve, we have, by 29],

$$\sum A_i P B_i \equiv 0 \ (\mathrm{mod}\ \pi).$$

Suppose, conversely, that a curve has the property that the sum of the angles from a variable point P to two fixed groups $A_1, A_2, \ldots; B_1, B_2, \ldots$ fulfils this condition. Let the group $A_1, A_2, \ldots$ have coordinates $(x_1, y_1), (x_2, y_2) \ldots$ while $B_1, B_2, \ldots$ have coordinates $(x_1', y_1'), (x_2', y_2') \ldots$. Let P, a given point of the curve, be the origin.

Take two curves of the same class with $(x_1, y_1), (x_2, y_2) \ldots$ and $(x_1', y_1'), (x_2', y_2') \ldots$ as complete sets of foci:

$$\phi_1 = \Pi(ux_i + vy_i + w) + (u^2 + v^2)\psi_1$$
$$\phi_2 = \Pi(ux_i' + vy_i' + w) + (u^2 + v^2)\psi_2.$$

Let us show that a curve of the system

$$\phi_1 - \rho\phi_2$$

has a focus at the origin.

Let $\qquad a_0 u^m + a_1 u^{m-1}v + \ldots + a_m v^m = \Pi(ux_i + vy_i)$
$$a_0' u^m + a_1' u^{m-1}v + \ldots + a_m' v^m = \Pi(ux_i' + vy_i').$$

By hypothesis

$$-\frac{a_1 - a_3 + a_5 - \ldots}{a_0 - a_2 + a_4 - \ldots} = -\frac{a_1' - a_3' + a_5' - \ldots}{a_0' - a_2' + a_4' - \ldots}.$$

Let $\qquad \dfrac{a_1 - a_3 + a_5 - \ldots}{a_1' - a_3' + a_5' - \ldots} = \dfrac{a_0 - a_2 + a_4 - \ldots}{a_0' - a_2' + a_4' - \ldots} = \rho$

$$(a_1 - a_3 + a_5 - \ldots)^2 + (a_0 - a_2 + a_4 - \ldots)^2$$
$$= \rho^2[(a_1' - a_3' + a_5' - \ldots)^2 + (a_0' - a_2' + a_4' - \ldots)^2]$$
$$\Pi(x_i^2 + y_i^2) = \rho^2 \Pi(x_i'^2 + y_i'^2).$$

Then $\phi_1 - \rho\phi_2$ has a focus at the origin, a generic point of the given curve.

Theorem 38] *If two curves of the same class m have the relation to the line at infinity frequently mentioned in this chapter, and if they share no minimal tangent, the locus of the foci, or a complete set of foci of curves linearly dependent on them in tangential co-ordinates, is a curve of order $2m-1$ with the multiplicity $m-1$ at each circular point. It is a locus of points such that the sum of the angles subtended thereat by corresponding foci of two complete sets is congruent to $0 \pmod{\pi}$.*

Theorem 39] *The locus of points whence m given line segments in general position, none of which is minimal, are seen at angles whose sum is congruent to $0 \pmod{\pi}$, is a curve of order $2m-1$ with a multiplicity $m-1$ at each circular point. It is the locus of the foci of curves linearly dependent, in tangential coordinates on two curves having the extremities of the given segments as two complete sets of foci.**

§ 5. Polars

The polar curves discussed in previous chapters are principally important because of their covariance under the group of projective transformations. Some of them, however, have metrical properties that are worth notice.

The point that divides in the ratio $-\xi_2/\xi_1$ the segment from (x, y) to (x', y') has the coordinates

$$\frac{\xi_1 x' + \xi_2 x}{\xi_2 + \xi_1}, \qquad \frac{\xi_1 y' + \xi_2 y}{\xi_2 + \xi_1},$$

or, in homogeneous form,

$$\xi_1 x_1' + \xi_2 x_1 : \xi_1 x_2' + \xi_2 x_2 : \xi_1 x_3' + \xi_2 x_3.$$

Let (x) be on the $(n-r)$th polar of (x') with regard to $a_x^n = 0$. Then, if our new point be on the curve,

$$\xi_1^n a_{x'}^n + n\xi_1^{n-1}\xi_2 a_{x'}^{n-1}a_x + \ldots + \xi_2^n a_x^n = 0 \qquad a_{x'}^{n-r} a_x^r = 0.$$

Remembering the relations of roots and coefficients of an equation,

$$\sum \left(-\frac{\xi_1^i}{\xi_2^i}\right)\left(-\frac{\xi_1^j}{\xi_2^j}\right)\ldots = 0.$$

* Cf. Darboux, p. 74.

If (x') be a point (O), (x) a point of this polar, while the intersections of OP with the original curve are $Q_1, Q_2 \ldots$,

$$\sum \left(\frac{PQ_i}{OQ_i}\right)\left(\frac{PQ_j}{OQ_j}\right)\ldots = 0. \tag{8}$$

Theorem 40] *If a point P be on the $(n-r)$th polar of a general point O with regard to a curve of order n, and if the line meeting them meet the curve in the points $Q_1, Q_2 \ldots$, then*

$$\sum \left(\frac{PQ_i}{OQ_i}\right)\left(\frac{PQ_j}{OQ_j}\right)\ldots = 0, \tag{8}$$

where the summation includes all sets of r different indices.

Dividing through by

$$\frac{PQ_1 PQ_2 \ldots PQ_n}{OQ_1 OQ_2 \ldots OQ_n},$$

$$\sum \frac{OQ_i OQ_j \ldots}{PQ_i PQ_j \ldots} = 0, \tag{9}$$

the summation including all sets of $n-r$ different indices.

Let us take the first polar, $r = n-1$,

$$\sum \frac{OQ_i}{PQ_i} = 0. \tag{10}$$

Since $OQ_i = PQ_i - PO$,

$$\frac{1}{PO} = \frac{1}{n} \sum \frac{1}{PQ_i} \tag{11}$$

For the line polar $r = 1$,

$$\frac{1}{OP} = \frac{1}{n} \sum \frac{1}{OQ_i}. \tag{12}$$

Theorem 41] *The line polar of a finite point is the locus of points, the reciprocals of whose distances from the given point is the average of the reciprocals of the distances from the latter to the intersection of lines through it and the given curve.*

We have already defined a point whose line polar is the line at infinity as a centre of our curve. When P is infinite, we have

$$\sum \frac{1}{OQ_i} = 0. \tag{13}$$

Theorem 42] *If through a centre of a curve a non-minimal line be drawn, the sum of the reciprocals of the distances from the centre to the intersections is 0.*

The general curve of order n has $(n-1)^2$ centres, whose centre
f gravity is the tangential centre by 7] of the present chapter.
,et us take this point as the origin. Then, in tangential coordinates, there will be no terms of the first order in u or v.
Ience, if u and v be fixed, i.e. if we take tangents in a fixed
lirection, the sum of the corresponding w's, i.e. the sum of the
listances of these tangents from the origin, is 0.

Theorem 43] *If a curve meet the infinite line in distinct non-
ingular points, its tangential centre is the centre of gravity of
ntersections of lines through that centre and tangents in any given
lirection. This property is shared by no other point.*

If we reciprocate a curve with regard to a circle, the foot of
he perpendicular from the centre of that circle on a tangent
s the inverse of the point reciprocal to the tangent. If we take
. centre of the curve as a centre of reciprocation, and the radius
.s unity, so that the distances to a point and its polar are
eciprocals, we get from 42] and 43]

Theorem 44] *The polar reciprocal of a curve in a circle whose
entre is one of its centres is a curve with that point as tangential centre.*

Suppose that the point O whose line polar we seek goes off
o infinity:
$$\sum PQ_i = 0.$$

Theorem 45] *The line polar of an infinite point, not on the
urve, is the locus of the centres of gravity of intersections with
ines through that infinite point.*

We shall call a line of this sort a 'diameter'. Let R be an
nfinite point, S the intersection of its line polar with the infinite
ine; let the line polar of S meet the infinite line in R', in general
lifferent from R. Conversely, if R' be given, its first polar
neets the infinite line in $(n-1)$ points S, and the first polar of
·ach meets the infinite line in $(n-1)$ points R. We have thus
. correspondence of indices 1 and $(n-1)^2$, with n^2-2n+2 co-
ncidences. We discard n of these which are at the ends of the
.symptotes, but only count simply. If we take the line polars
·f R and S as a pair of oblique axes, then for each x, the sum
·f the corresponding y's will be 0, and for each y the sum of
he corresponding x's will vanish, so that the equation of the
·urve will have no terms of degree $n-1$ in x or y, a canonical
·orm for the equation.

The first polars of the infinite points form a pencil of curves, all passing through the centres of the curve. A typical first polar will be

$$x' \frac{\partial f}{\partial x} + y' \frac{\partial f}{\partial y} = 0.$$

The centres of this latter curve satisfy the equations

$$x' \frac{\partial^2 f}{\partial x^2} + y' \frac{\partial^2 f}{\partial x \partial y} = 0 \qquad x' \frac{\partial^2 f}{\partial x \partial y} + y' \frac{\partial^2 f}{\partial y^2} = 0$$

$$\frac{\partial^2 f}{\partial x^2} \frac{\partial^2 f}{\partial y^2} - \left(\frac{\partial^2 f}{\partial x \partial y} \right)^2 = 0. \tag{14}$$

This gives a rather curious theorem due to Lucas:*

Theorem 46] *The locus of the centres of the first polars of points of the infinite line is the locus of points whose conic polars are parabolas or pairs of parallel lines.*

Let us find the intersections of the line

$$y = lx$$

with the first polar of its infinite point $(1, l, 0)$:

$$x \frac{\partial f}{\partial x} + y \frac{\partial f}{\partial y} = 0. \tag{15}$$

Theorem 47] *The locus of the intersections of a set of lines through a finite point with the first polars of their various infinite points is a curve of the same order as the given curve, with the same asymptotic directions. It will meet the given curve only at the ends of the asymptotes, and at the intersections with the first polar of the given point. It will pass through all the centres of the given curve.*

If the origin be a centre, the equation of the curve will lack terms of the first degree in x and y. In (16) the lowest terms in x and y are quadratic or higher.

Theorem 48] *The curve corresponding to a centre by theorem 47 will have a singular point there.*

If our radiating lines pass through (x_0, y_0) instead of passing through the origin, (16) is replaced by

$$(x - x_0) \frac{\partial f}{\partial x} + (y - y_0) \frac{\partial f}{\partial y} = 0, \tag{16}$$

where x_0 and y_0 appear to the first degree. Eliminating one of them between this and the equation of a straight line, we get

---

* See Lucas for this and the remaining theorems of the present section.

Theorem 49] *If a point trace a finite straight line, the curves corresponding thereto under 47] will trace a pencil. The centres of this pencil are the centres of the curve, the ends of the asymptotes and the* $(n-1)$ *points where the given line meets the first polar of its infinite point.*

As a check we notice

$$n^2 = (n-1)^2 + n + n - 1.$$

§ 6. Transversals

Let the equation of a curve in oblique coordinates be

$$f(x, y) = 0.$$

Changing origin to (x_0, y_0), but leaving the direction of the axes unaltered, we get

$$f(x, y) + \ldots + f(x_0, y_0) = 0.$$

Setting $y = 0$, the product of the roots will be $f(x_0, y_0)$ divided by a quantity independent of x_0 and y_0, and the same is true when $x = 0$. Hence, the ratio of these two is independent of x_0 and y_0, though depending on the direction of the axes.

Newton's Theorem 50] *If each of two non-parallel transversals with non-minimal directions meet a given curve in finite points only, the ratio of the products of the distances from the two sets of intersections to the intersection of the lines is independent of the position of the latter point.**

Theorem 51] *When the curve described in* 50] *meets the infinite line in distinct non-singular points, the ratio described will be unaltered if the curve be replaced by the asymptotes, or lines parallel to them, or any curve of this order with these asymptotic directions.*

Suppose that we have a finite polygon with no sides on minimal lines, and apply Newton's theorem to each vertex in turn. If a vertex have the coordinates (x_0, y_0) with respect to a fixed set of rectangular axes, and if the direction of the oblique axes correspond to angles ϕ_1 and ϕ_2, the product in question will be

$$\frac{f(\cos\phi_1, \sin\phi_1)}{f(\cos\phi_2, \sin\phi_2)}.$$

Going around the polygon and multiplying the results together, the product will be 1.

---

* Newton seems to have proved this only for a cubic Cf. Newton, vol. iii, p. 250.

Carnot's Theorem 52] *If $P_1, P_2...$, be the vertices of a finit polygon with no minimal sides, and if the side $P_i P_j$ meet a curv in P_{ij1}, $P_{ij2}...$, then*[*]

$$\frac{\prod_i P_1 P_{12i} \prod_i P_2 P_{23i} ... \prod_i P_N P_{N1i}}{\prod_i P_N P_{N1i} ... \prod_i P_2 P_{21i}} = 1. \qquad (17$$

Of course, if a side of the polygon be tangent or pass through a multiple point, we shall have to weight some of the distances thereon suitably.

If we take two points (x_0, y_0) and (x_1, y_1) and draw parallel transversals through them, the ratio of the products of the distances on the two will be

$$\frac{f(x_0, y_0)}{f(x_1, y_1)},$$

and this is independent of the direction of the transversals.[†]

Theorem 53] *If through two finite points parallel transversals be drawn which are not minimal lines, nor parallel to asymptotes of a given curve, the ratio of the products of the distances from the two points to the intersections of their respective transversals with a given curve is independent of the direction of the transversals.*

These last two theorems enable us to solve some simple problems in construction.[‡] Let P be a point near a given curve, Q an arbitrary point in the plane. Draw two arbitrary lines through P, and two through Q parallel thereto. Newton's theorem enables us to tell the direction of the line connecting the two intersections that are close to P and so, in the limit, the direction of the tangent.

Let P' and R be two points of this tangent, the former close to P, which is now supposed to be on the curve. $P'Q$ shall meet the curve in $\bar{P}$ close to P. The circle tangent to PP' at P and passing through $\bar{P}$ shall meet $P'Q$ again in $\bar{Q}$, so that

$$(P'P)^2 = P'\bar{P} . P'\bar{Q}.$$

We may eliminate $(PP')^2$ and $P'\bar{P}$ between this equation and (17) applied to the triangle $P'QR$, and thus find $P'\bar{Q}$ or, in the limit, $P\bar{Q}$, which enables us to construct the osculating circle.

---

[*] Cf. Carnot, p. 287.   [†] Chasles[1], p. 324.
[‡] Lucas, pp. 100 ff.

7. Evolutes

The evolute of a curve is the envelope of its normals, or the locus of the centres of curvature. When the original curve is algebraic, so is the evolute. The first thing to do is to find its Plücker characteristics.

We shall determine the order of the evolute by seeking its intersection with the line at infinity. The centre of curvature will be at infinity when the point in question is an inflexion, or, perhaps, when the point in question is at infinity itself. Let us take a finite inflexion at the origin

$$y = \sigma_3 x^3 + \sigma_4 x^4 + \dots .$$

The homogeneous Cartesian coordinates of the corresponding centre of curvature are

$$\rho \bar{x} = xy'' - y'(1 + y'^2) = 3\sigma_3 x^2 + \dots$$
$$\rho \bar{y} = yy'' + (1 + y'^2) \quad = 1 + b_4 x^4 + \dots$$
$$\rho \bar{z} = y'' \qquad\qquad = 6c_3 x + \dots .$$

This shows that the evolute will meet the infinite line simply at the end of the x-axis.

Let us assume that our original curve meets the line at infinity in distinct non-singular points, and that the asymptotes have two-point contact.

Let the y-axis be such an asymptote. To find the corresponding power series, development beginning with homogeneous coordinates. Then, instead of having $\dfrac{y}{z}$ as a power series in terms of $\dfrac{x}{z}$ or vice versa, we shall have $\dfrac{x}{y}$ as a power series in $\dfrac{z}{y}$, i.e.

$$\frac{x}{y} = a_2 \frac{z^2}{y^2} + a_3 \frac{z^3}{y^3} + \dots ,$$

or

$$y = \frac{b_{-1}}{x} + b_0 + b_1 x + \dots .$$

Then we find the homogeneous coordinates for the corresponding point on the evolute

$$\bar{x} = \alpha_0 + \alpha_1 x + \alpha_2 x^2 + \alpha_3 x^3 + \dots$$
$$\bar{y} = \qquad\qquad \beta_2 x^2 + \beta_3 x^3 + \dots$$
$$\bar{z} = \qquad\qquad\qquad \gamma_3 x^3 + \dots .$$

A horizontal line meets the curve twice at the end of the x-axis, but the line at infinity meets it three times there. There is, then, a cusp at the end of that axis, the infinite line being the cuspidal·tangent. This gives the order of the evolute.

To find the class we have merely to see how many normals pass through a general point, and this we found in 15] to be $m+n$. Finally the genus is that of the given curve, for they correspond birationally.

Theorem 54] *If a curve of order n, class m, and genus p meet the infinite line in distinct non-singular points, none of which is circular, and if the asymptotes have two-point contact, the leading Plücker characteristics of the evolute are*

$$n' = 3n+\iota \qquad m' = m+n \qquad p' = p \qquad \iota' = 0. \qquad (18)$$

It is particularly noticeable that there are no inflexions. The evolute may well have complicated singularities, in which case the genus will have an interpretation to be worked out in a subsequent chapter. Of the $m+n$ tangents to the evolute from a circular point, n coincide with the infinite line, the points of contact being the infinite cusps, the other m are the minimal tangents to the original curve, which are both tangents and normals.

Theorem 55] *A curve of the sort described in 54] has the same foci as its evolute.*

If the centre of a circle of fixed radius move along a certain curve, the envelope is defined as a 'parallel' to that curve. The parallel is usually irreducible when the original curve is, for the two points of contact of a circle with an adjacent circle are not usually rationally separable. In some cases the parallel curve is reducible, as when the locus of the centres is a straight line or a circle. Let the equation of the curve traced by the centre be

$$f(\xi, \eta) = 0.$$

For a parallel curve we have

$$x = \xi + \frac{r\frac{\partial f}{\partial \xi}}{\sqrt{\left(\frac{\partial f}{\partial \xi}\right)^2 + \left(\frac{\partial f}{\partial \eta}\right)^2}} \qquad y = \eta + \frac{r\frac{\partial f}{\partial \eta}}{\sqrt{\left(\frac{\partial f}{\partial \xi}\right)^2 + \left(\frac{\partial f}{\partial \eta}\right)^2}}.$$

Eliminating ξ and η we have the equation desired. Let us find its Plücker characteristics, assuming that the original curve has the restrictions mentioned in 54]. There is clearly a point of the second order at the end of each asymptote of the original curve. If the tangents fell together in general, they would in the particular case where the centre traced a straight line, but we know that in that case they certainly do not. Hence there is a node at the end of an asymptote. If the parallel curve meet the infinite line again, it must be at one of the circular points at infinity. Consider the system of circles

$$[x-\xi(t)]^2+[y-\eta(t)]^2 = r^2.$$

To find their envelope, we differentiate to t:

$$[x-\xi(t)]\xi'(t)+[y-\eta(t)]\eta'(t) = 0.$$

We could only have infinite values for x or y with a finite ξ, η when

$$\xi'^2+\eta'^2 = 0,$$

that is to say, when the locus of the centre has a minimal tangent. We get from this two important facts:

A) When the minimal tangents to the original curve are distinct, the parallel curve has an ordinary singularity of order m at each circular point.

B) Two near circles of the same radius are tangent when, and only when, their line of centres is minimal. Hence the points of contact with the minimal tangents are the only branch points of the one-to-two correspondence between the original curve and its parallel. We have first of all the order of the parallel

$$n' = 2(m+n).$$

We get from VIII (14)

$$2m+4(p-1) = 2(p'-1)$$

$$p' = 2p+m-1.$$

Since parallel curves have the same evolute, an inflexion of the original curve will correspond to two inflexions on the parallel

$$\iota' = 2\iota.$$

Since parallel tangents in a non-minimal direction to the original curve correspond to pairs of tangents in that direction to the parallel curve, we have

$$m' = 2m.$$

Theorem 56] *If a curve of order n, class m, etc., fulfil the requirements of 54], and if the minimal tangents be distinct and non-singular, the Plücker characteristics of a parallel curve are found to be*[*]

$$n' = 2(m+n) \qquad m' = 2m \qquad \iota' = 2i \qquad \kappa' = 2\kappa + 6m$$

$$p' = m + 2p - 1. \tag{19}$$

The evolute of an algebraic curve is always algebraic. When is the converse true, i.e. when is a given algebraic curve the evolute of another such curve ? Certainly this is not universally the case; the involute of a circle is clearly transcendental. Let the equation of the evolute be

$$f(x, y) = 0.$$

The evolute and involute are in one-to-one correspondence. If (ξ, η) be the point of the involute corresponding to (x, y) on the evolute, and if s be the parameter of arc for the latter curve, we shall have

$$\xi = x + (\omega - s) \frac{\dfrac{\partial f}{\partial y}}{\sqrt{\left(\dfrac{\partial f}{\partial x}\right)^2 + \left(\dfrac{\partial f}{\partial y}\right)^2}},$$

$$\eta = y - (\omega - s) \frac{\dfrac{\partial f}{\partial x}}{\sqrt{\left(\dfrac{\partial f}{\partial x}\right)^2 + \left(\dfrac{\partial f}{\partial y}\right)^2}}.$$

If the evolute be algebraic, everything here is rational or

$$\frac{\omega - s}{\sqrt{\left(\dfrac{\partial f}{\partial x}\right)^2 + \left(\dfrac{\partial f}{\partial y}\right)^2}} = \frac{P(x, y)}{Q(x, y)}, \tag{20}$$

the right-hand side being supposed to be rational. Conversely, when this holds there is a birational relation between evolute and involute, and the latter is algebraic.

We may carry this further. Equation (20) shows us that the arc of the evolute is a two-valued algebraic function of x and y.

[*] Cf. Cayley[1] and Roberts[2].

Suppose, conversely, this is the case. Consider the values of the integral

$$s = \int\limits_{x_0,\, y_0}^{x,\, y} \frac{\sqrt{\left(\dfrac{\partial f}{\partial x}\right)^2 + \left(\dfrac{\partial f}{\partial y}\right)^2}}{\dfrac{\partial f}{\partial y}}\, dx \qquad \textbf{(21)}$$

around a closed contour of the Riemann surface for y in terms of x.

A) $\sqrt{\left(\dfrac{\partial f}{\partial x}\right)^2 + \left(\dfrac{\partial f}{\partial y}\right)^2}$ returns to its original value. Then this integral is 0, otherwise, by going around often enough, we could make s infinitely multiple-valued.

B) $\sqrt{\left(\dfrac{\partial f}{\partial x}\right)^2 + \left(\dfrac{\partial f}{\partial y}\right)^2}$ changes sign. If 2ω be the value, and if we go around twice, the value is 0. It thus appears that the two values of the integral (21) are s and $2\omega - s$. Hence s is a two-valued algebraic function of x and y on the surface, and the sum of the roots is 2ω.

$$s^2 - 2\omega s + \frac{R(x,y)}{S(x,y)} = 0.$$

But
$$\frac{ds}{dx} = \frac{\sqrt{\left(\dfrac{\partial f}{\partial x}\right)^2 + \left(\dfrac{\partial f}{\partial y}\right)^2}}{\dfrac{\partial f}{\partial y}}$$

$$\frac{\omega - s}{\sqrt{\left(\dfrac{\partial f}{\partial x}\right)^2 + \left(\dfrac{\partial f}{\partial y}\right)^2}} = \frac{P(x,y)}{Q(x,y)}.$$

We finally get

Humbert's Theorem 57] *The necessary and sufficient condition that an algebraic curve should have an algebraic involute is that the length of arc should be a two-valued algebraic function of the coordinates of the extremities. This function is a root of a quadratic equation whose coefficients are rational functions of x and y.**

* Cf. Humbert[4], p. 136.

BOOK II

THE SINGULAR POINTS

CHAPTER I

THE REDUCTION OF SINGULARITIES

§ 1. Quadratic transformations

WE have, in the course of our work, frequently been obliged to transform algebraic curves in various ways. We have changed from rectangular to oblique axes, which is the same thing as an affine transformation, we have spoken of projective properties, which are unaltered under a collineation of the plane, we have transformed by inversion, and we have pointed out that the genus of a curve is unaltered by any birational transformation.

Let us pick from this list the familiar inversion in a circle. If the centre be the origin, and the radius r, the transformation is written

$$x' = \frac{r^2 x}{x^2 + y^2} \qquad y' = \frac{r^2 y}{x^2 + y^2}; \qquad x = \frac{r^2 x'}{x'^2 + y'^2} \qquad y = \frac{r^2 y'}{x'^2 + y'^2} \quad (1)$$

We may describe this transformation in language of projective geometry in the following way. The polar of a point (x, y) with regard to a circle

$$x^2 + y^2 = r^2$$

has the equation

$$x'x + y'y = r^2;$$

this is brought to intersect the line from (x, y) to the centre

$$y'x - x'y = 0.$$

The intersection (x', y') is the point corresponding to (x, y). The transformation consists in replacing a point in general position by a point conjugate with regard to a fixed conic, on a line from the first point to a fixed point. The transformation is one to one, involutory, that is to say, identical with its inverse. A general straight line goes into a circle, i.e. a conic through three fixed points, the centre of inversion and the circular points at infinity. These are the only points which do not transform into determinate points. We proceed to show how the transformation can be modified in such a way that the three exceptional points enter symmetrically.

Consider the totality of conics through four given points, of which no three are collinear. If a point be taken which is not a vertex of that triangle which is self-conjugate with regard to all these conics, its polars with regard to them will not be identical, but will pass through the one point which is conjugate to the first with regard to all these conics. The relation between the two points is a reciprocal one.

Theorem 1] *If each point in the plane be replaced by the point of concurrence of its polars with regard to a pencil of conics through four points, no three of which are collinear, the result is an involutory transformation of the plane which is one-to-one for all points except the vertices of that triangle which is self-conjugate with regard to all the conics.**

The transformation described in 1] shall be called a 'standard quadratic transformation'. The vertices of the common self-conjugate triangle shall be called 'fundamental points', its sides 'fundamental curves' or 'lines'. The fundamental points are the only ones which are not uniquely transformed, each is, so to speak, 'exploded' into the opposite fundamental line. All points on a fundamental line, other than the two fundamental points thereon, are transformed into the opposite fundamental point. Each fundamental line is completely determined by the fundamental points on it, and two fundamental lines meet only in a fundamental point. These properties are characteristic of one-to-one algebraic transformations of the plane, as we shall see in Book IV.

If a point *P* trace a straight line, its polars with regard to the various conics will trace pencils which are projective with the original range, and so with one another. As the line connecting the centres of two such pencils is not self-corresponding, the point *P'* where all these various polars meet traces a non-degenerate conic, which is the locus of the poles of the given line with regard to these various conics. It has many points which are easy to find. We thus get

Theorem 2] *If a point trace a straight line not through a funda-*

---

* Apparently discovered by Magnus, q.v. For a bibliography see Döhlemann[1], p. 49.

mental point of a standard quadratic transformation, the corresponding point, under the transformation, will trace a conic through the three fundamental points, the six points each harmonically separated from a point of the line by two centres of the pencil of conics, and the double points of the involution which the pencil of conics cuts on the given line.

This conic, for obvious reasons, is called the 'eleven-point' conic.

Feuerbach's Theorem 3] *The locus of the centres of all conics through the vertices and orthocentre of a triangle, which conics, when not degenerate, are rectangular hyperbolas, is a circle through the middle points of the sides, the points half-way from the orthocentre to the vertices, and the feet of the altitudes.**

Theorem 4] *If a point trace a straight line through a single fundamental point, the corresponding point, in a standard quadratic transformation, will trace a line through the same fundamental point. When a point approaches a fundamental point, the corresponding point approaches a definite position on the opposite fundamental line depending on the tangent at the fundamental point to the curve on which the first point approached.*

We leave aside the possibility of approaching a point by a non-algebraic curve with no tangent at that point, e.g. approaching the origin on $y = x \sin \dfrac{1}{x}$.

Theorem 5] *If a point trace a curve with an ordinary singularity of order k at a fundamental point, yet with no fundamental tangent at that point, the corresponding curve will meet the opposite side of the triangle in just k distinct points, no one of which is fundamental.*

If one of the tangents at a fundamental point approach a limiting position which is fundamental, the corresponding point on the opposite side will approach a limiting fundamental position.

To find the order of the curve into which a given curve is transformed, we find how many non-fundamental intersections the first curve has with a conic through the three fundamental points, as this is the transform of a straight line, and the order of a curve is the number of intersections with a general line.

* Cf. Feuerbach.

Theorem 6] *A curve of order n with multiplicities r_1, r_2, and r_3 at the three fundamental points will be transformed into a curve of order $2n-(r_1+r_2+r_3)$ with multiplicities $n-(r_2+r_3)$, $n-(r_3+r_1)$, $n-(r_1+r_2)$ at the fundamental points.*

It is time to express our standard quadratic transformation analytically. Let us take the three fundamental points as O_1, O_2, and O_3 in a trilinear system. If one of the points common to all the conics be $(1, 1, 1)$, and we are at liberty to assume that is the case, for we may take the unit point where we choose, the other centres of the pencil of conics are $(-1, 1, 1)$, $(1, -1, 1)$, $(1, 1, -1)$. The conics may be written

$$a_1x_1^2+a_2x_2^2+a_3x_3^2 = 0 \qquad (2)$$

where

$$a_1+a_2+a_3 = 0. \qquad (3)$$

The canonical equations for the standard quadratic transformation are then

$$\rho x_1' = x_2x_3 \qquad \rho x_2' = x_3x_1 \qquad \rho x_3' = x_1x_2$$
$$\sigma x_1 = x_2'x_3' \qquad \sigma x_2 = x_3'x_1' \qquad \sigma x_3 = x_1'x_2', \qquad (4)$$

or, more simply,

$$x_1' : x_2' : x_3' = \frac{1}{x_1} : \frac{1}{x_2} : \frac{1}{x_3}. \qquad (5)$$

Let us put

$$x_i = y_i\epsilon \qquad x_j = y_j\epsilon \qquad x_k = y_k \neq 0$$

$$\frac{1}{\epsilon}x_i' = y_jy_k \qquad \frac{1}{\epsilon}x_j' = y_ky_i \qquad \frac{1}{\epsilon}x_k' = y_iy_j\epsilon.$$

Then seeking the limit as $\epsilon \to 0$,

$$\sigma x_i' = y_jy_k \qquad \sigma x_j' = y_ky_i \qquad \sigma x_k' = 0,$$

a definite position on $x_k = 0$.

To give an analytic proof of 6], let us note that if the point $(1, 0, 0)$ have the multiplicity r_1 for a curve $f(x_1, x_2, x_3) = 0$, the highest power of x_1 is $n-r_1$, and so for the other fundamental points. When we make the substitution $x_j'x_k'$ for x_i, we have an equation of order $2n$. Since every term will involve $x_2'x_1'$ and $x_3'x_1'$ together to the power r_1 at least, we may divide out $x_1'^{r_1}$ and similarly for x_2' and x_3'. The transformed curve is a reducible one of order $2n$ and contains the three fundamental lines counted r_1, r_2, and r_3 times respectively. The residue is of order $2n-(r_1+r_2+r_3)$; its multiplicity at the fundamental points is given by the non-fundamental intersections of the original curve with the fundamental lines.

In the standard quadratic transformation, as in inversion, the net of all lines is carried into a net of conics. This can be done in a variety of other ways. If we generalize inversion projectively so that corresponding points are collinear with a fixed point, which we shall take as O_3, and conjugate with regard to a fixed conic whose equation shall be $x_1 x_2 - x_3^2 = 0$, the transformation takes the slightly altered form

$$\begin{aligned} x_1' = x_1 x_3 \qquad & x_2' = x_2 x_3 \qquad && x_3' = x_1 x_2 \\ x_1 = x_1' x_3' \qquad & x_2 = x_2' x_3' \qquad && x_3 = \omega_1' x_2'. \end{aligned} \tag{6}$$

This is known as a 'Hirst transformation', and is essentially like a standard quadratic one, being factorable into such a transformation and a very simple collineation which merely interchanges x_1 and x_2.

Here are other cases of quadratic transformations. Suppose the totality of lines is simply carried into conics through three distinct points in any one-to-one fashion. This may be written

$$\begin{aligned} \rho x_1' = a_{11} x_2 x_3 + a_{12} x_3 x_1 + a_{13} x_1 x_2 \qquad & \sigma x_1 = c_{11} x_2' x_3' + c_{12} x_3' x_1' + c_{13} x_1' x_2' \\ \rho x_2' = a_{21} x_2 x_3 + a_{22} x_3 x_1 + a_{23} x_1 x_2 \qquad & \sigma x_2 = c_{21} x_2' x_3' + c_{22} x_3' x_1' + c_{23} x_1' x_2' \\ \rho x_3' = a_{31} x_2 x_3 + a_{32} x_3 x_1 + a_{33} x_1 x_2 \qquad & \sigma x_3 = c_{31} x_2' x_3' + c_{32} x_3' x_1' + c_{33} x_1' x_2' \end{aligned} \tag{7}$$

and is factorable into a standard quadratic transformation and a collineation.

Let us look for a quadratic transformation where straight lines are carried into a net of conics which are tangent to one another at a given point, and pass through a second point. Let the conics be tangent to $x_1 = 0$ at O_2 and pass through O_1. Then the transformation and its inverse can be put in the form

$$\begin{aligned} \rho x_1' = x_1 x_3 \qquad & \sigma x_1 = x_1'^2 \\ \rho x_2' = x_1 x_2 \qquad & \sigma x_2 = x_2' x_3' \\ \rho x_3' = x_3^2 \qquad & \sigma x_3 = x_1' x_3'. \end{aligned} \tag{8}$$

We see that the transformation is not involutory, but the inverse is of the same general sort. Any birational transformation of the plane where lines go into conics tangent at one point, and passing through another can be factored into such a transformation and a collineation. In non-homogeneous Cartesian coordinates this may be put in a form which Nöther often used:[*]

$$x' = x \qquad x = x'$$
$$y' = xy \qquad y = \frac{y'}{x'}. \tag{9}$$

Still another plan is to have the straight lines of the plane transformed into osculating conics. Here is an involutory transformation of this sort where the conics touch $x_1 = 0$ at O_3, and osculate one another:

$$\rho x_1' = -x_1^2 \qquad\qquad \sigma x_1 = -x_1'^2$$
$$\rho x_2' = x_1 x_2 \qquad\qquad \sigma x_2 = x_1' x_2' \tag{10}$$
$$\rho x_3' = x_3 x_1 - x_2^2 \qquad \sigma x_3 = x_3' x_1' - x_2'^2.$$

Any one-to-one quadratic transformation where lines go into such conics can be factored into the product of this and a collineation.

It is possible also to have quadratic transformations between different planes. Here is a simple example due to Steiner.[†]

We start with two planes, and two skew lines outside of both; neither of these lines may intersect the line of intersection of the two planes. We project one plane on the other, not by means of lines through a fixed point, but by lines intersecting the skew lines. If a line be given in one plane, it will determine, in general, a regulus with the two skew lines. The projecting lines will generate a second regulus which meets the second plane in a conic through the intersection with the two skew lines and the point on the second plane where it meets the line in the first that intersects the two skew lines.

Theorem 7] *The product of any number of collineations and standard quadratic transformations is a birational transformation of the plane with but a finite number of points which have not unique mates. As a point approaches one of these along a curve with a definite tangent there, the corresponding point will approach a definite position on a certain corresponding curve.*

Analytically, a transformation of this sort may be written, with its inverse,

$$x_i' = \phi_i(x_1, x_2, x_3) \qquad \sigma x_i = \phi_i'(x_1', x_2', x_3'). \tag{11}$$

Let the three homogeneous polynomials ϕ_i be of degree n. Then the equations

$$n_1 x_1 + n_2 x_2 + n_3 x_3 = 0$$

$$n_1' \phi_1 + n_2' \phi_2 + n_3' \phi_3 = 0$$

must have n variable intersections. These equations are equivalent to

$$n_1 \phi_1' + n_2 \phi_2' + n_3 \phi_3' = 0$$

$$n_1' x_1' + n_2' x_2' + n_3' x_3' = 0,$$

so that the polynomials ϕ_i' are of order n.

Theorem 8] *A one-to-one algebraic transformation of the plane is of the same order as its inverse.*

We mean, of course, by the 'order' of the transformation, the order of the curve into which a general straight line is transformed.

It is an interesting fact that there is no theorem corresponding to 8] in a space of higher dimensions. The net of curves

$$n_1' \phi_1 + n_2' \phi_2 + n_3' \phi_3 = 0$$

which correspond to straight lines are assumed to have only ordinary singularities, and to intersect in distinct points. Since they are transformed into straight lines, by Riemann's theorem 3'] of Chapter VIII of the last book, they must be of genus 0. The only assumptions we shall make about the singular points are that at specified points (other assumptions would be nonlinear) they shall have multiplicities $r_1, r_2, \ldots$. Then by Bertini's theorem 10] of Ch. VII, Book I, there are no other singularities of the general curve. On the other hand, two of these curves must have but one variable intersection to correspond to the single variable intersection of two lines. Hence

$$\sum r_i(r_i - 1) = (n-1)(n-2)$$

$$\sum r_i^2 = n^2 - 1$$

$$\sum r_i = 3(n-1) \tag{12}$$

$$\sum \frac{r_i(r_i+1)}{2} = \frac{n(n+3)}{2} - 2.$$

The last equation shows that the conditions imposed by the fixed points are independent and sufficient, for the curves form a net. A birational transformation of the plane is called a Cremona transformation after the geometer who first studied the problem of such transformations in a general form.* We have so far seen examples only of Cremona transformations of the first or second orders. Here is an example of a transformation of any desired order. Consider the totality of rational curves of the nth order with a common point of order $n-1$, and $2(n-1)$ common simple points. We see that equations (12) are fulfilled. If there were more than a net of these curves, there would be more than one through two given points which is inadmissible; there would be too many intersections. Let O_3 be the singular point. We may find a curve of order $n-1$ with multiplicity $n-2$ at O_3, which passes simply through each of the other $2(n-1)$ points. This has no other intersections with the curves of order n, so it cannot correspond to a curve but to a special point. This curve and the pencil of lines through O_3 must go into a pencil of curves of order n consisting of a fixed part of order $n-1$ and a pencil of lines, each of which has but one variable intersection with the curves of order n which correspond to lines in the inverse transformation. That shows that in the inverse transformation we have curves of order n with a singular point of order $n-1$. They could have no other common singular points, hence the other special points must be $2(n-1)$ simple points, i.e. the transformation is of the same type as its inverse. Such a transformation is called a De Jonquières transformation.† Quadratic and linear transformations come under this general head, but we may have De Jonquières transformations of any order.

If we have a product of a succession of standard quadratic transformations and collineations, we produce a Cremona transformation of as high order as we please. Conversely, a Cremona transformation which can be factored into a product of standard quadratic transformations and linear transformations shall be called 'factorable'. We have seen that such is the case when lines go into conics through three distinct points. Consider a quadratic transformation of the type (8). Let us follow this by a standard quadratic transformation with the same O_1, O_2, O_3. The result would be a transformation where a line is carried into a conic through O_1, O_2 and a fixed point on the new line O_2O_3, i.e. a transformation of the type (7), and this is factorable.

* Cf. Cremona[1], pp. 54 ff.   † Cf. De Jonquières[1].

Let us now take a transformation of the type (10) where straight lines are carried into conics that osculate at O_3. If we follow by a standard quadratic transformation, the result will be a transformation where straight lines are carried into cubics with a node at O_3, a simple point at O_1 and O_2, and all tangent to one another at a point O_2' of O_1O_2. If we follow by a standard quadratic transformation with the fundamental points O_1, O_2', O_3, the cubics go into conics tangent to one another at O_3 and passing through a fixed point of O_1O_3, i.e. the product is of the type (8).

Theorem 9] *A quadratic Cremona transformation is always factorable.*

Let us next consider the De Jonquières transformation. If O_3 be at the singular point for a set of curves of order n, and O_1, O_2 be simple points common to them, then, if we make a standard quadratic transformation, it will carry these curves of order n, by 6], into curves of order $n-1$, with multiplicity $n-2$ at O_3, and $2(n-1)$ other simple common points, the product is a De Jonquières transformation of lower order.

Theorem 10] *A De Jonquières transformation is always factorable.*

These last two theorems have little to do with our present interests, but will be important at a later stage of the present work where we shall prove the grand theorem that all Cremona transformations are factorable.

§ 2. The effect on singularities

Suppose that we have an irreducible curve of order n, which has at O_3 a singular point of order r, which is not necessarily ordinary, but may be *of any description*. Let O_1, O_2 be two other points in the plane such that

a) neither is on the curve,

b) the lines O_1O_3 and O_2O_3 meet the curve each in $n-r$ distinct points besides O_3,

c) the line O_1O_2 meets the curve in n distinct points.

Let us make a standard quadratic transformation with O_1, O_2, O_3 as fundamental points. We are at once able to say about the transformed curve:

α) It is of order $n_1 = 2n-r$.

β) It has an ordinary singular point of order n at O_3.

γ) It has an ordinary singular point of order $n-r$ at O_1 and O_2.

δ) Corresponding to every singular point of the original curve, beside that at O_3, the new curve has a singular point of the same order, s_i.

The new curve will meet O_1O_2 not only in O_1 and O_2, but r times elsewhere. To make the most discouraging assumption, suppose it has a singular point O_3' of order r on O_1O_2. Let us start again and make a second quadratic transformation with fundamental points O_1', O_2', O_3', related to the new curve as the points O_1, O_2, O_3 were to the original curve. The third curve has the following properties:

α) Its order is $n_2 = 2n_1 - r$.

β) It has an ordinary singular point of order n_1 at O_3'.

γ) It has ordinary singular points of order n_1-r at O_1' and O_2'.

δ) It has three ordinary singular points of order n, $n-r$, and $n-r$ respectively.

ϵ) Corresponding to every singular point of the second curve, besides that at O_3', the new curve has a singular point of the same order.

Our third curve has r intersections with $O_1'O_2'$ to be accounted for; if these do not consist in a point of order r, we have made progress, if they do, we make a third transformation like these two, and so on. Let us show that we cannot keep on indefinitely always getting a singular point of order r. Suppose, in fact, that we have transformed k times and still have a point of that order appearing on a fundamental line. Two features of the product of all our transformations must be noted.

1) *We have introduced no new singular points but ordinary ones*.

2) The orders of all the singular points of the first curve other than the one operated on are unaltered.

The order of the last curve is

$$n_k = 2n_{k-1} - r.$$

It has singular points of the following orders:

n	$n-r$	$n-r$
n_1	n_1-r	n_1-r
n_2	n_2-r	n_2-r
. . .	. . .	. . .
n_{k-1}	$n_{k-1}-r$	$n_{k-1}-r$
r	s_1	$s_2\ldots$

Now, by Book I, Ch. VIII, the reasoning leading to 1] for the original curve

$$\frac{(n-1)(n-2)}{2} - \frac{r(r-1)}{2} - \sum \frac{s_i(s_i-1)}{2} \geqslant 0$$

and, applied to the kth transformed curve,

$$\frac{(n_k-1)(n_k-2)}{2} - \frac{n_{k-1}(n_{k-1}-1)}{2} - 2\frac{(n_{k-1}-r)(n_{k-1}-r-1)}{2} -$$

$$- \frac{n_{k-2}(n_{k-2}-1)}{2} - 2\frac{(n_{k-2}-r)(n_{k-2}-r-1)}{2} -$$

$$\cdots \cdots \cdots \cdots \cdots \cdots \cdots$$

$$- \frac{n(n-1)}{2} - 2\frac{(n-r)(n-r-1)}{2} -$$

$$- \frac{s_1(s_1-1)}{2} - \frac{s_2(s_2-1)}{2} - \cdots \geqslant 0.$$

But $\qquad n_{j+1} = 2n_j - r,$

$$\frac{(n_{j+1}-1)(n_{j+1}-2)}{2} = \frac{(2n_j-r-1)(2n_j-r-2)}{2}$$

$$= \frac{(n_j-1)(n_j-2)}{2} + \frac{n_j(n_j-1)}{2} + 2\frac{(n_j-r)(n_j-r-1)}{2} - \frac{r(r-1)}{2},$$

$$\frac{(n_{j+1}-1)(n_{j+1}-2)}{2} - \frac{n_j(n_j-1)}{2} - 2\frac{(n_j-r)(n_j-r-1)}{2}$$

$$= \frac{(n_j-1)(n_j-2)}{2} - \frac{r(r-1)}{2}.$$

This reduction may be applied again and again, beginning with the last curve and working backwards until we finally get

$$\frac{(n-1)(n-2)}{2} - k\frac{r(r-1)}{2} - \frac{s_1(s_1-1)}{2} - \frac{s_2(s_2-1)}{2} - \cdots \geqslant 0.$$

It is clear from this that there must be an upper limit to k, which means that eventually the point of order r has been broken up into points of lower order. We may attack each of these in the same way, and each of the singularities of the original curve which are not ordinary: every singularity so attacked can, eventually, be ground to pieces, and nothing new but ordinary singularities are introduced. We thus get

Nöther's Transformation Theorem 11] *Any irreducible curve may be carried by a factorable Cremona transformation into one with none but ordinary singular points.* *

The tremendous importance of this theorem will be more and more evident as our work proceeds. We see right now that if we wish to reach a property of curves which is unaltered by a linear or standard quadratic transformation, it is sufficient to do so for a curve with only ordinary singularities.

We have seen that in the case of an irreducible curve the expression $\frac{(n-1)(n-2)}{2} - \sum \frac{s_i(s_i-1)}{2}$ cannot be negative. There will be a similar expression for a reducible curve, which we need not here develop. We may, then, reason on a reducible curve, as we reasoned above on an irreducible one, getting

Theorem 12] *Any two curves may be carried by a factorable Cremona transformation into two with only ordinary singularities, which are nowhere tangent to one another.*

Here is a still more important result. We saw in Book I, Ch. II, Theorem 6], that in the vicinity of a point (x_0, y_0) which is either non-singular or an ordinary singularity, where no tangent is vertical, there are a given number of developments for y in integral powers of $x - x_0$. More generally we may say that the whole neighbourhood of this point is expressed by a certain number of developments:

$$x_i = \rho_\nu y_i + a_{\nu i1}t_\nu + a_{\nu i2}t_\nu^2 + \dots . \tag{13}$$

This fact will be invariant under a factorable Cremona transformation.

Puiseux's Theorem 13] *The whole neighbourhood of any point y) of an algebraic plane curve may be uniformly represented by a certain finite number of convergent developments in power series†*

$$x_i = \rho_\nu y_i + a_{\nu i1}t_\nu + a_{\nu i2}t_\nu^2 + \dots . \tag{13}$$

It is a tempting idea that perhaps we may push the simplification of a curve by reducible Cremona transformations even further. A study of this question must be postponed to a later chapter, as it involves many facts which we have not yet

---

* Nöther[5], pp. 267 ff. There are many proofs in existence, that here given is from Bertini[2].
                                                          † Puiseux, pp. 397 ff.

exhibited. If, however, we ease the restrictions under which we are working so that the transformation employed is birational, that is to say, one to one and algebraic for the curve alone, and not for the whole plane, as is a Cremona transformation, we are able right now to get a much greater simplification. The scheme which we shall follow is the following. We first exhibit a one-to-one correspondence between a plane and a certain cubic surface. We show how, in applying this to a particular curve, one singularity may be completely exploded so that the plane curve goes into a space curve with one less singular point. Then we project the space curve back on the plane, introducing new singularities, all of which are nodes. Then we begin all over again.

The totality of cubic curves are linearly dependent on ten, for there are ten coefficients in the general cubic equation. Through k points will pass, in general, $10-k$ linearly independent cubics. The curves through eight points will form a pencil, all of whose curves go through a ninth point. Consider six points in the plane, which are not on a conic, nor are any three collinear. They will impose on a cubic not less than six independent conditions. If they imposed less than six, we might impose four more, and make the cubic go through four arbitrary collinear points. It would then have to 'swallow' the line on which those points lay, and the rest of it would have to be a conic through the six given points, which, by hypothesis, do not lie on any one conic. Let us call them the six 'fundamental points' of the present discussion. Take four linearly independent cubic curves through them.

$$f_0(x,y) = 0 \qquad f_1(x,y) = 0 \qquad f_2(x,y) = 0 \qquad f_3(x,y) = 0. \quad (14$$

The general curve of the linear series which they determine the general cubic through the fundamental points, may be written
$$u_0f_0 + u_1f_1 + u_2f_2 + u_3f_3 = 0. \quad (15$$

If the general cubic had a singularity at one of the fundamental points, so would that cubic of the system which consisted of a conic through five of the points and an arbitrary line through the sixth, an absurd conclusion. On the other hand we know by Bertini's theorem 10] of Book I, Ch. VII, that the general cubic of the system does not have a singular point not common to all the curves.

Consider a point which is not fundamental. There will be one cubic of the system with a double point there. If there were more than one, there would be a pencil of them. But two cubics of the pencil would then have ten intersections and so be reducible with a common part, and this common part must either be a line through two fundamental points, or a conic through five. But, in neither case would the cubics of the pencil have a common double point. There will be a pencil of cubics with a node at each fundamental point, the tangents being variable.

Let us now write the four equations

$$\rho x_0 = f_0(x, y) \quad \rho x_1 = f_1(x, y) \quad \rho x_2 = f_2(x, y) \quad \rho x_3 = f_3(x, y). \quad (16)$$

If (x, y) move all over the plane, including the infinite line, the corresponding point in three-space will trace a surface which is of the third order.

We see, in effect, that the plane sections of the surface correspond to the cubics of our linear system. Two of our cubics have but three variable intersections, hence two planes, or a line, meet the surface in but three variable points. Each non-fundamental point of the plane will correspond to a single definite point of the surface. How about a fundamental point? Let this be at the origin, and let us write (16) in the form

$$\rho x_i = a_i x + b_i y + \dots .$$

If x and y vanish, (x) becomes indeterminate. Let us write

$$x = x'\epsilon \qquad y = y'\epsilon,$$

substituting, dividing by ϵ, since we have homogeneous co-ordinates on the left, and then putting $\epsilon = 0$, we get

$$\sigma x_i = a_i x' + b_i y'.$$

This shows that as x' and y' vary, approaching 0, (x) will trace a straight line on the cubic surface. We shall call this a fundamental line.

The cubic surface has no singular point. A singular point has the property that every plane section through it has a singularity there. If this singular point were not on a fundamental line, it would correspond to a point of the plane which was singular for every cubic through it, and 'there ain't no such animal'. If it were on a fundamental line a doubly infinite set of plane cubics would have singularities at a fundamental point. One of these would include a line connecting two fundamental points, the rest would be a reducible conic through the other four singular points with a double point at one—impossible. The curve in a tangent plane at a general point of the surface will correspond to the cubic which has a double point at an assigned position in the plane. The pencil of cubics with a fundamental double point, say the origin, will be given by multipliers (u) which satisfy the equations

$$(ua) = (ub) = 0$$

and so will correspond to the sections of the surface through the corresponding fundamental line. A point of the surface, not on a fundamental line, will lie on one plane through each of the six fundamental lines, and so correspond to the single non-singular point common to six cubics each with one fundamental point singular. The relation between plane and surface is, thus, one to one except for fundamental points of the plane, and fundamental lines of the surface.

Our transformation from plane to surface has been sufficiently developed. Let us apply it to the simplification of curves. Suppose that we have a plane curve whose only singular points are ordinary. Let us take just one of them whose multiplicity is r, as fundamental in the transformation described above. A cubic curve of the system will meet this in $3n-r$ variable points, so that will be the order of the corresponding space curve. The space curve will have singular points of the same description as the plane curve, except that the one at the fundamental point has been shattered into r distinct non-singular points along a fundamental line.

Let V' be a point of the space curve. The lines through there meeting the curve again trace a cone. If V be a point of the surface, not on this cone, the line VV' meets the curve but once, hence, by the 'in general' principle of Book I, Ch. I, a line through V which meets the curve once will not automatically meet it twice. We may thus project the space curve from V back into a plane curve which is in one-to-one correspondence with the original curve. What singularities has this new plane curve? It has singular points of the same description as those of the original curve except for the one exploded, also some introduced by projecting back from V. These can only be of the second order, for a line meets a cubic surface but three times, and we may assume that V does not lie on one of the twenty-seven straight lines which are easily shown to lie on the surface. They correspond to the six fundamental points, the six conics through five fundamental points, and the fifteen lines each through two of them. It is easy to see there are no others. Well, what will be the nature of these double points? If V lie on a tangent to the space curve, the point of contact will go into a cusp; we can avoid that by taking V not on the developable generated by the tangents. Again, if a line through V meet the space curve twice, we wish the two tangents to be in different planes through that line, otherwise we should project into a plane curve with two mutually tangent branches at a point. We must place V so that it lies on no line meeting the curve in two points with coplanar tangents. How many lines are there which meet the curve in two points with coplanar tangents? If there were a two-parameter family, then every tangent would meet every other one. If we have a set of lines of which each two are coplanar, then either all go through a point or all lie in a plane. If all our tangents were in a plane, the space curve would be a plane curve of order 3, and our transformation would be virtually accomplished as the order would be 3. It would either be non-singular or transformable into a conic.

If all the tangents went through a point, say the origin, we should have

$$\frac{dx}{x} = \frac{dy}{y} = \frac{dz}{z}.$$

The only solutions are sets of straight lines through the origin, a trivial case we may exclude. Hence there is only a one-parameter family of lines meeting the curve in two points with coplanar tangents, and we may assume V is not on them. Lastly, V must not lie in a tangent plane to the cubic surface at a singular point of the space curve, for fear of 'squashing' the latter in projecting back, nor on a line connecting a singular point with another point of that curve. If we keep V away from these four one-parameter systems of lines, the only singular points introduced are nodes, one singular point of the old curve has been eliminated, and the new and old curves are in birational correspondence. We can do this same trick over and over again till only nodes remain. Lastly, if we remember Nöther's reduction theorem 11] just proved, we have

Clebsch's Transformation Theorem 14] *Any algebraic plane curve may be birationally transformed into one with no singular points but nodes.**

* The literature of this particular subject is very extensive. For a general discussion see Bliss. My authority for giving the credit of discovering it to Clebsch is Klein, see his footnote to Bertini[1]. The idea of using the cubic surface in this way is due to Bertini, but he neglects certain precautions whose necessity was pointed out by Walker, q.v.

CHAPTER II

DEVELOPMENT IN SERIES

§ 1. Development of the branches at a point*

WE shall begin the present chapter by repeating a theorem proved in the last.

Puiseux's Theorem 1] *The whole neighbourhood of any point (y) of an algebraic plane curve may be uniformly represented by a certain finite number of convergent developments in power series*

$$x_1 = \rho_\nu y_1 + a_{\nu 11} t_\nu + a_{\nu 12} t_\nu^2 + \dots$$
$$x_2 = \rho_\nu y_2 + a_{\nu 21} t_\nu + a_{\nu 22} t_\nu^2 + \dots \qquad \textbf{(1)}$$
$$x_3 = \rho_\nu y_3 + a_{\nu 31} t_\nu + a_{\nu 32} t_\nu^2 + \dots.$$

Each point of the neighbourhood, except (y), will correspond to a single value for ν and t_ν.

Our present task is to find a direct way of determining such power-series development, without having recourse to quadratic transformations. After that we shall study the nature of the curve in the vicinity of a point, by studying the power series directly.

It is to be noted that the highest common factor of all the exponents of t_ν in any one triad must be 1, otherwise there would not be a one-to-one correspondence between the points and the values of t_ν. The totality of points which make these series convergent shall be called a 'branch', the point (y) the 'origin' thereof. The neighbourhood of any point is made up of a finite number of branches.

The power-series developments at an ordinary singular point, or cusp, have already been determined in Book I, Ch. II, so if we know the system of transformations which carry a given point into an ordinary singularity, we can get all the power-series developments. This is the method of Nöther.† We shall follow a modification of the classical method of Puiseux developed by Appell and Goursat.‡

To simplify matters, let us assume that the singular point in which we are interested is the origin of a Cartesian system. We

---

* In the present chapter I have maintained close contact with Jordan[1]. Another very important reference is Enriques-Chisini, vol. ii.
† Cf. Nöther[5], p. 267.　　　　　　‡ Cf. Appell et Goursat, pp. 184 ff.

apply to the region the method of Newton, used in Book I, Ch. III, to study the neighbourhood of a real singularity. The exponents of x and y are plotted as integral points in the first quadrant of a plane. Some of them are connected by segments of a broken line in such a way that on each segment lie at least two of these marked points, and the others are shut off from the origin by the straight line on which the segment lies. Let the equation of the curve be

$$\cdot \sum A_i x^{\alpha_i} y^{\beta_i} = 0 \tag{2}$$

$$r\alpha_p + s\beta_p = \ldots = r\alpha_\lambda + s\beta_\lambda = \ldots = r\alpha_q + s\beta_q;$$

$$\frac{\beta_q - \beta_p}{\alpha_p - \alpha_q} = \frac{\beta_q - \beta_\lambda}{\alpha_\lambda - \alpha_q} = \frac{\beta_\lambda - \beta_p}{\alpha_p - \alpha_\lambda} = \frac{r}{s}. \tag{3}$$

Put $x = x'^r$, $y = y'x'^s$ and divide by $(x')^{r\alpha_\lambda + s\beta_\lambda}$,

$$(y')^{\beta_p} \phi(y') + x'\psi(x', y') = 0. \tag{4}$$

The degree of ϕ is $\beta_q - \beta_p$, and it has this number of roots, distinct or coincident, different from 0. When x' is close to 0, by the Fundamental Continuity Theorem 4] of Book I, Ch. I, (4) will have $\beta_q - \beta_p$ roots close to those of

$$\phi(y') = 0.$$

Consider this equation more closely.

The exponents are of the form $\beta_\lambda - \beta_p = \dfrac{r}{s}(\alpha_p - \alpha_\lambda)$. Since r and s are relatively prime, $\beta_\lambda - \beta_p$ must be divisible by r. Let us rewrite the equation $\quad \bar{\phi}(y'^r) = 0. \tag{5}$

Suppose that, looked upon as an equation in y'^r, it has a simple root $y_0'^r$, as an equation in y' it has r roots y_0', $\theta y_0'$, $\theta^2 y_0'$, ..., $\theta^{r-1} y_0'$; $\theta^r = 1$.

Close to these we have sets of r developments:

$$y' = y_0' + a_{01}x' + \ldots$$
$$y' = \theta y_0' + a_{11}x' + \ldots$$
$$y' = \theta^2 y_0' + a_{21}x' + \ldots$$
$$\cdot \quad \cdot \quad \cdot \quad \cdot \quad \cdot \quad \cdot$$
$$y = y_0'x'^s + a_{01}x'^{s+1} + \ldots$$
$$y = \theta y_0'x'^s + a_{11}x'^{s+1} + \ldots$$
$$y = \theta^2 y_0'x'^s + a_{21}x'^{s+1} + \ldots$$
$$\cdot \quad \cdot \quad \cdot \quad \cdot \quad \cdot \quad \cdot$$

$$y = y_0' x^{\frac{s}{r}} + a_{01} x^{\frac{s+1}{r}} + \dots$$

$$y = \theta y_0' x^{\frac{s}{r}} + a_{11} x^{\frac{s+1}{r}} + \dots$$

$$y = \theta^2 y_0' x^{\frac{s}{r}} + a_{21} x^{\frac{s+1}{r}} + \dots$$

. . . .

If, in the first equation of the last set, we replace $x^{\frac{1}{r}}$ by $\theta^k x^{\frac{1}{r}}$, we get

$$y = x^{\frac{s}{r}} [\theta^{ks} y_0' + c_{01} x^{\frac{1}{r}} + \dots]$$

$$y' = \theta^{ks} y_0' + c_{01} x' + \dots.$$

and this must be one of the previous r developments for y' in terms of x'. Hence, there are but r developments of the present set for y in terms of $x^{\frac{1}{r}}$, and these are found from one of their number by permuting the values of $x^{\frac{1}{r}}$.

Suppose, now, that (5) looked upon as an equation in y^r has nothing but multiple roots. Let y_0' be one of them, and write

$$y' = y_0' + \bar{y}';$$

we get from (4) $\qquad \Theta(x', \bar{y}') = 0,$

and this curve has a multiple point at the origin. If we could find for this a development of the sort

$$\bar{y}' = \bar{y}_0' x'^{\frac{s'}{r'}} + \bar{a}_1 x'^{\frac{s'+1}{r'}} + \dots$$

$$y = y_0' x^{\frac{sr'}{rr'}} + \bar{a}_1 x^{\frac{sr'+rs'}{rr'}} + \dots,$$

and we have the desired result again. In fact we shall always reach this eventually unless a continual change of variable in this way never produces a drop in the order of the singularity. Let us show that such cannot be the case. Suppose that there is no drop at the start, and the original curve and (4) have singular points of the same order at their respective origins, $\phi(y')$ is an equation in y'^r, and if it is to have only one root which is not 0, we must have $r = 1$

$$x = x' \qquad y = y' x'^s,$$

while (4) takes the form

$$(y' - y_0')^{\beta_q} + x' \psi(x', y') = 0.$$

If we put $\qquad y' = y_0' + y'' \qquad y = y_0' x^s + y'' x^s$

$$\Theta(x, y'') = 0 \qquad y = y_0' x^s + y_0'' x^{s+s'} + y'''.$$

If Θ has just as bad a singularity we may keep on indefinitely
But we know that eventually fractional powers will begin, and
the lowest of these is not indefinitely large. Hence the singularity must eventually improve, and the process come to
an end.

Let us consider some special cases.

A) An ordinary singularity with no vertical tangent.

The broken line has but one segment, given by the terms of
lowest order

$$0 = (y - l_1 x)(y - l_2 x)...(y - l_k x) + ...$$

$$\frac{r}{s} = 1 \qquad \alpha_p = k \qquad \beta_p = 0 \qquad \alpha_q = 0 \qquad \beta_q = k$$

$$y = l_1 x + a_{12} x^2 + ...$$

$$y = l_2 x + a_{22} x^2 + ... \tag{6}$$

. . . .

or

$$x = t, \qquad y = l_1 t + a_{12} t^2 + ...$$

$$x = t, \qquad y = l_2 t + a_{22} t^2 + ...$$

. . . .

B) A cusp with a non-vertical tangent.

$$0 = (y - lx)^2 + f_3(x, y) + ... \qquad f_3(1, l) \neq 0$$

$$r = s = 1 \qquad y = y' x'$$

$$0 = (y' - l)^2 + x' f_3(1, l) + ...$$

$$y' = l + \bar{y}'$$

$$0 = \bar{y}'^2 + x' f_3(1, l) + ...$$

Here

$$\alpha_p = 1 \qquad \beta_p = 0 \qquad \alpha_q = 0 \qquad \beta_q = 2 \qquad r = 2 \qquad s = 1$$

$$x' = x''^2 \qquad \bar{y}' = y'' x''$$

$$0 = y''^2 + f_3(1, l) + ...$$

$$y'' = \sqrt{-f_3(1, l)} + a_1 x'' + ...$$

$$y' = l + \sqrt{-f_3(1, l)} \, x^{\frac{1}{2}} + a_1 x + ...$$

$$y = lx + \sqrt{-f_3(1, l)} \, x^{\frac{3}{2}} + a_1 x^2 + ...,$$

or $\qquad x = t^2 \qquad y = lt^2 + \sqrt{-f_3(1, l)} \, t^3 + a_1 t^4 + ... \tag{7}$

C) A cusp with a vertical tangent.

$$0 = x^2 + f_3(x, y) + \dots \qquad f_3(0, 1) \neq 0$$

$$\alpha_p = 2 \qquad \beta_p = 0 \qquad \alpha_q = 0 \qquad \beta_q = 3 \qquad r = 3 \qquad s = 2$$

$$x = x'^3 \qquad y = y'x'^2$$

$$0 = 1 + y'^3 f_3(0, 1) + \dots$$

$$y' = \sqrt[3]{-\frac{1}{f_3(0, 1)}} + a_1 x' + \dots$$

$$y = \sqrt[3]{-\frac{1}{f_3(0, 1)}} \, x^{\frac{2}{3}} + a_1 x + \dots,$$

or $\quad x = t^3 \qquad y = \sqrt[3]{-\dfrac{1}{f_3(0, 1)}} \, t^2 + a_1 t^3 + \dots$ \hfill (8)

Suppose that at a point (y) a curve have k developments of the type (1). To find its intersections with a curve $\phi(x_1, x_2, x_3) = 0$ we write

$$\phi_1 \phi_2 \dots \phi_k = 0,$$

where we mean by ϕ_i the result of substituting the ith triad in ϕ. In the vicinity of (y) our curve ϕ will also consist in a certain number of branches. The equation just written shows that the number of intersections of the two curves is the sum of the number of intersections that one has with the various branches of the other. This applies to either curve, which gives

Theorem 2] *The total number of intersections which two curves have at any point is the sum of the number of intersections which each branch of the one with that point as origin has with each branch of the other with that origin.*

We may determine the number of intersections in another way. Let us have (x_0, y_0) as a point common to the two curves, such that no other intersection has the abscissa x_0. If y_i on one curve and $\bar{y}_j$ on the other correspond to the same abscissa x, the expression $\Pi(y_i - \bar{y}_j)$, which is rational in x, will vanish as many times for $x = x_0$ as there are intersections there.

Theorem 3] *If two curves meet at a point (x_0, y_0) and have no other intersections with this same abscissa, the number of intersections at that point is the multiplicity of x_0 as a root of the resultant of the corresponding polynomials when looked upon as polynomials in y.*[*]

[*] For an elaborate discussion of the number of intersections treated in this way see Segre[3], pp. 1 ff.

Our theorem 3] shows that the problem of finding how many intersections two curves have at a common point is, by 2], the problem of counting the intersections of two branches with the same origin. This we shall study in very great detail. In order to do so intelligently, we must make a more detailed study of the series-developments like (1).

§ 2. Invariant numbers for branches

Suppose that we get a development for $y - y_0$ in fractional powers of $x - x_0$ by the method of Puiseux developed in the last section:

$$y - y_0 = a_0(x - x_0) + a_k(x - x_0)^{\frac{\rho_k}{\rho_0}} + a_l(x - x_0)^{\frac{\rho_l}{\rho_0}} + \dots .$$

Introducing the auxiliary parameter t we may write this

$$x = x_0 + t^{\rho_0} \qquad y = y_0 + a_0 t^{\rho_0} + a_k t^{\rho_k} + \dots \qquad a_0 a_k \neq 0;$$

we note at once that ρ_0 gives the number of intersections with a non-tangent line through (x_0, y_0). The equation of the tangent will be

$$y - y_0 = a_0(x - x_0),$$

and the number of additional intersections with the curve is $\rho_k - \rho_0$. The number ρ_0 is called the 'order' of the branch, and $\rho_k - \rho_0$ its class.*

Theorem 4] *The number of intersections which a tangent at the origin of a branch has with the branch at that point is the sum of order and class.*

This theorem appears a little ridiculous, since the class was defined as the excess intersections possessed by the tangent, but we shall find another independent definition later. Let us write our branch in the more general form

$$\begin{aligned} x_1 &= y_1 + b_{10}s^{\sigma_0} + b_{11}s^{\sigma_1} + \dots \\ x_2 &= y_2 + b_{20}s^{\sigma_0} + b_{21}s^{\sigma_1} + \dots \\ x_3 &= y_3 + b_{30}s^{\sigma_0} + b_{31}s^{\sigma_1} + \dots . \end{aligned} \qquad (9)$$

The order will be the first exponent for which the three coefficients are not proportional to $y_1 : y_2 : y_3$. There must be such a term, otherwise the branch would be a single point. If there be successive terms with coefficients proportional to $y_1 : y_2 : y_3$, even if there be an infinite number of such, we may group them all together at the beginning. It is not possible that the three

* These names are due to Halphen[1], vol. iv, pp. 4 ff.

coefficients in one column are linearly dependent on (y) and the first three not proportional to the y_i's, as then the tangent would be entirely contained in the branch, a case we naturally exclude. Let us, then, group together all the terms whose coefficients are proportional to the y_i's and all proportional to the first set of coefficients not proportional to the y_i's, and then write the subsequent terms. We get

$$x_1 = y_1[1+p_1s+p_2s^2+\ldots]+a_{10}[s^{\rho_0}+q_1s^{\rho_0+1}+\ldots]+a_{11}s^{\rho_1}+\ldots$$

$$x_2 = y_2[1+p_1s+p_2s^2+\ldots]+a_{20}[s^{\rho_0}+q_1s^{\rho_0+1}+\ldots]+a_{21}s^{\rho_1}+\ldots$$

$$x_3 = y_3[1+p_1s+p_2s^2+\ldots]+a_{30}[s^{\rho_0}+q_1s^{\rho_0+1}+\ldots]+a_{31}s^{\rho_1}+\ldots.$$

Since our coordinates are homogeneous we may first divide out $[1+p_1s+p_2s^2+\ldots]$ and write

$$\tau^{\rho_0} = \frac{s^{\rho_0}+q_1s^{\rho_0+1}+\ldots}{1+p_1s+p_2s^2+\ldots}.$$

Then s is an analytic function of τ whose derivative does not vanish with τ, we may solve for $s = \tau+l_2\tau^2+\ldots$

$$x_1 = y_1+a_{10}\tau^{\rho_0}+a_{11}\tau^{\rho_1}+\ldots$$

$$x_2 = y_2+a_{20}\tau^{\rho_0}+a_{21}\tau^{\rho_1}+\ldots \tag{10}$$

$$x_3 = y_3+a_{30}\tau^{\rho_0}+a_{31}\tau^{\rho_1}+\ldots$$

$$|ya_0a_i| \neq 0.$$

The class of the branch is then $\rho_1-\rho_0$.

Theorem 5] *The order and class of a branch are unaltered by a collineation of the plane.*

An algebraic curve, as we have often pointed out, may be looked upon as the envelope of its tangents, quite as well as the locus of its points. If we apply this to our branch (10), we get

$$\rho u_1 = \begin{vmatrix} x_j & x_k \\ x_j' & x_k' \end{vmatrix}.$$

Dividing through by t^{ρ_0-1}

$$u_1 = \rho_0 \begin{vmatrix} y_j & y_k \\ a_{j0} & a_{k0} \end{vmatrix} + \rho_1 \begin{vmatrix} y_j & y_k \\ a_{j1} & a_{k1} \end{vmatrix} t^{\rho_1-\rho_0}+\ldots. \tag{11}$$

If, then, we remember that a curve and its dual are symmetrically related, the tangents to the one correspond to the points of the other, we get

Theorem 6] *The order and class of a branch of a curve are the class and order of the polar reciprocal branch with regard to a general conic.*

Theorem 7] *The number of tangents to a curve from the origin of a branch accounted for by the tangent to the branch is equal to the sum of the order and class.*

We must now turn aside to study some arithmetical properties of series of integral powers, which give us further invariant numbers for the branches of a curve.

Definition. Given a set of positive integral powers of a variable t,

$$T = a + a_0 t^{\rho_0} + a_1 t^{\rho_1} + \dots . \qquad (12)$$

An exponent shall be said to be 'characteristic' if the coefficient be not 0, and be not divisible by the highest common factor of the preceding exponents. Every time a characteristic exponent appears, the highest common factor is reduced, hence:

Theorem 8] *The number of characteristic exponents of a series of increasing positive integral powers is, necessarily, finite.*

Let the characteristic exponents in the series (12) be ρ_0, ρ_α, ρ_β. Let S be such a function of T that

$$\frac{dS}{dT} \neq 0 \qquad T = a$$

$$S = S_0 + A_1(T-a) + \dots \qquad A_1 \neq 0$$

$$T - a = t^{\rho_0}[a_0 + a_1 t^{\rho_1 - \rho_0} + \dots]$$

$$[T-a]^\rho = t^{\rho \rho_0}[a_0^\rho + \rho a_0^{\rho-1}(a_1 t^{\rho_1-\rho_0}\dots) + \frac{\rho(\rho-1)}{2} a_0^{\rho-2}(\qquad)^2 \dots].$$

If we substitute in S, the lowest power of t appearing with a non-vanishing exponent is t^{ρ_0}. An exponent between ρ_0 and ρ_α must come from a term where the outside exponent $\rho \rho_0$ is less than ρ_α and so is divisible by ρ_0. The terms taken from the inside have exponents less than ρ_α, and so these are divisible by ρ_0. The earliest characteristic exponent is ρ_α, and this can only come from $T-a$, for when the sum of the inside and outside exponents is ρ_α and the outside is greater than 0 but divisible by ρ_0, the inside must be greater than 0 and less than $\rho_\alpha - \rho_0$, and so divisible by ρ_0, and this is a contradiction as ρ_α is not divisible by ρ_0. The coefficient of ρ_α is $A_1 a_\alpha$, which, by hypothesis, is not 0. By similar reasoning the next characteristic exponent is ρ_β from the term $A_1 a_\beta \tau^{\rho\beta}$.

Theorem 9] *If T be an analytic function of t in the vicinity of $t = 0$, and if S be an analytic function of T in the vicinity of $T(0)$, and if the derivative of S do not vanish there, then when S and T are expressed as positive integral powers of t, they have the same characteristic exponents, and proportional coefficients for them.*

Theorem 10] *If $T(0) \neq 0$, then terms with characteristic exponents in the development of $\dfrac{1}{T}$ in terms of τ are*

$$-\frac{a_0}{a^2}\tau^{\rho_0}, -\frac{a_\alpha}{a^2}\tau^{\rho_\alpha}.$$

Let us next suppose that we have two series,

$$c + c_0\tau^{\rho_0} + c_1\tau^{\rho_1} + \dots \qquad c_0 \neq 0,$$
$$d + d_0\tau^{\rho_0} + d_1\tau^{\rho_1} + \dots .$$

An exponent shall be said to be 'characteristic' for the two series, if it appear in at least one, and be not divisible by the highest common factor of all smaller exponents that appear in either series. We shall also assume that if ρ_λ be a characteristic exponent,

$$\begin{vmatrix} c_0 & c_\lambda \\ d_0 & d_\lambda \end{vmatrix} \neq 0.$$

Let us change the independent variable, writing

$$t^{\rho_0} = c_0\tau^{\rho_0} + c_1\tau^{\rho_1} + \dots$$
$$\tau = t[c_0^{-\frac{1}{\rho_0}} + p_1 t + p_2 t^2 + \dots]. \qquad (13)$$

The lowest exponent in the parenthesis which is not divisible by ρ_0 is $\rho_\alpha - \rho_0$. Suppose there were a lower one, ρ_i, the lowest of all such. Then $c_0\tau^{\rho_0}$ would give a term $t^{\rho_0 + \rho_i}$. This would have to be cancelled in the expansion for t^{ρ_0} by terms coming from higher powers of τ, say $c_j\tau^{\rho_j}$. The outside t would have an exponent greater than ρ_0 but less than ρ_α, and so divisible by ρ_0; the power of t taken from the inside would have to be less than ρ_i, yet not divisible by ρ_0, and similarly in the expansion for τ there would have to be a term to a power less than ρ_i not divisible by ρ_0, which contradicts the hypothesis.

If $\rho_0 < \rho_i < \rho_\alpha$, the term τ^{ρ_i} will not produce a t^{ρ_α}, for ρ_i is divisible by ρ_0 and the exponent of the term taken from the inside is less than $\rho_\alpha - \rho_0$ and so divisible by ρ_0, whereas ρ_α is not so divisible. Hence, such an expression as t^{ρ_α} can only come from τ^{ρ_0} and τ^{ρ_α}, and as the two must cancel one another in the expansion of t^{ρ_0}, the coefficient of $t^{\rho_\alpha - \rho_0}$ in (13) must be $-\dfrac{c_\alpha c_0^{-\frac{\rho_\alpha + 1}{\rho_0}}}{\rho_0}$.

In general, the characteristic exponents in the expansion (13) are $\rho_0 - \rho_\alpha$, $\rho_0 - \rho_\beta, \dots$, and the corresponding coefficients are

$$-\frac{c_\alpha c_0^{-\frac{\rho_\alpha + 1}{\rho_0}}}{\rho_0} \, , \quad -\frac{c_\beta c_0^{-\frac{\rho_\beta + 1}{\rho_0}}}{\rho_0} \dots .$$

Now let us substitute for τ in the second equation. The coefficient of t^{ρ_0} will be $\dfrac{d_0}{c_0}$. An exponent between ρ_0 and ρ_α will be divisible by the former. The next characteristic exponent will be ρ_α with the coefficient $\dfrac{\begin{vmatrix} c_0 & c_\alpha \\ d_0 & d_\alpha \end{vmatrix}}{c_0^{\frac{\rho_\alpha}{\rho_0}}} \neq 0$, and, in general, the characteristic exponents are ρ_0, ρ_α, $\rho_\beta, \dots$ and the coefficients

$$\frac{d_0}{c_0} \, , \quad \frac{\begin{vmatrix} c_0 & c_\alpha \\ d_0 & d_\alpha \end{vmatrix}}{c_0^{\frac{\rho_\alpha}{\rho_0} + 1}} \, , \quad \frac{\begin{vmatrix} c_0 & c_\beta \\ d_0 & d_\beta \end{vmatrix}}{c_0^{\frac{\rho_\beta}{\rho_0} + 1}} \dots .$$

Theorem 11] *Given two series*

$$c + c_0 \tau^{\rho_0} + c_1 \tau^{\rho_1} + \dots$$
$$d + d_0 \tau^{\rho_0} + d_1 \tau^{\rho_1} + \dots$$

with the characteristic exponents ρ_0, ρ_α, ρ_β, and with the restriction on the coefficients that if ρ_λ be a characteristic exponent $\begin{vmatrix} c_0 & c_\lambda \\ d_0 & d_\lambda \end{vmatrix} \neq 0$, *then if $c_0 \neq 0$, and if we write*

$$t^{\rho_0} = c_0 \tau^{\rho_0} + c_1 \tau^{\rho_1} + \dots ,$$

the second series when expressed in terms of t will have the same characteristic exponents as the original two series.

Suppose, lastly, that we have a branch written in the normal form (10). An exponent shall be defined as 'characteristic' if it be not divisible by the highest common factor of all the exponents

that have previously appeared in any one of the series. We **know**, by the way that the normal form was derived, that

$$|ya_0a_\lambda| \neq 0.$$

Theorem 12] *The characteristic exponents of a branch in normal form are unaltered by a linear transformation of the plane.*

Let us assume that y_3 is not equal to 0. By theorem 10] $\dfrac{1}{x_3}$ has the same characteristic exponents as x_3, with the coefficients $-\dfrac{a_{3\alpha}}{y_3^2},\ -\dfrac{a_{3\beta}}{y_3^2},\dots$. These will also be the characteristic exponents of $\dfrac{x_1}{x_3},\ \dfrac{x_2}{x_3}$, the coefficients being

$$-\frac{\begin{vmatrix} y_1 & y_3 \\ a_{1\alpha} & a_{3\alpha} \end{vmatrix}}{y_3^2},\qquad -\frac{\begin{vmatrix} y_2 & y_3 \\ a_{2\alpha} & a_{3\alpha} \end{vmatrix}}{y_3^2},\dots.$$

These could not both vanish, for then we should have

$$y_1 : y_2 : y_3 = a_{1\alpha} : a_{2\alpha} : a_{3\alpha},$$

which is contrary to the definition of the normal form. We may, therefore, write

$$x = \frac{x_1}{x_3} = x_0 + c_0 \tau^{\rho_0} + c_1 \tau^{\rho_1} + \dots$$

$$y = \frac{x_2}{x_3} = y_0 + d_0 \tau^{\rho_0} + d_1 \tau^{\rho_1} + \dots.$$

It appears, then, that these two series have the same characteristic exponents as the three series of the branch. We thus get from 11]

Theorem 13] *If a branch of a curve be written in the normal form*

$$x_1 = y_1 + a_{10} \tau^{\rho_0} + a_{11} \tau^{\rho_1} + \dots$$

$$x_2 = y_2 + a_{20} \tau^{\rho_0} + a_{21} \tau^{\rho_1} + \dots \tag{10}$$

$$x_3 = y_3 + a_{30} \tau^{\rho_0} + a_{31} \tau^{\rho_1} + \dots$$

$$|ya_0a_i| \neq 0,$$

it may also be written in the simplified form

$$x = x_0 + t^{\rho_0} \qquad y = y_0 + a_0 t^{\rho_0} + a_1 t^{\rho_1} + \dots. \tag{14}$$

The characteristic exponents are the same for the two forms.

§ 3. Intersections of two branches

Definition. Given two branches with a common origin (y),

$$x_1 = y_1 + a_{10}\tau^{\rho_0} + a_{11}\tau^{\rho_1} + \dots \qquad \bar{x}_1 = y_1 + A_{10}T^{R_0} + A_{11}T^{R_1} + \dots$$
$$x_2 = y_2 + a_{20}\tau^{\rho_0} + a_{21}\tau^{\rho_1} + \dots \qquad \bar{x}_2 = y_2 + A_{20}T^{R_0} + A_{21}T^{R_1} + \dots$$
$$x_3 = y_3 + a_{30}\tau^{\rho_0} + a_{31}\tau^{\rho_1} + \dots \qquad \bar{x}_3 = y_3 + A_{30}T^{R_0} + A_{31}T^{R_1} + \dots$$

If we put $T = \tau^{\frac{\rho_0}{R_0}}$, the infinitesimal order in τ of the expression

$$\rho_0 \sqrt{\begin{vmatrix} \xi_1 & \xi_2 & \xi_3 \\ x_1 & x_2 & x_3 \\ \bar{x}_1 & \bar{x}_2 & \bar{x}_3 \end{vmatrix}}$$

where (ξ) is an arbitrary point, shall be called the 'propinquity' of the two.

It is evident that it is unaltered by a linear transformation of the plane or by dividing through by any analytic function of τ which does not vanish with that variable, or by the replacement of τ by an analytic function thereof which is defined for $\tau = 0$ and whose derivative does not vanish for that value. The propinquity will, thus, remain unaltered under all those transformations which carry our form (14) into the form (10). But when we have two branches in the form (14),

$$x = x_0 + t^{\rho_0} \qquad\qquad \bar{x} = x_0 + T^{R_0}$$
$$y = y_0 + a_0 t^{\rho_0} + a_1 t^{\rho_1} + \dots \qquad \bar{y} = y_0 + A_0 T^{R_0} + A_1 T^{R_1} + \dots \qquad (15)$$

the propinquity, which is merely the infinitesimal order of the expression $\rho_0\sqrt{y - \bar{y}}$, turns out to be the smaller of the two quantities $\dfrac{\rho_{\mu+1}}{\rho_0}$, $\dfrac{R_{\mu+1}}{R_0}$

$$a_i = A_i \qquad \frac{\rho_i}{\rho_0} = \frac{R_i}{R_0} \qquad i = 0, 1, \dots, \mu \qquad (16)$$

Let us now see just how many intersections the two branches (15) have at (x_0, y_0). We write them in the form of fractional power series

$$y = y_0 + a_0(x - x_0) + a_1(x - x_0)^{\frac{\rho_1}{\rho_0}} + \dots$$
$$\bar{y} = y_0 + A_0(\bar{x} - x_0) + A_1(\bar{x} - x_0)^{\frac{R_1}{R_0}} + \dots .$$

The number of intersections is, then, the degree in $x - x_0 = \bar{x} - x_0$ of the expression $\Pi(\bar{y}_j - y_i)$, where y_i is given each of its ρ_0 values, and $\bar{y}_j$ each of its R_0. If $a_0 \neq A_0$, this is clearly $\rho_0 R_0$.

Theorem 14] *If two branches have different tangents, the number of their intersections is the product of their orders.*

This will lead immediately to a new proof of the fundamental intersection theorem 10] of Book I, Ch. II.

To find the number of intersections in the general case, let us pick that determination of $\bar{y}-y_0$ and that one of $y-y_0$ which yield the greatest number of intersections. Let us assume that, in that case we have the relations (16) with the additional inequality. Let us call these the determinations* $\bar{y}_1-y_0$, y_1-y_0. How many determinations of $y-y_0$ are identical with y_1-y_0 up to the term $a_\mu(x-x_0)^{\frac{\rho_\mu}{\rho_0}}$? Such a determination is obtained by replacing $(x-x_0)^{\frac{1}{\rho_0}}$ by $\theta^m(x-x_0)^{\frac{1}{\rho_0}}$ where $\theta^{\rho_0}=1$. We must have
$$\theta^{m\rho_0} = \theta^{m\rho_1} = \theta^{m\rho_\mu} = 1$$
$$m\rho_0 \equiv m\rho_1 \equiv ... \equiv m\rho_\mu \equiv 0 \ (\mathrm{mod}\,\rho_0).$$

For how many different values of $m \leqslant \rho_0$ can these congruences be satisfied? Let the highest common factor of $\rho_0, \rho_1,...,\rho_\mu$ be δ_μ.
$$\rho_0 = \lambda_0\delta_\mu, \quad \rho_1 = \lambda_1\delta_\mu,..., \quad \rho_\mu = \lambda_\mu\delta_\mu$$
$$m\rho_i = m\lambda_i\delta_\mu \equiv 0 \ (\mathrm{mod}\,\lambda_0\delta_\mu)$$
$$m\lambda_i \equiv 0 \ (\mathrm{mod}\,\lambda_0).$$

Let $m = pq$, $\lambda_0 = p\sigma$, for λ_0 cannot divide every λ_i as δ_μ would not be the highest common factor of the ρ_i's:
$$pq\lambda_i \equiv 0 \ (\mathrm{mod}\,p\sigma)$$
$$q\lambda_i \equiv 0 \ (\mathrm{mod}\,\sigma).$$

Now σ cannot divide q by hypothesis, and it could not divide λ_0 and λ_i, for then the highest common factor of the ρ_0's would be $\delta_\mu\sigma$. Hence $\sigma = 1$,
$$m = q\lambda_0.$$

But $m \leqslant \rho_0 = \lambda_0\delta_\mu$. Hence $q \leqslant \delta_\mu$. The condition is necessary and sufficient, or m takes δ_μ different values.

The difference between each of these and $\bar{y}_1-y_0$ is $(x-x_0)^{\frac{\rho_\mu+1}{\rho_0}}$. In the same way we find that the number of determinations which coincide with $\bar{y}_1-y_0$ up to and including the term $\lambda_{-1}(x-x_0)^{\frac{\rho_\lambda-1}{\rho_0}}$ is δ_λ, but from these we must, of course, deduct

---

* The next few pages are very close to Jordan[1].

those which coincide further. The total number of coincidences with values $\bar{y}_1 - y_0$ will be

$$\sum_{i=0}^{i=\mu} (\delta_{\lambda-1} - \delta_\lambda) \frac{\rho_\lambda}{\rho_0} + \delta_\mu \frac{\rho_\mu}{\rho_0}.$$

We pass from $\bar{y}_1 - y_0$ to another value $\bar{y}_m - y_0$ by replacing $(x-x_0)^{\frac{1}{R_0}}$ by $\theta^{\frac{m}{R_0}}(x-x_0)^{\frac{1}{R_0}}$, i.e. by replacing A_i by $\theta^{\frac{mR_i}{R_0}} A_i$, but at the same time we shall replace a_i by $\theta^{m\frac{\rho_i}{\rho_0}} a_i$ since $\frac{\rho_i}{\rho_0} = \frac{R_i}{R_0}$.

Hence the total number of intersections is

$$R_0 \left[\sum_{\lambda=1}^{\lambda=\mu} (\delta_{\lambda-1} - \delta_\lambda) \frac{\rho_\lambda}{\rho_0} + \delta_\mu \frac{\rho_{\mu+1}}{\rho_0} \right].$$

It remains to show that this is an integer:

$$\frac{\rho_\lambda}{\rho_0} = \frac{R_\lambda}{R_0} \qquad R_\lambda = \frac{\rho_\lambda}{\rho_0} R_0$$

$$\frac{\rho_0}{R_0} = \frac{\rho_\lambda}{R_\lambda} = \frac{\delta_\lambda}{\Delta_\lambda} \qquad \frac{R_0}{\rho_0} \delta_\mu \rho_{\mu+1} = \Delta_\mu \rho_{\mu+1}.$$

Lastly, let us notice that if ρ_λ be divisible by $\delta_{\lambda-1}$, then $\delta_{\lambda-1} = \delta_\lambda$ so that we need consider only the characteristic exponents.

Theorem 15] *Given two branches with a common origin* (y) *in normal form*

$$x_i = y_i + a_{i0} t^{\rho_0} + a_{i1} t^{\rho_1} + \dots$$
$$\bar{x}_i = y_i + A_{i0} T^{R_0} + A_{i1} T^{R_1} + \dots$$

with orders R_0 *and* ρ_0 *respectively. Let the highest common factor of the characteristic exponents* $\rho_0, \rho_\alpha, \dots, \rho_\lambda$ *be* δ_λ *and that of the characteristic exponents* $R_0, R_\beta, \dots, R_\lambda$ *be* Δ_λ. *If we put* $t^{\rho_0} = T^R$ *and if the propinquity be* $\frac{\rho_{\mu+1}}{\rho_0}$, *then the number of intersections of the two branches is*

$$\sum_{i=1}^{i=\mu} (\delta_{\lambda-1} - \delta_\lambda) R_\lambda + \Delta_\mu \rho_{\mu+1}, \tag{17}$$

whereas, if the propinquity be $\frac{R_{\mu+1}}{R_0}$, *it is*

$$\sum_{i=1}^{i=\mu} (\delta_{\lambda-1} - \delta_\lambda) R_\lambda + \delta_\mu R_{\mu+1}. \tag{18}$$

Since the only exponents involved are the characteristic ones, finite in number, and $\rho_{\mu+1}$, $R_{\mu+1}$, we shall get the same number of intersections if we disregard the subsequent terms in the power series, and treat our curves as if they were rational curves completely given by the polynomials which remain out of the series.

Theorem 16] *In finding the intersections of two branches with a common origin, we may replace each given curve by a rational curve having in the given position a singular point whose branches are of the same order, same characteristic exponents, and same propinquity with the branches of the other curve.**

§ 4. The effect of a quadratic transformation on a branch

It is time to see what effect a standard quadratic transformation will have upon the significant numbers connected with a branch. There are five different cases which might be studied but we shall merely take up two, that where the origin of the branch is not a fundamental line, and that where it is at a fundamental point but the tangent to the branch is not a fundamental line. In the first case our branch can be written

$$x_1 = y_1 + t^{\rho_0}$$
$$x_2 = y_2 + a_0 t^{\rho_0} + a_1 t^{\rho_1} + \dots$$
$$x_3 = y_3 = 1.$$

Writing $x_i' = x_j x_k$,

$$x_1' = x_2 = y_2 + a_0 t^{\rho_0} + a_1 t^{\rho_1} + \dots$$
$$x_2' = x_1 = y_1 + t^{\rho_0}$$
$$x_3' = y_1 y_2 + (y_1 a_0 + y_2) t^{\rho_0} + a_0 t^{2\rho_0} + a_1 y_1 t^{\rho_1}.$$

The order will still be ρ_0 since the continued proportion

$$y_2 : y_1 : y_1 y_2 = a_0 : 1 : y_1 a_0 + y_2$$

could not hold when no (y) vanishes. The characteristic exponents will be as before, for the three-rowed determinant associated with a characteristic exponent ρ_1 is

$$\begin{vmatrix} y_2 & a_0 & a_\lambda \\ y_1 & 1 & 0 \\ y_1 y_2 & y_1 a_0 + y_2 & y_1 a_\lambda \end{vmatrix} = a_\lambda y_1 y_2 \neq 0.$$

---

* This concept has been much elaborated by Brill[1].

Suppose that we have a second branch with propinquity $\frac{\rho_{\mu+1}}{\rho_\mu}$

$$\bar{x}_1 = y_1 + T^{R_0}$$

$$\bar{x}_2 = y_2 + A_0 T^{R_0} + A_1 T^{R_1} + \ldots$$

$$\bar{x}_3 = y_3 = 1$$

$$\bar{x}_1' = y_2 + A_0 T^{R_0} + \ldots$$

$$\bar{x}_2' = y_1 + T^{R_1}$$

$$\bar{x}_3' = y_1 y_2 + (y_1 A_0 + y_2) T^{R_0} + \ldots$$

$$\sqrt[\rho_0]{|\bar{\xi} \bar{x}' \bar{x}^r|} = \rho t^{\frac{\rho_{u+1}}{\rho_0}} + \ldots .$$

Theorem 17] *If two branches have a common origin which i*
not on a fundamental line for a standard quadratic transformation
their orders, characteristic exponents, and propinquity will not b
altered by the transformation.

Theorem 18] *The number of intersections which two curves hav*
at a point which is not on a fundamental line of a standard quad
ratic transformation will be equal to the number of intersection
which the transformed curves have at the transformed point.

Let us now assume that our singular point is a fundamenta
one for the transformation, but the tangent is not fundamental
We may write the branch

$$x_1 = t^{\rho_0}$$

$$x_2 = a_0 t^{\rho_0} + a_1 t^{\rho_1}$$

$$x_3 = 1$$

$$x_i' = \frac{1}{t^{\rho_0}} x_j x_k$$

$$x_1' = a_0 + a_1 t^{\rho_1 - \rho_0} \ldots$$

$$x_2' = 1$$

$$x_3' = a_0 t^{\rho_0} + a_1 t^{\rho_1}.$$

Here we have several cases to deal with.

A) $\rho_1 - \rho_0 < \rho_0$. The order of the branch has been reduced.
We might think that the characteristic exponents had been
reduced also to $\rho_\alpha - \rho_0$, but such is not the case, for the corresponding two-row determinants are 0. The characteristic ex-

ponents are as before, for the terms involving them appear only in x'_3, and the two-row determinants are of the form

$$\begin{vmatrix} a_1 & 0 \\ 0 & a_\lambda \end{vmatrix} \neq 0.$$

B) $\rho_1 - \rho_0 \geqslant \rho_0$. The order has been untouched, but the characteristic exponents reduced by ρ_0.

Theorem 19] *When the origin of a branch of higher order than the first is fundamental for a standard quadratic transformation, but the tangent is not, either the order or the characteristic exponents will be reduced by the transformation, and neither can be increased.*

Theorem 20] *Every curve may be reduced by a factorable Cremona transformation into one with only branches of the first order.*

Suppose, now, that we have two curves with branches of the first order tangent to one another at a fundamental point, we write them

$$x_1 = t$$
$$x_2 = a_1 t + a_2 t^2 + \ldots + a_\mu t^\mu + a_{\mu+1} t^{\mu+1}$$
$$x_3 = 1$$
$$\bar{x}_1 = t$$
$$\bar{x}_2 = a_1 t + a_2 t^2 + \ldots + a_\mu t^\mu + A_{\mu+1} t^{\mu+1}$$
$$\bar{x}_3 = 1.$$

The transformed branches will be

$$x'_1 = a_1 + a_2 t + \ldots + a_{\mu+1} t^\mu + \ldots \qquad \bar{x}'_1 = a_1 + a_2 t + \ldots + A_{\mu+1} t^\mu + \ldots$$
$$x'_2 = 1 \qquad \qquad \bar{x}'_2 = 1$$
$$x'_3 = a_1 t + a_2 t^2 + \ldots + a_{\mu+1} t^{\mu+1} + \ldots \qquad \bar{x}'_3 = a_1 t + a_2 t^2 + \ldots + A_{\mu+1} t^{\mu+1} + \ldots,$$

and the propinquity will be cut down from $\mu + 1$ to μ.

Theorem 21] *Any two curves may be carried by a factorable Cremona transformation into two with only ordinary singularities, which are nowhere tangent to one another.*

This is merely theorem 2] of the last chapter.

Our theorem 16] may be generalized very easily by taking a general analytic transformation of the plane. Let us prove the obvious proposition that the number of intersections of two curves at a point where the Jacobian of the transformation does not vanish will remain unaltered.

$$x = x_0 + t^{\rho_0} \qquad y = y_0 + a_0 t^{\rho_0} + a_1 t^{\rho_1} + \ldots.$$

Let
$$x'-x_0' = \alpha_1(x-x_0)+\beta_1(y-y_0)+\ldots$$
$$y'-y_0' = \gamma_1(x-x_0)+\delta_1(y-y_0)+\ldots$$
$$\begin{vmatrix} \alpha_1 & \beta_1 \\ \gamma_1 & \delta_1 \end{vmatrix} \neq 0.$$

The transformed branches will be
$$x' = x_0'+(\alpha_1+\beta_1 a_0)t^{\rho_0}+\ldots$$
$$y' = y_0'+(\gamma_1+\delta_1 a_0)t^{\rho_0}+\ldots.$$

We could not have
$$\alpha_1+\beta_1 a_0 = 0$$
$$\gamma_1+\delta_1 a_0 = 0,$$
for then
$$\begin{vmatrix} \alpha_1 & \beta_1 \\ \gamma_1 & \delta_1 \end{vmatrix} = 0.$$

The order of the branch is unaltered. In the expansion of x' the exponents between ρ_0 and ρ_α must be divisible by ρ_0, and so are not characteristic; the first characteristic exponent is ρ_α, provided the corresponding two-row determinant is not 0. This can only come from $y-y_0$, hence the determinant is
$$\begin{vmatrix} \alpha_1+\beta_1 a_0 & \beta_1 a_\alpha \\ \gamma_1+\delta_1 a_0 & \delta_1 a_\alpha \end{vmatrix} = \begin{vmatrix} \alpha_1 & \beta_1 \\ \gamma_1 & \delta_1 \end{vmatrix} a_\alpha \neq 0.$$

In the same way we shall have the characteristic exponents $\rho_\beta, \rho_\gamma, \ldots$ for the two-row determinants will take a form like that just given.

Suppose that we have a second branch
$$\bar{x} = x_0+T^{R_0} \qquad \bar{y} = y_0+A_0 T^{R_0}+A_1 T^{R_1}$$
$$\bar{x}' = x_0'+(\alpha_1+\beta_1 A_0)T^{R_0}+\ldots$$
$$\bar{y}' = y_0'+(\gamma_1+\delta_1 A_0)T^{R_0}+\ldots$$

$$\sqrt[\rho_0]{\begin{vmatrix} \xi & x' & \bar{x}' \\ \eta & y' & \bar{y}' \\ 1 & 1 & 1 \end{vmatrix}} = \sqrt[\rho_0]{\begin{vmatrix} \zeta & [(\alpha_1+\beta_1 a_0)t^{\rho_0}+\ldots] & [(\alpha_1+\beta_1 T^{R_0})+\ldots] \\ \eta & [(\gamma_1+\delta_1 a_0)t^{\rho_0}+\ldots] & [(\gamma_1+\delta_1 T^{R_0})+\ldots] \\ 1 & 1 & 1 \end{vmatrix}}$$

If we put $t^{\rho_0} = T^{R_0}$ and call $\dfrac{\rho_{\mu+1}}{\rho_\mu}$ the propinquity of the two original branches, the expression above takes the form

$$\rho t^{\frac{\rho_{\mu+1}}{\rho_0}}+\ldots.$$

Theorem 22] *The number of intersections of two curves at a point where the Jacobian of an analytic transformation does not vanish is unaltered by that transformation.*

This theorem is so evident that one seldom bothers to prove it. Let the reader devise another proof suitable for non-algebraic curves.

CHAPTER III

CLUSTERING SINGULARITIES

§ 1. The general idea of clustering singularities

In the last chapter we showed in detail how the number of intersections of two branches with a common origin may be determined from their characteristic exponents and propinquity. The same problem may be studied by watching the effect of successive standard quadratic transformations on two intersecting curves.

Suppose that two curves of order n_1, n_2 respectively share a point whose order for the one is r_1 and for the other r_2. The number of intersections there will depend on a certain number of the coefficients and exponents in the power-series developments for the different branches. If we take the chosen point as fundamental, while no tangent thereat is so, then the three fundamental lines will meet the first curve elsewhere in n_1, n_1-r_1, n_1-r_1 points, all distinct we may assume, and the second one, likewise, in n_2, n_2-r_2, n_2-r_2 distinct points. The transformed curves will have ordinary singularities of just these orders in the three fundamental points, and we may imagine the tangents to one distinct from the tangents to the other.

Let N be the number of intersections which the original curves have at the given fundamental point. The number of their other intersections will be, by Bézout's theorem 9], Book I, Ch. I, n_1n_2-N, and such of these as are not on fundamental lines will be carried over into equal groups of intersections for the transformed curves by the last theorem of the preceding chapter. The total number of $(2n_1-r_1)(2n_2-r_2)$ intersections of the new curves are accounted for in the following way:

A) n_1n_2 intersections at the first fundamental point;

B) $(n_1-r_1)(n_2-r_2)$ intersections at each of the other fundamental points;

C) n_1n_2-N intersections not on any fundamental line;

D) N' intersections on the fundamental line opposite the singular point:

$$(2n_1-r_1)(2n_2-r_2) = n_1n_2+2(n_1-r_1)(n_2-r_2)+n_1n_2-N+N'$$
$$= (2n_1-r_1)(2n_2-r_2)+r_1r_2-N+N'$$
$$N = r_1r_2+N'.$$

Theorem 1] *If an intersection of two curves be fundamental for a standard quadratic transformation, though neither curve touches a fundamental line there, and if they be quadratically transformed into curves with only ordinary singularities and different tangents at these three fundamental points, then the number of intersections which the first two curves have at the given fundamental point is the product of the orders of this point for the two curves, plus the number of intersections which the transformed curves have on the opposite fundamental line.*[*]

It appears, thus, that our original curves intersect as though they had two ordinary singular points of order r_1 and r_2 respectively in common, as well as other complicated singularities infinitely near, yet the latter are necessarily of slightly improved structure, as we saw in 19] of the last chapter. Let us fix our attention, for the moment, on a single curve f.

The singular point shall be O_3, the other fundamental points O_1 and O_2. The first transformed curve shall be f'. It will have singular points at O_1, O_2, O_3, and a series of singularities of orders r'_{11}, r'_{12}, etc., at points $O'_{31}, O'_{32}, \ldots$ of O_1O_2. The total number of intersections with O_1O_2 at these points will be r_1, but this may well exceed the sum of their orders if there be tangency at any point. Let us take an arbitrary conic through O_1, O_2, O_3, and Q_1, Q_2 as two arbitrary points thereon. Let us make a Hirst quadratic transformation of the type (6) of Book II, Ch. I, using as fundamental the points Q_1, Q_2, and Q_3 the pole of Q_1Q_2 with regard to the conic. All points of the conic but Q_1, Q_2 are non-fundamental in this transformation and stay in place, the general structure and intersections of curves passing through them will be unaltered. This will be the case with O_1, O_2, and O_3. Our curve f' is carried into a curve ϕ' of order $2(2n-r_1)$ with ordinary singularities of order n_1-r_1, n_1-r_1, and n_1 at O_1, O_2, and O_3 respectively, and with points of like structure to O'_{31}, O'_{32}, etc., at the transforms of these. Now take two points Q'_1, Q'_2 infinitely near to Q_1 and Q_2 on the same conic, and Q'_3 the pole of their line, and transform again in the same way. The product of these two Hirst transformations will be a factorable Cremona transformation, which differs infinitesimally from the identity, an infinitesimal Cremona transformation in fact, which carries f' into a curve ϕ'' of order $4(2n_1-r_1)$ with singularities exactly like those of f', besides three of high order but simple structure at Q_1', Q_2', Q_3'.

The curve ϕ'' lies infinitely near f' and has singular points exactly like O_{31}', O_{32}', etc., but off the line O_1O_2. Hence, when we transform this by our original standard quadratic transformation, we shall get a curve which lies infinitely near f and the fundamental lines counted twice, with an ordinary singular point of order r_1 at O_3, and other singularities infinitely near of the structure of O_{31}', O_{32}', etc.

As an example of how this process works, consider a curve with a 'beak' at the point O_3:

$$0 = (p_1x_1+p_2x_2)^2x_3^{n-2}+\psi_5[(p_1x_1+p_2x_2),x_2]x_3^{n-5}+\cdots.$$

This will become

$$0 = (p_1x_2+p_2x_1)^2x_1^{n-2}x_2^{n-2}+\psi_5[(p_1x_2+p_2x_1)x_1]x_1^{n-5}x_2^{n-5}x_3^3+\cdots.$$

Let us write
$$x_1 = p_1+\lambda\xi_1$$
$$x_2 = -p_2+\lambda\xi_2$$
$$x_3 = \lambda\xi_3$$

and substitute. We have two roots $\lambda = 0$, except when

$$p_2\xi_1+p_1\xi_2 = 0,$$

when there are three. Hence the transformed curve has a cusp on $x_3 = 0$ at the point $(p_1, -p_2, 0)$. Moving this off a slight distance and transforming back, we have a curve, infinitely near our original one, with a node, and a cusp infinitely near thereto.

Our original singular point at O_3 will be the limit of an ordinary singularity, and a number of approaching singularities. But each of these may be analysed in the same way into ordinary singularities and others approaching. Continuing thus we find, no matter how complicated the original singular point is, it may be treated as a limit of approaching ordinary singular points.

Theorem 2] *Any singular point is the limit of a system of converging ordinary singular points, whose orders are given by those of the points to which it is carried in a standard quadratic transformation, the corresponding numbers for these points, and so on.*

We shall say that we have at O_3, under these circumstances, clustering singular points $O_3, O'_{31}, O'_{32}, ..., O''_{3i_1}, O''_{3i_2} ...$ of orders $r_1, r_{11}, r_{12}, ..., r_{1i_1}, r_{1i_2}, ...$, or that O_3 is the leader of a 'train of infinitely near singularities'. This means that O_3 has the multiplicity r_1, its first transforms have the multiplicities $r_{11}, r_{12}, ...$, theirs in turn the multiplicities $r_{1i_1}, ...$. The positions of the clustering singularities are known in the sense that the positions of their first transforms are known when the transformations are chosen, and so on for the second and subsequent transforms. Thus a second curve shall be said to have a certain multiplicity at one of the clustering points if its corresponding transform have that multiplicity at the corresponding transformed point. There are two points of view, the inexact one where we visualize these points as nestling very close to O_3 and approaching it as a limit, and the exact one where we consider our language as a way of speaking of a point on a curve, the transformed points on a transformed curve, and so on. In any case the conditions requiring a curve to have assigned multiplicities at clustering singularities are linear in its coefficients. We get from a repeated application of theorem 1]

Theorem 3] *The number of intersections two curves have at a point is the sum of the products of the orders of multiplicity for the two curves of that point and all the following infinitely near points where each has an order greater than* 0.

§ 2. Singularities of a single branch

It is time to try to link up this geometrical idea of clustering singularities with the arithmetical analysis of a single branch. This is necessary in order to make sure that they represent something inherent in the curve and not an artificial superstructure introduced through the quadratic transformations. We see from what went before theorems 19] and 20] of the last chapter that if the order of a branch be less than its class, the order is not reduced by a quadratic transformation, but the characteristic exponents are. If there be any terms with exponents between ρ_0 and ρ_α, the next characteristic exponent, the class cannot be less than the order, and the order of the branch will not be reduced by a quadratic transformation. Let us look for δ_α, the highest common factor of ρ_0 and ρ_α.

$$\rho_\alpha = q_0\rho_0 + \sigma_1$$
$$\rho_0 = q_1\sigma_1 + \sigma_2$$
$$\sigma_1 = q_2\sigma_2 + \sigma_3$$
$$\cdot \quad \cdot \quad \cdot \quad \cdot \quad \cdot \quad \cdot$$
$$\sigma_{\lambda-2} = q_{\lambda-1}\sigma_{\lambda-1} + \delta_\alpha$$
$$\sigma_{\lambda-1} = q_\lambda\delta_\alpha.$$

These equations show that we can make q_0-1 successive transformations without reducing the order of the branch, i.e. there are q_0 points of order ρ_0 clustering together, then q_1 of order σ_1, q_2 of order σ_2, and then q_λ of order δ_α. There may be still others of this order, but they will involve the term t^{ρ_β}, whereas so far we have only involved the terms t^{ρ_0}, t^{ρ_α}.

In order to proceed further we must watch closely how our characteristic exponents are affected by the various quadratic transformations. At first they were

$$\rho_0,\ \rho_\alpha,\ \rho_\beta,...,\ \rho_\lambda,....$$

After one quadratic transformation

$$\rho_0,\ \rho_\alpha-\rho_0,\ \rho_\beta-\rho_0,...,\ \rho_\lambda-\rho_0.$$

After a second

$$\rho_0,\ \rho_\alpha-2\rho_0,\ \rho_\beta-2\rho_0,...,\ \rho_\lambda-2\rho_0.$$

After q_0-1

$$\rho_0,\ \rho_0+\sigma_1,\ \rho_\beta-\rho_\alpha+\rho_0+\sigma_1,...,\ \rho_\lambda-\rho_\alpha+\rho_0+\sigma_1.$$

Next there comes a change; the order of the point is altered. They are

$$\sigma_1,\ \rho_0,\ \rho_\beta-\rho_\alpha+\rho_0+\sigma_1,\ \rho_\lambda-\rho_\alpha+\rho_0+\sigma_1.$$

After q_1-1 transformations of this lot they are

$$\sigma_1,\ \sigma_1+\sigma_2,\ \rho_\beta-\rho_\alpha+2\sigma_1+\sigma_2,...,\ \rho_\lambda-\rho_\alpha+2\sigma_1+\sigma_2.$$

After the next

$$\sigma_2,\ \sigma_1,\ \rho_\beta-\rho_\alpha+2\sigma_1+\sigma_2,...,\ \rho_\lambda-\rho_\alpha+2\sigma_1+\sigma_2.$$
$$\cdot \quad \cdot \quad \cdot \quad \cdot \quad \cdot \quad \cdot \quad \cdot \quad \cdot \quad \cdot \quad \cdot$$
$$\delta_\alpha,\ \sigma_{\lambda-1},\ \rho_\beta-\rho_\alpha+2\sigma_1+2\sigma_2+,...,\ \rho_\lambda-\rho_\alpha+2\sigma_1+2\sigma_2+....$$

Here the second exponent shown is not characteristic, since the quantities $\sigma_1,\sigma_2,...$ are all divisible by δ_α we may keep on transforming till we get the series of characteristic exponents

$$\delta_\alpha,\ \rho_\beta-\rho_\alpha,...,\ \rho_\lambda-\rho_\alpha.$$

The highest common factor is now δ_β, and we may begin the process all over again.

Theorem 4] *The orders and numbers of the successive clustering singularities into which a complicated singularity may be decomposed are calculated from the quotients and the remainders in the process of finding the highest common factors of the successive characteristic exponents.*

This shows that the orders of these points are intrinsic to the form of the curve in that vicinity, and are not dragged in from the outside by the process of successive quadratic transformations.*

There are times when we are concerned not only with the orders of the clustering singularities but with their situations, which amounts to saying the directions of the tangents at the various singular points created by the quadratic transformations. We start as before:

$$x_1 = t^{\rho_0} \qquad x_1' = \frac{1}{t^2} x_2 x_3 = a_0 + a_1 t^{\rho_1 - \rho_0} + \ldots$$

$$x_2 = a_0 t^{\rho_0} + a_1 t^{\rho_1} \qquad x_2' = \frac{1}{t^2} x_3 x_1 = 1$$

$$x_3 = 1 \qquad x_3' = \frac{1}{t^2} x_1 x_2 = a_0 t^{\rho_0} + a_1 t^{\rho_1} + \ldots$$

These equations are not in proper shape to proceed. We work them by a simple linear transformation into

$$\bar{x}_1 = x_1' - a_0 x_2' + x_3' = a_0 t^{\rho_0} + a_1 t^{\rho_1 - \rho_0} + \ldots$$
$$\bar{x}_2 = x_2' = 1$$
$$\bar{x}_3 = x_3' = a_0 t^{\rho_0} + a_1 t^{\rho_1}.$$

The equation of the tangent $\bar{x}_1 - \bar{x}_3 = 0$ *is independent of* a_1. By a change of variable we may write these

$$x_1'' = t^{\rho_0}$$
$$x_2'' = t^{\rho_0} + A_1 t^{\rho_1 - \rho_0} + \ldots$$
$$x_3'' = 1.$$

Let us assume first that $\rho_1 = \rho_\alpha$, the first characteristic exponent. The equation of the tangent is $\bar{x}_2 - \bar{x}_1 = 0$, and A_1 is

* Cf. Nöther[4].

a function of a_0 and a_1. If we make q_0 of these transformations, we get

$$\xi_1 = A_1 T^{\sigma_1}$$
$$\xi_2 = 1$$
$$\xi_3 = A_1 T^{\sigma_1} + A_2 T^{\rho_0},$$

where the equation of the tangent is $\xi_1 - \xi_3 = 0$ independent of a_1, and A_1 is a function of a_0 and a_1. Proceeding thus we see that we have q_0 points of order ρ_0, q_1 of order σ_1, etc., whose positions are independent of a_1. They would have the same situations as those of a second branch:

$$x_1 = t'^{R_0} \qquad x_2 = a_0 t'^{R_0} + b_1 t'^{R_1} + \dots \qquad x_3 = 1.$$

Let
$$\frac{R_\alpha}{R_0} = \frac{\rho_\alpha}{\rho_0}$$
$$\rho_\alpha R_0 = R_\alpha \rho_0.$$

$\rho_\alpha = q_0 \rho_0 + \sigma_1$	Hence $R_\alpha = q_0 R_0 + S_1$
$\rho_0 = q_1 \sigma_1 + \sigma_2$	$R_0 = q_1 S_1 + S_2$
$\sigma_1 = q_2 \sigma_2 + \sigma_3$	$S_1 = q_2 S_2 + S$
. . . . .	. . . . .
$\sigma_{\lambda-1} = q_\lambda \delta_\alpha.$	$S_{\lambda-1} = q_\lambda \Delta_\lambda.$

The number of points of order δ_α depends upon the quantities σ as well as q and need not be the same for the two branches. In general,
$$S_1 = \frac{R_0}{\rho_0} \sigma_i.$$

We have supposed that ρ_1 and R_1 are characteristic exponents. Our branch will share with every other of the same order, class, and tangent:

q_0 clustering points of the order ρ_0

q_1 clustering points of the order σ_1

q_2 points of the order σ_2

. . . .

All these are independent of a_1 and the subsequent coefficients; they are said to be 'satellites' of the point first given.*

Theorem 5] *If the class of a branch be not divisible by the order, every other branch with the same origin, tangent thereat, and the same*

* This conception of satellite points is due to Enriques. Cf. Enriques-Chisini, vol. ii, pp. 364 ff.

ratio of order to class will share therewith a number of clustering satellite points whose orders are proportional to those for the first branch, and whose numbers are determined by the process of finding the highest common factor of order and class.

Let us return to the more general case for α and assume as before $\dfrac{\rho_\alpha}{\rho_0} = \dfrac{R_\alpha}{R_0}$. Suppose that this gives the propinquity of the two curves, then $a_0, a_1, ..., a_{\alpha-1}$ will take identical values for the two and the tangents will be the same until the terms t^{ρ_α} or T^{R_α} come into play.

Theorem 6] *If two branches have the same origin, and if their propinquity be given by the ratio of the first two characteristic coefficients of the two branches, then they share a number of clustering satellite points whose orders are proportional, and whose numbers are determined by the process of finding the highest common factor of the first two characteristic exponents.*

This theorem shows us that we are not, by any means, free to assume the order which clustering singularities of one curve shall have as points of another. The order never increases as we proceed; the order of a point is always as great as the sum of the orders of those that immediately follow, from the developments at the beginning of the present chapter. If two curves share satellite points, as determined above, we are by no means free to assume their orders for the one. Here is an example. Let us take a rational quintic curve:

$$x_1 = t^3 \qquad x_2 = at^3 + bt^5 \qquad x_3 = 1.$$

If we make a standard quadratic transformation we get

$$x_1' = a + bt^2 \qquad x_2' = 1 \qquad x_3' = at^3 + bt^5.$$

This curve has a cusp. A second quadratic transformation will carry the cuspidal branch into a branch of the first order tangent to a fundamental line. We may then say that the original curve has a cluster consisting of a triple point, a node, and a single point. Let us require a second curve to be non-singular at each of these three places. Its first transform must pass through the cusp and touch the cuspidal tangent, hence it must be of the form

$$\xi_1' = a + b\tau + ... \qquad \xi_2' = 1 \qquad \xi_3' = p\tau^2 + q\tau^3 + ...$$

Hence the original curve must have been of the form

$$\xi_1 = p\tau^2 + q\tau^3 + \dots \quad \xi_2 = ap\tau^2 + (aq + \beta p)\tau^3 + \dots \quad \xi_3 = a + \beta\tau + \dots,$$

and this has a cusp, and not a non-singular point at $(0, 0, 1)$.

A complicated singularity may well involve not one branch only but several, and a cluster may include points of different branches. It is easy to devise examples of such singularities by running a train of standard quadratic transformation backwards.

Although it is not always possible to assign the exact multiplicity for a curve of each of a number of clustering singularities of another curve, yet in some cases we may do so with a certain freedom, and, what is more, determine the number of independent linear conditions imposed. We saw in the reasoning that first led up to Nöther's fundamental theorem 15] of Book I, Ch. II, that if a curve have distinct ordinary singularities at assigned points and be of sufficiently high order compared with the orders of the singularities, the linear conditions imposed are independent. Moreover, no unexpected singularities are introduced in this way. Let us try to apply this to curves with clustering singularities.

Suppose that we have succeeded in proving that for every curve that can be resolved into one with only ordinary singular points by N standard quadratic transformations, and, perhaps, some collineations, if the order be sufficiently high, the imposition of permissible distinct singularities at a set of given distinct or clustering points will impose distinct linear conditions, and no unexpected singularities will appear. We wish to pass to the case of a curve that will require N quadratic transformations. Suppose there is a curve of order n which is very high, with just the assigned singularities, which singularities require N quadratic transformations to become unsnarled. Make a standard quadratic transformation with O_3 at a point of order r_0 as usual, getting a curve of order $2n - r_0$ with three ordinary singularities of order n, $n - r_0$, and $n - r_0$, and this can be unsnarled by $N - 1$ quadratic transformations. Now let n' be so large that independent linear conditions are imposed on a curve of order $2n' - r_0'$, which is required to have exactly the desired singularities at the singular points of the curve just constructed, except that at O_1, O_2, O_3 they are of orders $n' - r_0'$, $n_0' - r_0'$, and n' respectively.

Moreover, we may assume that undesired singularities are not introduced. Transforming back, we get a curve of order n' with exactly the singularities desired. With regard to the amount of freedom, let k be the number of conditions imposed on the curve of order $2n' - \rho'_0$ by the singular points other than O_1, O_2, O_3. Then the freedom of this latter curve, which is the freedom of the curve of order n', is

$$\frac{(2n'-r'_0)(2n'-r'_0+3)}{2} - \frac{n'(n'+1)}{2} - 2\frac{(n'-r'_0)(n'-r'_0+1)}{2} - k$$

$$= \frac{n'(n'+3)}{2} - \frac{r'_0(r'_0+1)}{2} - 1,$$

and this shows that the conditions imposed on the latter were independent, nor has it, necessarily, any undesired singular points.

Theorem 7] *The distinct or clustering singularities of a given curve will impose independent linear conditions conformable to their multiplicities and situation on a curve of sufficiently high order, and no undesired singular point is thereby necessarily created.*

CHAPTER IV

ADJOINT CURVES AND PLÜCKER'S EQUATIONS

§ 1. Adjoint curves in general

DEFINITION. A curve shall be said to be 'adjoint' to a given curve if at each distinct or clustering singularity of order r_i of the former, the latter has a multiplicity r_i-1 or more. The conditions imposed are called the 'adjunction conditions'.

In order to show that this definition is not completely vain, it is necessary to show that there do exist, in fact, adjoint curves, besides the curve itself and others of as high or higher order. We know that there are surely such curves when the singularities are distinct and consist in ordinary singular points and cusps. In particular the first polar of a general point is an adjoint, and the multiplicity at a singular point is not higher than desired. Let us prove that this is always the case. We assume that we have shown that if a curve can be carried into one with only ordinary singular points by $N-1$ quadratic transformations, a general first polar is an adjoint. Let f be a curve of order n, with a singular point of order r_0 at O_3 which requires N transformations. We may write its equation

$$f \equiv \sum a_{\lambda\mu\nu}x_1^\lambda x_2^\mu x_3^\nu = 0 \qquad \lambda+\mu+\nu = n.$$

The first transform will be

$$f' \equiv \sum a_{\lambda\mu\nu}x_1^{\mu+\nu}x_2^{\nu+\lambda}x_3^{\lambda+\mu-r_0} = 0.$$

We may assume that the point O_2 has no disturbing invariant relation to our curve f. Its first polar will be

$$\frac{\partial f}{\partial x_2} \equiv \sum \mu a_{\lambda\mu\nu}x_1^\lambda x_2^{\mu-1}x_3^\nu = 0.$$

The transformed curve will be

$$\phi' \equiv \sum \mu a_{\lambda\mu\nu}x_1^{\mu+\nu-1}x_2^{\nu+\lambda}x_3^{\lambda+\mu-r_0} = 0.$$

The first polar of O_2 with regard to f' is

$$\frac{\partial f'}{\partial x_2} \equiv \sum (\nu+\lambda)x_1^{\mu+\nu}x_2^{\nu+\lambda-1}x_3^{\lambda+\mu-r_0} = 0,$$

$$x_1\phi'+x_2\frac{\partial f'}{\partial x_2} \equiv nf'. \tag{1}$$

By assumption $\dfrac{\partial f'}{\partial x_2}$ is an adjoint to the curve f' which can be untied by $N-1$ quadratic transformations. Hence ϕ' is also an adjoint. The curve $\dfrac{\partial f}{\partial x_2}$ has the right multiplicity at O_3 for an adjoint, at the following singularities of that cluster, if there be any, and at the other singular points it also has the correct multiplicities since ϕ' has.

Theorem 1] *The first polar of a general point is an adjoint.*

Theorem 2] *The adjunction conditions are independent for an adjoint of sufficiently high order.*

We shall see in a later chapter that they are independent for every adjoint whose order is not less than $n-3$. When the order is below that number there may be no adjoints at all.

§ 2. Residuation

We saw in Book I, Ch. II, Nöther's fundamental theorem 15], that if two curves have in common only non-singular points, or ordinary singularities, with the respective orders r_i and s_i, then every curve which has a multiplicity r_i+s_i-1 or more at each such intersection can be written

$$f \equiv \psi'\phi + \phi'\psi = 0, \tag{2}$$

where ϕ' has multiplicity r_i-1 or more, and ψ' multiplicity s_i-1 or more. Let us assume that this theorem holds in every case where the common singularities can be unravelled by $N-1$ quadratic transformations, and let us consider the case where N are needed, and take one common singular point at O_3, the multiplicities there being r_0 and s_0, while the orders of the curves are n_1 and n_2. The order of the curve f shall be n. We make a standard quadratic transformation, getting the curves $\bar{f}, \bar{\phi}, \bar{\psi}$. If the order of f be sufficiently large, $\bar{f}$ will have high enough multiplicity at O_1, O_2, O_3 to fulfil the requirements. At the other intersections of $\bar{\phi}$ and $\bar{\psi}$ it will do so, since f does so with regard to ϕ and ψ. The intersections of $\bar{\phi}$ and $\bar{\psi}$ can be unsnarled by $N-1$ quadratic transformations, by hypothesis; hence

$$\bar{f} \equiv \bar{\psi}'\bar{\phi} + \bar{\phi}'\bar{\psi} = 0.$$

At this point we are tempted to go ahead light-heartedly, make our standard quadratic transformation, and try to throw this equation back into the form (2). Unfortunately things are not quite as simple as that. The result of the substitution might not give us f, but $x_1^\lambda x_2^\mu x_3^\nu f$, and it is not perfectly clear that the extraneous factors can be divided out. We must make an elaborate table of orders and multiplicities.

	Order.	Multiplicity at O_1 and O_2.	Multiplicity at O_3.
$\bar{f}$	$2n-r_0-s_0-1$	$n-r_0-s_0+1$	n
$\bar{\phi}$	$2n_1-r_0$	n_1-r_0	n_1
$\bar{\psi}$	$2n_2-s_0$	n_2-s_0	n_2
$\bar{\phi}'$	$2(n-n_2)-r_0+1$	n_1-r_0-1	n_1-1
$\bar{\psi}'$	$2(n-n_1)-s_0+1$	n_2-s_0-1	n_2-1
$\bar{\phi}\bar{\psi}'$	$2n-r_0-s_0+1$	$n_1+n_2-r_0-s_0-1$	n_1+n_2-1

We may replace $\bar{\psi}'$ by $\bar{\psi}'+\theta\bar{\psi}$ and $\bar{\phi}'$ by $\bar{\phi}'-\theta\bar{\phi}$ where θ is a polynomial of order $2(n-n_1-n_2)+1$. When n is very large indeed, the number of degrees of freedom of this is of the same order of magnitude as $2n^2$. The number of conditions to be imposed on θ to give $\bar{\psi}'+\theta\bar{\psi}$ as high a multiplicity as f at O_1, O_2, O_3 is of the order of magnitude of $\dfrac{3n^2}{2}$ and so less than the above.

Hence we may imagine θ so chosen that $\bar{\psi}'+\theta\bar{\psi}$ has at least as high a multiplicity at O_1, O_2, O_3 as $\bar{f}$, and, by the identity $\phi'-\theta\bar{\phi}$, must have as high multiplicity also. When we transform back the extraneous factors x_1, x_2, x_3 will appear to as high powers on the right as on the left, and so divide out of the latter. Let us notice, lastly, that although we have assumed here that f is of very high order, when Nöther's theorem is established for curves of high order, we may establish it for curves of lower order exactly as in Ch. II of Book I.

Nöther's Fundamental Theorem 3] *Given two curves ϕ and ψ which intersect in distinct or clustering points. Every curve which has a multiplicity r_i+s_i-1 at least at a common point where ϕ has the multiplicity r_i and ψ the multiplicity s_i has an equation of the form*

$$f \equiv \psi'\phi + \phi'\psi = 0, \tag{2}$$

where ψ' has at least multiplicity s_i-1, and ϕ' multiplicity r_i-1.

The next theorem comes exactly as in Book I, Ch. II; we take over the definition word for word, it being understood that when we speak of singular points we mean distinct or clustering.

Definition. Two groups of non-singular points are said to be residual when they constitute the total non-singular intersection with an adjoint curve.

Residue Theorem 4] *If two groups be residual to a third, every group residual to the one is residual to the other.*

Two such groups are defined as co-residual.

Definition. Two groups of non-singular points are said to be 'pseudo-residual' with the excesses $\lambda_1, \lambda_2, \dots$ where $\lambda_i \geqslant -(r_i - 1)$ if they constitute the total non-singular intersection with a curve which has a multiplicity at least $r_i + \lambda_i - 1$ at each singular point where the given curve has the multiplicity r_i.

Gambier's Extension of the Residue Theorem 5] *If two groups be pseudo-residual to a third, then every group pseudo-residual to the first with an excess greater than or equal to the excess of the first less the excess of the second, is pseudo-residual to the second with a positive or 0 excess.*

§ 3. The genus

Definition. Suppose that a curve of order n has clustering or distinct singularities $O_3, O_{31}, O_{32}, \dots, O_{3ij}, \dots$, etc., of orders r_0, $r_{01}, \dots, r_{02}, r_{0ij}$, etc. The expression

$$\frac{(n-1)(n-2)}{2} - \frac{r_0(r_0-1)}{2} - \frac{\sum r_{0i}(r_{0i}-1)}{2} - \frac{\sum r_{0ij}(r_{0ij}-1)}{2} - \dots \equiv p \quad (3)$$

shall be defined as the 'genus' of the curve. Let us take a standard quadratic transformation with O_3 fundamental. The genus of the transformed curve is

$$\frac{(2n-r_0-1)(2n-r_0-2)}{2} - \frac{n(n-1)}{2} - 2\frac{(n-r_0)(n-r_0-1)}{2} -$$

$$- \frac{\sum r_{0i}(r_{0i}-1)}{2} - \frac{\sum r_{0ij}(r_{0ij}-1)}{2} \dots$$

$$= \frac{(n-1)(n-2)}{2} - \frac{r_0(r_0-1)}{2} - \frac{\sum r_{0i}(r_{0i}-1)}{2} - \frac{\sum r_{0ij}(r_{0ij}-1)}{2} - \dots.$$

$$= p.$$

If we keep on in this way we finally reach a curve with only ordinary singular points whose genus is that of the original one.

Theorem 6] *The genus of an algebraic curve is equal to that of any curve with only ordinary singular points and cusps to which it may be reduced by a factorable Cremona transformation.*

Theorem 7] *The genus of an algebraic curve is never negative.*

Suppose that two algebraic curves are birationally related. The same is true of two curves with only ordinary singular points to which they may be transformed. This gives

Riemann's Theorem 8] *The genus of a curve is unaltered by a birational transformation.*

It follows immediately that all our work on correspondences holds for curves with any sort of singular points.

Theorem 9] *The number of coincidences properly counted of a (ν, ν') correspondence of value γ on a curve of genus p is given by the Chasles-Cayley-Brill formula*

$$\nu+\nu'+2p\gamma. \tag{4}$$

We shall see later how to count coincidences at singular points. We find exactly as in Book I, Ch. VIII:

Theorem 10] *Given a g_N^r and certain points $A_1, A_2, A_3,..., A$ such that ∞^{r-j} adjoints cutting groups of the series meet the base curve $\nu_{ij}+j$ times at A_i, then the number of places other than the A_i's where a group has $r+1$ coincident points is*

$$(r+1)[N+r(p-1)]- \sum_{i,j} \nu_{ij}. \tag{5}$$

It must be understood that if A_i acts in this way for several branches, it must be counted just so many times. Exceptionally some of these other coincidences might fall on the A's.

Weber's Theorem 11] *If two curves of the same genus which is greater than 1 be in rational correspondence, that correspondence is birational.*

Theorem 12] *If a curve of genus greater than 1 be rationally transformed into itself, the transformation is birational.*

Lüroth's Theorem 13] *If x and y be rational functions of a parameter, neither a constant, the curve so defined has genus 0, and x and y may be expressed rationally in terms of a parameter which is rational in them.*

Zeuthen's Theorem. 14] *If there be a (ν, ν') correspondence between two curves of genus p and p' respectively, and if the number of branch points properly counted be β and β',*

$$\beta+2\nu'(p-1) = \beta'+2\nu(p'-1). \tag{6}$$

With regard to counting the branch points, the reader is referred back to the remarks on this subject at the very end of Ch. VIII of Book I.

4. Plücker's equations

It is evident that when it comes to a study of the Plücker characteristics of a curve, there must be an extension of the definitions previously given. The order is the number of inter-sections with a general straight line, or the maximum number assuming the curve is not reducible, with a multiple factor); the class is the number of tangents from a general point, or the order of a polar reciprocal curve. The genus we have just defined.

Definition. The difference between the order of a distinct point and the number of different branches there is called its cuspidal component'. It will be noted that this is 0 for a non-singular point or an ordinary singularity, but is equal to unity in the case of a cusp. The sum of the cuspidal components of all distinct points of a curve is called its 'cuspidal index'. We shall indicate this by the symbol κ. In the same way the dif-ference between the order of a tangent and the number of branches which touch it is called the 'inflexional' component. The sum of the inflexional components of all distinct tangents is called the inflexional index and marked ι.

To find the class of a curve, let us assume that this is the number of vertical tangents m. Vertical lines will determine on our curve an $n-1$ to $n-1$ correspondence of value 1, which will have $2n+2(p-1)$ coincidences, for such will be the case on a curve with only ordinary singularities, birationally equivalent to the given curve. m of these will be simple coincidences arising from the vertical tangents, none of which we assume singular. The others come from the singular points. Let such a point be the origin with a branch of order r_0. In this vicinity we may represent the branch by

$$x = t^{\rho_0} \qquad y = a_0 t^{\rho_0} + a_1 t^{\rho_1} + \dots .$$

The number of coincidences will be the same as if we limit ourselves to a finite number of terms of these series, i.e. consider the rational curve given by these terms, whose points are in

one-to-one correspondence with the values of t. When x is given
the corresponding values of t are t, θt, $\theta^2 t$,..., where $\theta^{\rho 0} = 1$. As
$\theta^\kappa t - t$ is of the same order of infinitesimal magnitude as t, by
Zeuthen's rule of Book I, Ch. VIII, theorem 16], the number
of coincidences is $\rho_0 - 1$. Extending this to all the branches at
that point, we get its cuspidal component, and extending to all
points, we get the cuspidal index κ. Thus

$$m + \kappa = 2n + 2(p-1) \tag{7}$$

$$n + \iota = 2m + 2(p-1) \tag{8}$$

$$\iota - \kappa = 3(m-n) \tag{9}$$

$$2p = (n-1)(n-2) - \sum \rho_i(\rho_i - 1) - \sum \rho_{ij}(\rho_{ij} - 1) - \\ - \sum \rho_{ijk}(\rho_{ijk} - 1) - \ldots \tag{10}$$

$$= (m-1)(m-2) - \sum \sigma_i(\sigma_i - 1) - \sum \sigma_{ij}(\sigma_{ij} - 1) - \\ - \sum \sigma_{ijk}(\sigma_{ijk} - 1) - \ldots \tag{11}$$

$$m = n(n-1) - \sum \rho_i(\rho_i - 1) - \sum \rho_{ij}(\rho_{ij} - 1) - \\ - \sum \rho_{ijk}(\rho_{ijk} - 1) - \ldots - \kappa \tag{12}$$

$$n = m(m-1) - \sum \sigma_i(\sigma_i - 1) - \sum \sigma_{ij}(\sigma_{ij} - 1) - \\ - \sum \sigma_{ijk}(\sigma_{ijk} - 1) - \ldots - \iota \tag{13}$$

These last equations suggest another method for finding m. Let
O_3 be a singular point, O_2 a point in general position. How often
does the first polar of the latter point meet the curve at O_3?
This will give the deduction from the class caused by O_3. We
previously found the equation

$$x_1 \phi' + x_2 \frac{\partial f'}{\partial x_2} \equiv n f'. \tag{1}$$

By theorem 8] of the present chapter, the number we seek
is $\rho_0(\rho_0 - 1)$ plus the number of intersections of f' and ϕ' at non
singular points of $x_2 = 0$ or of f' and $\dfrac{\partial f'}{\partial x_2}$ at such points. This
again will be the number of intersections with the first polar of
an arbitrary point at these points, plus the multiplicity of $x_3 =$
as a tangent from O_2, and this is the difference between the
order of O_3 and the sum of the orders of the non-fundamental
points on $x_3 = 0$, the difference between the order of O_3 and the
sums of the orders of the infinitely near points. Keeping on in
this way, the sums of the orders of the intermediate branch

points cancel out, until we get down to a case where all branches are linear, in which case each branch will have contributed an amount one less than its order. Applying this to all branches, we get (12).

We get further light on all these questions by using non-homogeneous coordinates. Assuming the point to be the origin, and no tangent vertical, the reduction in class caused by that point is the number of intersections of

$$f = 0 \qquad \frac{\partial f}{\partial y} = 0,$$

and that consists in finding the discriminant of f considered as an equation in y. Now we learned in Book I, Ch. I, that this discriminant is

$$\pi(y_i - y_j)^2.$$

Here two of the y's will sometimes belong to the same branch, sometimes to different branches; in any case the number of intersections may be obtained by the methods at the end of Ch. II of the present book.

Theorem 15] *The number of intersections which a curve has at a singular point with a general first polar is twice the sum of the orders of the infinitesimal distances from one another of the intersections with an infinitely near line whose distance from the point is considered an infinitesimal of the first order.*

BOOK III

SYSTEMS OF POINTS ON A CURVE

CHAPTER I

GENERAL THEORY OF LINEAR SERIES

§ 1. Linear systems of curves, and linear series

In the second section of Ch. VIII, Book I, we touched upon certain properties of linear series of point groups on a fixed base curve. We restricted ourselves at that time to a base curve with only ordinary singular points, and only gave such few theorems as were necessary to establish the idea of the positive value of a correspondence on a curve. It is time to cast aside the restriction and to take up the whole subject of linear series of point groups in great detail, for it has proved astonishingly fruitful in the modern development of the theory of algebraic curves, and the relations of that theory to the theory of algebraic functions. Theorems already proved in Ch. VIII, Book I, need only be stated here, not proved.

The variable groups of non-singular points which the curves of a linear series cut on a fixed base curve, which we assume irreducible, is called a 'linear series' of groups. It may be that all the groups of such a series contain certain fixed non-singular points. *We are at liberty to count these as part of each group or not as we please.*

Theorem 1] *If a base curve be rationally transformed, a linear series will go into a linear series.*

The number of points in each group of the series is called its 'order', the number of independent parameters on which it depends its 'dimension'. A series of order N and dimension r is called a g_N^r.

Theorem 2] *The dimension of a series can never exceed its order, and can only equal it in the case of a curve of genus 0.*

We see, in fact, that if a curve contain a g_N^N, by fixing $N-1$ points there will be left a g_1^1, that is to say, a pencil of curves $\phi_1 + z\phi_2 = 0$ with only one variable intersection. The coordinates of this intersection will depend rationally on the parameter z which, in turn, depends rationally on them. Hence the curve can be birationally transformed into a straight line, which is of genus 0.

We find, exactly as in the previous chapter,

Linear Group Theorem 3] *Any linear system of point groups may be cut by a system of adjoint curves.*

It is evident that the series could not have more degrees of freedom than the system of secant curves; if it have less, that is because different curves of the linear system can cut the same group. But if two curves, and so a pencil of curves, cut the same group, no curve of the pencil will have a variable intersection with the base curve, and a curve of the pencil through an assigned point of the base curve, which we suppose irreducible, must contain it entirely.

Theorem 4] *The dimension of a linear series cut on an irreducible base curve is the dimension of the linear system of secant curves, less the dimension of the complete sub-system, all of whose curves contain the given curve as a factor.*

Definition. A linear series is said to be 'complete' if it be not contained in another of the same order and higher dimension. We get just as before:

Theorem 5] *If a group of points be residual to one group of a complete series, it is residual to all the groups.*

Theorem 6] *The totality of adjoints of a given order on which no restriction is placed except that they pass through a certain number, perhaps 0, of fixed non-singular points on the base curve, will cut a complete series, and every complete series can be cut in this way.*

Theorem 7] *A linear series is contained in but one complete series.*

Let us look for the dimension of the series cut by the totality of adjoints of a given order, let us say $\nu = n-3+\alpha$.*

$$r+1 \geqslant \frac{(\nu+1)(\nu+2)}{2} - \sum \frac{r_i(r_i-1)}{2} - \sum \frac{r_{ij}(r_{ij}-1)}{2} - \cdots - \\ - \frac{(\nu-n+1)(\nu-n+2)}{2}.$$

The equality will hold if the adjunction conditions be independent, otherwise the inequality. The right-hand side gives

* The work from here to the end of the chapter follows closely the admirable article Bertini[3]. See also Segre[4]. The beginning of all such treatment is the classical discussion of Brill and Nöther, q.v.

the number of linearly independent curves of order ν less the ostensible number of adjunction conditions, and also less the ostensible number of linearly independent curves of order $\nu-n$; for each of these, with the given curve, will form an adjoint of the system. We rewrite this, replacing ν by its value $n-\alpha+3$,

$$r+1 \geqslant \frac{(n-2+\alpha)(n-1+\alpha)}{2} - \sum \frac{r_i(r_i-1)}{2} - \sum \frac{r_{ij}(r_{ij}-1)}{2} - \cdots - \frac{(\alpha-1)(\alpha-2)}{2}.$$

In order that ν should be at least as great as n, it is necessary and sufficient that $\alpha \geqslant 3$. But the last fraction vanishes for $\alpha = 1$ and $\alpha = 2$. Hence this formula holds for all positive values of α. We may write it in the better form

$$r \geqslant (p-2)+n\alpha.$$

On the other hand, if we seek N, the order of the series, we have

$$N = \nu n - \sum r_i(r_i-1) - \sum r_{ij}(r_{ij}-1) - \cdots$$
$$= n\alpha + 2(p-1).$$

Hence, finally, if the system of secant adjoints have an order $n-3+\alpha$, $\alpha > 0$,

$$N-r \leqslant p. \tag{1}$$

The equality holds when the adjunction conditions are independent, otherwise the inequality. If $\alpha = 0$, we have

$$r+1 \geqslant \frac{(n-1)(n-2)}{2} - \sum \frac{r_i(r_i-1)}{2} - \sum \frac{r_{ij}(r_{ij}-1)}{2} - \cdots$$

$$r+1 \geqslant p$$
$$N = n(n-3) - \sum r_i(r_i-1) - \sum r_{ij}(r_{ij}-1) - \cdots$$
$$= 2(p-1)$$

$$N-r \leqslant p-1. \tag{2}$$

The equality will hold if the adjunction conditions be independent, otherwise the inequality.

Definition. An adjoint of order $n-3$ or less is said to be 'special'. A series cut by special adjoints is called a 'special' series. The series cut by the totality of all special adjoints is called the 'canonical' series.

Suppose that a series is special and complete. Take a point P which does not belong to all of its groups and adjoin it to each group. Let the complete series be cut by the totality of special adjoints through a group (perhaps empty) G, and let an arbitrary line through P meet the base curve again in $Q_1, Q_2, ..., Q_{n-1}$. There is certainly one adjoint of order $n-2$ through the group G and the point P, the totality of adjoints of that order through those points will cut a complete series. But as such adjoints contain $n-1$ collinear points, they consist in the line through those points and a special adjoint, and the complete series they cut will consist in the original series, residual to G, and the fixed point P.

Reduction Theorem 8] *If a fixed point be added to each group of a special complete series, the resulting series is complete.*

Suppose, now, that we know about a certain g_N^r that

$$N - r \leqslant p - 1.$$

We may suppose the series complete, for the inequality will be strengthened when we pass from an incomplete series to a complete one. If $r = 0$ the series is certainly special, for we have seen that the dimension of the canonical series is certainly as great as $p - 1$, so that we can always pass a special adjoint through $p - 1$ points. Suppose that we have proved that for every series of dimension less than r, if the order less the dimension be not above $p - 1$, the series is special. Consider the adjoints which cut our series and which pass through an arbitrary point, not common to all of them. They will cut a g_{N-1}^{r-1} which must be special, since $(N-1) - (r-1) \leqslant p - 1$ by hypothesis. It is also complete as it is cut by the totality of adjoints through certain fixed points but otherwise not restricted. The special adjoints which cut it must all pass through the arbitrary fixed point, for if they did not, we should get a complete g_N^{r-1} by adding the point to the g_{N-1}^{r-1}, whereas there is a complete g_N^r. Since this point is arbitrary, any group in the original series can be cut by a special adjoint.

Special Series Theorem 9] *If the difference between the order and the dimension of a series be less than the genus of the curve, the series is special.*

Theorem 10] *If a complete series be not special, the difference between the order and the dimension is equal to the genus of the curve*

$$N - r = p. \tag{3}$$

If we read again the lines which follow (2) we see that this means that the adjunction conditions are independent for an adjoint of order greater than $n-3$. Consider next the canonical system of adjoints, or the 'pure' adjoint system, as it is sometimes called. If we add a fixed point to all its groups, we get a series of order $2p-1$, which is complete by the reduction theorem 8]. If the adjunction conditions were not independent, i.e. if the dimension of the canonical series were above $p-1$, then this new series would be special by 9], or all the special adjoint curves would pass through any chosen point, which is absurd.

Adjunction Theorem 11] *The adjunction conditions are independent for an adjoint of order greater than or equal to $n-3$.*

It is to be noted that this theorem may not be true for adjoints of lower orders. Consider a curve of the seventh order with nine double points. We may place these where we choose. In general there will be one adjoint of order $n-4=3$ through these nine double points. Suppose, however, they are the intersections of 2 cubics, that is to say, the centres of a pencil of cubics. There will be nine linearly independent curves of order seven with these as double points, and only a four-parameter sub-system will consist in a pair of cubics and a straight line. Hence there are plenty of our curves of the seventh degree which are not reducible. Moreover, by Bertini's theorem 10] of Book I, Ch. VII, the general curve will not have any other singular points. Hence, if we take one such irreducible curve it will have an infinite number of adjoints of order $n-4$, instead of a single one.

Theorem 12] *The order of the canonical series is $2p-2$, and its dimension $p-1$. It is the only series of that order and dimension.*

We see, in fact, that every such series must be special by 9], and complete, for it has all the freedom of the most general special series.

Theorem 13] *An irreducible curve of genus p has exactly p linearly independent and special adjoints.*

This theorem is of absolutely first importance in the theory of the integrals of algebraic functions.

Could the canonical series have a fixed point Q ? If it could, the residual series would be a complete special g_{2p-3}^{p-1}. If we add an arbitrary point P, we have a complete special g_{2p-2}^{p-1} by 8] and 9], and that would mean that all special adjoints went through this arbitrary point.

Theorem 14] *The canonical series has no fixed points.*

There are cases where the special adjoints have fixed points not on the base curve. If the latter be of genus 2, the special adjoints form a pencil, and when $n > 5$ this will have centres other than the singular points of the base curve.

Theorem 15] *The order and dimension of a series are invariant for birational transformation.*

Theorem 16] *The canonical series is birationally transformed into the canonical series of the transformed curve.*

Theorem 17] *A special series is birationally transformed into a complete series.*

§ 2. Sums and differences of series

Suppose that we have a complete series of order $N+N'$ and dimension s, $g_{N+N'}^s$, which contains a group G of N points. This will be a group of some complete series, let us say a g_N^r, which consists in groups cut by all adjoints of a certain order through a group $\bar{G}$. The $g_{N+N'}^s$ shall be cut by all adjoints of a certain order through a group Γ. The adjoints of this latter system, which contain G, will cut a complete $g_{N'}^{r'}$ whose groups are co-residual to $\bar{G}$ and so residual to all groups of the g_N^r. The complete series will contain every group of g_N^r and every group of $g_{N'}^{r'}$ and so be their sum, as defined in Ch. VIII of Book I.

Theorem 18] *If a complete series contain in one of its groups a group of a series of lower or equal order, it contains the complete series containing this group.*

We shall say in this case that the complete series of larger order 'contains' that of lesser order, and the latter is 'contained' in the former. The complete series whose order is the difference of their orders, and which contains groups obtained by taking groups of one series from the corresponding groups of the other, is also included in the series of larger order, and is defined as the 'difference' of the two series. Each of the series of lower order is said to be 'residual' to the other in the series of larger order.

Suppose that we have two series of the same order g_N^r, $g_N^{r'}$ which have a common g_N^σ (which, by 18], is complete) where $\sigma \geqslant 0$. Let the general adjoint cutting g_N^r be

$$\lambda_0\phi_0 + \lambda_1\phi_1 + \ldots + \lambda_\sigma\phi_\sigma + \lambda_{\sigma+1}\phi_{\sigma+1} + \ldots + \lambda_r\phi_r = 0,$$

and that cutting $g_{N'}^{r'}$ be

$$\mu_0\phi_0 + \mu_1\phi_1 + \ldots + \mu_\sigma\phi_\sigma + \mu_{\sigma+1}\psi_{\sigma+1} + \ldots + \mu_{r'}\psi_{r'} = 0.$$

Then the curves

$$\nu_0\phi_0 + \nu_1\phi_1 + \ldots + \nu_\sigma\phi_\sigma + \nu_{\sigma+1}\phi_{\sigma+1} + \ldots + \nu_r\phi_r + \nu_{r+1}\psi_{r+1} + \ldots +$$
$$+ \nu_{r+r'}\psi_{r'} = 0$$

will cut a series that includes each of the given series, nor could any series of lower dimension include them both:

Theorem 19] *If two series be of the same order and have a common series of dimension 0 at least, then the dimension of the smallest series of that order that includes them both is the sum of their dimensions, less the dimension of the largest series of that order they have in common.*

More generally, let us suppose that we have a g_N^r and a $g_{N'}^{r'}$ which include a common g_ν^ρ but no series of that order and higher dimension. We may assume g_ν^ρ complete, by 18], and assume the various series cut by the totality of adjoints of given orders through groups G, G', and Γ respectively. Let a group of g_N^r consist in the two groups $\bar{G}$ and $\bar{\gamma}$, where $\bar{\gamma}$ is a group of g_ν^ρ, while one group of $g_{N'}^{r'}$ consists of $\bar{G}'$ and $\bar{\gamma}'$, which latter is also a group of g_ν^ρ. $G + \bar{G}$ and Γ are both residual to $\bar{\gamma}$, and, hence, to every group of g_ν^ρ. The same is true of $G' + \bar{G}'$ and Γ. Hence $G + \bar{G}$ and $G' + \bar{G}'$ are co-residual. The series $\bar{G} + g_{N'}^{r'}$ is of order $N + N' - \nu$ and dimension r', $\bar{G}' + g_N^r$ is of the same order and dimension r. They include the series $\bar{G} + \bar{G}' + g_\nu^\rho$ of dimension ρ, but no other of that order and higher dimension, as such a series would include g_ν^ρ, which is complete. Hence they are included in a $g_{N+N'-\nu}^{r+r'-\rho}$.

Theorem 20] *If a g_N^r and a $g_{N'}^{r'}$ share a complete g_ν^ρ, $\rho \geqslant 1$ they are included in a $g_{N+N'-\nu}^{r+r'-\rho}$.*

Let us remark in conclusion, that as we can add two series, so we can find any positive integral multiple of a series, this being the complete series that includes groups of the given series to the number indicated by the multiple.

3. Representation in hyperspace*

Suppose that a g_N^r is cut by the linear system of adjoints:

$$u_0\phi_0+u_1\phi_1+...+u_r\phi_r=0. \tag{4}$$

Let us write

$$\rho X_0=\phi_0 \qquad \rho X_1=\phi_1,..., \qquad \rho X_r=\phi_r. \tag{5}$$

We have a point in a space of r dimensions, since the ϕ's are linearly independent, corresponding to each point of our given curve, and these points trace a curve. The order of this curve will be the number of intersections with a general hyperplane (u).

It is not clear, however, whether, conversely, each point of the curve in hyperspace will correspond to a single point of the base curve. How could two different points of the base curve correspond to a single point of the curve in hyperspace ? We must have

$$\phi_0(x')=\lambda\phi_0(x'') \qquad \phi_1(x')=\lambda\phi_1(x''),..., \qquad \phi_r(x')=\lambda\phi_r(x'').$$

If, then, $\qquad\qquad \sum u_i\phi_i(x')=0,$

we have also $\qquad\qquad \sum u_i\phi_i(x'')=0,$

so that every group which includes (x') will also include (x''). Conversely, if two points have this property, they will correspond to the same point in hyperspace.

Definition. A linear series, all of whose points are variable, is said to be 'simple' if all groups through a generic point do not necessarily include any other point. If every group through a generic point contain $\mu-1$ other points but no more, variable with the first, the series is said to be composed of an 'involution of grade μ.' Any algebraic system of variable point groups on a base curve which has the property that a generic point determines $\mu-1$ others variable with the first shall be called an involution. A linear series which is composed of an involution shall be called 'composite'. If the series be simple, the order of the space curve will be N, for the number of intersections with a hyperplane (u) is the number of variable points cut by the adjoint (u) in (4).

Theorem 21] *If a curve contain a simple series of order N and dimension r, it may be so birationally transformed into a curve of*

* The most complete treatment of this topic is Segre[4].

*order N in a space of r dimensions that groups of the series corre
spond to hyperplane sections of the curve. If it contain a series
of dimension r and order N composed of an involution of grade μ
there is a μ-to-one correspondence between the plane curve and a
curve of order μ in a space of r dimensions, the groups of the
given series corresponding to the hyperplane sections of the space
curve.*

Suppose that we are in a space of three dimensions, and on
a given curve we choose such a point that a line through it
meeting the curve once will not necessarily meet the curve
twice. There must be such points, for there is a three-parameter
system of lines meeting the curve once, and only a two-para
meter meeting it twice. This point will be the vertex of a cone
whence the curve is projected simply on a plane.

More generally, take a curve in a space of r dimensions. It
is not possible that every space of $r-2$ dimensions that meets
the curve once should meet it twice. We see, in fact, that the
number of parameters giving the spaces of $r-2$ dimensions
through a point of the space of r dimensions is the number of
sets of $r-2$ linearly independent straight lines through the
point, less the number through the point in a space of $r-2$
dimensions, and is $2(r-2)$. The number of parameters giving
the spaces of $r-2$ dimensions through a line in r dimensions
will similarly be $2(r-3)$. The lines through a point of a curve
which meet it again form a one-parameter system. The spaces
of $r-2$ dimensions through a point on the curve which meet it
again depend on $2r-5$ parameters, which is less than the para
meter number of the system of all spaces of $r-2$ dimensions
through that point. Hence we may find plenty of spaces of $r-2$
dimensions which meet the curve once, but no more.

Let P be a point of the curve; $V_1, V_2,..., V_{r-2}$ independent points
of a space of $r-2$ dimensions through P which does not meet
the curve again. Then a general space of $r-2$ dimensions
through the space of $r-3$ dimensions determined by $V_1, V_2,..., V_{r-2}$
which meets the curve once, will not, automatically, meet it
again; so that the curve may be simply projected from the space
of $r-3$ dimensions upon an arbitrary plane, for in r dimensions,
a plane and a space of $r-2$ dimensions meet once. This same
thing can be done even when some of the points V_i lie on the

given curve. A space curve may be simply projected into a plane curve in one-to-one correspondence with it. If the space of $r-3$ dimensions be given by

$$X_0 = 0 \qquad X_1 = 0 \qquad X_2 = 0,$$

and the plane on which we project be that where only the coordinates X_0, X_1, X_2 do not vanish, the relation between plane and space curve may be written

$$X_0 = x_0 \qquad X_1 = x_1 \qquad X_2 = x_2 \qquad X_{2+i} = \frac{P_i(x_0, x_1, x_2)}{Q_i(x_0, x_1, x_2)}$$
$$f(x_0, x_1, x_2) = 0, \tag{6}$$

where the polynomials P_i are all of the same degree, which is one greater than that of Q_i.

More generally, we may project a curve from any space into another of any number of dimensions greater than one, and the relation is birational.

Definition. A space curve is said to be 'normal' if it cannot be obtained by projection from a curve of the same order but contained only in a space of more dimensions;* a conic is an example of such a curve, for every curve of the second order lies completely in a plane through three of its points. So is a cubic in three-space. So is a non-singular quartic in three-space which is the total intersection of two quadrics. We see, in fact, that this curve would be projected from one of its own points upon a plane, and the resulting curve would be a cubic curve with no singular point, which has genus 1. But a curve of the fourth order which lay in a space of order four and no less would be projected by planes through two of its points into a conic, which has genus 0.

Suppose that we have in our space of r dimensions S_r, a curve which has the property that the linear series cut by the hyperplanes is not complete, but contained in a series of higher dimension cut by some other surfaces. This series is certainly contained in a g_N^{r+1}, which may or may not be complete. Let O be a point outside our space of r dimensions S_r, say the point $(0, 0, 0, ..., 1)$. Let the g_N^{r+1} be cut by the system of surfaces

$$u_0 \phi_0 + u_1 \phi_1 + ... + u_{r+1} \phi_{r+1} = 0,$$

* Cf. Severi-Löffler, p. 93.

so that by taking $u_{r+1} = 0$ we get groups cut by hyperplanes, then the groups cut by

$$u_0 \phi_0 + u_1 \phi_1 + ... + u_r \phi_r = 0$$

will be the same as those cut by the hyperplanes

$$v_0 X_0 + v_1 X_1 + ... + v_r X_r = 0,$$

or, by a simple change of variable, the same series are cut by

$$u_0 \phi_0 + u_1 \phi_1 + ... + u_r \phi_r = 0$$
$$u_0 X_0 + u_1 X_1 + ... + u_r X_r = 0.$$

For a point on the given curve, where $\phi_i = \phi_i(x_1, x_2, x_3)$, $f(x_1, x_2, x_3) = 0,$ $\phi_i = \lambda X_i.$

If we allow the subscript i to take also the value $r+1$, we have a curve in the space of $r+1$ dimensions whose projection from O is the given curve. Conversely, if a curve in S_r be not normal but the projection of a curve in a space of higher dimensions, the linear series cut by hyperplanes of the curve in higher space will be projected into a series which will contain as a subseries that cut by the hyperplanes of the lower space.

Theorem 22] *The necessary and sufficient condition that a curve in a space of any number of dimensions be normal is that the series cut by hyperplanes be complete.*

Theorem 23] *The necessary and sufficient condition that the space curve obtained from a plane curve as in Theorem 21] should be normal is that the series in question should be complete.*

§ 4. The Riemann-Roch theorem

Suppose that we have a group G of N points which belongs to a complete g_N^r, and that the special adjoints through it cut the base curve in a special and complete $g_{N'}^{r'}$. If this series exist at all, i.e. if $r' \geqslant 0$, then the original series is special. We may find such a group of r' points that they, with G, determine just one special adjoint. If we add a fixed point P to every group of g_N^r, the resulting series, by our reduction theorem 8], is special and complete; the same will hold if we add a second point, and so on till we have added an r'th. But if we add one more point, the new complete series will be non-special, and

$$N + r' + 1 - r = p,$$
$$N - r = p - (r' + 1).$$

Definition. The index of specialization of a group is defined as the number of linearly independent special adjoints through that group. In the present case the index of specialization of the group G is
$$i = r' + 1.$$

Theorem 24] *All groups of a linear series have the same index of specialization.*

Riemann-Roch Theorem 25] *The dimension of a complete series is equal to the sum of the order and index of specialization of any group, less the genus of the base curve*
$$r = N + i - p, \tag{7}$$
$$N - r = p - i. \tag{8}$$

This theorem is of such fundamental importance, both in the theory of plane curves and that of algebraic functions, that it is worth while to bring it into another form. Suppose that the equation of the base curve is
$$f(x, y) = 0,$$
and that we have a rational function of x and y, i.e. a rational function of f on the corresponding Riemann surface,
$$\zeta = \frac{P(x, y)}{Q(x, y)}.$$

Introducing homogeneous coordinates, we may assume P and Q of the same order. The pencil of curves which we may assume adjoints
$$P(x_1, x_2, x_3) - \zeta Q(x_1, x_2, x_3) = 0$$
will cut a g_N^1 on the base curve. Conversely, every g_N^1 will give rise to a rational function. The correspondence is not one to one as the transformation
$$\zeta = \frac{\alpha \zeta' + \beta}{\gamma \zeta' + \delta}$$
will not give a new function, but merely permute the terms of the series. The set of rational functions so found is called a 'body'. Since the only one-to-one analytic transformation of a straight line into itself is a projective one, and since the groups of a g_N^1 correspond to the points of a line, there is no other system of rational functions corresponding to the g_N^1.

Theorem 26] *There is a one-to-one correspondence between the one-dimensional linear series on a curve and the bodies of rational functions on the corresponding Riemann surface.*

It is worth noting in passing that we may choose the multipliers in such a way that the zeros of the function and its poles will constitute two groups of the series, provided that contains no fixed points.

Theorem 27] *If the groups of a g_N^1 have no fixed points, two such may be taken as zeros and poles of a rational function on the corresponding Riemann surface.*

It is to be noted that a fixed point may be counted, in special cases, as the limit of a variable point. We get around the difficulty by saying that there is a variable point 'next' to the fixed point, an absurd but useful form of words.

Suppose, now, that we have a group of N points. Let us seek the most general rational function that will have poles of the first order at some or all of these points, but which is finite everywhere else.

Let $\dfrac{P}{Q}$ be a rational function with these poles which is finite at every other point of the Riemann surface. Then P is an adjoint of the same order as Q, which meets the base curve at the remaining intersections of Q, and is not subjected to any other restrictions, i.e. it is one of the set of adjoints cutting the complete series to which the group belongs, and so depends on r parameters. If $\dfrac{P'}{Q'}$ be a second rational function with the same poles, we shall have, by Nöther's fundamental theorem applied to f and Q',
$$P'Q \equiv \theta f + \bar{P}Q',$$
and $\bar{P}$ is an adjoint of the order of Q', through the remaining intersections of f and Q'. On the Riemann surface $f = 0$ and $\dfrac{P'}{Q'} = \dfrac{\bar{P}}{Q}$, where $\bar{P}$ is an adjoint of the general system for P just given.

Riemann-Roch Theorem 28] *The most general rational function on a Riemann surface which has poles of the first order at some or all the points of a given group, but which is everywhere else finite, depends on a number of parameters equal to the sum of the order of the group and the genus of the curve, less the index of specialization.**

* Cf. Roch, p. 372.

Suppose that a special adjoint meets the curve in $N+N'$ $= 2p-2$ points. Let r and r' be the dimensions of the corresponding complete series. Then by (8)

$$r = r'+1 = p+r-N$$

$$r' = r-N+\frac{N+N'}{2}$$

$$N-2r = N'-2r'. \tag{9}$$

Brill and Nöther Theorem 29] *If the total group of the canonical series be divided into two parts, the difference between the number of points in each part and the double of the dimension of the complete series to which it belongs is the same.**

It is not at all clear whether the numbers which appear on the two sides of (9) be positive or negative. If a special adjoint go through N' points, it has

$$i-1 = r'+p'-N'-1$$

degrees of freedom.

The N other points will determine it completely, so that they impose that number of conditions thereon. This number cannot be greater than the number they impose on an unrestricted special adjoint which, by the Riemann-Roch theorem, is $N-r$:

$$N-r \geqslant r'+p'-N'-1$$

$$N-2r \geqslant r'-r-N'+\frac{N+N'}{2}$$

$$N-2r \geqslant \tfrac{1}{2}[(N-2r)-(N'-2r')] = 0.$$

Clifford's Theorem 30] *The dimension of a special series can never exceed one-half its order.*†

We shall be able later to sharpen this theorem somewhat. We saw in the Reduction Theorem 8] that if a series be special and complete, and if a point not common to all the cutting adjoints be added to each group, the resulting series is complete. We find a converse in the following way. Suppose that when we add a fixed point to each group of a g_N^r the result is a complete series. The original series is obviously complete; moreover, it is special since

$$N+1-r \leqslant p \qquad N-r \leqslant p-1.$$

---

* Cf. Brill and Nöther, p. 28.   † Cf. Clifford[1], p. 331.

Lastly, the fixed point could not be common to all the adjoints which cut the series. For if we apply the Brill and Nöther theorem to the g_N^r and the g_{N+1}^r, we see that this point must apply an independent condition on a special adjoint, through the remaining points residual to the g_N^r, and the g_{N+1}^r would be included in a g_{N+1}^{r+1} where this point becomes variable, *contra hypothesem*.

Theorem 31] *If a series all of whose groups contain a fixed point be complete, the series obtained by omitting this point is special and complete, and the special adjoints which cut it do not all pass through this point.*

If a g_N^r be special and complete, and if the series obtained by adding a point P to all its groups be incomplete, this point must be common to all special adjoints which cut its groups. We must have a g_{N+1}^{r+1} which is special. Residual to the g_N^r in the canonical series is a complete $g_{N'}^r$, and residual to the g_{N+1}^{r+1} is a complete $g_{N'-1}^r$. If we add the point P to the groups of the latter, we get our $g_{N'}^r$.

Theorem 32] *If a g_N^r and a $g_{N'}^r$ be complete special series, residual to one another, the necessary and sufficient condition that the series obtained by adding a point to the one be incomplete, is that that point be fixed for the other.*

§ 5. Simple series and composite series

Suppose that we have a composite $g_{\mu\nu}^r$, which is complete and not special,
$$\mu\nu - r = p \qquad \mu \geqslant 2 \qquad \nu \geqslant r$$
$$2r - r \leqslant p$$
$$\mu\nu \leqslant 2p.$$

If $N > 2p$, the series is surely not special.

Theorem 33] *If the order of a complete series be greater than twice the genus of the curve, the series is certainly simple.*

Suppose that we have a composite g_{2r}^r:
$$2r = \mu\nu \qquad \nu \geqslant 2 \qquad \mu \geqslant 2.$$
These are only reconcilable when we have equality, not inquality. If $2r = 2p$, we have a g_{2p}^p, otherwise the series is special.

Theorem 34] *If the order of a composite series be twice its dimension, it is made up of an involution of grade 2, and is either a g_{2p}^p or is special.*

Theorem 35] *If the canonical series be composite, every special adjoint through an arbitrary point will pass through a second point variable with it.*

Definition. A curve of genus 1 is defined as 'elliptic'.

A cubic curve is an example of such a curve, and it contains a g_2^1 cut by lines through a fixed point. If a curve have genus greater than 1, and if the canonical series be composite, a special adjoint through an arbitrary point passes through a second variable with the first. The special adjoints through $p-2$ fixed points will cut a g_2^1. Conversely, if the genus of a curve be greater than 1, and if the curve have a g_2^1, this series is a special one for $2-1 < p$. The $(p-1)$th multiple of this series is special, and has at least the dimension $p-1$, hence it is the canonical series, and the latter will consist in sets of $p-1$ pairs of the g_2^1, i.e. every special adjoint through an arbitrary point goes through its mate in the g_2^1. The canonical series is composite.

Theorem 36] *If the canonical series of a curve be composite, the curve contains a g_2^1, and if a curve of genus greater than 1 contain a g_2^1, the canonical series is composed of pairs of that series.*

Definition. A curve fulfilling the requirements of theorem 36] is defined as 'hyperelliptic'. If a hyperelliptic curve had two different g_2^1's, each would produce a one-to-one correspondence of value 1 on the curve. The product of the two would be a one-to-one correspondence of value -1 by theorem 12] of Book I, Ch. VIII, and the number of coincidences would be $2(1-p) < 0$ by the Chasles-Cayley-Brill formula, theorem 14] of the same chapter; and this is absurd.

Theorem 37] *A hyperelliptic curve has only one g_2^1.*

Let p be an odd number. Construct a curve of order $n = \dfrac{p+5}{2}$ with a singular point of order $n-3$ and no other singularity. This is easily done. The special adjoints are curves of order $n-3$ with a common singularity of order $n-4$ and so rational curves. These curves cut one of their number in a series whose order and dimension are $2n-7$. If all the curves through a certain point on the curve of order n had to pass through another point abstracting from these two we should get on one of these curves, a g_{2n-9}^{2n-8} series whose dimension exceeded its order; an absurdity. Hence this curve is not hyperelliptic. When p is even we take a curve of order n with a point of order $n-3$ and a double point, and proceed as before.

Theorem 38] *There exist curves of every genus which are not hyperelliptic.*

Suppose that a series g_N^r is not composite. Is it possible that every group through $s < r$ points in general position should contain necessarily other points ? We assume that s is the smallest number for which this is the case, and transform as in theorem 21] to a curve of order N in a space of r dimensions. Then, by hypothesis, every hyperplane through s points will pass through certain other points. The hyperplanes through $s-2$ fixed points will depend on $r-s+3$ of their number, and will not necessarily pass through other points, and hyperplanes through an additional fixed point do not necessarily pass through any other point, but those through two more are supposed to pass through $\sigma+2$. Since $r > s$, we may find four linearly independent hyperplanes through the $s-2$ points, or, what amounts to the same thing, four linearly independent adjoints of our original system, and make the transformation

$$\rho X_0 = \phi_0 \qquad \rho X_1 = \phi_1 \qquad \rho X_2 = \phi_2 \qquad \rho X_3 = \phi_3.$$

This will carry our original curve into a curve in three-dimensional space which has the property that a plane through an arbitrary point will not, necessarily, meet it in any other chosen point; but one through two points does meet it in other variable points. This again amounts to saying that we have a curve in three-space with the property that a line which meets it twice will meet it more than twice. Let us show that this is impossible for a curve which is not plane, a case ruled out here by the linear independence of four groups. Suppose, in fact, that a space curve had the assumed property. Let A and B be any two points. Let the line AB meet the curve again in C. Then every line through C meeting the curve once elsewhere will meet it twice elsewhere, and the curve will be doubly projected from C. The tangents at A and B are in the tangent plane to this cone, and so coplanar. If we have a set of lines of which each two are coplanar, then either all lie in a plane, or all pass through a point. If all the tangents to our curve lay in a plane, it would be a plane curve contrary to hypothesis.

If all the tangents went through a point, say the origin, the curve would satisfy the differential equation

$$\frac{dx}{x} = \frac{dy}{y} = \frac{dz}{z},$$

and so be a set of lines through the origin, which is equally inadmissible. It appears, then, there is no such curve.

Theorem 39] *If a series be not composite, it is not possible that all groups containing a number of general points, less than the dimension, should necessarily contain other variable points.*

Theorem 40] *If a curve be not hyperelliptic, the special adjoints through a certain number, less than $p-1$, of general points will not necessarily contain other points of the curve.*

Theorem 41] *If a curve be not hyperelliptic, the special adjoints through s points in general position will cut a complete g_{2p-s-2}^{p-s-1} with no fixed points.*

Applying this to $p-3$ points, we get a g_{p+1}^2.

Theorem 42] *A non-hyperelliptic curve of genus p may be birationally transformed into a curve of order $p+1$.*

Suppose that we have a simple g_N^r. r points in general position will determine one group. Suppose that it were possible to find in each group s points of such a nature that all groups containing them would contain certain other variable points. Such a group of points will belong to ∞^{r-s} groups of the series, so that the number of these groups would be $\infty^{r-(r-s)} = \infty^s$, which amounts to saying the points are arbitrary, contrary to 39].

Theorem 43] *If a series be simple, it is not possible that each group should contain a number of points, less than the dimension, such that all groups through them will necessarily pass through other points variable with them.*

Suppose that we have a special complete g_N^r. Pick out any set of $N-r$ points in a generic group. Suppose that they present $N-r-l$ conditions to a special adjoint. By the Riemann-Roch theorem, the dimension of the complete series to which they belong is l. Adding the r points remaining, we get, by the Reduction Theorem 8], a complete g_N^l contained in a complete g_N^r, which is absurd unless $l=r$, and this particular set of r points belongs to every group of the g_N^r. Our original series would then have r fixed points.

Theorem 44] *If a g_N^r be special and complete with no set of r fixed points, every set of $N-r$ or less points of a generic group will present independent conditions to a special adjoint.*

Since a group of N points of a special series presents $N-r$ conditions to a special adjoint, if we represent the curve by one of order $2p-2$ in a space of $p-1$ dimensions, $p+r-N$ linearly independent hyperplanes will pass through the corresponding group of points, which must therefore lie in a space of $N-r-1$ dimensions. This curve of order $2p-2$ in a space of $p-1$ dimensions, which we shall have frèquent occasion to mention, is called the 'canonical curve'.

Theorem 45] *The groups of a complete special g_N^r on a non-hyperelliptic curve will be represented on the canonical curve by groups in spaces of $N-r-1$ dimensions.*

We saw in Clifford's theorem 30] that for a special series $N \geqslant 2r$; suppose that $N = 2r$. On the canonical curve we have a group of points in a space of $r-1$ dimensions. Such a space will be determined by r points and meet the curve again in r more points, which is ruled out by the reasoning that led up to 39].

Theorem 46] *For a special complete series other than the canonical series, $N > 2r$.*

We get at once from 22]

Theorem 47] *The canonical curve is normal.*

If the canonical curve had a singular point, this would impose a single condition on a hyperplane, but deduct more than one from the number of variable intersections with the curve, giving a special series whose order was not more than double its dimension, which we have just seen to be impossible.

Theorem 48] *The canonical curve has no singular point.*

If two canonical curves be birationally related, so are the corresponding plane curves, which must have the same genus. Hence the canonical curves are of the same order in the same number of dimensions, and hyperplane sections correspond on the two.

Theorem 49] *If two canonical curves be birationally related, the relation is a projective one.*

Theorem 50] *If a non-hyperelliptic curve be birationally transformed into itself, the corresponding canonical curve is projectively transformed into itself.*

Even a non-hyperelliptic curve may be birationally transformed into a space curve with no singular point. The totality of adjoints of order $n-2$ will cut a complete series whose order is $n-2+2p$ and dimension $n-2+p$, and so by 34] is simple. Also, for this series $N < 2r$. Here we have corresponding a curve of order N in a space of r dimensions. If there were a multiple point of order s, the hyperplanes through it would cut a g_{N-s}^{r-1} which is special, but that violates Clifford's theorem.

CHAPTER II

ABELIAN INTEGRALS

§ 1. Integrals of the first sort*

SUPPOSE that we have a base curve of genus p whose equation is

$$f(x, y) = 0. \tag{1}$$

We assume, as usual, that this curve is irreducible. y is an algebraic function of x, n-valued in the Gauss plane, single-valued on the corresponding Riemann surface whose branch points correspond to points of the curve where there are branches of order higher than the first, and to points where the tangent is vertical. If P and Q be two polynomials whose ratio is not constant, the expression

$$Y = \frac{P(x, y)}{Q(x, y)} \tag{2}$$

is an n-valued function of x in the Gauss plane, or single-valued on the Riemann surface. We may call it a rational function of x on that surface. It has no singularities but poles and polar branch points. If we eliminate y between (1) and (2), we get

$$F(x, Y) = 0. \tag{3}$$

Conversely, a single-valued function of x on the Riemann surface with no singularities but poles and polar branch points possesses the property that the elementary symmetric functions of its n values will be single-valued functions of x in the Gauss plane whose only singularities are poles, and so rational functions. If this function be called Y it will be connected with x by an equation of the type (3).

Definition. When x and y are connected by an equation such as (1), an integral of the type

$$\int\limits_{x_0, y_0}^{x, y} \frac{P(x, y)}{Q(x, y)} \, dx \tag{4}$$

shall be called an 'Abelian integral'. The value will depend on

---

* As the subject-matter of the present chapter is vast, and a little outside the natural course of our investigations, we give some of the proofs in rather sketchy form. The reader anxious to refresh his knowledge is referred to Appell et Goursat, to Picard, vol. ii, or to Severi-Löffler.

the limits of integration, and on the path followed upon the Riemann surface. Looked upon as a function of x, it can have poles or logarithmic singularities. The poles may or may not have residues. Since the sum of the residues all over the Riemann surface must be 0, the number of poles with residues of the integrand must be at least two, if there be any at all. Every Abelian integral can be built up from others of the following types:

1) Rational functions of x and y.

2) Integrals which are everywhere finite, defined as 'integrals of the first sort'.

3) Integrals with nothing worse than poles, defined as of the 'second sort'.

4) Integrals with pairs of logarithmic singularities, 'integrals of the third sort'.

With regard to integrals of the second sort, it is sufficient for our present purposes to consider those which have a single pole of the first order, for it is easy to show that every other integral of the second sort is made up of a rational function and p linearly independent integrals of the first sort, and p of the second with one simple pole each.*

The kernel of the whole matter lies in the integrals of the first sort. How do we know that such things exist anyway? An everywhere finite analytic function in the Gauss plane is a constant; why should not the same be true on a Riemann surface? It is not true, however: there are everywhere finite integrals which are not constants. We shall proceed to build one up, putting on the necessary conditions as we go along, and then show them to be sufficient.

As a preliminary simplification, let us assume that our curve has no singularities but nodes, that there are no vertical asymptotes, and no vertical tangents are singular. We know by Clebsch's Transformation Theorem 14] of Book II, Ch. I, that this pleasant situation can always be reached by means of a factorable Cremona transformation. The genus of the curve will remain unaltered by the transformation, and the canonical series carried into the canonical series. The number of branch points will be

$$m = 2(n+p-1),$$

* Cf. Appell et Goursat, p. 300.

and they are the points where the tangents are vertical. Let us see what happens at infinity. The curve meets the infinite line in n ordinary points with non-vertical tangents, corresponding to n developments of the form

$$y = b_{i1}x + a_{i0} + \frac{a_{i1}}{x} + \frac{a_{i2}}{x^2} + \dots .$$

When we substitute in a rational fraction $\dfrac{P}{Q}$ and integrate right out to infinity, the result remains finite when, and only when,

$$\frac{P(x,y)}{Q(x,y)} = \frac{b_{-2}}{x^2} + \frac{b_{-3}}{x^3} + \dots ;$$

and this demands that the degree of Q shall be at least 2 greater than that of P.

The other points where the integral might become finite are the 0's of the integrand, i.e. the intersections of the base curve (1) with $Q = 0$.

If the integral is to remain finite, even when the integrand becomes infinite, the latter must do so to a fractional power, i e. we must be at a branch point. At these points we must have

$$\frac{\partial f}{\partial y} = 0.$$

Let $y_1, y_2, \dots, y_n$ be the n values of y corresponding to a single value of x. We write the function

$$\sum_i y_i^k \frac{P(x, y_i)}{Q(x, y_i)}.$$

Since this is symmetric function of the y's it is a rational function in x, which becomes infinite in the finite region at most to a fractional power, i.e. a polynomial in x, and its degree cannot exceed $k-2$, since the degree of Q exceeds that of P by 2 at least.

$$\frac{P(x,y_1)}{Q(x,y_1)} + \frac{P(x,y_2)}{Q(x,y_2)} + \dots + \frac{P(x,y_n)}{Q(x,y_n)} = 0$$

$$y_1\frac{P(x,y_1)}{Q(x,y_1)} + y_2\frac{P(x,y_2)}{Q(x,y_2)} + \dots + y_n\frac{P(x,y_n)}{Q(x,y_n)} = 0 \tag{5}$$

$$\cdot \quad \cdot \quad \cdot \quad \cdot \quad \cdot \quad \cdot \quad \cdot \quad \cdot \quad \cdot \quad \cdot \quad \cdot \quad \cdot \quad \cdot \quad \cdot$$

$$y_1^k\frac{P(x,y_1)}{Q(x,y_1)} + y_2^k\frac{P(x,y_2)}{Q(x,y_2)} + \dots + y_n^k\frac{P(x,y_n)}{Q(x,y_n)} = R_{n-k}(x).$$

If we take n of the equations, the determinant of the coefficients is

$$\begin{vmatrix} 1 & 1 & . & . & . & . & 1 \\ y_1 & y_2 & . & . & . & . & y_n \\ . & . & . & . & . & . & . \\ y_1^{n-1} & y_2^{n-1} & . & . & . & . & y_n^{n-1} \end{vmatrix} = \pm\,\Pi(y_i - y_j)$$

and will not vanish identically, so that the equations may be solved for the fractions $\dfrac{P(x, y_i)}{Q(x, y_i)}$. We solve them in the following ingenious way. Let us write

$$\frac{f(x, y)}{y - y_i} = A_0 y^{n-1} + A_1 y^{n-2} + \dots + A_{n-2} y + A_{n-1}.$$

We multiply our first equation (5) by A_{n-1}, the second by A_{n-2}, the last by A_0, and add. The coefficient of $\dfrac{P(x, y_i)}{Q(x, y_i)}$ will then be

$$\frac{f(x, y)}{y - y_i},\ y = y_i,\ \text{and so} = \frac{\partial f}{\partial y_i}.$$

That of $\dfrac{P(x, y_j)}{Q(x, y_j)}$ will be

$$\frac{f(x, y)}{y - y_i},\ y = y_j,\ \text{and so} = 0.$$

Hence we have

$$\frac{\partial f(x, y_i)}{\partial y_i} \frac{P(x, y_i)}{Q(x, y_i)} = \phi_{n-3}(x_i, y_i)$$

$$\frac{P(x, y)}{Q(x, y)} = \frac{\phi_{n-3}(x, y)}{\dfrac{\partial f}{\partial y}}. \tag{6}$$

Since $\dfrac{\partial f}{\partial y}$ vanishes to the first order at the nodes, $\phi_{n-3}(x, y)$ must do the same and so be a special adjoint. Suppose, conversely, that we take

$$\int \frac{\phi_{n-3}(x, y)}{\dfrac{\partial f}{\partial y}}\, dx,$$

where ϕ_{n-3} is a special adjoint. The integrand is everywhere finite except at points where the tangent is vertical, and at the nodes. In the former case, since

$$\frac{\partial f}{\partial x}\,dx + \frac{\partial f}{\partial y}\,dy = 0,$$

$$\frac{\phi_{n-3}dx}{\dfrac{\partial f}{\partial y}} = -\frac{\phi_{n-3}dy}{\dfrac{\partial f}{\partial x}}$$

and the integral is finite. At a node the numerator and denominator vanish to the first order, and the integral is finite; we have indeed an integral of the first sort, and there is no other. Remembering the number of linearly independent special adjoints, we get

Riemann's Integral Theorem 1] *Associated with an irreducible curve of genus p there are p linearly independent integrals of the first sort. The zeros of the integrands are groups of the canonical series, and every such group will give rise to exactly one integral of the first sort.*[*]

In determining these integrals we made a very particular assumption as to singularities of the transformed curve. How far did we make use of this fact in our demonstration? Only in showing that the curve ϕ_{n-3} was an adjoint; its order was determined by other considerations. Let a birational transformation carry $f(x, y)$ into $f'(x', y')$; the correspondence between integrals of the first sort on the two curves may be written in the form

$$\frac{\phi_{n-3}(x, y)}{\dfrac{\partial f}{\partial y}}\,dx \equiv \frac{\psi_{n'-3}(x', y')}{\dfrac{\partial f}{\partial y'}}\,dx'.$$

Let G be a group of the canonical series of f, G' the corresponding group of the canonical series of f', H' the group of f' cut by ψ. Let (x_0, y_0) and (x_0', y_0') be corresponding points of the groups G and G'. Since

$$\psi_{n-3}(x_0', y_0')\frac{dx'}{dx} = 0,$$

and we may safely assume that we are not at a branch point so that $\dfrac{dx'}{dx} \neq 0$, then $\psi_{n-3}(x_0', y_0') = 0$, or (x_0', y_0') belongs to the

---

[*] Riemann cit. especially pp. 130 ff.

group H', which is thus identical with G'. The p linearly independent curves ψ cut f' in the canonical series. The same is true of the p linearly independent special adjoints ϕ'. No system of curves but the special adjoints could cut the canonical series, for such curves would have to be adjoints to behave at the singular points like the adjoints $\dfrac{\partial f}{\partial y'}$. Hence ψ and ϕ' are identical.

Theorem 2] *The necessary and sufficient condition that an Abelian integral be of the first sort is that the integrand take the form*

$$\frac{\phi_{n-3}(x,y)}{\dfrac{\partial f}{\partial y}}$$

where $\phi_{n-3}(x,y) = 0$ *is the equation of a special adjoint.*

§ 2. Integrals of other sorts

Let us next consider the special integral of the second sort with a single pole of the first order. If two integrals of the first sort share a single pole of the first order, a linear combination of them will be of the first sort. Hence we have merely to consider an individual integral of the second sort with a given pole. As before, the degree of the denominator must exceed that of the numerator by two, at least. Let the single pole be (x_0, y_0), and write the integral

$$\int \frac{\psi(x,y)}{\left[(x-x_0)\dfrac{\partial f}{\partial x_0} + (y-y_0)\dfrac{\partial f}{\partial y_0}\right]\dfrac{\partial f}{\partial y}} \, dx, \tag{7}$$

where ψ is an adjoint of order $n-2$. By our previous reasoning this integral will be finite everywhere except at (x_0, y_0) if we can find an adjoint ψ to go through the remaining $n-2$ intersections of f with the tangent

$$(x-x_0)\frac{\partial f}{\partial x_0} + (y-y_0)\frac{\partial f}{\partial y_0} = 0.$$

We know that the adjunction conditions are independent, so that the number of degrees of freedom of ψ is

$$\frac{(n-2)(n+1)}{2} - \sum \frac{r_i(r_i-1)}{2} = n+p-2.$$

This freedom is so great that ψ need not consist in the tangent and a special adjoint; we may find an irreducible adjoint of order $n-2$ to fit. The integrand has the development in the vicinity of (x_0, y_0),

$$\frac{a_{-2}}{(x-x_0)^2} + \kappa + a_1(x-x_0) + a_2(x-x_0)^2 + \dots .$$

The term in $(x-x_0)^{-1}$ is lacking, as we could not have a single pole with residue. Hence the integral has the desired form

$$\frac{-a_{-2}}{(x-x_0)} + c + \kappa(x-x_0) + \frac{a_1}{2}(x-x_0)^2 + \frac{a_2}{3}(x-x_0)^3 + \dots .$$

If we take a group of points $P_1, P_2, \dots, P_p$ which are not on the same special adjoint, and if $E_1, E_2, \dots, E_p$ be the Abelian integrals of the second sort, each with a pole of the first order at the corresponding point P, while $I_1, I_2, \dots, I_p$ are p linearly independent integrals of the first sort, then it may be shown that every Abelian integral with no logarithmic singularity may be expressed in the form*

$$\sum \alpha_i E_i + \sum \beta_i I_i + \frac{P(x,y)}{Q(x,y)} . \tag{8}$$

There remain integrals of the third sort. These are found by the same considerations as those of the second sort, and take the form

$$\int \frac{\psi(x,y)}{\begin{vmatrix} x & y & 1 \\ x_1 & y_1 & 1 \\ x_2 & y_2 & 1 \end{vmatrix} \dfrac{\partial f}{\partial y}} \, dx, \tag{9}$$

where ψ is an adjoint of order $n-2$ through all the intersections of f with the straight line which appears in the denominator except (x_1, y_1) and (x_2, y_2).

§ 3. Abel's Theorem

Suppose that we have a rational one-parameter system of points on our base curve, i.e. a set cut by the rational system of curves

$$R(x, y, z) = 0,$$

* Cf. Appell et Goursat, pp. 338 ff.

where R is a polynomial not independent of z. Consider the integrals

$$\int_{x_0,y_0}^{x_1,y_1} \frac{P}{Q}\,dx + \int_{x_0,y_0}^{x_2,y_2} \frac{P}{Q}\,dx + \ldots + \int_{x_0,y_0}^{x_N,y_N} \frac{P}{Q}\,dx = F(z)$$

$$\frac{P(x_1,y_1)}{Q(x_1,y_1)}\frac{dx_1}{dz} + \frac{P(x_2,y_2)}{Q(x_2,y_2)}\frac{dx_2}{dz} + \ldots + \frac{P(x_N,y_N)}{Q(x_N,y_N)}\frac{dx_N}{dz} = \frac{dF}{dz},$$

where (x_1,y_1) $(x_2,y_2)\ldots$ are a group cut by a particular curve R for a given z and the integral

$$\int \frac{P(x,y)}{Q(x,y)}\,dx$$

is of the first or second sort. The left-hand side is an algebraic function which is single-valued, owing to its symmetry, hence the right-hand side is rational, and F the integral of a rational function, and so is rational except, perhaps, for logarithmic singularities. The latter cannot occur if

$$\int \frac{P(x,y)}{Q(x,y)}\,dx$$

be an integral of the first or second sort.

If our group of points depend rationally not on one variable but on several, we get a set of functions which are rational in each variable alone, and, hence, rational in all together[*] or involve at worst logarithmic singularities.

This gives us

Abel's Theorem 3] *The sum of the values of an integral of the first or second sort from a fixed point to the points of intersection with a curve depending rationally upon any number of parameters is a rational function of those parameters.*[†]

A rational function which is everywhere finite is a constant.

Theorem 4] *The sum of the values of an integral of the first sort from a fixed point to the points of intersection with a curve depending rationally on any number of parameters is a constant.*

The value of this constant will depend, naturally, on the point of departure of the integral, and the path followed on the Riemann surface. We may state the theorem by saying that the

---

[*] Cf. Osgood, vol. ii, p. 283.

[†] Cf. Abel, p. 515, also Severi-Löffler, p. 267, and Appell et Goursat, ch. ix.

sum of the values of the integral will not be altered by a slight displacement of the rational group of points.

If $(x_1, y_1), ..., (x_N, y_N)$ and $(x'_1, y'_1), ..., (x'_N, y'_N)$ be two groups of a linear series, or, as we have called them, two equivalent groups, and if

$$\int \frac{\phi(x, y)}{\frac{\partial f}{\partial y}} \, dx$$

be an integral of the first sort,

$$\sum_{i=1}^{i=N} \int_{x_i, y_i}^{x'_i, y'_i} \frac{\phi(x, y)}{\frac{\partial f}{\partial y}} \, dx = 0. \tag{10}$$

Suppose, conversely, that we have two groups of N points, and that this equation holds for every integral of the first sort. It can be shown by methods of the theory of functions which would carry us too far afield* that the groups (x_i, y_i) and (x'_i, y'_i) are equivalent, or that these necessary conditions are also sufficient.

The theorem is certainly very plausible when the conditions thus imposed upon the group (x'_i, y'_i) are independent. For the number of parameters on which the group depends will thus be $N - p$. On the other hand this will contain the complete g^r_N determined by the group (x_i, y_i), and the number of parameters of this is given by the Riemann-Roch Theorem 28] of the first chapter in the present book. We have thus

$$N - p \geqslant N - p + i.$$

Hence

$$i = 0 \qquad N - p = N - p.$$

Since the total system of points and the linear system included therein depend on the same number of parameters, it is natural to conclude that they are identical. This is not an exact proof, and of course is inapplicable when the conditions are not independent. We therefore state without proof:

Theorem 5] *The necessary and sufficient condition that two groups of the same order should be equivalent is that the sum of the values of each integral of the first sort from a fixed point to the point of one group should differ only by multiples of the periods of the integrals from the corresponding sum for the second group.*

* Cf. Severi-Löffler, p. 271.

CHAPTER III

SINGULAR POINTS OF CORRESPONDENCES

§ 1. The Chasles-Cayley-Brill Correspondence Formula

In Chapter VIII of Book I we developed the Chasles-Cayley-Brill correspondence formula, and drew a number of conclusions from it. The formula was developed only for curves with ordinary singular points and cusps, and we assumed there were no coincidences at cusps. In Chapter IV of Book II we showed that the formula holds even when the curve has any sort of singularities, but we assumed that no coincidences came on branches of order higher than the first. If they do, the formula still holds, since it is birationally invariant, and we can carry over to a curve with none but linear branches, but we must see how to count the coincidences on super-linear branches. We first restate the formula itself.

Chasles-Cayley-Brill Theorem 1] *The number of coincidences, rightly counted, of a (ν, ν') correspondence of value γ on a curve of genus p is*

$$\nu + \nu' + 2p\gamma. \tag{1}$$

Suppose that we have a branch of order ρ_0 at the origin, and that P and P' are corresponding points thereon,

$$x = t^{\rho_0} \quad y = a_0 t^{\rho_0} + a_1 t^{\rho_1} + \dots \quad x' = t'^{\rho_0} \quad y' = a_0 t'^{\rho_0} + a_1 t'^{\rho_1} + \dots$$
$$OP = p_0 t^{\rho_0} + p_\alpha t^{\rho_\alpha} \dots \quad OP' = p_0 t'^{\rho_0} + p_\alpha t^{\rho_\alpha}$$
$$\sqrt[\rho_0]{OP'} - \sqrt[\rho_0]{OP} = (t' - t)(A_0 + A_1 t + B_1 t' + \dots).$$

The correspondence arises from a certain number of equations

$$\theta_1(x, y, x', y') = \theta_2(x, y, x', y') = \dots = \theta_k(x, y, x', y') = 0,$$

and for the present purposes gives rise on the branch to a single equation

$$\phi(t, t') = \psi(t, t' - t);$$

the number of coincidences at the origin will be the multiplicity of t as a factor when we put $t' - t = 0$, or in the (t, t') plane the number of intersections of ψ with $t' - t = 0$ at the origin. That is the infinitesimal order in t of the product of the roots of this equation in $t - t'$, or the sum of the infinitesimal orders of the expressions $\sqrt[\rho_0]{OP'} - \sqrt[\rho_0]{OP}$ where t or $\sqrt[\rho_0]{OP}$ is the principal infinitesimal.

Theorem 2] *The number of coincidences $P' = P$ at the origin*

O of a branch of order ρ_0 is the sum of the infinitesimal orders of the distances $\sqrt[p_0]{OP'} - \sqrt[p_0]{OP}$ where the distance $\sqrt[p_0]{OP}$ is taken as an infinitesimal of the first order.

We repeat word for word theorem 11] of the last chapter of Book II.

Theorem 3] *Given a g_N^r and certain points $A_1, A_2,..., A_l$ such that ∞^{r-j} adjoints cutting groups of the series meet the base curve $\nu_{ij} + j$ times at A_i, then the number of places other than the A's where a group has $r+1$ coincident points is*

$$(r+1)[N+r(p-1)] - \sum_{ij} \nu_{ij}. \tag{2}$$

A coincidence of more than $r+1$ points would account for several of these.

As an example, let us look for the 'sextactic' points (it is hard to keep away from sex these days) of a curve of order n and class m, i.e. the number of points where a non-degenerate conic has six-point contact. We have here $N = 2n$ and $r = 5$. Assuming that the curve has only ordinary singular points and cusps, though the general case could be handled with a bit of care, we see that any conic through a cusp has two intersections there, a tangent conic has three, etc., so that the deduction for κ cusps will be 5κ. We must also cut out each inflexional tangent counted twice, for that is a conic; the deduction for the inflexions will thus be $\iota(0+0+0+0+1) = \iota$.

The number of sextactic conics is thus

$$12n + 30(p-1) - 5\kappa - \iota$$
$$= 12n + 30(p-1) - 5[2n-m+2(p-1)] - [2m-n+2(p-1)]$$
$$= 3[n+m+6(p-1)]. \tag{3}$$

Theorem 4] *If a curve of order n and class m have no singular points but ordinary ones and cusps, and no singular tangent but ordinary ones and inflexional ones, the number of sextactic conics is*[*]

$$3[n+m+6(p-1)].$$

Suppose that we have given a g_N^r and a g_M^1. How many groups of the latter contain $r+1$ points of a group of the former ? We shall call this number for the present purposes $\phi(N, r)$. Let P be a general point of the curve, Q a generic name for one of the

* First determined by Cayley[2], p. 217.

$M-1$ points going with it in the g_M^1. We pick r of these points Q and use them to determine a group of the g_N^r. The remaining points of the group shall be called P', so that to each point P will correspond $\binom{M-1}{r}(N-r)$ points P'. Conversely, when P' is given, there will correspond $(M-r)\phi(N-1,r-1)$ points P. Here are the indices of the correspondence: we must determine its coincidences, but this has to be done indirectly. When P is given there are $\binom{M-1}{r}$ sets of r points Q lying with it in a group of g_M^1, each individual Q lying in $\binom{M-2}{r-1}$. We may say, symbolically, that $\binom{M-2}{r-1}Q+P'$ is a group of a correspondence meaning, thereby, that all the points P' and each Q counted $\binom{M-2}{r-1}$ times is a group of a complete series which is the $\binom{M-1}{r}$th multiple of our g_N^r. This extended correspondence is the correspondence of P to P' plus $\binom{M-1}{r}$ times the correspondence of P to Q. The extended correspondence has the value 0. The number of coincidences is

$$\binom{M-1}{r}(N-r)+\phi(N-1,r-1)+2(M-1)\binom{M-2}{r-1}.$$

These are made up of the $2(M+p-1)$ coincidences of the g_M^1 each counted $\binom{M-2}{r-1}$ times, and the coincidences of the original correspondence coming in $\phi(N,r)$ groups of $r+1$ each:

$$\binom{M-1}{r}(N-r)+(M-r)\phi(N-1,r-1)+2(M-1)\binom{M-2}{r-1}$$
$$=2\binom{M-2}{r-1}(M+p-1)+(r+1)\phi(N,r)$$

$$(M-r)\phi(N-1,r-1)+N\binom{M-1}{r}+(M-1)\binom{M-2}{r-1}$$
$$=(r+1)\phi(N,r)+2\binom{M-2}{r-1}(M+p-1)$$
$$\phi(N-1,0)=N-1$$
$$\phi(N,1)=(N-1)(M-1)-p,$$

for we have the product of two correspondences of value 1:

$$\phi(N,1) = N\binom{M-1}{1} - \binom{M-2}{0}(M+p-1)$$

$$\phi(N-1,1) = (N-1)\binom{M-1}{1} - \binom{M-2}{0}(M+p-1).$$

Let us assume that

$$\phi(N,r-1) = N\binom{M-1}{r-1} - \binom{M-2}{r-1}(M+p-1),$$

so that

$$\phi(N-1,r-1) = (N-1)\binom{M-1}{r-1} - \binom{M-2}{r-1}(M+p-1)$$

$$(M-r)(N-1)\binom{M-1}{r-1} - (M-r)\binom{M-2}{r-1}(M+p-1) +$$

$$+ N\binom{M-1}{r} + (M-1)\binom{M-2}{r-1}$$

$$= (r-1)\phi(N,r) + 2\binom{M-2}{r-1}(M+p-1).$$

The total coefficient of N is

$$(M-r)\binom{M-1}{r-1} + \binom{M-1}{r} = (r+1)\binom{M-1}{r}$$

$$-(M-r)\binom{M-1}{r-1} + (M-1)\binom{M-2}{r-1} = 0.$$

If all the terms involving $(M+p-1)$ be moved to the left, the total coefficient will be

$$-(M-r)\binom{M-2}{r-1} - 2\binom{M-2}{r-1} = -(r+1)\binom{M-2}{r-1}$$

$$N(r+1)\binom{M-1}{r} - (r+1)\binom{M-2}{r-1}(M+p-1) = (r+1)\phi(N,r).$$

Theorem 5] *The number of groups of $r+1$ points common to a group of a g_N^r and a group of a g_M^1 is*[*]

$$N\binom{M-1}{r} - \binom{M-2}{r-1}(M+p-1). \tag{4}$$

[1] Cf. Severi-Löffler, pp 191, 192.

§ 2. The Jacobian series

Suppose that our base curve

$$f(x_1, x_2, x_3) = 0$$

is cut by the pencil of curves

$$\lambda\phi + \mu\psi = 0.$$

The g_N^1 so determined has a certain number of singular points arising from curves of the pencil that pass through singularities of the base curve to a higher degree than usual, and from contact. In either case we have

$$\frac{\partial(f, \phi, \psi)}{\partial(x_1, x_2, x_3)} = 0.$$

It will be possible, though not necessary, to assume that f has only ordinary singularities, a condition that can be brought about by a factorable Cremona transformation, as we saw in Nöther's transformation theorem 11] of Book II, Ch. I. Since a transformation of this sort will carry a Jacobian into a Jacobian, there is no loss. The group of singular points of the g_N^1 arising from coincidences between points on the same branch shall be called the 'Jacobian Group'.

Theorem 6] *The Jacobian group of a one-dimensional linear series is given by intersections of the base curve with the Jacobian curve of itself and two curves cutting the series.*

Now let us take two groups of a g_N^1 cut by the curves

$$\phi \equiv r_0\theta_0 + r_1\theta_1 + \ldots + r_r\theta_r,$$

$$\psi \equiv s_0\theta_0 + s_1\theta_1 + \ldots + s_r\theta_r,$$

the Jacobian Group of the g_N^1 cut by $\lambda\phi + \mu\psi$ will be given by

$$\sum \begin{vmatrix} r_i & r_j \\ s_i & s_j \end{vmatrix} \frac{\partial(f, \theta_i, \theta_j)}{\partial(x_1, x_2, x_3)} = 0. \tag{5}$$

The complete series containing all groups cut by this last system of curves is called the 'Jacobian series' of the given linear series.

Theorem 7] *The Jacobian groups of all g_N^1's of a g_N^r are contained in a complete $g_{2(N+p-1)}^R$.*

Let us return to the Jacobian group of a g_N^1. Let one of the centres of the pencil approach a limiting position on the base curve. The g_N^1 will approach a g_{N-1}^1, and the latter has a Jacobian group of $2(N+p-2)$ points, or two less than before. Hence, if all groups of a g_N^1 have a common point, this must be counted doubly in the Jacobian group.

Suppose, next, that we have a g_N^1 and a g_M^1. Let G' be a group of the latter. If we add this to the g_N^1 we get a series whose Jacobian group consists in that of g_N^1 plus twice the group G'. Applying this to each group of g_N^1, we get

Theorem 8] *The Jacobian series of the sum of two given series is the sum of the Jacobian series of one, and the double of the other series.*

We get a very curious result by interchanging the roles of the two series in this theorem. The sum of a Jacobian group of one series, plus twice a group of the second, is equivalent, in the sense of Book I, Ch. VIII, to the sum of a Jacobian group of the second plus twice a group of the first. Hence, by the arithmetical operations there explained, we see that the difference between a Jacobian group of one and twice a group of that one is equivalent to the difference between a Jacobian group of the other and twice a group of the other. Or, using the theory of sums and differences of series explained in the first chapter of the present book, we see that the difference between the Jacobian series and the double of a given series is independent of the series chosen. Let us take, in particular, the g_n^2 cut by all straight lines. The Jacobian group of a pencil of lines is the points of contact of tangents from the centre of the pencil and the extraordinary singular points, and so on the first polar of that centre. The Jacobian series is that cut by all adjoints of order $n-1$, and so is not special but a $g_{2(n+p-1)}^{p+2(n-1)}$. The difference between this and the double of the given series is that cut by all adjoints of order $n-3$, for one of these and a line counted twice is an adjoint of order $n-1$.

Theorem 9] *The canonical series is the difference between the Jacobian series of a given series and the given series counted twice.*

This gives immediately another proof of the theorem that the canonical series will be birationally transformed into the canonical series.

§ 3. The De Jonquières formula

We shall devote the present section to the repellant but interesting task of finding how many groups there are in a g_N^r

consisting in ρ different points having multiplicities $k_1, k_2, ..., \boldsymbol{k_\rho}$, where

$$\sum k_i = N \qquad \sum (k_i - 1) = r = N - \rho.$$

This means that, by imposing $k_i - 1$ conditions, we get a multiplicity k_i at least. When the multiplicity is greater than this, we count the coincidences as in theorem 2] of the present chapter. We need not assume that all of the k_i's have different values. Suppose the value k_1 is repeated α_1 times, the value k_2 α_2 times, and so on. Let us represent the number we seek by the curious symbol

$$\frac{[k_1 k_2 ... k_\rho]}{\alpha_1! \, \alpha_2! \, ...}.$$

To show the suitableness of the notation, suppose that $k_1 = k_2 = ... = k_{\alpha_1}$. The number of groups where these were distinguished would be $\alpha_1!$ times the number where they were indistinguishable, i.e.

$$\frac{[k_{11} k_{12} ... k_{1\alpha_1} ... k_\rho]}{\alpha_2! \, \alpha_3! \, ...} = \frac{\alpha_1! \, [k_1 k_2 ... k_\rho]}{\alpha_1! \, \alpha_2! \, ...}$$

$$[k_{11} k_{12} ... k_{1\alpha_1} ... k_\rho] = [k_1 k_2 ... k_\rho].$$

Suppose, next, that no two numbers of $k, k_1, k_2, ..., k_\rho, k_1 + k,$ $k_2 + k, ..., k_\rho + k$ are equal. Consider a g_{N+k}^{r+k} on our base curve. If we take such of the adjoints cutting this series as meet the curve k times at a chosen point ρ, there will be residual thereto a g_N^r. The number of groups with multiplicities $k_1, k_2, ...$ will be $[k_1 k_2 ... k_\rho]$. Let us take one such group, and call the first point $k_1 Q_1$, the second $k_2 Q_2$, and so on. They will correspond to P in a correspondence of value $k[k_1 k_2 ... k_\rho]$.

Conversely, if a point Q_1 be given, if we look upon it as k_i near points there will correspond thereto $k_i [k_1 k_2 ... k_i ... k_\rho]$ points P, etc.

It might seem natural to think that this number should be multiplied by k since the adjoints have k-point contact at P. But in finding the value of the correspondence we counted P *as a single point*, and then multiplied by k because the adjoints have k-point contact. The factor k_i is accounted for because the single P corresponds to k_i adjacent Q_1's. The coincidences of P and Q will come from points of multiplicity $(k + k_i)$, such a group counting as k_i coincidences. We thus get from Chasles-Cayley-Brill, theorem 1] of the present chapter,

$$\sum_i k_i[k_1k_2...k_\rho]+k_1[kk_2...k_\rho]+k_2[k_1k...k_\rho]+...+2pk[k_1k_2...k_\rho]$$
$$= k_1[(k+k_1)k_2...k_\rho]+k_2[k_1(k+k_2)...k_\rho]+...+$$
$$+k_\rho[k_1k_2...(k+k_\rho)]. \quad (6)$$

Next we must see what modifications are needed if some of the different numbers be equal.

a) $$k_1 = k_2 = ... = k_{\alpha_1}.$$

We should replace $[k_1k_2...k_\rho]$ by $\dfrac{[k_1k_2...k_\rho]}{\alpha_1!}$ and $[kk_2...k_\rho]$ by $\dfrac{[kk_2...k_\rho]}{(\alpha_1-1)}$.

But what were formerly α_1 types of coincidence are now replaced by one type, so we must divide by α_1. In the same way our expressions $[(k+k_1)k_2...k_\rho]$ should all be divided by $\alpha_1!$. Multiplying out this common divisor, we fall back on (6).

b) $$k = k_1.$$

This is somewhat like the last case, but $[k_1k...k_\rho]$ must be replaced by $\dfrac{[k_1k...k_\rho]}{2}$. The divisor 2 may be multiplied out as before, as 2 points P correspond to Q_2.

c) $k_1 = (k_2+k)$. Here we shall have to multiply and divide in certain cases by 2, but the net result is the same. Our formula (6) always holds.

It is now time to build by mathematical induction; the essential thing is to take the various steps in the right order.

$[1, 1, ...k_\rho]$ can be found from our formula (2) for all values of the last argument. Taking $k_1 = k_2 = ... = k_{\rho-2} = 1, k = k_{\rho-1}-1$ we find $[1, 1, ...k_{\rho-1}k_\rho]$ for all values of the last two arguments. Continuing in this way, we finally get $[k_1k_2...k_\rho]$, *and at every stage of the process one of the k's is equal to* 1.

We shall now proceed to show

$$[k_1k_2...k_\rho] = k_1k_2...k_\rho[\rho!+(\rho-1)!\,p\sum(k_i-1)+$$
$$+(\rho-2)!\,p(p-1)\sum(k_i-1)(k_j-1)+...+$$
$$+p(p-1)...(p-\rho+1)(k_1-1)(k_2-1)...(k_\rho-1)], \quad (7)$$

no two indices under a summation sign being supposed equal. By (2)

$$[1, 1, ... k_\rho] = (\rho-1)! \, k_\rho [\rho-1+k_\rho+(k_\rho-1)(p-1)]$$
$$= k_\rho[\rho!+(\rho-1)! \, p(k_\rho-1)],$$

so that the formula (7) holds at the first stage of the process. Suppose it holds at some stage, let us show that it holds at the next stage by showing that we get a true equation by substituting in (6).

We rewrite (6)

$$k_1\{[(k+k_1)k_2...k_\rho]-[k_1k_2...k_\rho]-[kk_2...k_\rho]\}+$$
$$+k_2\{[k_1(k+k_2)...k_\rho]-[k_1k_2...k_\rho]-[k_1k...k_\rho]\}+$$
$$\cdot \quad \cdot \quad \cdot \quad \cdot \quad \cdot \quad \cdot \quad \cdot \quad \cdot \quad \cdot \quad \cdot \quad \cdot \quad \cdot \quad \cdot \quad \cdot$$
$$-2pk[k_1k_2...k_\rho]=0, \qquad (8)$$

and if we write $k_1k_2...k_\rho = \Pi$, (7) may be written

$$[k_1k_2...k_\rho]$$
$$= \Pi p(p-1)...(p-\rho-1)\left[\frac{\Pi}{p-\rho}-\frac{\sum \dfrac{\partial \Pi}{\partial k_i}}{p-\rho+1}+\frac{\sum \dfrac{\partial^2 \Pi}{\partial k_i \partial k_j}}{p-\rho+2}-...\right]+$$
$$+(-1)^\rho\frac{1}{p}=0. \qquad (9)$$

We substitute in (8) and collect the terms. Since this is a formal identity, we may divide out $\Pi p(p-1)...(p-\rho+1)$. The total coefficient of $\dfrac{1}{p-\rho}$ will be $2(\rho-p)k\Pi$.

The total coefficient of $\dfrac{-1}{p-\rho+1}$ will be

$$\sum_i (k+k_i)\left[\sum_j \frac{\partial \Pi}{\partial k_j}+k\sum_j \frac{\partial^2 \Pi}{\partial k_i \partial k_j}\right]-\sum_i k_i \sum_j \frac{\partial \Pi}{\partial k_j}-$$
$$-k\left[\sum_i\left\{k\sum_j \frac{\partial^2 \Pi}{\partial k_i \partial k_j}+\frac{\partial \Pi}{\partial k_j}\right\}\right]-2kp\sum_j \frac{\partial \Pi}{\partial k_j}.$$

But

$$\sum_{ij} k_i \frac{\partial^2 \Pi}{\partial k_i \partial k_j} = (\rho-1)\sum_j \frac{\partial \Pi}{\partial k_j}.$$

Hence we get the coefficient $2k(\rho-p-1)\sum_j \dfrac{\partial \Pi}{\partial k_j}$.

In the same way the coefficient of $\dfrac{(-1)^{\sigma-1}}{p-(\rho-\sigma)}$, besides the partial derivatives, is $2k[\rho-p-\sigma]$. The result of substituting is

$$-2k\left[\Pi-\sum_i\frac{\partial\Pi}{\partial k_i}+\sum_{ij}\frac{\partial^2\Pi}{\partial k_i\partial k_j}\cdots\right]=-2k(k_1-1)(k_2-1)\cdots(k_\rho-1).$$

But we have already noted that one k_i is necessarily 1. Hence, on the left as on the right, we have 0; the substitution yielded correct results, and the formula steps up and is proved by induction.

De Jonquières Theorem 10] *The total number of groups of a g_N^r consisting in a point of multiplicity k_1, one of multiplicity $k_2,...,$ one of multiplicity k_ρ, where $\sum k_i=N$, $\sum(k_i-1)=r$, and where α_1 points have one multiplicity, α_2 another, etc., and $\Pi=k_1k_2...k_\rho$ is*

$$\frac{\Pi p(p-1)\cdots(p-\rho)}{\alpha_1!\,\alpha_2!\cdots}\left[\frac{\Pi}{p-\rho}-\frac{\sum_i\dfrac{\partial\Pi}{\partial k_i}}{p-\rho+1}+\frac{\sum_{ij}\dfrac{\partial^2\Pi}{\partial k_i\partial k_j}}{p-\rho+2}+\cdots\right]\qquad(10)$$

* De Jonquières[2], pp. 289 ff. The proof here given is an expansion of Zeuthen[6], pp. 240 ff.

CHAPTER IV

MODULI AND LIMITING VALUES

§ 1. The gap theorem of Weierstrass

SUPPOSE that we have $p-k$ general points of our base curve where $k \geqslant 0$. Their index of specialization is k, and the complete series of which they are a group will have the dimension $p-k+k-p=0$. Hence they cannot be the group of poles of a rational function. On the other hand, if we take $p+l$ points,

$$r = p+l-p = l.$$

Theorem 1] *The smallest number of points in general position which can be the group of poles for a rational function of x and y is one more than the genus of the curve.*

Theorem 2] *A necessary and sufficient condition that the dimension of the complete series which contains a given group should be other than 0, is either that the number of points is less than or equal to the genus, and the conditions imposed on a special adjoint not independent, or the number is greater than the genus.*

Suppose that we have a set of N points $P_1, P_2, ..., P_N$ on a base curve which is not hyperelliptic, and has the genus p. Let us assume that the points $P_1, P_2, ..., P_\mu$ impose independent conditions on a special adjoint, but that every special adjoint through them also goes through $P_{\mu+1}, P_{\mu+2}..., P_{\mu_1-1}$. We suppose that P_μ is the first point of the series having this property. The groups $P_1, ..., P_\mu$ and $P_1, ..., P_{\mu+1}$ have the same index of specialization, but for the second group $r = 1$. The point $P_{\mu+1}$ could not be fixed for this, for if it were, $P_1, ..., P_\mu$ would be a group of a complete g_μ^1. Neither could a previous point, say P_1, be fixed, for the order of these first μ points is immaterial; they merely impose independent conditions. $P_1, P_2, ..., P_\mu, P_{\mu+1}$ are a group of a complete series with no fixed point and are poles of a rational function. Since the points $P_{\mu+1}, P_{\mu+2}, ..., P_{\mu_1-1}$ enter symmetrically, we see that they are a group of a complete series with no fixed point, for a point fixed in this series would be fixed in the series of order $\mu+1$ just described. The point P_{μ_1} shall impose a new condition on all adjoints through $P_1, ..., P_{\mu_1-1}$. The group $P_1, P_2, ..., P_{\mu_1}$ belongs to a series of order μ_1 and of dimension

$\mu_1 - \mu - 1$, so that the index of specialization is $p - \mu - 1$. Suppose that all these special adjoints go through $P_{\mu_1+1}, ..., P_{\mu_2-1}$. Here we have a complete series of order $\mu_2 - 1$; the index of specialization is $p - \mu - 1$ as before, hence the dimension is $\mu_2 - \mu - 2$. Let us show there is no fixed point. If there were a fixed point with index $\geqslant \mu_1$, dropping that point we should have a series with index $p - \mu$, so that all special adjoints through $P_1, ..., P_\mu$ would pass through the remaining points, which is not the case. But if the subscript were $< \mu_1$, we should be in the same trouble as before when we assumed P_1 fixed.

Let P_{μ_2} be another point of our original set, and let us assume that all the special adjoints through $P_1, P_2, ..., P_{\mu_2}$ go also through $P_{\mu_2+1}, P_{\mu_2+2}, ..., P_{\mu_3-1}$, we may go through exactly the same reasoning as before, getting a new series of variable points. Keeping on in this way we shall get points $P_{\mu_1}, P_{\mu_2}, ..., P_{\mu_l}$ which impose new conditions on a special adjoint, so that $\mu + l = p - 1$ if the adjoint be now fixed, and go through various other points, perhaps $P_{\mu_l+1}, ...,$ of our group. If we take a last point P_{μ_l+1} not among these it will also impose another impossible condition (like the last of p points in general position), every succeeding point will determine a series of positive dimension. This gives

Weierstrass's Gap Theorem 3] *Given a succession of non-singular points which are on a non-hyperelliptic curve of genus p, but are not a group of the canonical series, the number of groups of the first k which cannot constitute the group of simple poles of a rational function is p.*

Taking the points 'next' to one another, we get a more familiar form:

Weierstrass's Gap Theorem 4] *Given a non-singular point of a non-hyperelliptic curve of genus p. The orders which it cannot possess as the single pole of a rational function are p in number.*[*]

Given a point in general position on a curve, a special adjoint with $(p-1)$-point contact will not, usually, have higher contact. There are exceptional curves, which we shall study later, where this can happen. The lowest multiplicity it can have as a single pole of a rational function is $p+1$. If the contact conditions were not independent, so that a special adjoint with $(p-1)$-point contact has really higher contact, the order of the lowest pole

* Weierstrass, p. 69.

is less; the point is called a Weierstrass point. We get at once, from Chapter III, theorem 3] of the present book:

Theorem 5]   *The number of Weierstrass points on a non-hyperelliptic curve of genus p is $p(p^2-1)$.*

It is to be understood here that if these adjoints have higher contact still, the number of coincidences, or of identical Weierstrass points, is greater.

§ 2. Moduli

Two curves of the same order cannot, clearly, be projected into one another, i.e. carried into one another by a linear transformation, unless they have the same Plücker characteristics. Even this is not a sufficient condition in the case of curves of order greater than 2. If we allow ourselves not merely linear transformations but birational ones, the hope of carrying two curves into one another is greatly strengthened. A non-hyperelliptic curve of genus p may be carried into a curve of order $2p-2$ in a space of $p-1$ dimensions with no singular point, the canonical series being carried into that cut by hyperplanes.

It appears, thus, that the N.S. condition that two non-hyperelliptic curves, necessarily of the same genus, should be capable of being birationally carried into one another is that the corresponding non-singular curves in higher space should be capable of being carried into one another by a linear transformation, i.e. that they should be projectively equivalent. The Weierstrass points on the plane curves will correspond to Weierstrass points on the space curves where tangent hyperplanes required to have a certain amount of contact will automatically have a higher contact. Let μ be the lowest integer for which it is true that all hyperplanes at a certain point with μ-point contact have higher contact, say $(\mu+1)$-point contact. This point counted $\mu+1$ times is a group of a complete $g^1_{\mu+1}$, as we saw by the reasoning which led up to Weierstrass's gap theorem. The pencil of secant hyperplanes cutting $g^1_{\mu+1}$ will have $2(\mu+1)$ of its members tangent to the space curve by Chasles-Cayley-Brill applied to the $g^1_{\mu+1}$, but μ of the coincidences are accounted for at the given point. There are $\mu+2p$ others, and the hyperplanes of their pencil making these contacts will have $\mu+2p-3$ cross ratios, invariant numbers for the curve under a projective transformation when the other points of contact are distinct.

It occurs to us at this point that perhaps the Weierstrass points coalesce in two or three places, so that there are really very few of them. We can get a limit here as follows.* Suppose that at a certain Weierstrass point ∞^{p-1-j} special adjoints meet a branch of the curve $j+v_j$ times. Applying Clifford's theorem 30], Book III, Ch. I, to the residual series, we have

$$2p-2-(v_j+j) \geqslant 2(p-1-j) \qquad v_j \leqslant j.$$

The number of Weierstrass points accounted for by this particular one (for this branch) is thus

$$v_1+v_2+...+v_{p-1} \leqslant 1+2+...+p-1 \leqslant \frac{p(p-1)}{2}.$$

Theorem 6] *No one Weierstrass point can account for more than* $\dfrac{p(p-1)}{2}$ *falling together on the same branch.*

It might occur to us that trouble would come at a very complicated singularity, but these theorems are birationally invariant, and we may suppose the curve transformed into one with no singularities but nodes. Remembering 5]:

Theorem 7] *The number of distinct Weierstrass points on the curve of order* $2p-2$ *in a space of* $p-1$ *dimensions is at least*

$$2p+6.$$

Since this number is greater than the order of the non-singular space curve, the Weierstrass points of the latter could not all lie in a space of lower dimensions.

Suppose, now, we had a non-hyperelliptic or elliptic curve that is carried into itself by an infinite number of birational transformations. In hyperspace we should have a curve carried into itself by an infinite number of collineations. There would therefore be an infinite number of these collineations which left all the Weierstrass points in place. But the number of the points we have just seen $\geqslant 2p+6$, and not more than $2p-2$ can lie in any hyperplane. The hyperplanes of closest contact at each of these points will also be invariant. If we take $p-2$ of the Weierstrass points determining a space of $p-3$ dimen-

* Cf. Segre[5], p. 90.

sions, not more than $2p-2$ Weierstrass points can lie in this space. Through it will pass a pencil of hyperplanes. There must be at least nine other Weierstrass points, and as at least eight Weierstrass points lie outside any hyperplane, at least three hyperplanes of the pencil go to other Weierstrass points. There are an infinite number of collineations carrying these three hyperplanes into themselves and so keeping invariant every hyperplane of the pencil and its set of intersections with the curve. Hence, as many points as we please are invariant, or all are. A hyperelliptic curve cannot be carried into itself by an infinite number of birational transformations, for its g_2^1 cannot be.

Theorem 8] *A curve of genus greater than 1 cannot be carried into itself by an infinite number of birational transformations.*

Let us try to discover just how many independent invariants a curve of genus p has under the group of all birational transformations. On how many parameters does the general g_N^r depend ? By Riemann-Roch for a non-special g_N^r

$$r = N-p.$$

The number of parameters in the system of all groups of N points is N, the number in our series is r, hence the sets of all complete g_N^r's depend on p parameters. Now consider an incomplete not special g_N^r. It is contained in a complete g_N^{N-p}. The number of g_N^r's in such a g_N^{N-p} is the number of sets of $r+1$ linearly independent polynomials in a set of $N-p+1$ such, or of spaces of r dimensions in a space of $N-p$ dimensions, it is the number of sets of $r+1$ independent points in a space of $N-p$ dimensions, less the number in a space of r dimensions, and so is $(r+1)(N-p-r)$. Adding p for the complete series, we get

Theorem 9] *The number of parameters on which depend the totality of non-special series of order N and dimension r on a curve of genus p is* $$(r+1)(N-r)-pr.$$

When $N > 2(p-1)$, the number of parameters for a g_N^2 is $3(N-2)-2p > 2$. Take the g_N^2 determined by

$$\lambda_0\psi_0+\lambda_1\psi_1+\lambda_2\psi_2 = 0.$$

Make the transformation

$$\rho X_i = \psi_i(x_1, x_2, x_3).$$

It will carry our curve into one of order N, and the given g_N^2 into that cut by all straight lines. It is to be noted that our given curve can be carried through this g_N^2 into a plane curve of order N in ∞^8 ways corresponding to the number of collineations of the plane into itself. If two different g_N^2's could give us the same set of curves of order N, the g_{N-1}^1 residual to a given point in the first g_N^2 would be carried by the first transformation into sets of $N-1$ points collinear with a fixed point, and be carried by the inverse of the second transformation into a set of $N-1$ points residual to a point P'. There would be a birational relation between the points P and P', and the curve would be birationally transformed into itself. We have just seen that for a non-hyperelliptic curve of genus greater than 2 this can only be done in a finite number of ways. Hence, the plane curves of order N derivable from our given curve in this way depend on

$$3(N-2)-2p+8 = 3N-2(p-1)$$

parameters.

Suppose, now, we replace our original curve of genus p by another not birationally equivalent, we get another plane curve of order N not projectively equivalent to the first. We saw in Lefschetz's theorem 4] of Book I, Ch. VII, that the total freedom of a curve of order N and genus p is

$$\frac{N(N+3)}{2} - \left(\frac{(N-1)(N-2)}{2} - p\right) = 3N+p-1.$$

Taking from this the number of parameters in a set projectively equivalent to a given curve, we get the number of parameters governing the sets, i.e. the number of birationally invariant numbers for a given curve:

$$3N+(p-1)-[3N-2(p-1)] = 3(p-1).$$

Theorem 10] *A non-hyperelliptic curve of genus greater than 2 has $3(p-1)$ independent birationally invariant numbers, no constants independent of the curve.*

These numbers are defined as 'moduli' of the curve.*

§ 3. Limiting values

The numbers N, p, and r are connected by a certain number of inequalities. These are reached by considering the multiples of

* Our proof of 10] is from Severi-Löffler, pp. 157 ff.

a given series.* Let us consider first the kth multiple of a g_N^r. Suppose, first, $k \leqslant \dfrac{N-1}{r-1}$. We may find k different sets of $r-1$ points of a generic group which have the property that an adjoint of the set cutting the given series through them will not necessarily go through any other of the N points. Our group must, therefore, impose at least $k(r-1)+1$ independent conditions on the adjoints which cut the kth multiple of the given series. Suppose, on the other hand,

$$k > \frac{N-1}{r-1} \qquad N-1 = l(r-1)+\lambda \qquad \lambda < r-1 \qquad k \geqslant l+1.$$

We may take l adjoints through the l groups, each of which contains, usually, no other point of the N, so that these will impose $l(r-1)$ conditions on the lth multiple of the series. The remaining λ points will impose independent conditions on one of our adjoints, so that the whole set will impose $l(r-1)+\lambda = N$ conditions on the $(l+1)$th multiple, and on every higher multiple

Theorem 11] *If a g_N^r have no fixed points and $r > 1$, the points of a generic group will impose at least $k(r-1)+1$ independent conditions on the kth multiple of the given series, when $k \leqslant \dfrac{N-1}{r-1}$, but N independent conditions when k is greater.*

The difference between the kth multiple and the given series is, by definition, a complete series, and so is the $(k-1)$th multiple. If r_k and r_{k-1} be the dimensions of the kth and $(k-1)$th multiples respectively, we have

$$r_{k-1} \leqslant r_k - k(r-1)+1 \qquad\qquad k \leqslant \frac{N-1}{r-1}$$

$$r_k - r_{k-1} \geqslant k(r-1)+1 \qquad\qquad k \leqslant \frac{N-1}{r-1}$$

$$r_k - r_{k-1} \geqslant N \qquad\qquad k \geqslant \frac{N-1}{r-1}$$

$$r = (r-1)+1$$
$$r_2 - r \geqslant 2(r-1)+1$$
$$r_2 \geqslant 3(r-1)+2$$
$$r_k \geqslant \frac{k(k+1)}{2}(r-1)+k \qquad\qquad k \leqslant \frac{N-1}{r-1}. \qquad (1)$$

---

* Cf. Castelnuovo.[2]

Let
$$\frac{N-1}{r-1}-1 \leqslant K < \frac{N-1}{r-1}.$$

Let us show that in this case the Kth multiple is not special. We see that the number of conditions a general group imposes on the Kth multiple is
$$\geqslant K(r-1)+1 \geqslant N-r+1.$$

But if the Kth multiple were special, so would the original series be special, and the highest number it can impose on any special adjoint is $N-r$ by Riemann-Roch. Hence the Kth multiple is not special or
$$N-r_K = p$$
$$p \leqslant K(N-1)-\frac{K(K+1)}{2}(r-1) \tag{2}$$
$$p \leqslant K\left[(N-r)-\frac{(K-1)}{2}(r-1)\right]. \tag{3}$$

Theorem 12] *If a curve of genus p contain a g_N^r with no fixed points, $r>1$,*
$$p \leqslant K\left[(N-r)-\frac{(K-1)}{2}(r-1)\right] \qquad \frac{N-1}{r-1}-1 \leqslant K < \frac{N-1}{r-1}.$$

It is clear that this inequality can be turned around in various ways.*

Suppose that the smallest multiple of a g_N^r which is not special is the hth,
$$h \leqslant K \leqslant \frac{N-1}{r-1}.$$
From (2)
$$r \leqslant \frac{2h(N-1)-2p}{h(h+1)}+1.$$

Since the $(h-1)$th multiple is special,
$$(h-1)N \leqslant 2(p-1)$$
$$h \leqslant \frac{2(p-1)}{N}+1.$$

We have a function of h which dominates r. The derivative to h is positive if
$$h(h+1)(N-1)-[h(N-1)-h](2h+1) > 0$$
$$2p > (N-1)(h-1)+\frac{(N-1)}{h}.$$

* Cf. Comesati.

This can be written

$$\frac{2(p-1)}{N} > (h-1) - \frac{(h+1)}{N} + \frac{1}{h} - \frac{1}{hN}.$$

But we know

$$\frac{2(p-1)}{N} \geqslant (h-1).$$

Hence the dominating function increases with h right up to its limit. If, therefore, we pick out such an integer ρ that

$$\frac{2(p-1)}{N} < \rho \leqslant \frac{2(p-1)}{N} + 1 \tag{4}$$

$$r \leqslant \frac{2[\rho(N-1)-p]}{\rho(\rho+1)} + 1. \tag{5}$$

Theorem 13] *An upper limit for the dimension of a series of order N with no fixed points on a curve of genus p is*

$$r \leqslant \frac{2[\rho(N-1)-p]}{\rho(\rho+1)} \qquad \frac{2(p-1)}{N} < \rho \leqslant \frac{2(p-1)}{N} + 1.$$

Let us try to turn things about so as to get a lower limit for N when r and p are given. We have from (2)

$$N \geqslant \frac{K+1}{2}(r-1) + \frac{p}{K} + 1.$$

But

$$N \leqslant (K+1)(r-1) + 1$$

$$\frac{K+1}{2}(r-1) \geqslant \frac{p}{K}$$

$$\frac{K(K+1)}{2} \geqslant \frac{p}{r-1}$$

Let us write

$$N \geqslant \frac{(h+1)}{2}(r-1) + \frac{p}{h} + 1 \qquad h \leqslant K.$$

This decreases as h increases as long as

$$\frac{h^2}{2} \geqslant \frac{p}{r-1}.$$

If, then, $\qquad \tau(\tau-1) < \dfrac{2p}{r-1} \leqslant \tau(\tau+1), \tag{6}$

$$N \geqslant \frac{(\tau+1)}{2}(r-1) + \frac{p}{\tau} + 1. \tag{7}$$

Theorem 14] *A lower limit for the order of a series with no fixed points of dimension r on a curve of genus p is*

$$N \geqslant \frac{(\tau+1)}{2}(r-1)+\frac{p}{\tau}+1 \qquad \tau(\tau-1) < \frac{2p}{r-1} \leqslant \tau(\tau+1).$$

Consider, in particular, $r = 2$,

$$N \geqslant \frac{(\tau+1)}{2}+\frac{p}{\tau}+1 \qquad \tau(\tau-1) < 2p < \tau(\tau+1)$$

$$\frac{1+\sqrt{8p+1}}{2} > \tau \geqslant \frac{-1+\sqrt{8p+1}}{2}.$$

If the curve be non-singular so that

$$2p = (n-1)(n-2)$$

$$\tau \geqslant n-2,$$

$$N \geqslant \frac{n-1}{2}+\frac{(n-1)(n-2)}{2(n-2)}+1 = n.$$

Theorem 15] *If a curve have no singular point, the lowest possible order for a series of dimension 2 is the order of the curve.*

This is also evident because if it were possible to have a series of dimension 2 and lower order, we might transform the curve into another of lower order, but every curve of lower order will certainly have a lesser genus.

Our determination of the number of g_N^r's on a curve of genus p was limited to non-special series. It is time to take up the case of special series also. Looking at the problem as one in the projective geometry of higher space, we have a space of $p-1$ dimensions carrying a curve of order $2p-2$. Suppose that a $(n-r)$-parameter system of hyperplanes cuts this curve in N variable points. By the Riemann-Roch theorem one of the groups will impose $N-r$ conditions on a hyperplane, so they will all lie in a space of $N-r-1$ dimensions that meets our curve N times. We know by the reasoning on page 266 that every space of this number of dimensions that meets the curve $N' < N$ times will not, necessarily, meet it N times.* To require a space

* This assumption is tacitly made in most discussions of the problem as

of $N-r-1$ dimensions, in one of $p-1$ dimensions, to go through a given point amounts to requiring $p-N+r$ hyperplanes to go through there, and imposes that number of restrictions. To require it to meet a given curve will impose one less restriction; to require it to meet the curve N times, *under our present assumption*, will impose $N[(p-1)-(N-r)]$ conditions. The spaces of $N-r-1$ dimensions in a space of $p-1$ dimensions depend on $(N-r)[(p-1)-(N-r-1)]$ parameters; hence, the number of parameters going with those which meet it N times is $r(N-r)-rp+N$. The series being complete, each group belongs to but one of these hyperplanes, but there are ∞^r groups in the series. Hence, the series depends on $(r+1)(N-r)-rp$ parameters.

There remain the non-complete series. Suppose that such a series has the index of specialization i. The number of g_N^r's through a group will be the number of linearly independent spaces of r dimensions in a space of $N-p+i$ dimensions, i.e. $(r+1)(N-p+i-r)$. We have seen that the number of parameters on which a complete g_N^{N-p+i} depends is

$$(p-i)(N-p+i+1)-p(N-p+i).$$

The g_N^r's are included in these, but no g_N^r is in more than one. Hence, the number of parameters determining the incomplete g_N^r is

$$(N-p+i+1)(p-i)-p(N-p+i)+(r+1)(N-p+i-r)$$

$$= (r+1)(N-r)-ip-i(N-p+i-r).$$

This number is not greater than the number for the complete series, hence

Theorem 16] *In a curve of genus p the special g_N^r's will depend on $(r+1)(N-r)-rp$ parameters.*

This theorem leads at once to the solution of the problem of finding the lowest order of curve to which a general curve of genus p can be birationally transformed. By Riemann-Roch, for $r=2$

$$N-2=p-i,$$

e.g. Brill and Nöther. The only complete discussion I have seen is Severi-Löffler, pp. 380–90. It is involved, and too long to reproduce here.

so that we shall have the minimum order when the series cut
by straight lines is special. Let

$$(r+1)(N-2) \geqslant rp \qquad r = 2$$
$$3(N-2) \geqslant 2p$$
$$3N \geqslant 2p+3$$

$$p = 3\rho \qquad N = 2\rho+1$$
$$p = 3\rho-1 \qquad N = 2\rho+2$$
$$p = 3\rho+1 \qquad N = 2\rho+3$$
$$p = 3\rho+2 \qquad N = 2\rho+4.$$

Theorem 18] *If a curve have the restriction imposed in theorem
17], the lowest order of any curve to which it can be birationally
transformed is*

$$p = 3\rho \qquad n = 2\rho+1$$
$$p = 3\rho-1 \qquad n = 2\rho+2$$
$$p = 3\rho+1 \qquad n = 2\rho+3$$
$$p = 3\rho+2 \qquad n = 2\rho+4.$$

CHAPTER V

CURVES OF SPECIAL TYPE

§ 1. Curves containing series of given sort

THE inequalities given at the close of the last chapter show that if a base curve be given, it may, or may not, contain series of given description. It is our next task to find properties of curves which do contain assigned series.

Suppose that a curve contain a g_N^1 and a g_M^1, neither with a fixed point, and with no common linear series of dimension greater than 0. Each series gives rise to a correspondence of value 1, hence the pairs of points in the same group in both series are the points of coincidence in a correspondence of value -1. The number of these pairs is, thus,

$$\tfrac{1}{2}[(N-1)(M-1)+(M-1)(N-1)-2p] = (N-1)(M-1)-p. \quad (1)$$

If the two series have a common group of k points, this will count for $\dfrac{k(k-1)}{2}$ pairs. Let the two series be cut by

$$X_0\phi_1+X_1\phi_2 = 0 \qquad X_0\psi_1+X_2\psi_2 = 0,$$

where the curves ϕ_2 and ψ_2 pass through the group of k points. Eliminating x and y between these and the equation of the base curve, we get
$$F(X_0, X_1, X_2) = 0,$$

a curve birationally related to the original one. We should expect from theorem 11] of Book I, Ch. I, that the order of this curve would be $N+M$, but the resultant is reducible; each of the k common points gives X_0 as a factor of the new curve, and a moment's calculation shows that it gives it only once. The order will, then, be $N+M-k$. When X_0 and X_1 are given there are N points (x,y), and so N values X_2; when X_0 and X_2 are given there are M points (x,y), and so M values X_1.

Theorem 1] *A curve which contains two one-dimensional series of orders N and M with no common linear series of dimension 1, but with a common group of k points, may be birationally transformed into a curve of order $N+M-k$ with a point of order $M-k$, and one of order $N-k$.*

We can always assume $N = M = p$, and $k = 2$, so that we can always transform birationally into a curve of order $2p-2$ with two points of multiplicity $p-2$. However, there are better ways to proceed. Suppose that our curve is of genus above 2 and is not hyperelliptic. We may find thereon a group of $p+1$ points which is not special, and a second non-special group sharing p with the first.

Theorem 2] *A curve of genus greater than 2 which is not hyperelliptic may be transformed birationally into a curve of order $p+2$.*

§ 2. Elliptic curves

A curve of genus 1 is defined as elliptic. If we take two random points, the dimension of their complete series is 1, for a curve with a g_2^r contains a g_1^1, and so is rational. We get from 1]:

Theorem 3] *An elliptic curve may always be birationally transformed into a non-singular cubic.*

Let us seek a canonical form for the equation of a cubic curve. By Plücker's equations of Book I, Ch. VII, it has nine inflexions. By Book I, Ch. II, theorem 19], corollary 5, a line connecting two inflexions passes through a third. Klein's equation of Book I, Ch. VII, shows that just three of these must be real for a real curve. The line connecting two conjugate imaginary inflexions will be real, and meet the cubic again in a real inflexion. There are three real inflexions by Klein's equation. They lie on a real line. Through each real inflexion will pass four lines to pairs of other inflexions. These lines are real, or conjugate imaginary in pairs. We know that one is real, that to the other two real inflexions, hence another is real also; so here are three real lines each with one real and two conjugate imaginary inflexions,

The conic polar of a point on a cubic is easily shown to be the locus of points harmonically separated from the given point by pairs of points of the curve. The conic polar of an inflexion is the inflexional tangent, and the polar of the inflexion with regard to a pair of lines containing each three other inflexions. If, thus, l_1, l_2, and l_3 be three real lines each with one real and two imaginary inflexions, the conic polars of all points on l_1 pass through the intersection of l_2 and l_3, and as this is not on the curve its line polar is l_1; l_1 does not go through there, the three are not concurrent, and may be taken as sides of the coordinate triangle. The line polar of each vertex is now the opposite side of the triangle, and the equation of the curve is seen to be*

$$a_1 x_1'^3 + a_2 x_2'^3 + a_3 x_3'^3 + b x_1' x_2' x_3' = 0.$$

Putting $x_i = \sqrt[3]{a_i x_i'^3}$,

$$x_1^3 + x_2^3 + x_3^3 - 6m x_1 x_2 x_3 = 0. \tag{2}$$

Suppose that A and B are any two points of the cubic, the line AB meeting the curve again at C. Let CT touch the curve at T. A line through A shall meet the curve again in A_1, A_2. The lines TA_1, TA_2 shall meet it again in B_1, B_2 respectively. The group $TT + A_1 A_2$ is residual to $A + C$, as is also B. Hence B_1, B_2, which are residual to T, T, A_1, A_2, are residual to B, or B, B_1, B_2 are collinear. We thus have a one-to-one algebraic relation between the lines through A and B, i.e. a projective relation, and the tangents from A correspond to the tangents from B. This gives

Theorem 4] *The cross ratio of four tangents to a non-singular cubic from a point of that curve is the same for all points of the curve.*[†]

It is clear that it is possible to express this cross ratio in terms of the coefficient m that appeared in equation (2). The work is tedious, but it is found that if r be one of these cross ratios,[‡]

$$\frac{(r^2 - r + 1)^3}{(r+1)^2 (r-2)^2 (2r-1)^2} = \frac{16(m + m^4)^3}{(1 + 20m^3 - 8m^6)^3}. \tag{3}$$

The lines through a point of the cubic cut a g_2^1. This is the only sort of g_2^1 that the curve has, for a point residual to one pair of a g_2^1 is residual to all, or all pairs are collinear with the same point. Every birational transformation will carry a g_2^1 into another.

Theorem 5] *An elliptic curve has but one independent modulus, a cross ratio determined by four double points of a g_2^1.*

A g_2^1 gives an involutory transformation of the curve into itself. The product of two of these is a one-to-one transformation of the curve into itself, depending on a correspondence of value -1. We shall call these, temporarily, 'product transformations'. They are not involutory, as we shall see more clearly in a subsequent chapter.

Suppose that we have a birational transformation of the cubic that carries A to A'. It will carry the single g_2^1 with A as a double point, into the single g_2^1, with A' as a double point, so that lines through the point I collinear with AA will be carried projectively into lines through the point I' collinear with $A'A'$, and the four tangents at I go to the four tangents at I'. Since the line IA corresponds to $I'A'$ and the cross ratios are equal, the relation between the two tetrads is uniquely determined, unless the four tangents form a harmonic or equi-harmonic set. Excluding these cases, when we know that A goes to A', and so I to I', if another line through I meet the curve in B_1B_2 and the corresponding line through I' meet it in $B_1'B_2'$, our transformation will be completely determined when we know whether B_2 goes to B_1' or to B_2'. Now we can find an involutory transformation to accomplish one of these results, and a product one to accomplish the other, whence we get

Theorem 6] *If an elliptic curve be neither harmonic nor equi-harmonic, the only birational transformations which carry it into itself are involutory ones and product ones.*

The product of two product transformations is a birational transformation of value -1 and so a product transformation. They form a continuous group, and this group depends on one parameter giving the fate of a chosen point.

Theorem 7] *The product transformations of an elliptic curve which is neither harmonic nor equi-harmonic into itself form a continuous one-parameter group.*

In a later chapter we shall express the coordinates of the points of a cubic curve in terms of an auxiliary parameter by means of elliptic functions. We shall there get a very simple expression for these two kinds of transformations in terms of elliptic functions. It will appear at once that two product transformations are commutative, but two involutory ones are not.

There are special cubic curves which permit of other birational transformations into themselves; we shall see an example in a later chapter.*

* The literature of birational transformations of cubic curves is large. See 'Topics' chs. vii and xv, and Segre[2].

§ 3. Hyperelliptic curves

The characteristic property of a hyperelliptic curve is that it has a genus greater than 1, yet contains a g_2^1 which must be complete and special, for if there be a g_2^2 there will be a g_1^1, and this characterizes a rational curve. If we take $p+2$ points in general position, no two being mates in the g_2^1, by the Riemann-Roch theorem, they characterize a g_{p+2}^2 by means of which the curve may be transformed birationally into a hyperelliptic curve of order $p+2$. There must be some singular points in order to have a genus p. If such a point be of order r, the lines through it will cut a g_{p+2-r}^1, which must be special; hence the mate of every point in the g_2^1 must be on the line to this point, or there is only one distinct singularity. Let this be the end of the y-axis, and let the g_{p+2}^1 be cut by the pencil of curves

$$\theta_1(x,y) + x'\theta_2(x,y) = 0.$$

Then $x = \dfrac{P(x')}{Q(x')}$, for only two intersections with the base curve depend on x', and these·have the same x. For y we have

$$\phi_0(x')y^2 + 2\phi_1(x')y + \phi_2(x') = 0. \tag{4}$$

The number of values of x' for which two of the y's fall together is $2p+2$, hence the degree of this equation must be $p+2$. When x' is given there are but two y's, hence there is a point of order p at the end of the y-axis, and there can be no other singularities, since the genus is p.

Theorem 8] *A hyperelliptic curve of genus p can be birationally transformed into a curve of order $p+2$ with a single singular point of order p.*

We can transform our curve (4) to a simpler one in the following fashion:

$$y = \frac{y' - \phi_1(x')}{\phi_0(x')}$$

$$y'^2 = \phi_0(x')[\phi_0(x')y^2 + 2\phi_1(x')y] + [\phi_1(x')]^2$$

$$y'^2 = -\phi_0(x')[\phi_2(x')] + [\phi_1(x')]^2$$

$$y'^2 = f_{2p+2}(x'). \tag{5}$$

Theorem 9] *A hyperelliptic curve of genus p can be birationally transformed into a curve with an equation of the type*

$$y^2 = f_{2p+2}(x'). \tag{5}$$

This curve is of higher degree than (4) but simpler equation. It has a point of multiplicity $2p$ at the end of the y-axis, and a number of other singularities clustering infinitely near, for there are no singularities at a finite distance, as, if there were, (4) would have such.

Theorem 10] *A hyperelliptic curve of genus p may be birationally transformed into a curve of order $2p+2$ with a point of multiplicity $2p$, and p double points clustering close to it.*

Let us seek the power-series development of our curve in the vicinity of the singular point by the methods of Book II, Ch. II. Using homogeneous coordinates,

$$y^2 = f_{2p+2}(x,z) = a_0 x^{2p+2} + a_1 x^{2p+1} z + \ldots$$
$$x = x'^p \qquad z = z' x'^{p+1} \qquad y = 1$$
$$z'^{2p} = a_0 + a_1 z' x' + \ldots$$

$$z' = (\sqrt{a_0})^{\frac{1}{p}} + \alpha_1 x' + \ldots \qquad z' = (-\sqrt{a_0})^{\frac{1}{p}} + \beta_1 x' + \ldots$$
$$z = (\sqrt{a_0})^{\frac{1}{p}} x^{\frac{p+1}{p}} + \ldots \qquad z = (-\sqrt{a_0})^{\frac{1}{p}} x^{\frac{p+1}{p}} + \ldots$$
$$x = t^p, \quad z = (\sqrt{a_0})^{\frac{1}{p}} t^{p+1} + \ldots \quad x = t^p, \quad z = (-\sqrt{a_0})^{\frac{1}{p}} t^{p+1} + \ldots . \quad (6)$$

Theorem 11] *If a hyperelliptic curve of genus p be birationally transformed to the form*

$$y^2 = f_{2p+2}(x),$$

there are at the singular point two branches of order p and class 1.*

The degree of our equation (5) may be slightly reduced as follows. The polynomial f has only simple roots, as we saw a few lines back. If α be one of these, and we write

$$x' = \alpha + \frac{1}{x} \qquad y' = \frac{y}{x^{p+1}} \qquad x = \frac{1}{x'-\alpha} \qquad y = \frac{y'}{(x'-\alpha)^{p+1}}$$
$$y'^2 = \psi_{2p+1}(x'). \quad (7)$$

Theorem 12] *A hyperelliptic curve of genus p may be birationally transformed into a curve of the form*

$$y^2 = \psi_{2p+1}(x). \quad (7)$$

This seems, on the whole, less useful than (5); the essential difference is that in the case of (5) the double points of the g_2^1 are the intersections with the x-axis, but in the case of (7) there is one at infinity.

* Cf. Severi-Löffler, p. 148.

When three of the vertical tangents to (5) are known, the others are given by the cross ratios they make with these three.

Theorem 13] *A hyperelliptic curve of genus p has $2p-1$ moduli.*

We could not have a hyperelliptic curve of genus p whose order was less than $p+2$, for the series cut by all lines in the plane would be special, but a general line through a point of the curve cannot connect it with its mate in the g_2^1. Suppose that the order is n, and that there are only ordinary singular points. We seek the class of the envelope of lines connecting pairs of the g_2^1. To find the number of tangents through an arbitrary point we must find the number of pairs of the g_2^1 which are in a group of the g_n^1 cut by radiating lines through an arbitrary point. The number we find at once by Chasles-Cayley-Brill.

Theorem 14] *If a hyperelliptic curve have only ordinary singular points, the class of the envelope of lines connecting pairs of the g_2^1 is $n-p-1$.*

Suppose that the system of adjoints which cuts the g_2^1 is

$$\phi_0(x,y)+t\phi_1(x,y)=0.$$

If we eliminate y between this and the equation of the curve, we get a reducible equation in x, the first part, dependent on t, will be quadratic in x.

$$P(t)x^2+2Q(t)x+R(t)=0.$$

The symmetric functions of the roots are rational in t, as also the coefficients in the equation of the line connecting the two points*

$$u_i=u_i(t).$$

We may generate our curve in the following fashion. Let a special adjoint ϕ cut the curve in pairs of points $A_1A_1', A_2A_2'...$. Let A_iA_i' be on

$$u_i=u_i(t).$$

Then $u\phi$ is an adjoint of order $n-2$ meeting f in $n-2$ other points. They, with the points $A_1A_1', A_2A_2'...$, are residual to one group of our g_2^1, hence there is a pencil of adjoints of order $n-2$ through these last points, and the group of $n-2$ cutting our g_2^1. Such a pencil may be written

$$u\phi-\mu\chi=0.$$

* Cf. Bobek, pp. 390 ff.

Let θ_2 be a conic meeting f in A_lA_l' and again in $2(n-1)$ points through which we can pass a pencil of adjoints of order $n-1$:

$$\theta_2\phi - \mu\psi = 0.$$

Whence we have $\qquad f \equiv u\psi - \theta_2\chi,$

enabling us to study the generation of f by sets of lines and conics.

§ 4. Polygonal curves

A curve containing a g_1^1 is rational, if it contain a g_2^1 it is rational, elliptic, or hyperelliptic.

Definition. A curve is said to be 'k-gonal' if it contain a g_k^1 all points variable but no series of dimension 1 and lower order. If the series be not special we must have $k=p+1$. The g_k^1 is surely complete, for if there were a g_k^2 there would be a g_{k-1}^1 contrary to definition. It is also special, for if $k=p+1$ by fixing $p-2$ points of a special adjoint, we should get a g_p^1.

Theorem 15] *A defining series for a polygonal curve is special and complete.*

A group of the g_k^1 imposes $k-1$ conditions on a special adjoint, so that all special adjoints through $k-1$ points of a group pass through the last one. We may, however, find $k-2$ points of a group which impose independent conditions, and these, with $p-k+2$ arbitrary points, will determine a g_p^1. We get from 1]

Theorem 16] *A k-gonal curve may be birationally transformed into a curve of order $p+2$ with a point of multiplicity $p-k+2$. The g_k^1 will be cut by lines through this point.*

Suppose that a curve is k-gonal, and that it has an adjoint of order $n-k-1$. The Riemann-Roch theorem tells us that a group of our g_k^1 imposes $k+1$ conditions on a special adjoint. Let us take two points in one of these groups, and pass a line through them, and a line in arbitrary direction through each of $k-3$ others of the k points. These $k-2$ lines, with the line through 2 and the particular adjoint, will make an adjoint of order $n-3$ through all but one of the k points, hence through all k, and they must lie on a line.

Theorem 17] *If a k-gonal curve of order n have an adjoint curve of order $n-k-1$, then the points of each group are collinear.*[*]

[*] Cf. Amodeo[1].

If the k-gonal curve had a special adjoint of order $n-k-2$, it certainly has plenty of order $n-k-1$. The curve of order $n-k-2$ and $k-1$ arbitrary lines, one through each point of a group, would have to go through the remaining variable point; an absurd conclusion.

Theorem 18] *A k-gonal curve cannot have an adjoint of order $n-k-2$.*

Suppose there is more than one adjoint of order $n-k-1$, i.e. an infinite number of them. The curve of this system through a generic point and $k-2$ lines in arbitrary directions through as many other points of the group of k would give, with the adjoint of order $n-k-1$, a special adjoint through all but one of the k points, hence through the last, i.e. all must lie on the adjoint of order $n-k-1$.

Theorem 19] *If a k-gonal curve contain an infinite number of adjoints of order $n-k-1$, the g_k^1 will be cut by a pencil of such adjoints.*

There has been a good deal of study of the moduli of k-gonal curves, but to pursue it would lead us too far.*

If a curve of order n have a multiple point of order $n-k$ it certainly has a g_k^1. Its genus will be greater if it have no other singular points than if it have one. Its polygonality could not be $k' < k$, for then although there can be no special adjoints of order $n-k'-2$, yet there are some of order $n-k-1$, a contradiction. Our curve is k-gonal.

Conversely, suppose we have a k-gonal curve of this order and genus. It cannot have a singularity of order greater than $n-k$, and the conditions for an adjoint of order $n-k-1$ are not incompatible. The points of a group of k are thus collinear by 17].

Let the g_k^1 be cut by the pencil

$$\phi \equiv t_1\phi_1 + t_2\phi_2.$$

The group cut by ϕ_1 shall be on a line l_1, that cut by the general ϕ on a line l. Since $\phi_1 l$ contains all the variable intersections of f and ϕ, we have, by Nöther's Fundamental Theorem 3], Book II, Ch. IV,

$$\chi l_1\phi = \psi l\phi_1 + \theta f.$$

The parameter $t_1 : t_2$ appears linearly on the left, hence it will

---

* Cf. Castelnuovo[1] and Segre, Beniamino[1].

appear linearly on the right, or we have a pencil of lines. The lines l have only k variable intersections with f since the curves ϕ only have that number, hence they pass through a fixed point of order $n-k$.

Theorem 20] *The necessary and sufficient condition that a k-gonal curve of order n should have the maximum compatible genus is that it should have a multiple point of order $n-k$ and no other singularities.**

§ 5. Φ-curves

Suppose that we have a curve of genus p. The canonical series is a g_{2p-2}^{p-1}. There will be a certain number of special adjoints which touch the base curve simply at $p-1$ points or, as a special case of this, more elaborately in fewer points; there are no simple intersections except at the singularities. We determine the number of these from the De Jonquières formula at the end of Ch. III:

$$\rho = p-1 \qquad k_1 = k_2 = ... = k_\rho = 2$$

$$\alpha_p = p-1 \qquad \Pi = 2^{p-1} \qquad \frac{\partial \Pi}{\partial k_i} = 2^{p-2}, \text{ etc.}$$

Substituting, we get

$$\frac{2^{p-1}p!}{(p-1)!}\left[\frac{2^{p-1}}{1} - \frac{(p-1)2^{p-2}}{2} + \frac{(p-1)(p-2)2^{p-3}}{2.3} - ...\right]$$

$$= 2^{p-1}\left[p . 2^{p-1} - \frac{p(p-1)}{1.2}2^{p-2}...\right]$$

$$= 2^{p-1}[2^p - (2-1)^p] = 2^{p-1}[2^p-1]. \qquad (8)$$

Theorem 21] *The number of groups of the canonical series which consist in $p-1$ pairs of adjacent points or the equivalent is, in general,*† $2^{p-1}[2^p-1]$.

A special adjoint which bears this relation to the base curve is called a Φ-curve. In some cases 21] does not hold, for there are an infinite number of curves. These cases deserve further study.‡ If the base curve have a one-parameter family of Φ-curves, every curve of the type

$$\lambda\Phi + \mu[\Phi + \Delta\Phi] = 0$$

will be a special adjoint through the intersections of Φ and

---

* Cf. Kupper, pp. 60 ff.   † Cf. Weber[2], p. 38.
‡ Cf. Kraus, pp. 245 ff.

$\Phi + \Delta\Phi$. If the parameter on which the curves depend be t, the pencil of curves

$$\lambda\Phi + \mu\frac{\partial\Phi}{\partial t} = 0$$

will pass through the $p-1$ points of contact of Φ with the base curve. We have also, by Nöther's fundamental theorem 3] of Book II, Ch. IV,

$$\left[\lambda\Phi + \mu\frac{\partial\Phi}{\partial t}\right]^2 \equiv \psi f + \Phi'\Phi;$$

here Φ' must be a special adjoint tangent to f where the latter meets $\lambda\Phi + \mu\dfrac{\partial\Phi}{\partial t}$. In other words, Φ' must be a Φ of our one-parameter system, and by a proper choice of $\lambda:\mu$ we may get any curve of the system this way. This gives a very pretty result.

Theorem 22] *If a base curve have a one-parameter system of Φ-curves, the points of contact of any two are a group of the canonical series.*

Take an arbitrary curve of the pencil

$$\lambda\Phi + \mu\frac{\partial\Phi}{\partial t} = 0,$$

and let l be an arbitrary line. Through the points of contact with f, and through $n-3$ of the intersections with l, we may pass ∞^2 adjoints of order $n-2$ cutting a g^2_{p+2}. Of these, ∞^1 will consist in l and the adjoints of the pencil above. We may thus transform the curve into one of order $p+2$ with a pencil of lines meeting it in only $p-1$ variable points, i.e. with a triple point. Consider any line through this point. There will be a pencil of adjoints of order $p-1$ through its $p-1$ variable intersections with the curve, and one curve of the pencil will consist in that line and a curve of order $p-2$. But the residual group is also a set of $p-1$ collinear points, hence the curve of order $p-2$ is that other line and a curve of order $p-3$ which is adjoint except, perhaps, for the triple point.

Theorem 23] *If a curve of genus p have an infinite number of Φ-curves it may be birationally transformed into a curve of order $p+2$ with a triple point and the equivalent of $\dfrac{(p+2)(p-3)}{2}$ other double points. These lie on a curve of order $p-3$ which acts as an adjoint at each of these singularities.*

Conversely, it is evident that such a curve is of the desired sort, for the curve of order $p-3$ and a line through the triple point counted twice gives us just the group we want.

Theorem 24] *If a curve have an infinite number of Φ-curves, its genus must be at least 3.*

The simplest curve of this sort is a quintic with a triple point. The canonical series is cut by a pair of lines through the triple point.

Suppose we have an s-parameter system of Φ-curves, $s > 1$. The index of specialization of a group of contacts will be at least $s+1$; we may pass a two-parameter system of special adjoints through one of our sets of $p-1$ points, and $s-2$ other arbitrary points, cutting the base curve in a g^2_{p+2}.

Theorem 25] *If a curve possess an s-parameter family of Φ-curves where $s > 1$, it may be birationally transformed into a curve of order $p-s+1$ and genus p.*

§ 6. Reducible curves

In all our work in the present chapter we have assumed that our base curve is irreducible. The study of series on a reducible curve is worth some attention.* Suppose, first, our base curve consists in two curves f_1, f_2 of orders n_1, n_2 and genera p_1 and p_2 respectively. Let a common singular point have the multiplicities of s_{1i}, s_{2i} for the two, while the multiplicities of not common singular points shall be r_{1i}, r_{2j}. An adjoint of the combined reducible curve must have at least the multiplicities $s_{1i}+s_{2i}-1$, $r_{1i}-1$, $r_{2j}-1$. It may be written

$$\phi \equiv \psi_2 f_1 + \psi_1 f_2, \tag{9}$$

where ψ_1 and ψ_2 are adjoints of the corresponding curves f_1, f_2.

Theorem 26] *Every adjoint of order n of a reducible curve $f_1 f_2$ can be written*
$$\phi \equiv \psi_2 f_1 + \psi_1 f_2,$$
where ψ_1 is an adjoint of order $n-n_2$ of f_1, and ψ_2 an adjoint of order $n-n_1$ of f_2.

Theorem 27] *Every special adjoint for a reducible curve $f_1 f_2$ can be written*
$$\phi \equiv \phi_2 f_1 + \phi_1 f_2,$$
where ϕ_1 is a special adjoint to f_1, and ϕ_2 is a special adjoint to f_2.

* For an extended study see Nöther[7].

Let us define p the genus of the reducible curve as we have defined genus for an irreducible one. We have, then,

$$p_1 = \frac{(n_1-1)(n_1-2)}{2} - \sum \frac{\rho_{1i}(\rho_{1i}-1)}{2} - \sum \frac{\sigma_{1i}(\sigma_{1i}-1)}{2}$$

$$p_2 = \frac{(n_2-1)(n_2-2)}{2} - \sum \frac{\rho_{2i}(\rho_{2i}-1)}{2} - \sum \frac{\sigma_{2i}(\sigma_{2i}-1)}{2}$$

$$p = \frac{(n_1+n_2-1)(n_1+n_2-2)}{2} - \sum \frac{\rho_{1i}(\rho_{1i}-1)}{2} - \sum \frac{\rho_{2i}(\rho_{2i}-1)}{2} -$$

$$- \sum \frac{(\sigma_{1i}+\sigma_{2i})(\sigma_{1i}+\sigma_{2i}-1)}{2}$$

$$p = p_1+p_2-1+n_1 n_2 - \sum \sigma_{1i}\sigma_{2i} = p_1+p_2-1. \tag{10}$$

This number is clearly an invariant for birational transformations; it will, by the last theorem, give us the number of linearly independent special adjoints.

The fundamental residuation theorems are based upon Nöther's fundamental theorem, which holds equally for reducible and irreducible curves. For a non-special complete series cut by the adjoints ψ_1, ψ_2,

$$N = N_1+N_2 \quad r = r_1+r_2 = N_1-p_1+N_2-p_2 \quad p-1 = p_1+p_2-2$$

$$N-r = p-1. \tag{11}$$

Theorem 28] *If a reducible curve consist in two irreducible parts, the difference between the order and dimension of a complete non-special series is one more than the genus.*

Theorem 29] *If a reducible curve consist in two irreducible parts, the canonical series is a g_{2p-2}^{p-1}.*

Consider a special series of order N_1+N_2.

$$N_1-r_1 = p_1-i_1 \quad\quad N_2-r_2 = p_2-i_2 \quad\quad i-1 = i_1-1+i_2-1$$

$$p+1 = p_1+p_2 \quad\quad N-r = p+1-(i+1) = p-i. \tag{12}$$

Riemann-Roch Theorem 30] *The difference between the order and dimension of a complete special series is equal to the genus of the curve less the index of specialization.*

It is perfectly easy to generalize these results to the case of a curve which is reducible and composed of s irreducible factors, all different.

Theorem 31] *If a curve f be made up of s irreducible factors*

abscissae. Eliminating y between f and the various curves ϕ
we have
$$\theta_0(x) = \theta_1(x) = \ldots = 0.$$

Let the highest common factor of these be $\theta(x)$ after fixed
common roots have been divided out. Each root of $\theta(x)$ will
give but one point of the group, in general. We may determine
our system of groups by the equations
$$f(x, y) = 0 \qquad \theta(x) = 0 \qquad r(x) + ys(x) = 0,$$
or, more generally,
$$f(x, y) = 0 \qquad F_1(x, y) = 0 \qquad F_2(x, y) = 0$$
$$\psi_0 = \psi_1 = \ldots = 0.$$

The equations ψ, as before, involve the coefficients of F_1 and
F_2. By adding, if needful, factors with constant coefficients to
the one or the other, we may make them both of degree ν
Their coefficients will correspond to points of an algebraic
variety of r dimensions, in a space of $\dfrac{\nu(\nu+3)}{2}$ dimensions. We
get from Book I, Ch. I, theorem 15], the fact that these co
ordinates in F_1 and F_2 can be rationally expressed in terms of
$r+1$ parameters, independent except for the fact that they are
connected by one polynomial equation. Expressing them so
and substituting, we get the canonical form for the equations
of our series
$$f(x, y) = F_1(x, y, X_0, \ldots, X_r) = F_2(x, y, X_0, \ldots, X_r)$$
$$= f'(X_0, \ldots, X_r) = 0. \quad (1$$

§ 2. Series of index 1

A linear series is of index 1. It seems natural to suppose that,
conversely, a series which is algebraic, and of index 1, is neces
sarily linear. This is, as a matter of fact, usually the case, but
there are exceptions. Here is an example. A linear series of
dimension 1 is rational and its groups are in one-to-one corre
spondence with the points of a line, or of any rational curve
Suppose we have a space curve whose genus is not 0 (i.e. a plane
curve in one-to-one algebraic correspondence therewith is not
rational). A quartic curve, the complete intersection of two
quadric surfaces nowhere tangent to one another, is an excellent
example. This can be projected into a binodal plane quartic

so that its genus is 1. Let the tangents to this space curve meet some other quadric in a curve whereon they determine a γ_2^1, and this will be of index 1 for, through a point of the new curve will usually pass but one tangent to the quartic. So on this space curve, or a plane curve to which it may be projected, we have a γ_2^1 of index 1, which is not a g_2^1, as then its groups would be in one-to-one correspondence with the points of a line, not with those of a curve of genus 1.

Suppose that we have a γ_N^1 of index 1 on a rational curve. We may transform birationally so that the curve of genus 1 is the x-axis:

$$F_1(x, x', y') = F_2(x, x', y') = f'(x', y') = 0.$$

Here f' must be the resultant of these two equations in x. Since there is but one group for each x,

$$x' = \frac{p(x)}{q(x)}.$$

Hence our series is cut by the pencil

$$x'q(x) - p(x) = 0.$$

Theorem 1] *A series of dimension and index* 1 *on a rational curve is linear.*

Suppose, next, that we have a γ_N^1 of index 1 which is rational. We may write it

$$f(x, y) = F_1(x, y, T) = F_2(x, y, T) = 0.$$

f must be a factor of the resultant of these two, and since there is but one T for each point on f,

$$T = \frac{P(x, y)}{Q(x, y)} \qquad T Q(x, y) - P(x, y) = 0.$$

Theorem 2] *A rational series of index and dimension* 1 *is linear.*

Theorem 3] *If a one-parameter system of series of dimension and index* 1 *be given, each series is linear.*

We shall prove this theorem early in the next chapter. The proof involves the use of Abelian integrals and had better be postponed till then. Let us pause to notice one interesting result. Suppose that on an algebraic surface

$$F(X, Y, Z) = 0$$

we have a one-parameter system of curves

$$X = \frac{P(U,V,x,y)}{S(U,V,x,y)} \qquad Y = \frac{Q(U,V,x,y)}{S(U,V,x,y)} \qquad Z = \frac{R(U,V,x,y)}{S(U,V,x,y)}$$

$$F(U,V) = f(x,y) = 0.$$

Here x and y are fixed for each curve of the system. Suppose further, each two curves of the system meet in one, and only one, variable point. Each point on the surface will give a finite number of curves, and so of points on f, so that f carries a γ_N^2. Residual to any point on $f = 0$ will be a γ_{N-1}^1, which by 3] is a g_{N-1}^1, and so is rational. Hence the curves on F are.

Theorem 4] *If an algebraic surface in three-dimensional space have a one-parameter family of algebraic curves, each two of which intersect in but one variable point, those curves are rational.*

Suppose now, we have a γ_N^2 of index 1. When any point is fixed we have a γ_{N-1}^1 of index 1 and, as there is a continuous system, a g_{N-1}^1. Let P_1, P_2 be a generic pair cut by a curve ϕ, while Q_1, Q_2 are a fixed pair cut by a curve ψ. Let ϕ_1 be another curve through Q_1, and ϕ_2 another curve through Q_2. Then $Q_1 P_2$ will be cut by $l\phi + m\phi_1$, and $Q_2 P_1$ by $l'\phi + m'\phi_2$. There are two different ways of expressing the curve which cuts $P_1 Q_1$:

$$\rho\phi + \sigma\phi_1 \qquad r\psi + s(l'\phi + m'\phi_2).$$

Hence

$$\phi = L\psi + M\phi_1 + N\phi_2,$$

or γ_N^2 traces a linear system of curves.

More generally, suppose we have a γ_N^r of index 1. Let $P_1, P_2, ..., P_r$ be a generic group cut by the variable curve ϕ. Let Q_1, Q_2 be two fixed points common to all the fixed curves $\phi_3, \phi_4, ..., \phi_{r+1}$. The system $Q_1, P_2, ..., P_r$ will be an $(r-1)$-parameter system of index 1 and so a g_{N-1}^{r-1}, and the same holds for $P_1, Q_2, P_3, ..., P_r$.

Let $Q_1, P_2, P_3, ..., P_r$ be cut by $\lambda_1\psi_1 + \lambda_3\phi_3 + ... + \lambda_{r+1}\phi_{r+1}$.

Let $Q_2, P_1, P_3, ..., P_r$ be cut by $\mu_2\psi_2 + \mu_3\phi_3 + ... + \mu_{r+1}\phi_{r+1}$.

If P_2 be fixed, the general curve through Q_1, P_2 would arise from an $(r-2)$-parameter sub-set of the first, and the general curve through P_1 from a linear combination of this and ϕ. Identifying this with a curve of the other set, we get

$$\phi = \rho_1\psi_1 + \rho_2\psi_2 + \rho_3\phi_3 + ... + \rho_{r+1}\phi_{r+1}.$$

Theorem 5] *Every algebraic series of index 1 and dimension greater than 1 is linear.**

3. Groups common to a γ_M^1 and a g_N^r

In the third chapter of the present book we determined the number of groups of $r+1$ points common to a group of a g_M^1 and a group of a g_N^r. We can extend the result to a γ_M^1 of index ν as follows. Let the number sought be $\phi(M, 1, \nu, N, r)$. Let P be a general point of our curve, Q one of the $\nu(M-1)$ residual points in γ_M^1. Choose out r of these in one group of M; they will determine one group of the g_N^r, cutting also in points P', so that to P will correspond $\nu\binom{M-1}{r}(N-r)$ points P'. Conversely, when P' is chosen, there are $\phi[M, 1, \nu, (N-1), (r-1)]$ groups of r points Q, and $(M-r)\phi[M, 1, \nu, (N-1), (r-1)]$ points P. Lastly, to each P corresponds $\nu(M-1)$ points Q, each lying in $\binom{M-2}{r-1}$ groups of g_N^r. The correspondence from P to P' with $\binom{M-2}{r-1}$ times the correspondence from P to Q will give a correspondence of value 0. The coincidences of this are the coincidences sought plus the double points, let us say d in number, of γ_M^1, each counted $\binom{M-2}{r-1}$ times. We thus get

$$\nu\binom{M-1}{r}(N-r)+(M-2)\phi(M, 1, \nu, (N-1), (r-1)]+$$
$$+2\nu(M-1)\binom{M-2}{r-1}$$
$$=(r+1)\phi(M, 1, \nu, N, r)+\binom{M-2}{r-1}d.$$

This equation is identical in form with that in the first section of the third chapter of the present book, except that we have replaced $\binom{M-1}{r}(N-r)$ by $\nu\binom{M-1}{r}(N-r)$, $2(M-1)\binom{M-2}{r-1}$ by $2\nu(M-1)\binom{M-2}{r-1}$, and $2(M+p-1)$ by d. Hence we get from equation (4) of that section

* Cf. Castelnuovo[9].

Theorem 6] *The number of groups of $r+1$ points common to a group of a γ_M^1 of index v which has d coincidences, and a g_N^r, is*

$$Nv\binom{M-1}{r} - \tfrac{1}{2}d\binom{M-2}{r-1} \qquad (2)$$

By an extension of the same methods we could find the number of groups of $M+\rho$ points common to a group of a γ_M^ρ and one of a g_N^r. The labour is rather forbidding, and we shall not pursue the subject further.†

§ 4. The defect of equivalence

Our formula (2) leads to another characteristic of a one-parameter series which is of considerable interest. Let us see how many groups of a γ_N^1 are in a g_{N+p-1}^{N-1} which is obviously complete and not special. This number z will be

$$z = v(N+p-1) - \tfrac{1}{2}d. \qquad (3)$$

It is defined as the 'defect of equivalence' of the γ_N^1. Suppose that it turns out to be 0. The algebraic work is as follows. Let the γ_N^1 be given by

$$f(x,y) = F_1(x,y,x',y') = F_2(x,y,x',y') = f'(x',y') = 0, \qquad (4)$$

while a g_{N+p-1}^{N-1} is given by

$$f = \lambda_1 \psi_1 + \lambda_2 \psi_2 + \ldots + \lambda_N \psi_N = 0. \qquad (5)$$

Assuming that the axes have general directions, so that two points of a group of the γ_N^1 do not, usually, have the same abscissae, we eliminate y from f, and F_1 also from f and F_2, getting
$$\theta_1(x,x',y') = \theta_2(x,x',y') = 0.$$

When $f' = 0$, these two equations have N common solutions given by
$$\chi(x,x',y') = 0.$$

Eliminating y between f and the general curve ψ, we have
$$\Theta(x,\lambda_1,\lambda_2,\ldots,\lambda_N) = 0.$$

If we write the condition that all the roots of $\chi = 0$ are roots of this and $f' = 0$, we have N equations in the N variables

$$\frac{\lambda_2}{\lambda_1}, \ldots, \frac{\lambda_N}{\lambda_1}, x', y'.$$

We assume that for the general curve ψ_i there are no permissible solutions, but if for a particular ψ_i there is one permissible solution, by theorem 6] of Book I, Ch. I, there are an infinite

* Cf. Severi-Löffler, pp. 191 ff.   † Cf. Torelli[1].

number. To get a particular ψ_i, take one group of our γ_N and p other points $P_1, P_2, \ldots$. They are a group of a complete g_{N+p}^N if the points P_i do not lie on a special adjoint. Residual to the point P_1 is a complete g_{N+p-1}^{N-1} that contains one group of our γ_N^1, and since the defect of equivalence is 0, by what was said above, this must contain every group of our γ_N^1. They are all residual to P_1. But by the same reasoning they are residual to $P_2, P_3, \ldots$. This amounts to saying that the fact that all the groups of γ_N^1 are in a certain g_{N+p}^N is not invalidated by requiring the groups to contain P_1 or the independent point P_2 or P_3, etc. In other words, we may require the groups of the g_{N+p}^N to contain all these points, so that the γ_N^1 is contained in a residual g_N^{N-p} or in a complete g_N^{N-p}.

Suppose, conversely, that our γ_N^1 is contained in a g_N^{N-p}. Then if we have a group of a g_{N+p-1}^{N-1} which contains one group of the γ_N^1, the residual group is residual to every group of the g_N^{N-p} and so determines a g_{N+p-1}^{N-1} which contains an infinite, not a finite, number of groups of γ_N^1. This could not be true of the general g_{N+p-1}^{N-1}, for these do not all share a common series, hence

$$z = 0.$$

Theorem 7] *The necessary and sufficient condition that an irreducible series of dimension 1 should be contained in a linear series of the same order is that its defect of equivalence should be 0.*

Theorem 8] *The number of double points of an irreducible series of dimension 1, order N, and index ν is not greater than $2\nu(N+p-1)$.*

Theorem 9] *When the upper limit given in 8] is reached, and only then, the defect of equivalence is 0.*[*]

A point P of our curve f belongs, by hypothesis, to ν groups of the γ_N^1, and so is residual to $\nu(N-1)$ points Q, each of which corresponds to that number of points P. If, now, all the groups through a variable point belong to a linear series, together they belong to the νth multiple thereof, the correspondence has the value ν and, by Chasles-Cayley-Brill,

$$d = \nu(N-1) + \nu(N-1) + 2\nu p = 2\nu(N+p-1).$$

Theorem 10] *If the ν groups of a γ_N^1 of index ν containing a variable point vary in a fixed linear series of order νN, then the defect of the given γ_N^1 is 0.*

* Cf. Castelnuovo[5], pp. 294 ff.

It is evident, conversely, that if the defect is 0, any set of ν groups is in the linear series which is the νth multiple of that containing the given series.

If the defect of equivalence be 0, the given series is included in a linear series, and its individual groups will correspond to the points of an algebraic curve in that linear space of higher dimensions whose points correspond to the groups of the linear series. But we learnt in the first chapter of Book I that an algebraic curve may always be given by expressing the co-ordinates of its points rationally in terms of two auxiliary para-meters which are connected by a polynomial equation. A series of defect 0 may always, thus, be written

$$f(x, y) = F_1(x, y, x', y') = f'(x', y') = 0. \tag{6}$$

Conversely, every series so written is contained in the series cut by F_1 when the coefficient of each term in x and y is an independent variable.

Theorem 11] *The necessary and sufficient condition that it be possible to represent a series of dimension 1 by three equations,*

$$f(x, y) = F_1(x, y, x', y') = f'(x', y') = 0, \tag{6}$$

is that the defect of equivalence be 0.

This can also be expressed in another form:

Theorem 12] *The necessary and sufficient condition that an algebraic transformation between two curves f and f' be expressible by a single additional equation $F_1(x, y, x', y') = 0$ is that the groups on one of the curves corresponding to the individual points of the other should form a series of defect* 0. *If one of the series have this defect the other will also.*[*]

There is another birationally invariant number connected with an algebraic series of dimension 1 that is important. That is the genus of the curve f' when we write the series in standard form:

$$f(x, y) = F_1(x, y, x', y') = F_2(x, y, x', y') = f'(x', y') = 0. \tag{1}$$

This is defined as the 'genus' of the series; it is the genus of any plane algebraic curve whose points are in one-to-one corre-spondence with its groups. Let us assume that our series is of index N' and simple if $N' > 1$, so that the N' groups containing an arbitrary point do not, necessarily, contain any other point.

* Cf. Castelnuovo[4].

To each point P of f will correspond N' points of f', to each of f', N points of f. We have on f' a series of index N and order N'. Let d' be the number of branch points of the series on f, that is to say, the number of points where two fall together, they correspond to as many double points of the series on f'. We thus get, by Zeuthen's formula of Book I, Ch. VIII (14)

$$d' + 2N'(p-1) = d + 2N(p'-1), \tag{7}$$

$$z = N'(N+p-1) - \frac{d}{2} = N(N'+p'-1) - \frac{d'}{2} = z'. \tag{8}$$

Theorem 13] *If the groups of a simple series of dimension* 1 *on a plane curve be represented by individual points on a second curve, then the individual points on the first will represent groups of a series on the second. The relation between the two curves and their series is a reciprocal one, the index of one series is the order of the other, the genus of one curve is that of the series on the other, and the two series have the same defect of equivalence.*

If $N' = 1$ we must have $d' = 0$, for if but one group go through a point, two cannot coalesce. The left-hand side of (7) is negative if $p = 0$. The right-hand side can only be negative if $p' = 0$, so that the series is rational, its defect is 0, and $z = 0$. Clearly we have a g_N^1; this gives another proof of 1]. We get by equally simple considerations

Theorem 14] *A series of dimension and index* 1 *on a curve of genus* 1 *has the genus* 1, *and no double points, or genus* 0 *and* $2N$ *double points.*

When $N' = 1$ and $d' = 0$, we get from (7) and (8), when N is replaced by M,

$$z = (M+p-1) - \frac{d}{2} = Mp'.$$

Combining with (2),

$$\phi(M, 1, 1, N, r) = N\binom{M-1}{r} - \binom{M-2}{r-1}[(p-1) - M(p'-1)] \tag{9}$$

$$\phi(M, 1, 1, N, 1) = (M-1)(N-1) - p + Mp' \tag{10}$$

$$\phi[M, 1, 1, N, (M-1)] = N - M + 1 - p + Mp' \geqslant 0. \tag{11}$$

Suppose that our γ_M^1 is of index 1 and that we have g_N^r. Let us pick $r-(M-1)$ general points of the curve. Residual thereto we shall have a $g_{N+M-r-1}^{M-1}$. If the points of a group of our γ_M^1

impose independent conditions on this, we get from (11), changing N to $N+d-r-1$,

$$(N+M-1-r)-M+1-p+Mp' \geqslant 0$$

$$N-r \geqslant p-Mp'. \tag{12}$$

This gives a generalization of the Riemann-Roch theorem.[*]

Theorem 15] *If a series of order* M, *dimension and index* 1, *and genus* p' *be given on a curve of genus* p, *and if*

$$N-r < p-Mp',$$

then a general group of the series will not impose independent conditions on a group of a g_N^r.

Suppose that our base curve has an involutory transformation into itself which is not of value 1. We have a γ_ν^1 of index 1 which is not linear. The order of the curve being n, consider an adjoint of order $n-\nu$. The order and dimension of the series cut by all such adjoints will be given by

$$N = n(n-\nu) - \sum r_i(r_i-1) = 2(p-1)+n(3-\nu)$$

$$r \geqslant \frac{(n-\nu)(n-\nu+3)}{2} - \sum \frac{r_i(r_i-1)}{2} = p-1+n(3-\nu)+\frac{\nu(\nu-3)}{2}$$

$$N-r \leqslant p-1-\frac{\nu(\nu-3)}{2}.$$

If $\qquad\qquad \dfrac{(\nu-3)}{2} > p', \ N-r < p-2p'.$

Theorem 16] *If a curve have an involutory transformation into itself of genus* $p' > 0$, *then an adjoint whose order is* ν *less than that of the given curve which passes through an arbitrary point will also pass through its mate in the involution if* $\dfrac{(\nu-3)}{2} > p'$.

A γ_M^1 of index 1 produces an $(M-1)$-to-$(M-1)$ transformation of the curve into itself. If this have a value γ in the Chasles-Cayley-Brill sense,

$$d = 2(M-1)+2p-2r = 2(M-1)+2p\gamma$$

$$\gamma = 1-\frac{z}{p}.$$

Theorem 17] *If the transformation of a curve into itself by a* γ_M^1 *have a value in the sense of the Chasles-Cayley-Brill theorem*

* Castelnuovo[4], p. 296.

this value is 1 *when the defect of equivalence is* 0, *otherwise it is less than* 1 *and the defect is divisible by the genus of the curve.*[*]

We shall see in the next chapter that, in general, a curve probably has no transformations which have no value.

A series of index and dimension 1 is certainly an involution. Let us assume that each of the N' groups through a generic point P goes through $\nu'-1$ other points, variable with P. If Q be one of these points, since one condition only is imposed by requiring a group to go through P and Q, all the groups which contain Q contain P also. The series being of order N and dimension 1, the N points of a group on f correspond to a single point on f'. The order of the $\sum$ series on f' is N', and if we multiply this by the index of the series on f' we get the totality of the points on f' in groups which contain a given point, or the totality of groups on f which contain points of a given group. This is $\dfrac{NN'}{\nu'}$, hence the index sought is $\dfrac{N}{\nu'}$; each branch point of f drags with it $\nu'-1$ others, so that the number of these is $\dfrac{d'}{\nu'}$.

Theorem 18] *If a composite γ_M^1 on a curve f be represented by the points of a curve f' in the usual way, the index of the series being greater than* 1, *and if all groups through a generic point of f go through $\nu'-1$ others variable therewith, then the index of the series of f' is the order of that on f divided by ν', and the defect on f' is that on f divided by ν'.*

A series of dimension 1 has a residual series which is of some interest. We start with a γ_N^1 and consider at the same time a certain g_{N+p}^N. Each group of the γ_N^1 will be residual to a group of p points of the g_{N+p}^N, and these will generate a γ_p^1 whose characteristic numbers we are to find. Let us assume, in the first place, that each group of our γ_N^1 is not, in general, equivalent to any other, and that the same is true of the γ_p^1. The groups of the two series are, then, in one-to-one correspondence, and the two have the same genus. If a point P be taken, the number of groups of the second series through it is the number of groups of the first series in the residual g_{N+p-1}^{N-1}, and this by the definition of defect is z. It remains only to find the defect

[*] Cf. Amodeo[2], p. 230.

of the second series. Let G_1, G_2 be two groups of γ_N^1, G_1', G_2' their residuals in the γ_p^1. Let $G_1 + E_1$ and $G_2 + E_2$ be two groups of a g_{N+p-1}^{N-1} in our g_{N+p}^p. Let E_1', E_2' be residual to E_1, E_2 in the canonical series. Adopting the notation for equivalent groups developed in Book I, Ch. VIII,

$$G_1 + G_1' \equiv G_2 + G_2'$$
$$G_1 + E_1 \equiv G_2 + E_2$$
$$E_1 + E_1' \equiv E_2 + E_2'$$
$$G_1 + E_1 + G_1' + E_1' \equiv G_2 + E_2 + G_2' + E_2'$$
$$G_1' + E_1' \equiv G_2' + E_2'.$$

There are, thus, z equivalent groups of the type $G' + E'$, or the new series has the old defect.

Theorem 20] *If a general group of a γ_N^1 be equivalent to no other, and if the same be true of a general group of the γ_p^1 residual to the given series in a certain g_{N+p}^N, then the two series have the same genus and defect, and the defect of the first is the index of the second.*[*]

We have assumed that no two groups of our γ_N^1 are equivalent, and no two of the residual are. When two groups of the residual are equivalent, they belong to a special g_p^1. The number of these by Theorem 17] of Ch. IV of the present book is ∞^{p-1}, while the number of g_{N+p}^p by theorem 9] of the same chapter is ∞^p. Hence, no two groups of the residual γ_p^1 in a general g_{N+p}^p are equivalent, and no one group is special. When in fact a group of the γ_p^1 is special, all groups of the g_p^1 are residual to the residual group of the γ_N^1, so that the g_p^1 forms part of the γ_p^1.

Theorem 21] *No two groups of a γ_p^1 residual to a γ_N^1 in a general g_{N+p}^N are equivalent, and no group is special when the γ_p^1 is irreducible. When there is a special group, the g_p^1 to which it belongs is part of the γ_p^1, unless that have a higher dimension.*

Suppose that a group of our original series is equivalent to $k-1$ others. To each group of γ_p^1 will correspond k of γ_N^1. The index of γ_p^1 will be not z but $\dfrac{z}{k}$. We find the index as before merely noting that G_1' goes with k groups G_1, and G_2' with k groups G_2.

---

[*] For this theorem and the three next theorems see Torelli[2].

Theorem 22] *If the general group of a γ_N^1 be equivalent to $k-1$ others, the index and defect of the residual γ_p^1 is $\dfrac{z}{k}$.*

If we start with a γ_p^1 which has no special groups, the residual $\bar{\gamma}_p^1$ plays the role of the original γ_N^1.

Theorem 23] *If no group of a γ_p^1 be special, the index and defect are equal.*

Suppose that l groups of a γ_p^1 are special. The residual γ_p^1 is residual to a reducible series composed of γ_p^1 and l g_p^1's. The defect and index of the total series are equal by 20], the defect of a g_p^1 is 0 and its index 1.

Theorem 24] *The defect of a γ_p^1 is the sum of its index and the number of special groups in the series.*

The defect of equivalence has, so far, only been defined for series of dimension 1. There are corresponding numbers for series of higher dimension. We start with a γ_N^ρ and take $\rho-b$ points in general position. Residual to them in the given series will be a $\gamma_{N+b-\rho}^b$. Let z_b be the number of groups of the latter in a general $g_{N+p-\rho}^{N-\rho}$. If $\rho=1$ and $b=0$, we get our previous z. We could not, of course, have $b>\rho$. If $z_b=0$, then a generic $g_{N+p-\rho}^{N-\rho}$ does not contain a group of our residual $\gamma_{N+b-\rho}^b$. If there be one $g_{N+p-\rho}^{N-\rho}$ that contains such a group, it must contain an infinite number of them, as we saw in the earlier case. As the total number of $g_{N+p-\rho}^{N-\rho}$'s is ∞^p, so the number containing an infinite number of these groups is at most ∞^{p-1}. Every group of $N+b-\rho$ points belongs to ∞^{p-b} groups of $N+p-\rho$. Hence there are ∞^p groups of $N+p-\rho$ points, each of which contains a group of $N+b-\rho$. But any group of $N+p-\rho$ points belongs to a $g_{N+p-\rho}^{N-\rho}$. Such series which contain groups of $\gamma_{N+b-\rho}^b$ each contain an infinite number of them, since $z_b=0$. Now take a $\gamma_{N+p+k-\rho}^{N+k-\rho}$ of such very high order that it contains every group of $\gamma_{N+b-\rho}^b$ and every $g_{N+p-\rho}^{N-\rho}$ that contains an infinite number of these. If we take any group of $\gamma_{N+b-\rho}^b$, there will be residual thereto in the large series a group of $k+p-b$ points of k which, in turn, is residual to a $g_{N+b-\rho}^{N-\rho}$ containing an infinite number of groups of the $\gamma_{N+b-\rho}^b$, all equivalent. Conversely, if a group of $\gamma_{N+b-\rho}^b$ be equivalent to an infinite number of others, a linear series which contains one group will contain an infinite number. But it cannot be true that every $g_{N+p-\rho}^{N-\rho}$ contains an infinite number of groups of $\gamma_{N+b-\rho}^{b}$, for then there would be ∞^{p+1} instead of ∞^{b}.

Theorem 25] *The N.S. condition, that each group of a $\gamma_{N+b-\rho}^{b}$ residual to $(\rho-b)$ points of a γ_{N}^{ρ} should be equivalent to an infinite number of others, is that $z_{b}=0$.*

Suppose $z_{b}=0$. z_{b+1} is the number of groups of a $\gamma_{N+b+1-\rho}^{b+1}$ residual to $(\rho-b-1)$ and contained in a $g_{N+p-\rho}^{N-\rho}$. If we fix a point P, we have a residual series with $z_{b}=0$. Hence, if we add P, which is perfectly general, we have a $\gamma_{N+b+1-\rho}^{b+1}$ with an infinite number of equivalent groups.

Theorem 26] *If $z_{b}=0$, then $z_{b+1}=0$.*

It is possible with the aid of these numbers to find an extension of the De Jonquières formula of Chapter III; the labour is excessive.†

* Cf. Allen, p. 345 ff.   † Ibid., p. 349.

CHAPTER VII

THE HIGHER THEORY OF CORRESPONDENCES

§ 1. General theorems

IN the present chapter we shall return once more to the theory of algebraic correspondences between curves, or of groups of points on curves, extending and completing results already obtained, and exhibiting new methods of study based on the theory of Abelian integrals. We begin with one or two of the formulae already established, the Chasles-Cayley-Brill formula for the coincidences of a correspondence of indices N and N' on a curve of genus p, when the correspondence has the integral or 0 value γ:

$$N+N'+2p\gamma. \tag{1}$$

If we have an N-to-N' correspondence between two curves of genera p and p' respectively, with β and β' branch points in each case, Zeuthen's formula at the end of Ch. IV of Book II gives

$$\beta+2N'(p-1) = \beta'+2N(p'-1). \tag{2}$$

If we use not the branch points on one curve but the double points of the series on the other, we may put this in the form

$$d'+2N'(p-1) = d+2N(p'-1). \tag{3}$$

Care must be taken when branch points on one curve correspond to branch points on the other; we assume such is not the case.

The general formula for an algebraic correspondence between two curves is nothing but the general formula for a one-dimensional series on one curve, and may be written, as in the last chapter,

$$f(x,y) = F_1(x,y,x',y') = F_2(x,y,x',y') = f'(x',y') = 0. \tag{4}$$

We get from theorem 9] of that chapter:

Theorem 1] *The necessary and sufficient condition that a N-to-N' correspondence between two curves of genera p and p' should have the maximum number of branch points is that the defect of the corresponding series should be 0.*

Theorem 2] *If an algebraic correspondence have the maximum permissible number of branch points, so does the inverse correspondence.*

We get at once from theorem 10] of the last chapter:

Theorem 3] *The necessary and sufficient condition that the groups corresponding to individual points in a correspondence on an irreducible curve be equivalent, is that the groups of individual points in the product of the correspondence and its inverse should be equivalent.*

Suppose that we have a 1-to-N' correspondence between two curves. As this must be rational in one sense, it must be possible to write it

$$x = \frac{\phi(x', y')}{\psi(x', y')} \qquad y = \frac{\chi(x', y')}{\psi(x', y')}.$$

A g_ν^1 in the (x, y) plane will be carried into a $g_{\nu N}^1$ in the (x', y') plane. Conversely, suppose we have

$$\phi_0(x', y') + t\phi_1(x', y') = 0. \qquad (5)$$

If we eliminate x' and y' between this and the two equations preceding, we get a polynomial in x, y, and t equated to 0, and so groups of points of a rational series which is contained in the linear series obtained by replacing the polynomials in t which multiply the individual products in x, y by independent variables, a linear series of dimension 1 on the x', y' curve will go into a series of defect 0. Two equivalent groups in the x', y' plane may be joined by a $g_{\nu'}^1$, hence they will go to two groups of a rational series; two equivalent groups. When we have an N-to-N' correspondence, we may factor it into the product to an N-to-1 and a 1-to-N' as in Ch. VIII of Book I.

Theorem 4] *An algebraic correspondence will carry a pair of equivalent groups into a pair of equivalent groups.*

The reader will not make the mistake of supposing that such a correspondence will necessarily carry a linear series into a linear series. It surely will in some cases, but not in all.

§ 2. Application of Abelian integrals

The subject of algebraic correspondences does not, in its nature, seem to involve essentially any transcendental considerations. It seems certain that with a modicum of skill we might derive all the properties of such correspondences by the methods of algebraic geometry. As a matter of fact no one has, so far, succeeded in doing this; certain fundamental problems have

only yielded to transcendental treatment. It is our present task
to show how such treatment is applied.*

We premise that we are dealing with a correspondence on an
irreducible curve of genus p, and this, as we saw in the second
chapter of the present book, has exactly p linearly independent
integrals of the first sort. Let us call them $u^1(x), u^2(x),..., u^p(x)$.
Each of these has $2p$ moduli of periodicity (not to be confused
with the $3(p-1)$ moduli of a curve as derived in Ch. IV of the
present book) corresponding to as many circuits on the Riemann
surface, as we shall see in more detail in the next chapter. We
may tabulate them in the canonical form:†

$$u^1 \sim (1, 0, 0,..., 0, a_{11}, a_{12},..., a_{1p})$$
$$u^2 \sim (0, 1, 0,..., 0, a_{21}, a_{22},..., a_{2p})$$
$$\cdot \quad \cdot \quad \cdot \quad \cdot \quad \cdot \quad \cdot \quad \cdot \quad \cdot \quad \cdot \quad \cdot \quad \cdot \quad \cdot \quad \cdot \qquad (6)$$
$$u^p \sim (0, 0, 0,..., 1, a_{p1}, a_{p2},..., a_{pp}).$$
$$a_{ij} = a_{ji}.$$

Suppose, next, that in our transformation a point (x) corresponds to N' points $(y^1), (y^2),..., (y^{N'})$ the expression

$$\sum_{i=1}^{i=N'} u^k(y^i)$$

is everywhere finite. Its derivative is a single-valued analytic
function with no singularities but poles, and so is rational.
Hence it is itself an Abelian integral of the first sort, so that
we may write

$$\sum_{i=1}^{i=N'} u^k(y^i) \equiv \sum_{i=1}^{i=p} \Pi_{ki} u^i(x) + \Pi_k, \qquad (7)$$

Here the constants Π_k depend on the paths of integration on
the Riemann surface. The p^2 constants Π_{ki} are called the
'characteristics' of the correspondence.

Let (x) move around one of the first p circuits, say the lth.
The increment of $u^l(x)$ will be 1, that of all the other u^i's will
be 0. The corresponding y's will move around the various circuits each an integral number of times in positive or negative
sense, hence

$$\Pi_{kl} = h_{kl} + \sum_{i=1}^{i=p} g_{il} a_{ki}. \qquad (8)$$

* The classical memoir on this subject is Hurwitz.
† Cf. Appell et Goursat, pp. 152 and 320.

If (x) had traced the $(p+l)$th circuit, we should have had

$$\sum_{j=1}^{j=p} \Pi_{kj} a_{jl} = H_{kl} + \sum_{i=1}^{i=p} G_{il} a_{ki}. \qquad (9)$$

The quantities g, h, G, H are integers or 0.

If in (8) we change l to j, multiply by a_{jl}, and add, we get, by comparing with (9),

$$\sum_{j} h_{kj} a_{jl} + \sum_{i,j} g_{ij} a_{ki} a_{jl} = H_{kl} + \sum_{i} G_{il} a_{ki}. \qquad (10)$$

We have here a linear equation connecting the moduli of periodicity, the coefficients being integers. It seems extremely unlikely that the general curve, i.e. every curve, of genus p has such a relation among these moduli. We shall therefore define as a 'curve of general moduli of periodicity' one where no such relation not a numerical identity exists, leaving open the question as to whether any such curves exist for the general p.[*] If, then, we have a curve of general moduli of periodicity, so that (10) is merely a numerical identity,

$$g_{ij} = H_{kl} = 0.$$

On the left the summation bears on the first subscript, on the right it bears on the second. Hence we must have

$$h_{kj} = 0, \ k \neq j \qquad G_{il} = 0, \ i \neq l \qquad h_{kk} = G_{ll} = -\gamma.$$

This can be neatly written in terms of the Kronecker indices:

$$g_{ij} = H_{kl} = 0 \qquad h_{ij} = -\gamma I_i^j \qquad G_{kl} = -\gamma I_k^l. \qquad (11)$$

Our equation (7) then becomes

$$\sum_{i} u^k(y^i) + \gamma u^k(x) = \Pi_k$$

$$\sum_{i} u^k(y^i) + \gamma u^k(x) = \sum_{i} u^k(y^{i'}) + \gamma u^k(x'). \qquad (12)$$

At this point we recall theorem 5] of Ch. II of the present book, which tells us that the N.S. condition that two groups of points should be equivalent is it should be possible to match them up one to one in such a manner that the sum of the differences of the values of every integral of the first sort at the different pairs of points should be congruent to 0 within the moduli of periodicity, and bear in mind the definition of the value of a correspondence given in Ch. VIII of Book I, and we

---

[*] Cf. Hurwitz, p. 565.

see that this constant γ is nothing more nor less than the 'value' of the correspondence.

Theorem 5] *On a curve of general moduli of periodicity, the only algebraic correspondences are those with integral or 0 values.*

The Chasles-Cayley-Brill correspondence formula gives the number of coincidences as

$$N+N'+2p\gamma = N+N'- \sum_i (h_{ii}+G_{ii}). \qquad (13)$$

It can be shown with the aid of θ functions that this expression will always give the number of correspondences.*

An upper limit to the number of coincidences may be reached in the following fashion. Consider a g^1_{p+1} where the group containing a general point does not contain one of the transformed points. Each group will be transformed into N' groups, and in the inverse correspondence each group to N groups. The groups of a g^1_{p+1} may be transformed birationally into the points of a line, on which we have here an N-to-N' correspondence. The $N+N'$ coincidence groups will include all the coincidence points there are.

Theorem 6] *The number of coincidences of an N-to-N' correspondence on a curve of genus p will never exceed $(N+N')(p+1)$ in number.*

Let us next pause a moment to prove theorem 3] of the last chapter, as we promised to do. Suppose that we have a one-parameter system of γ^1_N's of index 1. In each group the various points appear symmetrically. Let us apply our recent analysis to the transformation, including the identity induced by any one of the γ^1_N's, so that (x) appears as one of the corresponding points (y). We turn to equations (8), noting that Π_{kl} will change continuously, while the a_{ki}'s are constants, and the other quantities involved are integers. This is a contradiction unless the Π_{kl}'s are constants. Returning to (7), we have, by symmetry,

$$\sum_i \Pi_{ki}u^i(x) = \sum_i \Pi_{ki}u^i(y).$$

But the point (y) is any mate of (x) in any one of the correspondences, and so is any point of the curve. Hence we have

$$\sum_i \Pi_{ki}u^i(x) = \text{const.}$$

Substituting in (7), $\sum_i u^k(y^i) = c_k.$

* Cf. Hurwitz, p. 576.

The summation on the left covers all the points of a group, the constant on the right depends on the particular γ_ν^1 but not on (x), and so is constant for any particular γ_ν^1. Hence, by theorem 5] of Ch. II, the group (y) is a group of a linear series, and that is what we wished to prove.*

Consider, in place of our original correspondence, which we assume to be non-involutory, its inverse. The two could not have identical values for g, h, G, H, as we shall presently see from the formula for the product of two correspondences. On the other hand, they impose the same conditions on the moduli of periodicity, for if a curve admit a certain correspondence, it automatically admits the inverse. We rewrite (10)

$$\sum_j h_{kj}a_{jl} + \sum_{ij} g_{ij}a_{ki}a_{jl} = H_{kl} + \sum_i G_{il}a_{ki}. \tag{10}$$

If the coefficients for the inverse correspondence be g', h', G', H', and if we interchange k and l, we have from the inverse

$$\sum_i h'_{li}a_{ki} + \sum_{ij} g'_{ij}a_{li}a_{jk} = H'_{lk} + \sum G'_{jk}a_{lj}.$$

If these equations are to be identical we must have

$$h'_{li} = G_{il} \qquad G'_{jk} = h_{kj} \qquad H'_{lk} = -H_{kl} \qquad g'_{ij} = -g_{ji}. \tag{14}$$

Let us write the formulae for the product of two correspondences. In addition to (7) we shall have

$$\sum_s u^k(z^{rs}) = \sum_r \Pi' u^i(y^r) + \Pi'_k.$$

In (7) change k to j, multiply by Π'_k, and add

$$\sum_{rs} u^k(z^{rs}) = \sum_{ij} \Pi_{ji}\Pi_{kj}u^i(x) + \Pi''_k.$$

That is to say, for the product

$$\Pi''_{kl} = \sum \Pi_{jl}\Pi'_{kj}.$$

From (8) and (9) and the corresponding equations for the second transformation,

$$
\begin{aligned}
h''_{kl} &= \sum_j (h_{jl}h'_{kj} + g_{jl}H'_{kj}) \\
g''_{kl} &= \sum_j (h_{jl}g'_{kj} + g_{jl}G'_{kj}) \\
H''_{kl} &= \sum_j (H_{jl}h'_{kj} + G_{jl}H'_{kj}) \\
G''_{kl} &= \sum_j (H_{jl}g'_{jk} + G_{jl}G'_{kj}).
\end{aligned}
\tag{15}
$$

* Cf. Castelnuovo⁹, p. 732.

How many points have the same mates in two different correspondences ? This is the number of coincidences in the product of one and the inverse of the other. Applying (13), (14), and (15), we get*

$$N_1N_2' + N_2N_1' - \sum_{ij} [h_{ji}G_{ji}' - g_{ji}H_{ji}' - H_{ji}g_{ji}' + G_{ji}h_{ji}']. \qquad (16)$$

When the first has the value γ and the second the value γ', this becomes
$$N_1N_2' + N_2N_1' - 2p\gamma\gamma'. \qquad (17)$$

Definition. μ correspondences shall be said to be 'linearly dependent' if a set of constant multipliers $\lambda_1, \lambda_2, ..., \lambda_\mu$, not all zero, may be found, such that
$$\sum_s \lambda_s \Pi_{kl}^s = 0.$$
This will involve $\quad \sum_s \lambda_s h_{kl}^s + \sum_{s,i} \lambda_s g_{il}^s a_{ki} = 0.$

The first set of quantities are integers, the second complex, hence $\quad \sum_s \lambda_s h_{kl}^s = 0 \qquad \sum_{s,i} \lambda_s g_{il}^s a_{ki} = 0.$

The λ's are thus rational quantities; we may take them as integers since we are dealing with homogeneous quantities.

As the determinant of the a_{ki}'s is not 0, we have
$$\sum_s \lambda_s h_{kl}^s = \sum_s \lambda_s g_{il}^s = 0. \qquad (18)$$

The $2p^2$ quantities gh are integers; every set of such will be linearly dependent on $2p^2$ such sets, so that this is the maximum number of linearly independent correspondences on a curve of genus p.† If our μ correspondences be linearly dependent, we have
$$\sum_{r,s} \lambda_s u^k(y^{rs}) = c_k = \sum_{r,s} \lambda_s u^k(y^{rs'}).$$

Conversely, when this equation holds, since in (7) the p integrals $u^i(x)$ are linearly independent, we have
$$\sum_s \lambda_s \Pi_{ki}^s = 0,$$

or the correspondences are linearly dependent. We thus get from Ch. II, 5]:

Theorem 7] *The necessary and sufficient condition that μ correspondences be linearly dependent is that there be μ sets of multiples*

---

* This differs slightly from the value given by Hurwitz, p. 564. He defines as his second transformation what we have called the inverse thereof.

† Cf. Severi².

of groups of points corresponding to a variable point which vary in a linear series.

Here a negative integral multiple of a group has the meaning developed in Book I, Ch. VIII.

If our curve have general moduli of periodicity, if we take two correspondences of values γ_1 and γ_2, we have

$$\gamma_1 P + [Q_1 + Q_2 + ... + Q_{\nu_1}] \equiv \gamma_1 P' + [Q'_1 + Q'_2 + ... + Q'_{\nu_1}]$$
$$\gamma_2 P + [R_1 + R_2 + ... + R_{\nu_2}] \equiv \gamma_2 P' + [R'_1 + R'_2 + ... + R'_{\nu_2}]$$
$$\gamma_2 [Q_1 + Q_2 + ... + Q_{\nu_1}] - \gamma_1 [R_1 + R_2 + ... + R_{\nu_2}]$$
$$\equiv \gamma_2 [Q'_1 + Q'_2 + ... + Q'_{\nu_1}] - \gamma_1 [R'_1 + R'_2 + ... + R'_{\nu_2}].$$

Theorem 8] *Any two correspondences with integral or 0 values are linearly dependent, and any correspondence with an integral or 0 value is linearly dependent on the identity.*

Theorem 9] *If a curve have general moduli of periodicity, any two correspondences are linearly dependent.*

In addition to our equations (28) we shall get from (9)

$$\sum_s \lambda_s H^s_{kl} = \sum_s \lambda_s G^s_{kl} = 0.$$

These equations, with (14), give

Theorem 10] *If a set of correspondences be linearly dependent, so are their inverses, and the same set of linear multipliers appear in the two cases.*

The number of coincidences in the sth correspondence is

$$U^s = N^s + N'^s - \sum_i [h^s_{ii} + G^s_{ii}].$$

Multiplying through by λ_s and summing,

$$\sum_s \lambda_s U_s = \sum_s \lambda_s [N_s + N'_s].$$

Theorem 11] *If μ correspondences of indices $N_1, N'_1, N_2, N'_2,...$ and coincidences $U_1, U_2,...$ in number μ be linearly dependent with the multipliers $\lambda_1, \lambda_2,...$ then*

$$\sum_s \lambda_s U_s = \sum_s \lambda_s [N_s + N'_s].$$

§ 3. Representation in hyperspace*

In dealing with the periods of the various Abelian integrals of the first sort, we have to treat a large number of variables, connected by various linear equations. This suggests that the

* The material of the present section and the next is taken from the articles by Rosatti[1]

point of view and language of the projective geometry of hyper-space may throw an interesting sidelight on the whole question. Let us look into this matter.

Suppose that we have a projective space of $2p-1$ dimensions where a point has projective homogeneous coordinates

$$X_1, X_2, ..., X_{2p}$$

and a hyperplane the equation

$$(uX) = 0,$$

the quantities (u) being its projective coordinates. There are p linearly independent fundamental hyperplanes whose co-ordinates are

$$u^1 \sim (1, 0, 0, ..., 0, a_{11}, ..., a_{1p})$$
$$u^2 \sim (0, 1, 0, ..., 0, a_{21}, ..., a_{2p})$$
$$\cdot \quad \cdot \quad \cdot \quad \cdot \quad \cdot \quad \cdot \quad \cdot \quad \cdot \quad \cdot \quad \cdot \tag{6}$$
$$u^p \sim (0, 0, 0, ..., 1, a_{p1}, ..., a_{pp}).$$

These will constitute a bundle of hyperplanes having in com-mon a space of $p-1$ dimensions S_{p-1}.

Suppose that we take a rational point in our S_{2p-1}. We may multiply through by such a number that the homogeneous co-ordinates are $2p$ integers, and they will correspond to a definite path on the Riemann surface for our curve, the coordinate X_l telling us how many times the lth circuit has been traced in a positive or negative sense. We have a one-to-one correspon-dence between the closed paths and the rational points, in so far as a path is characterized by any constant multiple of the number of turns it takes about the various circuits.

Theorem 12] *The closed circuits on the Riemann surface corre-sponding to an irreducible algebraic curve of genus p may be represented by the rational points of a projective space of $2p-1$ dimensions, and the Abelian integrals of the first sort by the hyper-planes through a fixed space of $p-1$ dimensions S_{p-1}. The necessary and sufficient condition that the period of an Abelian integral about a certain path should be 0 is that the hyperplane corresponding to the integral should contain the rational point corresponding to the path.*

Let us next return to equation (7). If a point (x) describe the closed path (X), the corresponding points (y) will trace various paths and, perhaps, permute with one another, but the sum of their wanderings will be a series of closed paths which we shall call (Y), the transform of (X). Let the integral

$$\sum_i V_i' u^i(x)$$

correspond to the integral

$$\sum_{k,i} V_k u^k(y^i) = \sum_{k,i} V_k \Pi_{ki} u^i(x);$$

then

$$V_i' = \sum_k \Pi_{ki} V_k. \tag{19}$$

We have a collineation of the bundle of hyperplanes through S_{p-1}, and each such collineation will correspond to a transformation of our integrals of just this type. Let (x) trace the various circuits $X_1, X_2, ..., X_{2p}$ times, while $\sum (y'')$ traces them $Y_1, Y_2, ..., Y_{2p}$ times. The kth integral will be changed by

$$Y_k + \sum_l a_{kl} Y_{p+l}.$$

This may be written, by (8) and (9),

$$\sum_i \Pi_{ki} X_i + \sum_{i,j} \Pi_{ki} a_{ij} X_{p+j}$$

$$= \sum_i h_{ki} X_i + \sum_{i,l} g_{li} a_{kl} X_i + \sum_{k,j} H_{kj} X_{p+j} + \sum_{i,j} G_{ij} a_{ki} X_{p+j}$$

$$Y_k = \sum_i h_{ki} X_i + \sum_j H_{kj} X_{p+j} \tag{20}$$

$$Y_{p+l} = \sum_i g_{li} X_i + \sum_j G_{lj} X_{p+j}.$$

We have, thus, a collineation of our S_{2p-1} which carries S_{p-1} into itself, as an integral of the first sort goes into one of the first sort. Suppose, conversely, that we have a rational collineation of S_{2p-1} given by equations like (20) that carries S_{p-1} into itself, so that a hyperplane (V') of the bundle through there goes into another such hyperplane (V). The coordinates of these hyperplanes will be

$$U_k = V_k \qquad U_{p+l} = \sum_j a_{jl} V_j \qquad U_k' = V_k' \qquad U_{p+l}' = \sum_j a_{jl} V_j'.$$

The transformation contragredient to (20) is

$$U_i' = \sum_l h_{li} U_l + \sum_m g_{mi} U_{p+m}$$

$$U_{p+n}' = \sum_l H_{ln} U_l + \sum_l G_{ln} U_{p+l},$$

and this becomes immediately, by equations (8) and (9),

$$V_i' = \sum_k \Pi_{ki} V_i, \tag{19}$$

the desired relation among the hyperplanes of the bundle. It is to be noted that if the transformation have the value 0 all the Π_{ki}'s disappear, and the reasoning ceases to hold.

Definition. Two correspondences which have the same values for g, h, G, and H are said to be 'equivalent'. Two correspondences with the same value are equivalent. If they are of the same indices, we see from (8) and (7) that

$$\sum_i u'^k(y^i) = \sum_i u^k(z^i),$$

and we see by theorem 5] of Ch. II, present book, that the groups (y) and (z) are equivalent. Suppose, conversely, that these groups are equivalent. We get from (7) that the two correspondences have the same Π_{ki}'s, since the u^k's are linearly independent. Hence, if we subtract one set of equations (8) from the corresponding other set, and the same for the sets (9), since $|a_{ij}| \neq 0$

$$h_{ij} = h'_{ij} \qquad g_{ij} = g'_{ij} \qquad H_{ij} = H'_{ij} \quad G_{ij} = G''_{ij}.$$

Theorem 13] *If two correspondences have the same indices, and are equivalent, the groups in the two corresponding to a general point are equivalent, and if two correspondences have the same indices, and if the groups corresponding to a general point on the two be equivalent, the correspondences are equivalent.*

It is to be noted that if a correspondence have the value 0, all the g's and h's are 0, and equations such as (19) become illusory. We get from what immediately preceded the definition of equivalent correspondences

Rosatti's Theorem 14] *There is a one-to-one correspondence between the sets of equivalent correspondences, not of value 0, on an irreducible curve of genus p, and the rational collineations of a projective space of $2p-1$ dimensions which leave invariant a space of $p-1$ dimensions. The number of linearly independent correspondences will be that of linearly independent collineations.**

Theorem 15] *All correspondences with a value which is not 0 are represented by the identical collineation.*

Theorem 16] *If the product of two correspondences have a value not 0, they will be represented by mutually inverse collineations.*

---

* Rosatti[1], p. 6.

§ 4. Generalized values

The original definition of a value given in Ch. VIII of Book I was such an integer that the group of points $\sum_i Q_i + \gamma P$ was a group of a linear series, with an easy extension to the case where γ was negative. This amounts to

$$\sum_r u^k(y^r) + \gamma u^k(x) = \Pi_k.$$

And so, from (7), $\sum_i \Pi_{ki} u^i(x) + \gamma u^k(x) = 0.$

Since the integrals u^k are linearly independent,

$$\begin{vmatrix} \Pi_{11}+\gamma & \Pi_{12} & . & \Pi_{1p} \\ \Pi_{21} & \Pi_{22}+\gamma & . & \Pi_{2p} \\ . & . & . & . \\ \Pi_{p1} & \Pi_{p2} & . & \Pi_{pp}+\gamma \end{vmatrix} = \begin{vmatrix} \Pi_{11}+\gamma & \Pi_{21} & . & \Pi_{p1} \\ \Pi_{12} & \Pi_{22}+\gamma & . & \Pi_{p2} \\ . & . & . & . \\ \Pi_{1p} & \Pi_{2p} & . & \Pi_{pp}+\gamma \end{vmatrix} = 0.$$

The roots of this equation are the negatives of the roots of the characteristic equation of the collineation in the bundle given by (19).

Definition. The negatives of the roots of the characteristic equation of the collineation among the hyperplanes of the bundle through S_{p-1} shall be called the 'generalized values' of the correspondence.[*]

Theorem 17] *The number of generalized values of a correspondence cannot exceed the genus of the curve. If the correspondence have a value, this will be one of the generalized values.*

It may seem surprising that we should get the generalized values from the collineation in the bundle, rather than from the space collineation (20). The characteristic equations of the two are simply connected. Let us find

$$\begin{vmatrix} h_{11}-\rho & h_{12} & . & h_{1p} & H_{11} & . & H_{1p} \\ . & . & . & . & . & . \\ h_{p1} & h_{p2} & . & h_{pp}-\rho & H_{p1} & . & H_{pp} \\ g_{11} & g_{12} & . & g_{1p} & G_{11}-\rho & . & G_{1p} \\ . & . & . & . & . & . \\ g_{p1} & g_{p2} & . & g_{pp} & G_{p1} & . & G_{pp}-\rho \end{vmatrix} \times \begin{vmatrix} 1 & 0 & 0 & . & 0 & a_{11} & . & a_{1p} \\ . & . & . & . & . & . & . \\ 0 & 0 & 0 & . & 1 & a_{p1} & . & a_{pp} \\ 1 & 0 & 0 & . & 0 & \bar{a}_{11} & . & \bar{a}_{1p} \\ . & . & . & . & . & . & . \\ 0 & 0 & 0 & . & 1 & \bar{a}_{p1} & . & \bar{a}_{pp} \end{vmatrix}$$

---

[*] This concept is due to Rosatti[2].

where a_{ij} and $\bar{a}_{ij}$ are conjugate complex numbers. Multiplying columns into rows:

$$
\begin{vmatrix}
\Pi_{11}-\rho & \Pi_{12} & . & \Pi_{1p} & \sum_r \Pi_{1r}a_{r1}-a_{11}\rho & . & \sum_r \Pi_{1r}a_{rp}-a_{1p}\rho \\
. & . & . & . & . & . & . \\
\Pi_{p1} & \Pi_{p2} & . & \Pi_{pp}-\rho & \sum_r \Pi_{pr}a_{r1}-a_{1p}\rho & . & \sum_r \Pi_{pr}a_{rp}-a_{pp}\rho \\
\bar{\Pi}_{11}-\rho & \bar{\Pi}_{12} & . & \bar{\Pi}_{1p} & \sum_r \bar{\Pi}_{1r}\bar{a}_{r1}-\bar{a}_{11}\rho & . & \sum_r \bar{\Pi}_{1r}\bar{a}_{rp}-\bar{a}_{1p}\rho \\
. & . & . & . & . & . & . \\
\bar{\Pi}_{p1} & \bar{\Pi}_{p2} & . & \bar{\Pi}_{pp}-\rho & \sum_r \bar{\Pi}_{pr}\bar{a}_{r1}-\bar{a}_{1p}\rho & . & \sum_r \bar{\Pi}_{pr}\bar{a}_{rp}-\bar{a}_{pp}\rho
\end{vmatrix}
$$

$$
=
\begin{vmatrix}
\Pi_{11}-\rho & \Pi_{12} & . & \Pi_{1p} & 0 & 0 & . & 0 \\
\Pi_{21} & \Pi_{22}-\rho & . & \Pi_{2p} & & . & . & . \\
. & . & . & . & . & . & . & . \\
\Pi_{p1} & \Pi_{p2} & . & \Pi_{pp}-\rho & 0 & & . & . \\
0 & 0 & . & 0 & \bar{\Pi}_{11}-\rho & \bar{\Pi}_{12} & . & \bar{\Pi}_{1p} \\
. & . & . & . & . & . & . & . \\
0 & 0 & . & 0 & \bar{\Pi}_{p1} & & . & \bar{\Pi}_{pp}-\rho
\end{vmatrix}
\times
$$

$$
\times
\begin{vmatrix}
1 & 0 & . & 0 & a_{11} & . & a_{1p} \\
. & . & . & . & . & . & . \\
. & . & . & . & . & . & . \\
0 & 0 & . & 1 & a_{p1} & . & a_{pp} \\
1 & 0 & . & 0 & \bar{a}_{11} & . & \bar{a}_{1p} \\
. & . & . & . & . & . & . \\
0 & 0 & . & 1 & \bar{a}_{p1} & . & \bar{a}_{pp}
\end{vmatrix}
$$

Hence the first large determinant, which is characteristic for the collineations in S_{2p-1}, is equal to

$$
\begin{vmatrix}
\Pi_{11}-\rho & \Pi_{12} & . & \Pi_{1p} \\
. & . & . & . \\
\Pi_{p1} & & . & \Pi_{pp}-\rho
\end{vmatrix}
\cdot
\begin{vmatrix}
\bar{\Pi}_{11}-\rho & . & \bar{\Pi}_{1p} \\
. & . & . \\
\bar{\Pi}_{p1} & . & \bar{\Pi}_{pp}-\rho
\end{vmatrix}
$$

This gives a curious result, namely,

Theorem 18] *The negatives of the generalized values of a correspondence and the conjugate complex numbers are the roots of the characteristic equation of the corresponding collineation in higher space.*

If we take the characteristic determinant, and add to each of the first p rows a suitable combination of the last rows, we get

$$\begin{vmatrix} \Pi_{11}-\rho & \Pi_{12} & . & \Pi_{1p} & \sum_r \Pi_{1r}a_{r1}-a_{11}\rho & . & \sum_r \Pi_{1r}a_{rp}-a_{1p}\rho \\ . & . & & . & . & & . \\ \Pi_{p1} & \Pi_{p2} & . & \Pi_{pp}-\rho & \sum_r \Pi_{pr}a_{r1}-a_{p1}\rho & . & \sum_r \Pi_{pr}a_{rp}-a_{pp}\rho \\ g_{11} & g_{12} & . & g_{1p} & G_{11}-\rho & . & G_{1p} \\ . & . & & . & . & & . \\ g_{p1} & g_{p2} & . & g_{pp}-\rho & G_{p1} & . & G_{pp}-\rho \end{vmatrix}$$

In the same way we may add to each of the last p columns a suitable combination of the first three, getting

$$\begin{vmatrix} \Pi_{11}-\rho & \Pi_{12} & . & \Pi_{1p} & 0 & . & . & 0 \\ . & . & & . & & . & . \\ \Pi_{p1} & \Pi_{p2} & . & \Pi_{pp}-\rho & 0 & . & . & 0 \\ g_{11} & g_{12} & . & g_{1p} & \Pi'_{11}-\rho & 0 & . & \Pi'_{1p} \\ . & . & & . & & . & . \\ g_{p1} & g_{p2} & . & g_{pp} & \Pi'_{p1} & . & . & \Pi'_{pp}-\rho \end{vmatrix}$$

$$= \begin{vmatrix} \Pi_{11}-\rho & \Pi_{12} & . & \Pi_{1p} \\ . & . & & . \\ \Pi_{p1} & \Pi_{p2} & . & \Pi_{pp}-\rho \end{vmatrix} \times \begin{vmatrix} \Pi'_{11}-\rho & \Pi'_{12} & . & \Pi'_{1p} \\ . & . & & . \\ \Pi'_{p1} & \Pi'_{p2} & . & \Pi'_{pp}-\rho \end{vmatrix}$$

Comparing this with (14) and theorem 18], we get

Theorem 19] *The generalized values of a correspondence and its inverse are conjugate complex numbers.*

The sum of the roots of the characteristic equation for the collineation in S_{2p-1} is $\sum h_{ii} + \sum G_{jj}$, and this we know is the negative of the sum of the generalized values and the conjugate complex numbers. We thus get from (13)

Theorem 20] *The number of coincidences of a correspondence is the sum of the indices and the generalized values of the correspondence and its inverse.*

§ 5. (p, p) Correspondences

There are a certain number of particular types of correspondence which can be studied fruitfully by special methods invented to suit each case. As a first example,* let us take a correspondence with the indices p and p and limit ourselves to correspondences with value.

* Cf. Scorza.

If the value γ of the correspondence be positive, there exists a $g^r_{p+\gamma}$ which we may assume complete. If this be not special, we have $r = \gamma$, and the group corresponding to a given point is residual to the group consisting in that point counted γ times. The number of coincidences is $2p + 2p\gamma$, and this by theorem 10] of Book II, Ch. IV, is $(\gamma+1)^2 p$, so that we must have $\gamma = 1$. When the series is special, we have

$$p + \gamma - \rho = p - i \qquad \gamma + i = \rho,$$

counting the coincidences by two methods, then, we have

$$p + p + 2p\gamma = 2p(\gamma+1) = (\gamma+1+i)[p+\gamma+(\gamma+i)(p-1)];$$

and since
$$\gamma + 1 \leqslant \gamma + i + 1,$$
$$2p \geqslant [p+\gamma+(\gamma+i)(p-1)]$$
$$p \geqslant (\gamma+i)p - i, \qquad\qquad \text{since } p - 1 \geqslant 0,$$
$$i = 0 \qquad \gamma = 1.$$

Theorem 21] *The only* (*p, p*) *correspondences of positive value are those given by a non-special* g^1_{p+1}.

If there exist a (*p, p*) correspondence of negative value, that value must be -1, as otherwise the number of coincidences would be negative. The group corresponding to a variable point (*x*) could not be special. For if it belonged to a special complete series, then by the reduction theorem 8] of the first chapter of the present book we should get another complete series by adding a fixed point (*y*) to each group. But by the definition of a correspondence of value -1, the group consisting of (*y*) and the mates of (*x*) is equivalent to that consisting of (*x*) and the mates of (*y*). If *p* points do not belong to a special group, certainly $p+1$, which include them, do not. Let (*y*) be a fixed point, $(y^1), (y^2),..., (y^p)$ be other fixed points not belonging to a special group. If (*x*) be a variable point, there will be a g^1_{p+1} with the group $(x), (y^1),(y^2),..., (y^p)$. Let (*x*) correspond to the *p* points $(x^1), (x^2),..., (x^p)$, which with (*y*) form a group of this. We thus get a (*p, p*) correspondence of value -1, and there are no others of a different kind.

Theorem 22] *The only* (*p, p*) *correspondences of negative value are those of value* -1. $p+1$ *points in general position will determine such a correspondence. They have no coincidences.*

Could we have a (p, p) correspondence of value 0 ? The curve must contain a special and complete g_p^ρ, and all its groups are residual to $p-2$ fixed points. If $\rho = 1$ the curve must be rational, for its points are in one-to-one correspondence with the groups of a g_p^1 or a pencil of curves. But there $p = 0$, and there is no series left. Hence we must have $\rho > 1$. We may construct a correspondence of this sort in the following fashion. Take a curve of order p with a given point of order $p-3$ and $p-5$ given double points. The number of conditions imposed does not exceed

$$\frac{(p-2)(p-3)}{2} + 3(p-5) = \frac{p(p+1)}{2} - 12,$$

so that we have not asked too much, and we may be sure by putting the singular point at the origin and applying the reasoning that led to Lefschetz's theorem 4] of Book I, Ch. VII, that just this curve exists. Its genus is also equal to p. Our correspondence shall consist in making each point correspond to the p points conjugate to it with regard to a fixed conic.

§ 6. Birational correspondences

A $(1, 1)$ correspondence will give a birational transformation of the curve into itself, and conversely. If the value be negative, the genus must be 1 or 0. When the genus is 0 we have what amounts to a birational transformation of a straight line into itself, and this is of course a projective transformation. When the genus is 1 the negative value can only be -1.

If the value be 0, the curve has a g_1^1, and so is rational. Suppose the value is positive, say γ. Our curve has a complete $g_{\gamma+1}^\rho$. Now by hypothesis we may have γ of these points coalesce in a general point, and the other point is then determined, we must have $\gamma = \rho$. But then, if we pick $\gamma - 1$ arbitrary points, we shall have residual thereto a g_2^1.

Theorem 23] *The only curves of general modulus of periodicity which can be birationally transformed into themselves are curves of genus 0 or 1 or hyperelliptic curves.*

Let us now give an example of a birational correspondence which has no value. We have so far never shown that any valueless correspondences exist.*

* Cf. Burkhardt[1].

We take the cubic curve

$$y^3 + x^2 - 1 = 0$$

and make the transformation

$$x' = x \ . \quad y' = -\left(\frac{1+\sqrt{3}i}{2}\right)y \quad y = -\left(\frac{1-\sqrt{3}i}{2}\right)y'.$$

Here corresponding points are collinear with a fixed point not on the curve. The curve has no singular point, so the genus is 1. The coincidences are the two finite and one infinite inflexions on the x-axis, each counting but once, as we see by Zeuthen's rule of Ch. VIII, Book I, so that if there were an integral value γ we should have
$$3 = 1 + 1 + 2\gamma,$$
which is absurd.

Here is another example. Suppose that we have an irrational γ_ν^1 of index 1:

$$f(x,y) = F_1(x,y,x',y') = F_2(x,y,x',y') = f'(x',y') = 0.$$

When we take (x,y) on f, since the index is 1 we have but one corresponding point (x',y'), but each (x',y') corresponds to ν points (x,y). We have a ν-to-1 correspondence between two curves of genera p and p' respectively, but on the former curve a $(\nu-1)$-to-$(\nu-1)$ correspondence. Suppose this had the value γ.

$$\gamma P_1 + P_2 + \ldots + P_\nu \equiv P_1 + \gamma P_2 + \ldots + P_\nu$$

$$P_3 + \ldots + P_\nu \equiv P_3 + \ldots + P_\nu$$

$$(\gamma-1)P_1 \equiv (\gamma-1)P_2 \equiv (\gamma-1)P_3 \equiv \ldots$$

$$\gamma P_1 + \ldots + P_\nu \equiv \gamma Q_1 + \ldots + Q_\nu$$

$$(\gamma-1)Q_1 \equiv (\gamma-1)Q_2 \equiv (\gamma-1)Q_3 \equiv \ldots$$

$$(\gamma-1)(\nu+\gamma-1)P_1 \equiv (\gamma-1)(\nu+\gamma-1)Q_1.$$

If $\gamma = 1$, our γ_ν^1 is a g_ν^1, *contra hypothesem.*

If
$$\nu + \gamma - 1 = l \neq 0,$$

we have exactly the same contradiction encountered at the bottom of page 124, unless $\nu = \gamma = 1$ and the curve is rational. If

$$\nu + \gamma - 1 = 0,$$

the number of coincidences is

$$2(\nu-1)(1-p),$$

which is negative unless $p=1$ or $p=0$.

Theorem 24] *An irrational series of index 1 on a curve of genus greater than 1 gives rise to a correspondence without value.*[*]

If we have a one-to-one or birational correspondence between two curves, or of a curve with itself, there may be some points where the correspondence degenerates. How can this be ? Assuming that neither curve is hyperelliptic, let them be replaced by curves of order $2p_1-2$ in a space of p_1-1 dimensions, and of order $2p_2-2$ in a space of p_2-1 dimensions, which curves have no singular points. The birational relation between the original curves must correspond to a projective relation between the new curves, and a projective relation has no exceptions. Hence, any exception in the original birational relation must come from a point on the original curve which did not correspond to a single point on the space, i.e. a singular point. When the curves are hyperelliptic, there is a one-to-one relation between their g_2^1's and this relation must be without exception, since the g_2^1's correspond to points on a line, which are birationally transformed only by a projective transformation. Hence, the exceptions here can come only from singular points or double points of the g_2^1's.

Theorem 25] *If two curves be birationally related, no points can be exceptional except singular points or double points of the g_2^1's if they be hyperelliptic.*

§ 7. Halphen's transformation

In the treatment of birational transformations which we have given so far we have discussed the effects but said little about the means by which they are produced. It will be well to take one particular type of transformation and carry it through in detail. This is named after Halphen.[†]

We start with a curve

$$f(x_1, x_2, x_3) = 0,$$

and let each point (x) thereof correspond to the point (y) which is on the tangent at (x) and is conjugate to (x) with regard to

---

[*] Cf. Severi-Löffler, pp. 186 ff. and 402.   [†] Halphen[2], p. 420 ff.

a given conic. If we take such trilinear coordinates that the conic has the equation

$$(xx) = 0,$$

$$\rho y_i = \begin{vmatrix} x_j & x_k \\ \dfrac{\partial f}{\partial x_j} & \dfrac{\partial f}{\partial x_k} \end{vmatrix}. \tag{21}$$

If the curve be given parametrically so that

$$x_i = x_i(t) \qquad x_i' = \frac{dx_i}{dt},$$

$$\sigma y_i = (xx')x_i - (xx)x_i'. \tag{22}$$

Each generic point (x) of our curve will correspond to a single (y). When (y) is given, its polar with regard to the fixed conic will cut the given curve in a number of points. Let us show that usually there is but one of them whose tangent goes through (y). Let (x) be a general point of our curve or, let us say, merely a non-singular point, P any other point on its tangent. There are ∞^3 conics where P is the pole of the line from (x) to the point of contact of another tangent from P, hence at most ∞^4 conics where this is true for some point P on the tangent, and so plenty of conics where it is not true. Hence (x) may be made to go into a point that corresponds to (x) alone, or the transformation will be, in general, one to one.

Returning to our equation (21) we may interpret $\left(\dfrac{\partial f}{\partial x}\right)$ as the pole of the tangent to f with regard to the fixed conic. Moreover,

$$nf = \left(\frac{\partial f}{\partial x} x\right) = 0$$

$$d(nf) = \left(\left[d\frac{\partial f}{\partial x}\right]x\right) + \left(\frac{\partial f}{\partial x} dx\right) = 0 \qquad \left(\frac{\partial f}{\partial x} dx\right) = 0.$$

Hence
$$\left(\left[d\frac{\partial f}{\partial x}\right]x\right) = 0.$$

The relation between (x) and $\left(\dfrac{\partial f}{\partial x}\right)$ is a reciprocal one; each is the pole of the tangent to the curve traced by the other.

Theorem 26] *A curve and its polar reciprocal with regard to the fixed conic have the same Halphen transform.*

Let us next take a branch of the first order:

$$x_i = z_i + a_i t + b_i t^2 + c_i t^3 + \ldots \tag{23}$$

$$x_i' = a_i + 2b_i t + 3c_i t^2 + \ldots \tag{24}$$

$$(xx) = (zz) + 2(az)t + [(aa) + 2(by)]t^2 + \ldots \tag{25}$$

$$(xx') = (az) + [(aa) + 2(bz)]t + 3[(ab) + (cz)]t^2 + \ldots \tag{26}$$

$$y_i = [(az)z_i - (zz)a_i] + \{[(aa) + 2(bz)]z_i - (az)a_i - 2(zz)b_i\}t + \ldots \tag{27}$$

Since the original branch is simple,

$$(az)z_i - (zz)a_i \not\equiv 0.$$

The new branch will not be simple if

$$[(az)z_i - (zz)a_i] = \rho\{[(aa) + 2(bz)]z_i - (az)a_i - 2(zz)b_i\}.$$

Multiply through by z_i and add:

$$0 = \rho[(aa)(zz) - (az)^2].$$

We have already seen $\rho \neq 0$. If the second factor vanish, the line from (a) to (z) touches the conic. But if we multiply through by a_i and add, we get

$$0 = (az)^2 - (aa)(zz) = 2\rho[(az)(bz) - (zz)(ab)].$$

This means that the lines from (z) to (a) and to (b) are conjugate with regard to the conic. The first of these is tangent, hence either (z) is the point of contact, or (z), (a), and (b) are collinear on a tangent, which would be an inflexional tangent to the original curve. If, then, we take care that the conic does not touch the original curve, or touch an inflexional or singular tangent, the original branch of the first order will become a branch of the first order.

Let us assume that our original curve has no singular points but ordinary ones, that the fundamental conic does not touch it nor pass through a singular point nor touch a singular tangent, then the new curve will have nothing but branches of the first order, and all the original singular points will have been exploded into non-singular points. Let us show that we can arrange things so that the transformed curve has no singularity worse than a node.

If the transformed curve is to have a singular point of order 3 or more, three or more collinear points of the original curve must have their tangents concurrent at the pole of the line on which they lie. If there be only a one-parameter family of lines which cut the curve in three points with concurrent tangents, we may choose the conic so that such a line and point of concurrence shall never be polar and pole with regard to it, for there are ∞^5 conics in the plane, and only ∞^3 with a given polar and pole. But perhaps every line in the plane meets the curve in three points with concurrent tangents. Let us show that this is impossible in the case of an irreducible curve. Suppose it were the case, and that the curve touched the line at infinity at the end of the y-axis, so that each vertical line met the curve in two points with parallel tangents. Analytically this gives the equations

$$f(xy) = f(x\bar{y}) = 0$$

$$\frac{dy}{dx} = \frac{d\bar{y}}{dx} \qquad \bar{y} = y+k.$$

The curve can be carried into itself by a parallel translation, and so by an infinite number of them, and this is only possible if it consists in one or more parallel lines, a trivial case.

We must next show that the transformed curve does not, necessarily, have a tacnode, i.e. a point where two branches of the first order touch. If we return to equation (27), we see that we can give to t such a value that although (x) and (z) correspond to the same point (y) they will not give proportional values (y'). That means that of the ∞^3 conics that carry the branches at (x) and (z) into two branches at (y), the intersection of their tangents, there are at most ∞^2 which make those branches tangent, and give a tacnode. Hence there are, at most, ∞^4 transformations that produce a tacnode, or we can avoid this and carry our curve, which has nothing but branches of the first order, into one with no singularities but nodes.

We pause at this moment to note that the transformed curve has no cusps. Its order is found, by Chasles-Cayley-Brill, to be the sum of the order and class of the original curve, and the two are of the same genus. For the original curve

$$\kappa = 0 \qquad m = 2n+2(p-1). \tag{28}$$

For the transformed curve,

$$p' = p \qquad \kappa' = 0 \qquad n' = 3n+2(p-1) \qquad m' = 3m. \tag{29}$$

Now let us see what will be the effect of a Halphen transformation on a branch of any order, it being assumed that the origin thereof is not on the conic and the tangent does not touch the conic, whose equation is still $(xx) = 0$.

$$x_1 = t^{\rho_0} \qquad x_2 = a_1 t^{\rho_1} + \ldots \qquad x_3 = 1$$

$$\lambda x_1' = \rho_0 \qquad \lambda x_2' = \rho_1 a_1 t^{\rho_1 - \rho_0} + \ldots \qquad \lambda x_3' = 0$$

$$(xx) = 1 + t^{2\rho_0} + \tfrac{1}{2} \sum_{i,j} a_i a_j t^{\rho_i + \rho_j}$$

$$\lambda(xx') = \rho_0 t^{\rho_0} + \tfrac{1}{2} \sum_{i,j} (\rho_i + \rho_j) a_i a_j t^{\rho_i + \rho_j - \rho_0}$$

$$\mu y_1' = -\rho_0 + \tfrac{1}{2} \sum (\rho_i + \rho_j - 2\rho_0) a_i a_j t^{\rho_i + \rho_j} + \ldots$$

$$\mu y_2' = -\rho_1 a_1 t^{\rho_1 - \rho_0} - \rho_2 a_2 t^{\rho_2 - \rho_0} - (\rho_1 - \rho_0) t^{\rho_1 + \rho_0} + \ldots$$

$$\mu y_3' = \rho_0 t^{\rho_0} + \tfrac{1}{2} \sum (\rho_i + \rho_j) t^{\rho_i + \rho_j - \rho_0}.$$

If $\rho_0 \leqslant \rho_1 - \rho_0$ the order is unaltered, but the characteristic exponents have been reduced. If $\rho_0 > \rho_1 - \rho_0$ the order has been reduced, and the characteristic exponents not increased. Hence, neither order nor characteristic exponents is ever increased, and one at least is reduced. Keeping on with successive transformations, we see that the order of the branch can be brought down to 1, and that of no other branch has been increased. Thus we may carry over, step by step, to a curve which has only branches of the first order. Two such branches with contact of order c will be carried into two with contact of lower order. Remembering what we learned about such a curve two pages back, we reach

Theorem 27] *Any curve may be carried by a succession of Halphen transformations into one whose only singularities are nodes.*

Let us next turn from the Halphen transformation to its inverse. We see at once from theorem 26] that the inverse curve is not unique, and we are led to the idea that there are an infinite number of curves that are carried over into a given curve. Let the transformed curve be

$$y_i = y_i(t).$$

Let (r) and (s) be the points of contact of tangents from (y) to the conic. $(rr) = (rs) = (ry) = (sy) = 0.$

An arbitrary point conjugate to (y) is

$$x_i = r_i(t) + \phi(t) s_i(t)$$

$$x_i' = r_i'(t) + \phi(t) s_i'(t) + \phi'(t) s_i(t).$$

Since (y), (x), and (x') are collinear,

$$|rr'y|+\phi[|rs'y|+|sr'y|]+\phi^2|ss'y|+\phi'|rsy| = 0. \qquad \textbf{(30)}$$

Theorem 28] *The problem of finding the curves of which a given curve is the Halphen transform, leads to a Ricatti equation.*

(r) and (s) are two solutions; the familiar properties of the cross ratios of four solutions of a Ricatti equation suggest that the different solutions of the inverse of Halphen's problem have interesting relations to one another.

$$(rr) = (ss) = (rr') = (ss') = 0 \qquad (ry) = (sy) = 0$$

$$|rr'y|^2 = \begin{vmatrix} (rr) & (rr') & (ry) \\ (r'r) & (r'r') & (r'y) \\ (yr) & (yr') & (yy) \end{vmatrix} = 0$$

$$|ss'y| = 0.$$

Hence (30) becomes $\qquad A\phi+B\phi' = 0.$

If ϕ_1 and ϕ_2 be two solutions,

$$\phi_1\phi_2'-\phi_2\phi_1' = 0.$$

This shows that the ratio of ϕ_1 to ϕ_2 or the cross ratio of these two points with (r) and (s) is constant. We get the situation clearly in mind by considerations of non-Euclidean geometry. Let us take the fixed conic as the Absolute for a Cayleyan system of non-Euclidean measurement, the distance of two points being a constant multiple of the logarithm of the cross ratio which they make with the intersection of their line with the conic. Thus two solutions of the Ricatti equations give two curves cutting constant distances on their common system of normals, i.e. geodesically parallel.

Theorem 29] *If the fundamental conic of a Halphen transformation be taken as the Absolute for a non-Euclidean system of measurement, then a given curve and its geodesic parallels have the same Halphen transforms.*

An algebraic curve will always have an algebraic Halphen transform. Is every algebraic curve the Halphen transform of another? Certainly not; there is no reason to expect that the Ricatti equation given above will lead to an algebraic curve, and it usually will not. We are face to face with a question very closely analogous to that faced in Book I, Ch. X: when will an algebraic curve have an algebraic involute? The various

solutions of the Ricatti equation give us sets of moving points
P, whose tangents are concurrent in Q the pole of the line on
which all the f's lie. This line, being conjugate to the tangents,
is the common normal to all the P curves; its envelope, which is
the polar reciprocal of the Halphen transform, is their common
evolute. Since a curve and its polar reciprocal in a conic are
algebraic together, the question becomes simply this: when is
a given algebraic curve the evolute of some algebraic curve
in a Cayley system of measurement ? The method of treatment
thus becomes exactly that of Book I, Ch. X, and the result
stated in Humbert's Theorem 57] is correct if we replace 'arc'
by 'cosine of constant multiple of arc'.

§8. Rational determination of the characteristics of a curve

As a last application of the Halphen transformation, let us
approach a problem which may have occurred already to the
thoughtful reader. Logically it should have been discussed
much sooner, but we lacked the tools to do so in the easiest way.

What do we mean by saying that an algebraic curve is
'given' ? What is given ? The algebraist will say the equation
is given, and nothing else. But we have frequently assumed
that we knew not only the equation but the situation of the
singular points, and that would enable us by Puiseux's method
to determine the power-series developments, as well as the effect
on genus and class. But when we have nothing available but
the equation, the determination of the situation of the singular
points may lead us to irreducible equations of high order, so
that we do not really know where these points are, or what they
amount to. Let us see if we can go at the matter otherwise.

Let us first seek the class of the curve. This is obtained from
the tangential equation, which in turn comes from eliminating
x and y from

$$f(x, y) = 0 \qquad \frac{u}{w} = \frac{\dfrac{\partial f}{\partial x}}{\dfrac{\partial f}{\partial 1}} \qquad \frac{v}{w} = \frac{\dfrac{\partial f}{\partial y}}{\dfrac{\partial f}{\partial 1}}.$$

The resulting equation may be reducible. There may be
extraneous factors which are the tangential equations of the

singular points counted to a suitable degree. As each singular point of a curve is also a singular point of the Hessian, to as high or higher order, the same extraneous factors will appear in the tangential equation of the Hessian, and may be removed by a H.C.F. process.

We next note that a Halphen transformation will always improve the structure of a curve, provided that we avoid certain dangerous positions of the fundamental conic. If the curve have the homogeneous equation

$$f(x_1, x_2, x_3) = 0$$

and the conic have the equation

$$c_1 x_1^2 + c_2 x_2^2 + c_3 x_3^2 = 0,$$

we may improve it by the transformation

$$\rho y_i = \begin{vmatrix} c_j x_j & c_k x_k \\ \dfrac{\partial f}{\partial x_j} & \dfrac{\partial f}{\partial x_k} \end{vmatrix}.$$

By repeating the process a sufficient number of times, varying the c's, we can come to a curve with no singular points but nodes. How do we know when we have got there ? By seeing if the intersections of two arbitrary first polars are distinct. This also can be accomplished by rational means. We may find the class of the transformed curve as above. Knowing the order and class, and that the cuspidal index is 0, we can determine the genus, which is the genus of the original curve. Of this curve we know the order, class, and genus, hence all the other Plücker characteristics.

Theorem 30] *If the equation of a curve be given, its Plücker characteristics may be determined by rational processes.**

It goes without saying that we use the word 'may' in the poetical sense, that only a finite number of operations are, demonstrably, necessary. No man or superman could put the thing through successfully in a complicated case. Another method would be to find the order of the evolute of a general curve projectively equivalent to the given one, for this order, by (18) of the last chapter of Book I, is $3n+\iota$. This gives us ι, and with n, m, and ι we have all we need.

---

* Cf. Nöther². His method is much longer than this.

CHAPTER VIII

PARAMETRIC REPRESENTATION OF THE GENERAL CURVE. A SKETCH

§ 1. Riemann surface for the general curve

WE have had occasion at various times to note that a curve of genus 0 is rational, that is to say, we may express x and y as rational functions of an auxiliary parameter, which, in turn, depends rationally on them. We shall see in the last section of the present chapter that the coordinates of points on a curve of genus 1 may be rationally expressed in terms of Weierstrass elliptic functions. In each of these cases the parametric representation, once obtained, offers the easiest way to study a number of the properties of the curve. It is the main task of the present chapter to show that the coordinates of the points on any curve can be expressed in terms of an auxiliary parameter, to 'uniformize' the curve as the somewhat cacophonous technical expression goes. We shall apply the method of uniformization to prove one or two fundamental theorems, leaving open the question whether there be many facts about the general curve that can be better found in this way than any other. A complete study of all the questions in the theory of algebraic functions which are involved in uniformization would lead us very far afield indeed; we have therefore entitled the chapter a 'sketch', and shall live up to that designation, giving the reader, anxious to go into the matter further, references to original sources.

Let us begin with a curve of genus $p > 1$,

$$f(x, y) = 0. \tag{1}$$

As we shall deal exclusively with birationally invariant properties, we may assume that the curve has been suitably simplified, that is to say:

 a) It has no singular points but nodes.

 b) It meets the line at infinity in distinct non-singular points.

 c) It has no vertical asymptotes.

 d) No inflexional tangent, nor tangent at a node, is vertical.

If, then, we construct the Riemann surface for y as a function of x, whatever 'construct' may mean in this connexion, the only branch points are simple ones where two values of y coalesce, and they correspond to points of contact of vertical tangents in number

$$m = 2(n+p-1). \tag{2}$$

Let the superposed sheets of the surface be $s_1, s_2, ..., s_n$, the corresponding values of y for a particular $x, y_1, y_2, ..., y_n$. It may be shown by a discussion that is much too long to reproduce here, that a Riemann surface may be constructed with the following characteristics.*

The branch points being $P_1, P_2, ..., P_m$, there is a line of passage P_1P_2 for the sheets s_1, s_2, along P_3P_4 for the sheets s_2, s_3, and so on, along $P_{2n-5}P_{2n-4}$ for the sheets s_{n-2}, s_{n-1}. The values y_{n-1} and y_n will permute about each of the points $P_{2n-3}, P_{2n-2}, ..., P_m$. We connect them in pairs by lines of passage for these two sheets. The number of these is

$$\tfrac{1}{2}[m-2(n-4)] = p+1.$$

This Riemann surface is not simply connected. We make it so by drawing two types of cuts. Each line of passage $P_{2(n-1+i)-1}P_{2(n-1+i)}$ shall be surrounded by a very close cut C_i lying wholly on s_{n-1}. The number of these will be p. We get p more as follows. We start with a point on the line of passage $P_{2n-3}P_{2n-2}$ and make a circuit D_i partly in s_{n-1}, partly in s_i, which crosses this line and $P_{2(n-1+i)-1}P_{2(n-1+i)}$ and surrounds $P_{2n-3}P_{2(n-1+i)-1}$. The number of these is p. The opposite sides of these cuts are treated as different arcs of the boundary, just as though the surface were slit along them and opened up. We get finally a simply connected region bounded by $4p$ different arcs. They form p sets of four corresponding to the same subscript, the first and third corresponding to a cut D, the second and fourth to a cut C.

Let us look at the periods of the various types of integrals as we follow a cut C or a cut D closely. For an integral of the first sort there will be $2p$ of these. The value of an integral taken almost completely around a cut C will be the difference of its values at two near points separated by D, and the same

---

* Cf. Picard, p. 367 ff. This type is called the Lüroth-Clebsch, and was first described by these analysts in the *Math. Annalen*, vol. iv, 1870. See also Enriques-Chisini, vol. i, pp. 381 ff.

is true when the roles of the letters are interchanged. The difference between the two values of an integral between the same two points, when taken by two distinct paths, will be of the form

$$\sum_i m_i c_i + n_i d_i.$$

The general integral of the first sort may be written

$$r_1 u_1 + r_2 u_2 + \ldots + r_p u_p,$$

where $u_1, u_2, \ldots, u_p$ are linearly independent integrals of the first sort. Let us see if we can choose the multipliers r to satisfy the equations

$$\sum_i r_i c_{ij} = 0 \ (j \neq k) \qquad \sum_i r_i c_{ik} = 1,$$

where c_{ij} is the period for u_k around the cut D_i. If the determinant of the coefficients were 0 we could find an integral of the first sort with a period 0 for every one of the first p circuits, and this is not possible.*

Hence we may solve these equations for each value of k. We thus get p linearly independent integrals, known as normal integrals, whose periods follow the scheme already outlined in Ch. VIII:

	D_1	D_2	.	.	.	D_p	C_1	C_2	.	.	.	C_p	
u_1	1	0	.	.	.	0	a_{11}	a_{12}	.	.	.	a_{1p}	
u_2	0	1	.	.	.	0	a_{21}	a_{22}	.	.	.	a_{2p}	(3)
.	.	.	.	.	.	.	.	.	.	.	.	.	
.	.	.	.	.	.	.	.	.	.	.	.	.	
u_p	0	0	.	.	.	1	a_{p1}	a_{p2}	.	.	.	a_{pp}	

where $a_{ij} = a_{ji}$ by Cauchy's integral.

Let us next consider an integral of the second sort. We learned in formula (7) of Ch. II of the present book that we get such an integral by writing

$$v = \alpha_1 u_1 + \alpha_2 u_2 + \ldots + \alpha_p u_p + \int \frac{\psi(x,y)}{\left[(x-x_0)\dfrac{\partial f}{\partial x_0} + (y-y_0)\dfrac{\partial f}{\partial y_0}\right]\dfrac{\partial f}{\partial y}} \, dx,$$

where (x_0, y_0) is a point of the curve, and ψ is an adjoint of order

---

* Cf. Picard, pp. 407 ff.

$n-2$ that does not include the tangent line appearing in the denominator as a factor.

We may determine the multipliers α_i, so that the period of this for each circuit D_i is 0. We assume that the residue of the integral at the single pole (x_0, y_0) is 1. Let l_k be the period for the circuit C_k, which does not include (x_0, y_0). We determine this indirectly as follows. Consider the integral

$$\int v\, du_k = \int v \frac{du_k}{dx}\, dx = \int v\, \frac{\phi_k(x, y)}{\dfrac{\partial f}{\partial y}}\, dx,$$

where ϕ_k is a special adjoint giving u_k. Cauchy's integral formula tells us that if a circuit include no pole of $f(t)$, and if $\theta(t)$ have a single pole with residue 1 at a point z inside this circuit,

$$f(z) = \frac{1}{2\pi i} \int \theta(t) f(t)\, dt,$$

Applying this to v, since v is everywhere finite save at (x_0, y_0) where the residue is 1, the value of this integral is

$$2\pi i \frac{\phi_k(x_0, y_0)}{\dfrac{\partial f}{\partial y_0}}.$$

But we may reckon it otherwise. On opposite sides of D_k the values of v differ by l_k, the period for u_k is 1. On opposite sides of C_k the values of v are the same. Hence for the two arcs D_k and the two arcs C_k we get l_k.

On opposite sides of D_l the values of v differ by l_k, but the period of u_k is 0. On opposite sides of C_l the values of v differ by 0. Hence, integrating all around,

$$l_k = 2\pi i \frac{\phi_k(x_0, y_0)}{\dfrac{\partial f}{\partial y_0}}.$$

The periods of v are

D_1	D_2	.	. D_p	C_1	C_2	.	.	C_p
0	0	.	. 0	$2\pi i \dfrac{\phi_1(x_0, y_0)}{\dfrac{\partial f}{\partial y_0}}$	$2\pi i \dfrac{\phi_2(x_0, y_0)}{\dfrac{\partial f}{\partial y_0}}$	.	.	$2\pi i \dfrac{\phi_p(x_0, y_0)}{\dfrac{\partial f}{\partial y_0}}.$

§ 2. Uniformization

Our next task is to form a new type of Riemann surface, which usually has an infinite number of sheets.* We begin with the n-leaved surface of the Lüroth-Clebsch type just described, which we shall call the surface S_1. Take a second such surface and attach it to the first along one of the cuts C in such a way that the included lines of passage coincide. Let this become a line of passage for the new surface $S_1 S_1'$. The new surface will hang together and be bounded. What we have done amounts essentially to this. We actually effect the cuts C and D on our two surfaces, getting two simply connected figures each bounded by $4p$ arcs C, D. We attach the two boundaries C_k of one to the two boundaries C_k of the other, and then obliterate these as boundaries. We have a new simply connected figure with a great number of boundaries, but not these particular two. We call this figure S_2. We take another Riemann surface analogous to S_1 or S_1', attach it to S_2 along a C_i or D_j cut, and obliterate that as before, getting a new surface S_3 and so on, till we get a surface S_n. Let us construct a Green's function g_n for this surface looked upon as a simply connected region of the plane of $x = \xi + i\eta$ bounded by a curvilinear polygon of a very great number of sides. This function is analytic except at a single pole 0, in the vicinity of which it takes the form $\log \dfrac{1}{r} + \theta(\xi, \eta)$, vanishes on the boundary, and is a solution of Laplace's equation

$$\frac{\partial^2 g}{\partial \xi^2} + \frac{\partial^2 g}{\partial \eta^2} = 0.$$

The proof that this function exists would lead us too far afield.†

At this point there are two possibilities open to us:

A) $\lim\limits_{m \to \infty} g_n(\xi, \eta) = g(\xi, \eta).$

Let h_n be the conjugate function to g_n; we write

$$t_n(x) = e^{-g_n - i h_n}.$$

This is an analytic function of $x = \xi + i\eta$ which will take a

* Cf. Osgood, vol. i, pp. 750 ff. † Ibid., pp. 661 ff.

particular value t_n where $|t_n| < 1$ but once on S_n, hence we may show that if

$$\text{limit } g_n = g; \text{ limit } h_n = h, \text{ limit } t_n = t = e^{-g-ih}.$$

If, thus, S be the infinitely many-leaved Riemann surface which is the limit of S_n, there will be but one point thereon which will give an assigned value to t, where* $|t| < 1$.

Hence x is a single-valued function of t, and so is y, since that is single-valued in x on the Riemann surface, and we have

$$x = x(t) \qquad y = y(t) \qquad t = e^{-\psi(x)}. \tag{4}$$

Suppose that we pass from one sheet of our infinitely many-leaved Riemann surface to another. This will correspond to a functional relation $\qquad t' = f_i(t).$

This transformation is single-valued and analytic, and carries the interior of the unit circle conformally into itself, hence it is linear.† The passage across a cut will correspond to one of these substitutions, and we have an infinite discontinuous group generated by $2p$ original linear transformations, all of which leave the unit circle invariant. If we mean by a fundamental domain within this circle a connex two-dimensional region which contains just one point equivalent under the group to every point within the given circle while the points of the boundary are equivalent in pairs, then we may bound such a domain by $4p$ arcs of circles orthogonal to the unit circle. The interior and one-half the boundary of such a region will correspond uniformly to the points on the given curve.

B) $\lim\limits_{n\to\infty} g_n = \infty$.

We arrive here at a similar result.‡ The group for t will be the doubly periodic group of elliptic function theory. We shall shortly see how we fall on this same group in the case of a curve of genus 1. If two curves correspond uniformly to the points of the same parallelogram they are in one-to-one correspondence with no exception. In such a correspondence the worst possible trouble would be a pole, hence the relation is birational, or both curves have genus 1.

Fundamental theorem 1] *The coordinates of the points of any algebraic curve of genus greater than 1 can be expressed as analytic*

---

functions of an auxiliary parameter t analytic in them. Each point of the curve will correspond to an infinite number of values of this parameter connected together in such a way that all are obtained from one by the linear transformations of an infinite discontinuous group. The total group is generated by independent transformations equal in number to double the genus of the curve, each transformation leaving invariant a certain circle.

Functions of this sort are defined as 'automorphic', and the group is called an 'automorphic group'.*

Instead of starting with the Riemann surface and working over to the group, it is possible to reverse the process as follows.†

We start with a fundamental circle, and form a fundamental domain by means of arcs of $4p$ circles orthogonal thereto, and corresponding in pairs under $2p$ circular transformations that leave the fundamental circle invariant. Let

$$t' = \frac{\alpha_i t + \beta_i}{\gamma_i t + \delta_i}$$

be a typical transformation of the set. A function F is said to be 'Theta-fuchsian' of degree ν if

$$F(t') = F(t)(\gamma_i t + \delta_i)^{2\nu}.$$

Three such functions, $x_1(t), x_2(t), x_3(t)$, will necessarily be connected by a relation

$$f(x_1, x_2, x_3) = 0.$$

The functions

$$x = \frac{x_1(t)}{x_3(t)} \qquad y = \frac{x_2(t)}{x_3(t)}$$

will be automorphic, and the genus of f will be p. Poincaré undertakes to show by a very arduous and delicate process of counting constants that any curve of genus p can be reached in this way.

§ 3. Applications of uniformization

Suppose that we have a curve of genus p uniformized, so that we may write

$$x = x(t) \qquad y = y(t) \qquad t = e^{-\psi(x)}, \tag{4}$$

* The credit for discovering this wonderful theorem is to be divided between Klein and Poincaré. Their original studies have required a great deal of elaboration before being finally perfected, the most indefatigable worker in the field being Koebe cit. The most recent account is to be found in Ford.

† This is the original method of Poincaré, especially pp. 108 ff.

where $x(t)$, $y(t)$ are automorphic functions, as explained above. An integral of the first sort will take the form

$$\int \frac{\phi_k(x, y)}{\dfrac{\partial f}{\partial y}} \, dx = \int \Phi_k(t) \, dt$$

$$\Phi_k(t) = \frac{\phi_k[x(t), y(t)]}{\dfrac{\partial}{\partial y} f[x(t), y(t)]} \frac{dx}{dt}. \tag{5}$$

The only poles of

$$\frac{\phi_k(x, y)}{\dfrac{\partial f}{\partial y}},$$

when f has been simplified as indicated at the beginning of the present chapter, are the finite points with vertical tangents. Here

$$x - x_0 = a_2(y - y_0)^2 + a_3(y - y_0)^3 + \dots$$

$$\frac{\partial f}{\partial y} = (y - y_0)[d_0 + d_1(y - y_0) + \dots] \qquad d_0 \neq 0.$$

$$y - y_0 = l_1(t - t_0) + l_2(t - t_0)^2 + \dots$$

$$\frac{dx}{dt} = \frac{dx}{dy} \cdot \frac{dy}{dt} = (y - y_0)[g_0 + g_1(t - t_0) + \dots].$$

$$\Phi_k(t) = h_0 + h_1(t - t_0) + h_2(t - t_0)^2 + \dots,$$

so that Φ_k is finite even at the branch points.

Suppose that we have a group of N points corresponding to the parameter values $t_1, t_2, \dots, t_N$. We may find an integral of the second sort $\psi_i(t)$ such that it has simple poles at the points t_i and nowhere else, and the scheme of periods is

D_1	D_2	.	.	.	D_p	C_1	C_2	.	.	.	C_p
0	0	.	.	.	0	$2\pi i \Phi_1(t_i)$	$2\pi i \Phi_2(t_i)$	.	.	.	$2\pi i \Phi_p(t_i)$.

The function

$$\rho_1 \psi_1 + \rho_2 \psi_2 + \dots + \rho_N \psi_N$$

will be an integral of the second sort with a simple pole at each of our N points, otherwise finite, the periods about the circuits D being all 0. If those about the circuits C are also 0, the function is single-valued and so rational on our original Riemann surface. Conversely, every rational function on our Riemann surface $\dfrac{\rho(x,y)}{\phi(x,y)}$ with simple poles at some of the points corre-

sponding to $t_1, t_2, ..., t_p$ when looked upon as a function of t is of just this type.

The dimension of the complete series of which $t_1, t_2, ..., t_N$ is a group will be the number of linearly independent numerators which go with the proper denominator or the number of linearly independent integrals of the second sort

$$\rho_1 \psi_1 + \rho_2 \psi_2 + ... + \rho_N \psi_N.$$

Since the periods for the circuits C are to be 0,

$$\rho_1 \Phi_1(t_1) + \rho_2 \Phi_1(t_2) + ... + \rho_N \Phi_1(t_N) = 0$$
$$\cdot \quad \cdot \quad \cdot \quad \cdot \quad \cdot \quad \cdot \quad \cdot \quad \cdot \quad \cdot \quad \cdot \quad \cdot \quad \cdot \quad \cdot$$
$$\rho_1 \Phi_p(t_1) + \rho_2 \Phi_p(t_2) + ... + \rho_N \Phi_p(t_N) = 0.$$

We therefore construct the matrix

$$\begin{Vmatrix} \Phi_1(t_1) & \Phi_1(t_2) & . & \Phi_1(t_N) \\ . & . & . & . \\ \Phi_p(t_1) & \Phi_p(t_2) & . & \Phi_p(t_N) \end{Vmatrix}. \tag{6}$$

Let the rank of this be $N-r$. Then all solutions of the equations are linearly dependent on r of them, or the dimension is r.

Let us see next how many linearly independent special adjoints there are through the group. As the relation of x to t is one-to-one, we need not fear

$$\frac{dx}{dt} = 0.$$

The non-singular intersections of

$$\phi_k(x,y) = f(x,y) = 0$$

will correspond exactly to the roots of $\Phi_k(t)$. We seek the number of linearly independent functions

$$\sigma_1 \Phi_1 + \sigma_2 \Phi_2 + ... + \sigma_p \Phi_p$$

which vanish for the values $t_1, t_2, ..., t_N$. This search leads to the matrix

$$\begin{Vmatrix} \Phi_1(t_1) & \Phi_2(t_1) & . & \Phi_p(t_1) \\ . & . & . & . \\ \Phi_1(t_N) & \Phi_2(t_N) & . & \Phi_p(t_N) \end{Vmatrix}, \tag{7}$$

which is essentially the same as (6). The rank of this is, by definition of i, $p-i$, and that of the other $N-r$. This proves the Riemann-Roch theorem.*

Our system of uniformization leads at once to the Weierstrass points. If t_0 be such a point, there is an equation

$$\rho_1\Phi_1(t)+\rho_2\Phi_2(t)+...+\rho_p\Phi_p(t)=0,$$

which has a root $t=t_0$ of multiplicity p or greater. The derivatives of this function up to the $(p-1)$th must vanish, or

$$\begin{vmatrix} \Phi_1(t_0) & . & . & . & \Phi_p(t_0) \\ \Phi_1'(t_0) & . & . & . & \Phi_p'(t_0) \\ . & . & . & . & . & . \\ \Phi_1^{(p-1)}(t_0) & . & . & \Phi_p^{(p-1)}(t_0) \end{vmatrix}=0. \tag{8}$$

This is a Wronskian determinant, and could not vanish identically unless the functions were linearly dependent, which they are not.

§ 4. Curves of genus 1

The methods just developed do not apply to curves of genus 1 or 0. These deserve further study beyond that already given. We confine ourselves in the present section to curves of genus 1, elliptic curves, as we have called them. We saw in Ch. V of Book III that every such curve could be birationally transformed into a non-singular cubic. If we place this curve so that there is an inflexion at the end of the y-axis, the line at infinity being the inflexional tangent, the equation becomes

$$x^3+Ax^2+Bxy+Cy^2+Dx+Ey+F=0.$$

The conic polar of this inflexion is the infinite line and

$$Bx+2Cy+E=0,$$

which we take as the x-axis, so that $B=E=0$, the Cartesian coordinate system being perhaps oblique. The line polar of the end of the x-axis will go through the infinite inflexion, and we take this as the y-axis. Lastly, we may multiply x and y by suitable constants to get the new canonical form

$$y^2=4x^3-g_2x-g_3. \tag{9}$$

* This proof was communicated to the author by Prof. Osgood verbally in Nov. 1927. See also Picard, p. 432.

This curve has a single Abelian integral of the first sort:

$$u = \int\limits_{\infty}^{x} \frac{dx}{y}, \tag{10}$$

so that we have, conversely, a parametric representation in terms of the Weierstrass doubly periodic elliptic functions*

$$x = \wp(u) \qquad y = \wp'(u) \qquad \wp(u+2m_1\omega_1+2m_2\omega_2) = \wp(u). \tag{11}$$

Consider the intersections of the cubic with a curve of order n, which is necessarily adjoint, since the cubic is non-singular. Let the corresponding parameter values be $u_1, u_2, ..., u_{3n}$. Then by Abel's theorem 4] of Ch. II, present book,

$$u_1 + u_2 + ... + u_{3n} \equiv K \pmod{2\omega_1, 2\omega_3}.$$

Consider, in particular, a straight line

$$u_1 + u_2 + u_3 \equiv K \pmod{2\omega_1, 2\omega_3}.$$

Corresponding to the line at infinity we have $u = 0$, so that $K = 0$. Hence three points are collinear when, and only when,

$$u_1 + u_2 + u_3 \equiv 0 \pmod{2\omega_1, 2\omega_3}. \tag{12}$$

A curve of order n may degenerate into n lines, hence we have here also $K = 0$.

$$u_1 + u_2 + ... + u_{3n} \equiv 0 \pmod{2\omega_1, 2\omega_3}. \tag{13}$$

If we have a system of curves of a given order whose only limitation is that they pass through fixed points of the cubic, we know, by theorem 6] of Ch. I, Book III, that they will cut a complete series. For the variable points of such a series we shall have

$$u_1 + u_2 + ... + u_N \equiv C \pmod{2\omega_1, 2\omega_3}.$$

Conversely, any such set will be residual to any set where

$$u_{N+1} + u_{N+2} + ... + u_{3n} \equiv -C \pmod{2\omega_1, 2\omega_3},$$

so that they form a linear series which is complete since the number of points exceeds the number of parameters by 1, the genus of the base curve.

Theorem 2] *The coordinates of the points of a curve of genus 1 may be expressed as rational functions of the Weierstrass elliptic functions $\wp(u)$ and its derivative $\wp'(u)$. The N.S. condition that a series of groups of N points should form a complete linear series*

---

* This is, of course, classic. Cf. E. C. Burkhardt[2], p. 46, or White, p. 123.

is that the sum of the corresponding coordinate values u should be constant, within the moduli of periodicity.

If
$$\sum u_i + \sum u_i' \equiv 0 \pmod{2\omega_1, 2\omega_3}$$
$$\sum u_i + \sum u_i'' \equiv 0 \ (\quad ,, \qquad ,, \quad)$$
$$\sum v_i + \sum u_i' \equiv 0 \ (\quad ,, \qquad ,, \quad)$$

Then
$$\sum v_i + \sum u_i'' \equiv 0 \ (\quad ,, \qquad ,, \quad).$$

This is, of course, nothing more nor less than the residue theorem.

The only birational transformations of the curve into itself which have the value 1 are of the type

$$u + u' \equiv K \pmod{2\omega_1, 2\omega_3}. \tag{14}$$

The points with parameter values u, $-u'$, and $-K$ being collinear. A birational correspondence with negative value can only have the value -1, as otherwise the number of coincidences would be negative. The product of a correspondence of positive value, with one of value -1, would be one of value $-\gamma$, hence $\gamma = 1$, or the only birational correspondences of positive value are those of value 1 given by (14). As the product of a correspondence of value 1 and one of value -1 is one of value 1, so every correspondence of value -1 is the product of two of value 1, and can be written

$$u' - u \equiv 0 \pmod{2\omega_1, 2\omega_3}. \tag{15}$$

Clearly there can be no birational transformation of value 0, for then our curve would have a g_1^1 and be rational.

If the tangent at u_i meet the curve again at u, we have

$$2u_i + u \equiv 0 \pmod{2\omega_1, 2\omega_3}.$$

The four points whose tangents pass through u correspond to the coordinate values

$$u_1 = -\frac{u}{2} \quad u_2 = -\frac{u}{2} + \omega_1 \quad u_3 = -\frac{u}{2} + \omega_3 \quad u_4 = -\frac{u}{2} + \omega_1 + \omega_3$$

$$\frac{u_1 - u_2}{u_1 - u_3} \times \frac{u_4 - u_3}{u_4 - u_2} = \left(\frac{\omega_1}{\omega_3}\right)^2. \tag{16}$$

This number is independent of u and is a function of the only birational invariant or modulus which the curve possesses.

Suppose that, more generally, we have a birational transformation of the curve into itself:

$$u' = f(u).$$

Since this function is single-valued and analytic, with a single-valued inverse, it must be linear, or we shall have

$$u' = \frac{\alpha u + \beta}{\gamma u + \delta},$$

We have thus three types of transformation:

$$u' = \frac{1}{u} \qquad u' = \alpha u \qquad u' = u + \beta.$$

The first of these cannot be algebraic, for it will not carry a complete series into a complete series. The third is familiar. The only interest is in transformations of the type

$$u' = \alpha u.$$

As these must carry periods into periods, we must have

$$\alpha \omega_1 = a_{11}\omega_1 + a_{13}\omega_3 \qquad \alpha \omega_2 = a_{31}\omega_1 + a_{33}\omega_3, \qquad (17)$$

where a_{ij} are integers. Dividing through by α, and noting that working inversely, the coefficients which express ω_1 and ω_2 in terms of $\frac{\omega_1}{\alpha}$ and $\frac{\omega_2}{\alpha}$ must be integers, we have

$$a_{11}a_{33} - a_{13}a_{31} = \pm 1.$$

On the other hand, the compatibility conditions of equations (17) give us

$$\begin{vmatrix} a_{11}-\alpha & a_{13} \\ a_{31} & a_{33}-\alpha \end{vmatrix} = \alpha^2 - (a_{11}+a_{33})\alpha \pm 1 = 0.$$

If α be real, so is $\alpha - a_{11}$, but the theory of elliptic functions tells us that $\frac{\omega_1}{\omega_3}$ is complex.* Hence

$$a_{13} = a_{31} = 0 \qquad a_{11}a_{33} = \pm 1 \qquad \alpha = \pm 1.$$

We are thus led back to something familiar. If α be complex,

$$(a_{11}+a_{33})^2 \mp 4 \leqslant 0.$$

Either $\qquad (a_{11}+a_{33}) = 0 \qquad \alpha = \pm i,$

or $\quad (a_{11}+a_{33}) = \pm 1 \qquad \alpha = \pm \omega$ or $\alpha = \pm \omega^2; \qquad \omega^3 = 1.$

* Burkhardt², p. 34.

Conversely, it can be shown that, under these circumstances, we have an algebraic transformation of our curve.* It is to be noted that

$$\frac{\omega_1}{\omega_3} = \frac{p+qi}{r}$$

where p, q, r are integers, illustrating the principle already mentioned that correspondences without value do not exist on curves of general moduli of periodicity.

* Cf. Abel[2], especially pp. 426 ff. Our discussion follows Segre[2].

CHAPTER IX

RATIONAL CURVES

§ 1. Binary apolar forms

WE learned in theorem 3] of Ch. VII, Book I, that the co-ordinates of the points on a curve of genus 0 can be rationally expressed in terms of an auxiliary parameter, and in Lüroth's Theorem 22] of Ch. VIII that if x and y be rational functions, not both constants, of an auxiliary parameter, the curve so defined, if irreducible, is of genus 0. The general parametric representation of a curve of order n and genus 0 is, thus,

$$\rho x_1 = f_1(t) \qquad \rho x_2 = f_2(t) \qquad \rho x_3 = f_3(t). \qquad (1)$$

For many purposes it is better to use two homogeneous parameters instead of the single parameter t. Reverting to the Clebsch-Aronhold symbolic notation explained in Ch. V, Book I, we write
$$a_\xi \equiv a_1\xi_1 + a_2\xi_2, \text{ etc.}$$

$$\rho x_1 = a_\xi^n \qquad \rho x_2 = b_\xi^n \qquad \rho x_3 = c_\xi^n. \qquad (2)$$

There are two invariant operators frequently employed in connexion with these forms, which we explained when we first took up invariants in that chapter. There is first the polar process or polar operator

$$\frac{1}{n}\left[\eta_1 \frac{\partial f}{\partial \xi_1} + \eta_2 \frac{\partial f}{\partial \xi_2}\right], \qquad (3)$$

and the Cayley operator

$$\frac{1}{n_1 n_2}\begin{vmatrix} \dfrac{\partial}{\partial \xi_1} & \dfrac{\partial}{\partial \xi_2} \\ \dfrac{\partial}{\partial \eta_1} & \dfrac{\partial}{\partial \eta_2} \end{vmatrix} F(\xi_1, \xi_2, \eta_1, \eta_2) \qquad \begin{matrix} \xi_1 = \eta_1 \\ \xi_2 = \eta_2 \end{matrix} \qquad (4)$$

where n_1 is the order in ξ_1, ξ_2, and n_2 the order in η_1, η_2. The rth polar of (η) with regard to a_ξ^n is $a_\eta^r a_\xi^{n-r}$. If we apply the Cayley operator k times to $a_\xi^{n_1} b_\xi^{n_2}$, we get

$$|ab|^k a_\xi^{n_1-k} b_\xi^{n_2-k}.$$

This we have defined as the kth transvectant of a_ξ^n on b_ξ^n. It is also $(-1)^k \times$ the kth transvectant of b_ξ^n on a_ξ^n.

Definition. Two binary forms of the same order are said to be 'apolar' if the last transvectant of the one on the other is 0.

If the given forms be a_ξ^n and $a'_\xi{}^n$, the condition for apolarity is

$$|aa'|^n = 0. \tag{5}$$

If we prefer a non-symbolic notation, and write

$$a_\xi^n \equiv a_0\xi_1^n + na_1\xi_1^{n-1}\xi_2 + \dots + \binom{n}{r}a_r\xi_1^{n-r}\xi_2^r + \dots$$

$$a'_\xi{}^n \equiv a'_0\xi_1^n + na'_1\xi_1^{n-1}\xi_2 + \dots + \binom{n}{r}a'_r\xi_1^{n-r}\xi_2^r + \dots,$$

then (5) takes the form

$$a_0a'_n - na_1a'_{n-1} + \dots + (-1)^r\binom{n}{r}a_ra_{n-r} + \dots = 0. \tag{6}$$

Since the a''s are perfectly arbitrary, this simply tells us that the a's are connected by a linear homogeneous equation.

Theorem 1] *If the coefficients of a binary form be subjected to a linear homogeneous condition, the form is apolar to a given form, and conversely.*

Theorem 2] *k binary forms of the nth order which are linearly independent are apolar to $n+1-k$ linearly independent forms of that order.*

If the roots of our second form be $(\eta_1^1\eta_2^1),(\eta_1^2\eta_2^2),\dots,(\eta_1^n\eta_2^n)$, so that

$$a_\xi^n \equiv a'_0|\xi\eta^1| \cdot |\xi\eta^2| \dots |\xi\eta^n|,$$

the condition for apolarity is

$$a_{\eta^1}a_{\eta^2}\dots a_{\eta^n} = 0. \tag{7}$$

Theorem 3] *The N.S. condition that two binary forms of the same order should be apolar is that if we polarize the first with regard to a root of the second, and that polar with regard to a second root, and so on, the root of the last form so obtained should be the last root of the second form.*[*]

Suppose that the second form has a root η of multiplicity r so that

$$a'_\xi{}^n \equiv |\xi\eta|^r a''_\xi{}^{n-r}.$$

The apolarity condition is

$$a_\eta^r|aa''|^{n-r} = 0.$$

Theorem 4] *If the second of two apolar binary forms of order n have a root of multiplicity r, then that factor of the form which*

---

[*] Cf. Pitarelli.

is independent of that root is apolar to the rth polar of that root with regard to the first form.

The most interesting case is where $r = n$.

Theorem 5] *If a binary form have only one distinct root it is apolar to every form of the same order which shares that root.*

Theorem 6] *A binary form of order n is apolar to as many perfect nth powers as it has distinct roots.*

Theorem 7] *If a binary form of order n be apolar to any form with n distinct roots, then it is a linear combination of the n polynomials of that order, each of which has as its only root one of those n.*

§ 2. Determination of the equation of a rational curve

Suppose that we have the three equations (1). How do we find the corresponding trilinear equation of the curve ? We must first eliminate ρ twice, giving

$$f_3(t)x_1 - f_1(t)x_3 = 0 \qquad f_3(t)x_2 - f_2(t)x_3 = 0,$$

and then eliminate t. This operation may become very cumbersome in practice. Here is another which is shorter but less obvious.* We start with a cubic:

$$x_i = a_i t^3 + b_i t^2 + c_i t + d_i.$$

We write this in three different forms:

$$(a_i t - b_i)t^2 + c_i t + d_i \cdot 1 + x_i(-1) = 0$$
$$(a_i t)t^2 + (b_i t + c_i)t + d_i \cdot 1 + x_i(-1) = 0$$
$$(a_i t)t^2 + (b_i t)t + (c_i t + d_i) \cdot 1 + x_i(-1) = 0.$$

Giving i the values 1, 2, 3, we get three proportions:
$t^2 : t : 1 : (-1)$

$$= |cdx| : -\{|adx|t + |bdx|\} : \{|acx|t + |bcx|\} : -\{|acd|t + |bcd|\}$$
$$= \{|bdx|t + |cdx|\} : -|adx|t : \{|abx|t + |acx|\} : -\{|abd|t^2 + |acd|t\}$$
$$= \{|bcx|t + |bdx|\} : -\{|acx|t + |adx|\} : |abx|t : -\{|abc|t^2 + |abd|t\}.$$

Hence
$$|adx|t^2 + \quad |bdx|t \quad + |cdx| = 0$$
$$|acx|t^2 + [|bcx| + |adx|]t + |bdx| = 0$$
$$|abx|t^2 + \quad |acx|t \quad + |adx| = 0$$

$$\begin{vmatrix} |adx| & |bdx| & |cdx| \\ |acx| & |bcx| + |adx| & |bdx| \\ |abx| & |acx| & |adx| \end{vmatrix} = 0.$$

* Cf. Rowe.

The generalization to a curve of order n is easily effected, but clumsy to put into words.

§ 3. Groups of intersections

Let us revert to our parametric form (2) and ask under what circumstances will the points corresponding to the parameter values $(t_1^1 t_2^1), (t_1^2 t_2^2), \ldots, (t_1^n t_2^n)$ lie on a line. There are $n-2$ linearly independent binary forms or order n apolar to $a_\xi^n, b_\xi^n, c_\xi^n$. Call these $A_\xi^n, B_\xi^n, \ldots$. If $(t_1^1 t_2^1), (t_1^2 t_2^2), \ldots$ be roots of a form that is apolar to all of these, that form must be a linear combination of $A, B, \ldots$. The N.S. condition is, then,[*]

$$\Pi_i A_{t^i} = \Pi_i B_{t^i} = \ldots = 0. \tag{8}$$

Theorem 8] *The N.S. condition that n sets of parameter values $(t_1^1 t_2^1), (t_1^2 t_2^2), \ldots$ for the curve (2) should correspond to points of a line is that they should satisfy the $n-2$ equations (8) where $A_\xi^n, B_\xi^n, \ldots$ are $n-2$ linearly independent binary forms apolar to $a_\xi^n, b_\xi^n, c_\xi^n$.*

Let us generalize so as to find out when $n\nu$ points lie on a curve of order ν:

$$\phi^\nu(x_1, x_2, x_3) = 0.$$

This polynomial is a linear combination of terms of the form

$$x_1^p x_2^q x_3^r \qquad p+q+r = \nu.$$

If, thus, $A_\xi^{n\nu}, B_\xi^{n\nu}, \ldots$ be a complete set of forms of order $n\nu$ apolar to $(a_\xi^n)^p (b_\xi^n)^q (c_\xi^n)^r$,

$$\Pi_i A_{t^i} = \Pi_i B_{t^i} = \ldots = 0. \tag{9}$$

The reasoning is reversible. This gives

Theorem 9] *The N.S. condition that $n\nu$ sets of parameter values should give the complete intersection with a curve of order ν is that all the equations (9) should be satisfied, where $A_\xi^{n\nu}, B_\xi^{n\nu} \ldots$ are the complete set of forms of order $n\nu$ apolar to all forms $(a_\xi^n)^p (b_\xi^n)^q (c_\xi^n)^r$, $p+q+r = \nu$.*

There is a more beautiful way of exhibiting these conditions when the parameter values giving the singular points are known. Suppose, first, there are no singular points but nodes corresponding to the pairs of parameter values

$$(\eta_1^1 \eta_2^1), (\zeta_1^1 \zeta_2^1); \; (\eta_1^2 \eta_2^2), (\zeta_1^2 \zeta_2^2); \ldots.$$

We may multiply through by such constants that

$$a_{\eta^1}^n = a_{\zeta^1}^n, \qquad a_{\eta^2}^n = a_{\zeta^2}^n \ldots.$$

---

[*] See the important, though obscurely written, Meyer[1].

Under these circumstances the form $|\xi\eta^i|^n - |\xi\zeta^i|^n$ is apolar to $a_\xi^n = b_\xi^n = c_\xi^n$, and so, by theorem 8],

$$\prod_{j=1}^{j=n} |t^j\eta^i| = \prod_{j=1}^{j=n} |t^j\zeta^i| \qquad i = 1, 2, ..., \frac{(n-1)(n-2)}{2}. \qquad \textbf{(10)}$$

We have here a set of necessary conditions for collinear points. To show that they are sufficient we must show that among the $\frac{(n-1)(n-2)}{2}$ forms $|\xi\eta^i|^n - |\xi\zeta^i|^n$ there are $n-2$ which are linearly independent.

Suppose the number is $n-k$. There will be apolar thereto $k+1$ forms
$$a_\xi^n = b_\xi^n = c_\xi^n = ... = l_\xi^n.$$
If we write
$$\rho x_1 = a_\xi^n \qquad \rho x_2 = b_\xi^n \qquad \rho x_3 = c_\xi^n ... \rho x_{k+1} = l_\xi^n,$$
we have in a space of k dimensions
$$x_1 : x_2 : ... : x_{k+1},$$
a space curve of order n with at least $\frac{(n-1)(n-2)}{2}$ double points corresponding to the parameter values $(\eta_1^i\eta_2^i)$, $(\zeta_1^i\zeta_2^i)$. But if $k > 2$ we can project down to a rational plane curve of order less than n, with at least $\frac{(n-1)(n-2)}{2}$ double points, which is absurd.

We can extend the process as before. A necessary condition that νn points $(t_1^1 t_2^1), (t_1^2 t_2^2),...$ should be on a curve of order ν is

$$\prod_{j=1}^{j=n\nu} |t^j\eta^i| = \prod_{j=1}^{j=n\nu} |t^j\zeta^i| \qquad i = 1, 2, ..., \frac{(n-1)(n-2)}{2}. \qquad \textbf{(11)}$$

To prove the condition sufficient, we proceed as in the case before. If we have not here a complete set of forms
$$[x_1(\xi)]^p [x_2(\xi)]^q [x_3(\xi)]^r$$
apolar to $|\xi\eta^i|^{n\nu} - |\xi\zeta^i|^{n\nu}$, but if there be certain others $A_\xi^{n\nu}, B_\xi^{n\nu},...$, then the two curves
$$X_{p+q+r} = (a_\xi^n)^p (b_\xi^n)^q (c_\xi^n)^r$$
$$X_{p+q+r} = (a_\xi^n)^p (b_\xi^n)^q (c_\xi^n)^r \qquad X_\alpha = A_\xi^{n\nu} \qquad X_\beta = B_\xi^{n\nu}$$
lying in spaces of a different number of dimensions have the same double points $(\eta^i), (\zeta^t)$, which leads to a contradiction.

Theorem 10] *If the curve* (2) *have no singular points but nodes corresponding to pairs of parameter values* $(\eta^i), (\zeta^i)$, *the N.S. condition that points* (t^j) *should be a complete intersection is that* (11) *shall be satisfied.*

Suppose that two of our intersections tend to coalesce at a node

$$t_1^1 = \eta_1^1 + \delta_1 \qquad t_2^1 = \eta_2^1 + \delta_2 \qquad t_1^2 = \zeta_1^1 + \epsilon_1 \qquad t_2^2 = \zeta_2^1 + \epsilon_2,$$

where $\delta_1, \delta_2, \epsilon_1, \epsilon_2$ are infinitesimals,

$$|t^1 \eta^1| = |\delta \eta^1| \qquad |t^1 \zeta^1| = |\eta^1 \zeta^1| + |\delta \zeta^1|$$

$$|t^2 \eta^1| = |\zeta^1 \eta^1| + |\epsilon \eta^1| \qquad |t^2 \zeta^1| = |\epsilon \zeta^1|$$

$$\lim \frac{|t^1 \eta^1| . |t^2 \eta^1|}{|t^1 \zeta^1| . |t^2 \zeta^1|} = -\lim \frac{|\delta \eta_1|}{|\epsilon \zeta_1|}.$$

Our conditions for non-singular intersections with an adjoint will be

$$\prod_{j=1}^{j=n\nu-(n-1)(n-2)} |t^j \eta^i| = K \prod_{j=1}^{j=n\nu-(n-1)(n-2)} |t^j \zeta^i|. \tag{12}$$

Conversely, when these equations are given, we can find such infinitesimals that they are the limiting forms for (11). They therefore give the N.S. conditions for a set of points to be the non-singular intersections with an adjoint. An easy proof of the residue theorem will come at once.

Suppose that our curve has a singular point of order k given by parameter values $(\eta_1^1 \eta_2^1), (\eta_1^2 \eta_2^2), \ldots, (\eta_1^k \eta_2^k)$, so that

$$a_{\eta^1}^n = a_{\eta^2}^n = \ldots = a_{\eta^k}^n; \quad b_{\eta^1}^n = \ldots = b_{\eta^k}^n; \quad c_{\eta^1}^n = \ldots = c_{\eta^k}^n.$$

Let $$p_1 + p_2 + \ldots + p_k = 0.$$

We have $k-1$ linearly independent sets of p's, and the form

$$p_1 |\xi \eta^1|^n + p_2 |\xi \eta^2|^n + \ldots + p_k |\xi \eta^k|^n$$

is apolar to a_ξ^n, b_ξ^n, c_ξ^n. We thus get $k-1$ conditions

$$p_1 \prod_{j=1}^{j=n} |t^j \eta^1| + p_2 \prod_j |t^j \eta^2| + \ldots + p_k \prod_j |t^j \eta^k| = 0. \tag{13}$$

These are necessary for the points to be collinear. There will be similar conditions for the other singular points. We show that these conditions are sufficient exactly as before.

§ 4. Equations and conditions for singularities*

Let us rewrite the homogeneous parametric equations for our given curve

$$\rho x_1 = a_\xi^n \qquad \rho x_2 = b_\xi^n \qquad \rho x_3 = c_\xi^n. \qquad (2)$$

If (u) be the tangent at the point (η),

$$\left(u\,\frac{\partial x}{\partial \eta_1}\right) = \left(u\,\frac{\partial x}{\partial \eta_2}\right) = 0 \qquad (14)$$

$$u_1 = |bc|\,b_\eta^{n-1}c_\eta^{n-1} \qquad u_2 = |ca|\,c_\eta^{n-1}a_\eta^{n-1} \qquad u_3 = |ab|\,a_\eta^{n-1}b_\eta^{n-1}. \qquad (15)$$

The polynomial in (ξ), (ux) is divisible by $|\xi\eta|^2$, hence we get the remaining intersections with the tangent, the tangential points as they are sometimes called, by writing

$$\frac{1}{|\xi\eta|^2}\left[\,|bc|\,b_\eta^{n-1}c_\eta^{n-1}a_\xi^n + |ca|\,c_\eta^{n-1}a_\eta^{n-1}b_\xi^n + |ab|\,a_\eta^{n-1}b_\eta^{n-1}c_\xi^n\,\right] = 0.$$

This may also be written

$$\frac{1}{|\xi\eta|^2}\begin{vmatrix} a_\xi^n & b_\xi^n & c_\xi^n \\ a_\eta^{n-1}a_1 & b_\eta^{n-1}b_1 & c_\eta^{n-1}c_1 \\ a_\eta^{n-1}a_2 & b_\eta^{n-1}b_2 & c_\eta^{n-1}c_2 \end{vmatrix} = 0.$$

By Taylor's theorem,

$$a_\xi^n = \left(\frac{\xi_2}{\eta_2}\right)^n\left[a_\eta^n + n a_\eta^{n-1}a_1\,\frac{|\xi\eta|}{\xi_2} + \frac{n(n-1)}{1.2}\,a_\eta^{n-2}a_1^2\,\frac{|\xi\eta|^2}{\xi_2^2} + \cdots\right].$$

Substituting in the determinant above, we get, after a little manipulation,

$$F(\xi,\eta) \equiv |bc|.|ca|.|ab|\,a_\eta^{n-2}b_\eta^{n-2}c_\eta^{n-2}\xi_2^{n-2} + |\xi\eta|\phi(\xi,\eta) = 0. \qquad (16)$$

To find the points where a tangential coincides with a point of contact, we put $\xi_i = \rho\eta_i$:

$$|bc|.|ca|.|ab|\,a_\xi^{n-2}b_\xi^{n-2}c_\xi^{n-2} = 0. \qquad (17)$$

The degree is $3(n-2)$. The roots are the inflexions each counted μ times and the cusps each counted ν times:

$$\mu\iota + \nu\kappa = 3(n-2).$$

By Plücker's equations, when $p = 0$,

$$\iota + 2\kappa = 3(n-2).$$

Theorem 11] *If the rational curve* (2) *have no singular points but ordinary ones and cusps, and no singular tangents but ordinary and inflexional ones, the roots of* (17) *give the inflexions counted once and the cusps each counted twice.*

---

* The present section is based on Meyer[2].

When the curve has higher singularities, we see by continuity that this equation gives the total inflexional index of each tangent counted once, and the total cuspidal index of each point counted twice.

If, for present purposes, we indicate the resultant of two binary forms ϕ_1, ϕ_2 by $R(\phi_1, \phi_2)$ and remember that the discriminant of a binary form is the resultant of its two partial derivatives, we see that the points of contact of bitangents are obtained from (16) by writing

$$R\left(\frac{\partial F}{\partial \xi_1}, \frac{\partial F}{\partial \xi_2}\right) = 0. \tag{18}$$

Now the partial derivatives of F are of degree $(n-3)$ in (ξ), and degree $2(n-2)$ in (η). Hence (18) is of degree $4(n-2)(n-3)$.

We have from Plücker's equations

$$2\tau + \kappa(m-3) + 2\kappa(n-3) = 4(n-2)(n-3).$$

We shall find among the roots of (18) the points of contact of bitangents, and of tangents from the cusps. Also, if (η) be a cusp, the coordinates of the tangent are illusory, and we get other solutions.

Theorem 12] *If a rational curve be limited as in the last theorem, the equation* (18) *is reducible. One factor gives the points of contact of bitangents, a second those of tangents from cusps, and a third the tangential points of the cusps, each counted twice.*

If we look upon (16) as an equation in (η) and write its discriminant, we get

$$R\left(\frac{\partial F}{\partial \eta_1}, \frac{\partial F}{\partial \eta_2}\right) = 0. \tag{19}$$

The degree in (ξ) is

$$2(2n-5)(n-2) = 2\delta + 2\kappa + (n-3)(\iota + 2\kappa).$$

Two (η)'s corresponding to the same (ξ) will coincide if that point be a node, for then we have coincident tangents to one branch from a point on another, if the point be a cusp, or if it be a tangential point of a cusp or an inflexion.

Theorem 13] *If a rational curve be limited as in the last two theorems, the equation* (19) *will be reducible. The roots give the nodes (or equivalent ordinary singularities), the cusps, and the* *tangential points of the cusps each counted twice, and the tangential points of the inflexions.*

The general rational curve has no cusps. Hence, for the general curve (18) will merely give the points of contact of bitangents, and (19) the nodes and the tangential points of inflexions. What conditions must be imposed on our equations (2) that at least one cusp should be present ?

The conditions for a cusp at (η) are

$$\frac{a_\eta^{n-1}a_1}{a_\eta^{n-1}a_2} = \frac{b_\eta^{n-1}b_1}{b_\eta^{n-1}b_2} = \frac{c_\eta^{n-1}c_1}{c_\eta^{n-1}c_2}$$

$$|bc|b_\eta^{n-1}c_\eta^{n-1} = |ca|c_\eta^{n-1}a_\eta^{n-1} = |ab|a_\eta^{n-1}b_\eta^{n-1} = 0. \qquad (20)$$

If we equate the first two only to 0, then either

$$c_\eta^{n-1}c_1 = c_\eta^{n-1}c_2 = 0$$

or else the third vanishes. The resultant of the first two is then reducible. The first factor gives the required cuspidal condition, the second is a power of the discriminant of c_η^n. The resultant of the first two is of degree $[4(n-1)]$ in the actual, as distinguished from the symbolic, coefficients of the form c_η^n. The discriminant of this form is of degree $2(n-1)$ in these coefficients, hence, as the cuspidal condition must appear somewhere, the discriminant can come in to the first power only.

Theorem 14] *The resultant of the first two polynomials (20) is reducible. One factor is the discriminant of the form c_η^n, the other factor equated to 0 gives the N.S. condition for the existence of a cusp. It is of degree $2(n-1)$ in the coefficients of each of the given binary forms.*

If we return to (16) and set

$$|bc|.|ca|.|ab|a_\eta^{n-2}b_\eta^{n-2}c_\eta^{n-2} = 0, \qquad (21)$$

we get an equation to determine the points whose tangents have three-point contact. These are inflexions, cusps, and points of undulation, that is, points, when such exist, which are nonsingular, but whose tangents have at least four-point contact. These are all intersections with the Hessian, but whereas at an inflexion the Hessian cuts across simply, at a point of undulation, which counts for two adjacent inflexions, it is tangent, and at a cusp it has a singularity. The discriminant of the left-hand side of (21) must be factorable. One factor gives the cuspidal, the other the undulational condition. Its degree in the actual coefficients of each form is $6n-14$.

We may look for the points of undulation elsewhere. The roots of (18), in the general case where there are no cusps, go together in pairs, giving the pairs of points of contact of bi-tangents. Let us write it

$$d_\eta^{4(n-2)(n-3)} \equiv e_\eta^2 f_\eta^2 g_\eta^2 \ldots \qquad \text{to } 2(n-2)(n-3) \text{ factors.}$$

The condition that two roots of a pair should fall together is

$$|ee'|^2 . |ff'|^2 . |gg'|^2 \ldots = 0.$$

This is of the second degree in the coefficients of (18), and so of degree $4(n-3)$ in the coefficients of each of the original forms

$$6n-14 = 4(n-3)+2(n-1).$$

Theorem 15] *The discriminant of the left-hand side of* (21) *is factorable. The vanishing of one factor gives the cuspidal condition, that of the other the undulational one.*

BOOK IV
SYSTEMS OF CURVES

CHAPTER I

POSTULATION OF LINEAR SYSTEMS BY POINTS

§ 1. Fundamental properties of linear systems

WHEN we first began the study of linear systems of point-groups on a base curve, we said that such groups were defined by linear systems of curves. These secant curves served only to determine the groups, now it is time to study them for their own sakes. The knowledge which we have acquired from the study of point groups will be vitally important in this study.

Definition. The system of all curves of a given order linearly dependent on $r+1$ linearly independent curves of that order shall be called an 'r-parameter linear system'. Since the general curve has $\dfrac{(n+1)(n+2)}{2}$ independent coefficients, the total system of these curves is in one-to-one correspondence with the points of a projective space of $N = \dfrac{n(n+3)}{2}$ dimensions. An r-parameter linear system will correspond to the points of a space of r dimensions therein. Through it will pass $N-r-1$ linearly independent hyperplanes.

Theorem 1] *If the coefficients of a curve of order n be subjected to $\dfrac{n(n+3)}{2} -r-1$ independent linear conditions, but are otherwise entirely free, there will result an r-parameter linear system and conversely, every r-parameter linear system can be reached in this way.*

The general r-parameter irreducible algebraic system of curves may be expressed in the following fashion outlined in Book I Ch. I, theorem 15]:

$$\sum a_{pqs}x_1^p x_2^q x_3^s = 0 \qquad p+q+s=n$$
$$a_{pqs} = a_{pqs}(x_0, x_1, ..., x_{r+1}) \tag{1}$$
$$\phi(x_0, x_1, ..., x_{r+1}) = 0.$$

Here all of the functional symbols stand for homogeneous polynomials, and all variables are homogeneous. The degree of the variety ϕ is called the 'index' of the system. It will be the number of intersections with the general linear S_{N-r}. The totality of curves through r given points will also correspond to points of a line S_{N-r} though not the general S_{N-r}, for the requirement of passing through an assigned point is a special type of linear requirement on the coefficients of the curve. The general S_{N-r} and an S_{N-r} which requires a curve to pass through *some* r points could only intersect the variety of r dimensions in a different number of points if the requirement to pass through *some* r points imposed a peculiar restriction on a curve. But every curve passes through as many points as we please, so the requirement to pass through *some* r cannot be peculiar, or the index of the system is the number of curves through r general points.

The index of a linear system is 1. Conversely, a one-parameter algebraic system of index 1 would be represented by an algebraic curve of the first order, i.e. a straight line. We may give it by equations of the form

$$a_{pqr} = b_{pqr} + tc_{pqr},$$

so that we have a pencil of curves.

Suppose that we have proved that every $(r-1)$-parameter system of index 1 is linear. The general curve through a point (x_1, y_1) will be

$$\lambda_1\psi_1 + \lambda_2\psi_2 + \ldots + \lambda_r\psi_r = 0.$$

Let ψ_0 be a curve of the system which does not contain (x_1, y_1). Since the general curve of the system meets ψ_0 somewhere, and all of the curves of the system through any point of ψ_0 are linearly dependent on ψ_0 and an $(r-1)$-parameter linear system through (x_1, y_1), the general form for the linear system will be

$$\lambda_0\psi_0 + \lambda_1\psi_1 + \ldots + \lambda_r\psi_r = 0.$$

Theorem 2] *An algebraic system of curves of the same order, whose index is 1, is a linear system.*

We get at once from Book I, Ch. VII, 10],

Bertini's Theorem 3] *The general curve of a linear system has no singular point which is not a fixed point for all curves of the system.*

Suppose that the general curve of a linear system is reducible, and that it has two irreducible parts, one of degree n_1, the other of degree n_2. If both were variable and the degrees different, there would be a variable singular point, which is intolerable. If the orders of the two were different, one at least would have to be a fixed curve. If $n_1 = n_2$, and both parts were variable, since two could not intersect in a general point and produce a singularity; there would be but one curve of order n_1 through a general point, or the system consists in groups of curves of a pencil.

Theorem 4] *If the general curve of a linear system be reducible, then either all curves of the system have a fixed factor, or else the system consists in groups of curves of a pencil.*

§ 2. Systems defined by simple points

The easiest way to define a linear system is to require the curves to pass through a certain number of specified non-singular points. These points shall be called 'base points' for the system. The base is said to be 'complete' if every curve through the assigned points does not, necessarily, pass through any other points. Eight points will not form a complete base for a system of cubics, for all cubics through eight points pass through a ninth.

If we have n points, we can pass a line through each in any desired direction.

Theorem 5] *n or fewer points will form a complete base for a curve of order n.*

The curves of order n through n or less than n points pass through no other points, of necessity, hence we get from 4]

Theorem 6] *If the order of the curves be at least as large as the number of base points, the curves are not, necessarily, reducible.*

A base shall be said to be 'normal' for curves of a given order if the conditions which its points impose be independent. If the number of conditions be less by s than the number of points, the base is said to have the 'superabundance' s. Thus, nine points are usually a normal base for a cubic, but the intersections of two cubics have superabundance 1. If a base be not complete, the base obtained by adding the new points which must be common to all curves of a certain order through the original points is superabundant. To determine the super-abundance of a group of points $(x_1, y_1), (x_2, y_2), ..., (x_\nu, y_\nu)$ we examine the rank of the matrix

$$\begin{Vmatrix} x_1^n & x_1^{n-1} y_1 & . & . & y_1^n & x_1^{n-1} & . & . & x_1 & y_1 & 1 \\ . & . & . & . & . & . & . & . & . & . & . \\ . & . & . & . & . & . & . & . & . & . & . \\ x_\nu^n & x_\nu^{n-1} y_\nu & . & . & y_\nu^n & x_\nu^{n-1} & . & . & x_\nu & y_\nu & 1 \end{Vmatrix}$$

If the rank be $\nu-s$, we can pick $\nu-s$ of these points which will impose independent conditions on a curve of order n, but a larger number will not impose independent conditions.

Theorem 7] *The superabundance of a group of points for curves of a certain order is equal to the difference between the number of points in the group and those in the largest normal sub-group.*

We get immediately from Book I, Ch. II, theorem 25],

Theorem 8] *If two curves intersect only in ordinary points, their intersections form a normal base for every curve whose order is as great as the sum of their orders. If the order of the new curve be the sum of their orders less l, the superabundance is $\frac{1}{2}(l-1)(l-2)$.*

If the order of the two curves be n_1 and n_2 where $n_1 \geqslant n_2$, the superabundance of their intersections for a curve of order $n_1 = n_1 + n_2 - n_2$ is $\frac{1}{2}(n_2-1)(n_2-2)$.

Theorem 9] *The superabundance of the group common to two curves for a curve of the greater order is the genus of the general curve of the lesser order.*[*]

Suppose that we have a group of ν points which lie on a single curve of order n. The number of conditions which they impose is $\nu-s$. If they lie on more than one such curve, and if they have the superabundance s, the dimension of the system of curves of order n through them is

$$r+1 = \frac{n(n+3)}{2} - \nu + s.$$

This exceeds by 1 the dimension of the series which the curves of the system cut on one of their number. The dimension of this complete series is thus

$$r = \frac{n(n+3)}{2} - \nu + s - 1.$$

---

* Cf. Gambier[1], p. 206.

The order of the series is

$$N = n^2 - v.$$

The general curve has no singularity by Bertini's Theorem 3], hence its genus is

$$p = \frac{n(n-3)}{2} + 1,$$

$$N - r = p - s. \tag{2}$$

We thus get, by the Riemann-Roch Theorem 25] of Book III, Ch. I,

Theorem 10] *If a group of simple points be complete or incomplete for curves of a given order, and lie on more than one such curve, its superabundance is equal to the index of specialization of the residual group common to two such curves.*

It is curious that the problem of finding superabundant groups for curves of a given order should thus be thrown back upon that of finding them for curves of order three less.

The index of specialization of a group of points on a curve of genus p is surely 0 if the number of points exceed $2p-2$. Hence we have

$$s = 0 \text{ if } n^2 - v > n(n-3); \text{ i.e. if } n > \frac{v}{3}.$$

Theorem 11] *A group of points is normal for a curve whose order exceeds one-third of the number of points in the group.*

We may generalize our theorem 10] to a small extent by considering the series which our curves cut on a curve of higher order. This obviates the difficulty of finding the series desired when there is but one curve of order n through the points of the base. Let us find the series cut on a curve of order $n+\alpha$.

$$N = n^2 + \alpha n - v \quad r = \frac{n(n+3)}{2} - v + s \quad p = \frac{(n+\alpha)(n+\alpha-3)}{2} + 1$$

$$1 = p + r - N = s + \frac{(\alpha-1)(\alpha-2)}{2}. \tag{3}$$

Theorem 12] *The superabundance of a group of points for curves of a certain order is less by $\dfrac{(\alpha-1)(\alpha-2)}{2}$ than the index of specialization of the residual group cut by these curves on a general curve of order α greater through the given group.*

We may generalize 11] in another way. If $s > 0$, the residual group is special, and so by Clifford's Theorem 30] of Book III, Ch. I,

$$n^2 - \nu \geqslant n(n+3) - 2\nu - 2 + 2s \qquad \nu - 3n \geqslant 2(s-1). \qquad (4)$$

Theorem 13] *If ν points lie on an infinite number of curves of order n, their superabundance cannot exceed $\dfrac{\nu - 3n}{2} + 1$.*

It is quite easy to construct groups of points having various amounts of superabundance if we proceed step by step. Let us take a quartic. The smallest superabundant group contains twelve points; it will be residual to four collinear points and so consist in the intersections with a cubic. Fifteen points, if they lie on two quartics, have superabundance 2, and sixteen superabundance 3.*

§ 3. Postulation by means of singular points

The postulation of linear systems by simple points generalizes very easily to postulation by means of singular points. The terms base, complete, normal, going over immediately. We shall say that a base is 'complete for singular points', if the curves of given order through it do not necessarily have other singular points of higher multiplicity than desired, or, what comes to the same thing, these curves have really the genus imposed upon them by the conditions assumed. Let the base points be $P_1, P_2, \ldots$, their respective multiplicities $r_1, r_2, \ldots$. It has the superabundance s if the system of curves through it have the dimension

$$\frac{n(n+3)}{2} - \sum \frac{r_i(r_i+1)}{2} + s.$$

We shall confine our attention to those cases where there is more than one curve of the system with the given base.

Theorem 14] *If a base be complete for singular points, then all the curves of the system, but at most a sub-system depending on a lesser number of parameters, have the same adjoints of every order. The genus of the general curve is the dimension of the system of special adjoints.*

Consider next the series which the curves of the system cut on one of their number. This shall be defined as the 'charac-

---

* Ibid., p. 165, where quite an elaborate table is given.

teristic series' of the system. Its order is defined as the 'grade' of the system, no fixed intersections being counted.

$$N = n^2 - \sum r_0^2 \qquad r = \frac{n(n+3)}{2} - \sum \frac{r_i(r_i+1)}{2} + s - 1$$

$$p = \frac{n(n-3)}{2} + 1 - \sum \frac{r_i(r_i-1)}{2}. \tag{5}$$

Let us now show that this series is complete. Let f be a curve of the system which we take as base curve, f_1 another generic curve, which cuts f not only in the base but in the group G_1. Let an adjoint ϕ_1 cut f in two groups G_1, G_2. Let G_2' be a group of the complete series defined by G_1, i.e. a general group residual to G_2, the two being cut by the adjoint ϕ_2. Consider the curve $f_1\phi_2$. It will have at P_i the multiplicity $2r_i - 1$, and will contain the groups G_1, G_2, G_2'. Hence, by Nöther's fundamental theorem 3], Book II, Ch. IV,

$$f_1\phi_2 \equiv \theta f + \phi_1 f_2.$$

Here f_2 is a curve of the same order as f_1, and it has at P_i the multiplicity $r_i - 1$ *at least*. We proceed to show that, in fact, it has the multiplicity r_i. Let us suppose that this point is the origin and that no other point of the base is infinitely near, a state of affairs that can always be brought about by a succession of quadratic transformations, and they will not alter the statement of the theorem we wish to prove about the completeness of the series of groups. Let us write our various polynomials in terms of ascending powers of x and y, using a superscript to indicate the degree of the polynomials:

$$f_1 \equiv f_1^{r_0} + f_1^{r_0+1} + \dots$$
$$\phi_1 \equiv \phi_1^{r_0-1} + \phi_1^{r_0} + \dots$$
$$\phi_2 \equiv \phi_2^{r_0-1} + \phi_2^{r_0} + \dots$$
$$\theta \equiv \theta^{r_0-2} + \theta^{r_0-1} + \dots$$
$$f \equiv f^{r_0} + f^{r_0+1} + \dots$$
$$f_2 \equiv f_2^{r_0-1} + f_2^{r_0} + \dots.$$

Since $f_1\phi_2$ has no term of order $2r_0 - 1$, there can be no such term on the right of the above identity, or

$$\theta^{r_0-2}f^{r_0} + \phi^{r_0-1}f^{r_0-1} \equiv 0.$$

Since there are no base points infinitely near the origin, we may assume that f is not tangent to ϕ_1 at the origin, so that f^{r_0} and $\phi_1^{r_0-1}$ have no common factor. But the factors of f^{r_0} cannot all fit into $f_2^{r_0-1}$. Hence $f_2^{r_0-1} \equiv 0$, or f_2 has the multiplicity r_0 at the origin, or r_i at P_i. It is a curve of our system, so that a curve of our system will cut each group of the complete series determined by G_1. A linear series which includes a complete series of the same order is itself complete. We have

Theorem 15] *The characteristic series cut by the curves of a linear system determined by base points on the general curve of the system is complete.*

We get from the equations above for the series

$$N-r = p-s, \tag{6}$$

and so, from Riemann-Roch,

Theorem 16] *If the dimension of a linear system of irreducible curves determined by a base complete for singular points be as great as 1, the superabundance of the base is the index of specialization of the characteristic series.**

We may generalize exactly as we did before, getting

Theorem 17] *If a base of a linear system be complete for singular points, for curves of a certain order, the superabundance is the excess above $\dfrac{(\alpha-1)(\alpha-2)}{2}$ of the index of specialization of the series cut on curves of order α greater with the same base.*

Theorem 18] *If a base be complete for singular points for curves of a certain order, and if those curves be necessarily rational and exist in infinite numbers, then the base is normal.*

In the case of a pencil of curves we have

$$N = 0 \qquad r = 0 \qquad p = s.$$

Theorem 19] *The superabundance of a pencil of curves is equal to the genus of the general curve of the pencil. This is the greatest superabundance for any base for curves of that genus.*

We get by Clifford's Theorem 30] of Ch. I, Book III:

If $s > 0$,
$$2(p-1) \geqslant N \geqslant 2r,$$
$$2(s-1) \geqslant \sum r_i - 3r \geqslant 0. \tag{7}$$

---

* This really beautiful theorem is due to Castelnuovo[6].

§ 4. Fundamental curves and special adjoints

Definition. A curve is said to be 'fundamental' for a linear system if the curves of the system do not meet it in variable points. If, thus, we require a curve of the system to go through a point of the fundamental curve not common to all curves of the system, it must include the fundamental curve or be included therein. Considering not the whole fundamental curve but its irreducible factors, we may assume that the order does not exceed that of the curves of the system. If the system of curves be a pencil, each individual curve is fundamental. The line at infinity is fundamental for any one-parameter linear family of circles. We see that in general but one condition is imposed on a curve of the system to make it include the fundamental curve. Hence, if the tangents at a base point be variable, it will take more than one additional condition to give a particular curve a higher multiplicity than the general curve, or the fundamental curve will not have a higher multiplicity. We may always reach this condition for base points by a factorable Cremona transformation, so let us suppose for the moment that this is the case. Let the order of the general curve be n, the multiplicity at the base point P_i, r_i, the order of a fundamental curve shall be ν and the multiplicity of P_i, s_i.

$$\sum r_i s_i = n\nu. \tag{8}$$

The order of the residual curve which goes with the fundamental curve to make a curve of the system is $n-\nu$, the multiplicity at P_i is r_i-s_i. Let us find the genus of the residual curve. This will be its ostensible genus, for the condition of having an additional singular point is not linear, while that of including the fundamental curve is linear. Also, this curve is irreducible by 4], a fixed part being added to the fundamental curve. The genus of the general residual curve is, thus,

$$\frac{(n-\nu)(n-\nu-3)}{2} - \sum \frac{(r_i-s_i)(r_i-s_i-1)}{2} + 1$$
$$= p + \frac{\nu(\nu+3)}{2} - \sum \frac{s_i(s_i+1)}{2}.$$

Now $\dfrac{\nu(\nu+3)}{2} - \sum \dfrac{s_i(s_i+1)}{2} \leqslant 0$ as the fundamental curve cannot be variable. If the lower sign hold, i.e. if the base be normal for the fundamental curve, the genus of the general residual is p, so that it has p linearly independent special adjoints, and these, with the fundamental curve, give p linearly independent special adjoints for the original system of curves. We shall show in a later chapter that a factorable Cremona transformation will carry a special adjoint into a special adjoint, or the variable parts of special adjoints called the 'pure adjoint system' into variable parts. Hence we may announce

Theorem 20] *If an infinite linear system be given by a base complete for singular points, the genus of an irreducible curve residual to a fundamental curve is equal to the genus of the general curve of the system, less the superabundance of the base for the fundamental curve. When the base is normal for this fundamental curve, it forms a part of every special adjoint to the original system, while the residual curves have the genus of the original system.*

It is to be noted that a linear system may have different sets of fundamental curves and residual curves. Thus, for the conics through three points, each line connecting two is a fundamental curve, and the lines through the third point are the residual curves. These lines, like the original conics, have the genus 0.

The essential part of theorem 19] is that the special adjoints are reducible. Suppose, conversely, that the general special adjoint of a curve is reducible. By Bertini's theorem 3], either all have a common part, or they are $p-1$ groups of curves of a pencil. In the latter case the pencil will cut a g_2^1 on the original curve, which must be hyperelliptic.

Theorem 21] *If the special adjoints of a curve be reducible without a common factor, the curve is hyperelliptic.*

Suppose there is a common factor. Since the canonical series on one of the curves of our system has no fixed points, this fixed part must be fundamental.

Theorem 22] *If the special adjoints of a linear system determined by a base complete for singular points have a fixed part, this will be fundamental for the given system, and the base points are all singular.*

The difference between the actual freedoms of the original

linear system and the system residual to a fundamental curve is 1. The difference between the apparent freedoms is

$$\frac{n(n+3)}{2} - \sum \frac{r_i(r_i+1)}{2} - \left[\frac{(n-\nu)(n-\nu+3)}{2} - \sum \frac{(r_i-s_i)(r_i-s_i+1)}{2} \right]$$

$$= -\left[\frac{(\nu-1)(\nu-2)}{2} - \sum \frac{s_i(s_i-1)}{2} \right] + 1. \quad (9)$$

Since the apparent freedom equals the actual freedom less the superabundance, we have

Theorem 23] *If a linear system have an irreducible fundamental curve, its apparent genus is the difference between the superabundance of the original and residual systems.*

Theorem 24] *If a linear system of curves have an irreducible fundamental curve, its genus cannot exceed the superabundance of the system.*

It is to be noted that we say genus, not apparent genus, here. The theorem appears for the apparent genus from 22], the actual genus is less than the apparent when there are unsuspected singularities, otherwise equal to it.

Suppose that our base is not necessarily complete, but is determined by k of its points which lie on a cubic. This cubic with any special adjoint will constitute a curve of the system, or all the base points lie in the cubic. If the system were superabundant, the intersections of a general curve with a curve made up of the cubic and a special adjoint would be a special group of the former, by 10], but this is impossible unless the cubic is fundamental. There could not be an infinite number of such cubics.

Theorem 25] *A superabundant system must have at least nine base points.*

Let us calculate the apparent genus of a special adjoint. This is

$$p' = \frac{(n-4)(n-5)}{2} - \sum \frac{(r_i-1)(r_i-2)}{2} = p + \sum r_i - 3n - [\sum 1 - 9].$$

$$(10)$$

where $\sum 1$ means number of base points.

If the base points do not lie on a cubic $\sum 1 > 9$. Comparing with (5),
$$r - s < 2p - 1 - p'. \quad (11)$$

On the other hand, by (7)

$$s' \geqslant \sum \frac{(r_i-1)-3(n-9)}{2}+1 = \frac{p'-p}{2}+1 > 0.$$

Theorem 26] *If the base points do not lie on a cubic, and if $r-s \geqslant p+1$, the base system is normal for an irreducible special adjoint.*

§ 5. Situation of the singular points

The groups of points so far considered, whether normal or superabundant, were generally supposed to lie on more than one curve of given order. The situation becomes a good deal more complicated when there is but one curve, as we are not able to use 15]. As an example we shall take up one of the most important unsolved problems in the whole theory of plane curves, the situation of the permissible singular points.

A curve of order n can have any number of nodes up to $\frac{(n-1)(n-2)}{2}$, but we can assign arbitrary positions to at most $\frac{n(n+3)}{6}$. When the curve has more double points than this, where do they lie ?

If the order of the curve be less than six the question has no point. We can place the nodes where we please, provided we do not have three on a line, or six on a conic. When it comes to a curve of the sixth order, quite a new situation arises.* The maximum permissible number of double points is ten; we have apparently enough parameters to allow us to place nine double points where we please, thereby exactly determining the sextic curve. But through nine points we may always pass a cubic, and this counted twice would give us a sextic fulfilling the desired conditions; consequently the double points of a non-degenerate sextic must form a superabundant base. They could not be the base points of a pencil of cubics, for a cubic of the pencil through a non-singular point of one of the sextics would intersect it nineteen times. Consider the single cubic through these nine double points. If we express the curve parametrically with the aid of elliptic functions, as explained at the end of

* Cf. Halphen[3].

Ch. VIII, Book III, the nine values corresponding to the nodes of the sextic will be connected by the relation

$$2(u_1 + u_2 + \ldots + u_9) \equiv 0 \pmod{2\omega_1, 2\omega_3}.$$

We could not have

$$u_1 + u_2 + \ldots + u_9 \equiv 0 \pmod{2\omega_1, 2\omega_3},$$

for then our nine points would lie on another cubic. Hence

$$u_1 + u_2 + \ldots + u_9 = k\omega_1 + l\omega_3,$$

where either $k \neq 0$ or $l \neq 0$. We construct such a set of points in the following fashion. We start with $P_1, P_2, \ldots, P_8$, arbitrary points, no 3 on a line, no 6 on a conic. Let Q_9 be the remaining base of the pencil of cubics through $P_1, \ldots, P_8$. Let the tangent at Q_9 to one of these curves meet that curve again at T. Then we may take for P_9 the point of contact of any one of the other three tangents to this cubic from T, besides the tangent at T and TQ_9. The proof is immediate.

Suppose, conversely, we have nine points on a cubic with this relation. The number of linearly independent sextics tangent to the cubic at these points is $28 - 17$ (not $28 - 18$) $= 11$. If the curves of a pencil have usually the same tangent at a base, but one condition need be imposed to require a double point there. Hence there is a pencil of sextics with double points at these nine points, and that is just what is desired.

Suppose the points $P_1, \ldots, P_8$, are given, no three on a line, no six on a conic, what will be the locus of P_9? Let ϕ_1 and ϕ_2 be two cubics through $P_1, \ldots, P_8$, and f a non-degenerate sextic with these as double points. The general sextic with these eight double points is

$$\lambda\phi_1^2 + \mu\phi_1\phi_2 + \nu\phi_2^2 + \rho f = 0.$$

If (x) be another singular point of such a sextic,

$$2\lambda\phi_1 \frac{\partial\phi_1}{\partial x_i} + \mu\left[\phi_2 \frac{\partial\phi_1}{\partial x_i} + \phi_1 \frac{\partial\phi_2}{\partial x_i}\right] + 2\nu\phi_2 \frac{\partial\phi_2}{\partial x_i} + \rho \frac{\partial f}{\partial x_i} = 0.$$

These equations will be satisfied by ∞^1 sets of solutions λ, μ, ν, ρ if 2 be the rank of the matrix

$$\left\| \begin{array}{cccc} \phi_1 \dfrac{\partial\phi_1}{\partial x_1} & \left(\phi_2 \dfrac{\partial\phi_1}{\partial x_1} + \phi_1 \dfrac{\partial\phi_2}{\partial x_1}\right) & \phi_2 \dfrac{\partial\phi_2}{\partial x_1} & \dfrac{\partial f}{\partial x_1} \\ \cdot & \cdot \quad \cdot \quad \cdot \quad \cdot \quad \cdot \quad \cdot \quad \cdot & \cdot & \cdot \\ \cdot & \cdot \quad \cdot \quad \cdot \quad \cdot \quad \cdot \quad \cdot \quad \cdot & \cdot & \dfrac{\partial f}{\partial x_3} \end{array} \right\|$$

The N.S. condition for this is

$$\frac{\partial(\phi_1, \phi_2, f)}{\partial(x_1, x_2, x_3)} = 0.$$

This curve of order 9 is the locus required. It has a triple point at each of the positions $P_1, ..., P_8$ and passes simply through each of the double points of cubics of the pencil $\lambda\phi_1 + \mu\phi_2 = 0$. These characteristics determine it completely. P_9 can be any general point on this curve.

Suppose, now, that our sextic is rational, and so has ten double points. How must they lie ? We have a pencil of sextics with double points $P_1, ..., P_9$. How many of them have a tenth double point ? If f_1 and f_2 be two cubics of the pencil, the first polars of three general points (y), (z), and (r), with regard to a curve $\lambda f_1 + \mu f_2 = 0$, must be concurrent.

$$\lambda\left(y\frac{\partial f_1}{\partial x}\right) + \mu\left(y\frac{\partial f_2}{\partial x}\right) = 0 \qquad \lambda\left(z\frac{\partial f_1}{\partial x}\right) + \mu\left(z\frac{\partial f_2}{\partial x}\right) = 0$$

$$\lambda\left(r\frac{\partial f_1}{\partial x}\right) + \mu\left(r\frac{\partial f_2}{\partial x}\right) = 0$$

$$\begin{vmatrix} \left(y\frac{\partial f_1}{\partial x}\right) & \left(y\frac{\partial f_2}{\partial x}\right) \\ \left(z\frac{\partial f_1}{\partial x}\right) & \left(z\frac{\partial f_2}{\partial x}\right) \end{vmatrix} = \begin{vmatrix} \left(z\frac{\partial f_1}{\partial x}\right) & \left(z\frac{\partial f_2}{\partial x}\right) \\ \left(r\frac{\partial f_1}{\partial x}\right) & \left(r\frac{\partial f_2}{\partial x}\right) \end{vmatrix} = \begin{vmatrix} \left(r\frac{\partial f_1}{\partial x}\right) & \left(r\frac{\partial f_2}{\partial x}\right) \\ \left(y\frac{\partial f_1}{\partial x}\right) & \left(y\frac{\partial f_2}{\partial x}\right) \end{vmatrix} = 0.$$

Here are three curves of the tenth order. A point common to the first two is also a point of the third, unless

$$\left(z\frac{\partial f_1}{\partial x}\right) = \left(z\frac{\partial f_2}{\partial x}\right) = 0.$$

The first two have 100 intersections. A rather dreary calculation shows that they meet 8 times at each of the points $P_1, ..., P_9$. Hence they have 28 other intersections. The curves

$$\left(z\frac{\partial f_1}{\partial x}\right) = \left(z\frac{\partial f_2}{\partial x}\right) = 0$$

have 25 intersections, of which 9 are at $P_1, ..., P_9$. Deducting the 16 others from the 28, we have left 12.

Theorem 27] *Given a pencil of sextic curves with nine common double points, twelve curves of the pencil have a tenth double point.*

We find the sets of 10 points quite simply after this. Let P_9 be a simple general point of the curve of order 9 with triple points at $P_1, ..., P_8$. Then must P_8 be a point of the curve of order 9 with double points $P_1, ..., P_7, P_9$. The twelve singular points P_{10} must be common to these two curves. They have 81 intersections all told, of which 9 are at each of the points $P_1, ..., P_7$ and 3 at each of the points P_8, P_9, and that leaves just 12.

Theorem 28] *A necessary and sufficient condition that* 10 *points should be singular points of a sextic is that each set of* 9 *should be so.*

We pass to curves of order 7. Here we have to use a totally different technique. We may choose 11 singular points for such a curve at random. If a curve of order 7 have 12 double points its genus is 3, the canonical series is a g_4^2. Let P be a point of the curve. Residual thereto in the canonical series will be a g_3^1 of which, by Book III, Ch. III, theorem 5], 2 groups contain 3 collinear points Q. Each of these lines meets the base curve in 4 other points, so that to P will correspond 8 points P'. Conversely, when P' is given, the lines through it cut the curve in a g_6^1 which by the same theorem has 8 groups of 3 points Q lying in a group of the g_4^2, leaving but one residual point. To each P' will thus correspond 8 points P. We have between P and P' an 8-to-8 correspondence. If the curve be of general moduli of periodicity, so that the correspondence has a value γ, the number of coincidences is $\nu + \nu' + 3p\gamma = 16 + 6\gamma$, and this cannot be 0, so that there is a special adjoint ϕ^4 which cuts the base curve in 4 collinear points

$$f \equiv \chi^3 \phi^4 + (ux)\psi^6, \tag{12}$$

the curve ψ^6 will have to be tangent to ϕ^4 at each singular point, so that the condition is thrown back on that of finding a sextic and quartic which touch 12 times. Now take the question from the other end. Start with a conic and construct a quartic to touch it four times. Through these points of contact passes a second quartic. The second quartic counted twice contains all the intersections of the conic and the first quartic. Hence the remaining intersections, by Book I, Ch. II, theorem 19], lie on a sextic which touches the first quartic in the twelve other intersections with the second one. The quartic and sextic being ϕ^4 and ψ^6, we return to equation (12). We have ten arbitrary coefficients in χ^3 and three in (ux), and we can use these to make f have a singular point wherever the quartic and sextic touch, twelve times in all.

Theorem 29] *The twelve points of contact of a quartic and sextic may be taken as singular points for a curve of the seventh order, and if a curve of that order have twelve double points, and have general moduli of periodicity, then the double points are points of contact of a quartic and sextic.**

The step upwards to the case where the curve has thirteen or more singular points does not seem to go through smoothly; still less easy is the step up to curves of higher order. We shall give in a later chapter a little more information on this question, taking the matter from a different point of view. In general, however, we must confess right now that the important and intriguing problem of finding general conditions for the situation of the singular points of curves of high order, or of general order, when the number of these points is large, is very far indeed from solution. A solution of this problem would be a great step in advance.

* This theorem is apparently due to Gambier[2], p. 266. This writer assumes without proof that the four collinear points are always there.

CHAPTER II

THE TRANSFORMATION OF LINEAR SYSTEMS

§ 1. Invariants of linear systems

IF we have a linear system given by base points, and apply thereto a standard quadratic transformation, some of its characteristics will be altered, others unaltered. The order of the general curve will probably be changed, so will the number, multiplicity, and situation of the base points. On the other hand, the superabundance will not change, nor the order and dimension of the characteristic series, nor the genus of the general curve.

Theorem 1] *If a linear system determined by a complete base be subjected to a factorable Cremona transformation, its dimension will be unaltered, as will be the order of the characteristic series, the superabundance of the base, and the genus of the general curve.*

Let three base points of our linear system be O_1, O_2, O_3 of orders r_1, r_2, r_3 respectively; suppose that they are distinct and not collinear, and $n > r_i + r_j$. Let us effect a standard quadratic transformation with O_1, O_2, O_3 as fundamental. The order of the new linear system will be

$$n' = 2n - (r_1 + r_2 + r_3).$$

The situation and nature of the base points will be essentially unchanged except that the orders of O_1, O_2, O_3 are now

$$n - (r_2 + r_3) \qquad n - (r_3 + r_1) \qquad n - (r_1 + r_2).$$

Consider a special adjoint of the first system. The transformed curve will have the order

$$\bar{n} = 2(n - 3) - (r_1 - 1) - (r_2 - 1) - (r_3 - 1) = n' - 3.$$

The multiplicities at the fundamental points are

$$n - 3 - (r_2 - 1) - (r_3 - 1) = n - (r_2 + r_3) - 1,$$
$$n - (r_3 + r_1) - 1, \qquad n - (r_1 + r_2) - 1,$$

so that a special adjoint is carried into a special adjoint.

Suppose, next, that O_3 is not a base point. The curve of order n goes into one of order

$$n' = 2n - (r_1 + r_2).$$

The fundamental points are base points of orders

$$n-r_2 \qquad n-r_1 \qquad n-(r_1+r_2).$$

A special adjoint will go into a curve of order

$$\bar{n} = 2(n-3)-(r_1-1)-(r_2-1) = n'-4,$$

with multiplicities

$$n-r_2-2 \qquad n-r_1-2 \qquad n-(r_1+r_2)-1.$$

However, the line $O_1 O_2$ is fundamental for the transformed system: if we add it to the curve of order $n'-4$ we get a special adjoint of the transformed system, and every special adjoint of that system has $O_1 O_2$ as a factor. We may proceed in the same way when O_2 ceases to be a base point, and finally when O_1 ceases to be.

Suppose, next, that $n = r_1+r_2$. O_3 will not be a base point of the transformed system. $O_1 O_2$ is fundamental originally. It should be split off from each special adjoint. What is left is a curve of order $n-4$ which has, in the first case, multiplicities r_1-2, r_2-2, and r_3-1. It is carried as before into a curve of order $n'-3$, which is a special adjoint. In the second case we get a special adjoint if we add the line $O_1 O_2$ as before.

Definition. If the curves of a linear system given by base points have a genus greater than 1, the variable parts of their special adjoints are called the 'pure adjoint system'. The special adjoints are also called 'special adjoints of index 1'. The special adjoints to them are called 'special adjoints of index 2', etc.

Theorem 2] *If a linear system given by base points be subjected to a factorable Cremona transformation, the pure adjoint systems of all indices are transformed covariantly, as are the special adjoints if fundamental curves be added or subtracted.*

Let us see under what circumstances we can alter the number of base points by means of a standard quadratic transformation. A new base point will be introduced at O_3 if the sum of the multiplicities at O_1 and O_2 is less than n. After the transformation $O_1 O_2$ will be a fundamental line. It will be a new fundamental line unless it was a fundamental line before. If it was a fundamental line before, it must have had fixed base points other than O_1, O_2 since $r_1+r_2 < n$. Hence, after the transformation the curves will have fixed tangents at O_3 or base points infinitely near O_3. If this cannot happen, we cannot introduce a base point without introducing a fundamental curve. Conversely, suppose O_1O_2 comes in as a new fundamental curve. If it have base points other than O_1, O_2, then the curves of the original system had the same tangents at O_3, or there were infinitely near base points. If that be excluded, O_1 and O_2 must be the only base points on it after the transformation, hence the curve did not go through O_3 before the transformation, but must afterwards, since the line was not fundamental before, so that a new base point is involved. If introducing base points with fixed tangents changes the number of fundamental curves, abolishing such base points will make just the opposite change.

Theorem 3] *If two linear systems with distinct base points be connected by a factorable Cremona transformation, the difference between the number of base points and of fundamental curves is the same for both.**

We could doubtless extend this theorem to include curves with infinitely near base points by introducing the corresponding conception of infinitely near fundamental curves, but it is doubtful whether the attempt would be worth while.

§ 2. Curves transformable into straight lines

We have frequently had occasion to notice that every rational curve can be birationally transformed into a straight line. A great many rational curves can be carried into straight lines by factorable Cremona transformations. We are naturally tempted to believe that every rational curve can be so transformed. This is not the case.

A curve of order $n-3k$ with multiplicities r_i-k where the original curve has multiplicities r_i has been defined as a special adjoint of index k. It may be a kth pure adjoint, or contain that as a factor, the remainder being a fundamental curve or fundamental curves of that pure adjoint system. We prove exactly as we did in the case for the pure adjoint system that if we transform a special adjoint of index k by a standard quadratic transformation, we either get a special adjoint of that

* Cf. Jung[1]. This article is carelessly written, the writer does not consider the case of infinitely near base points.

index, or a part of one, the rest being one or more fundamental lines counted k times, or, if the special adjoints of this index be only such lines, we get no curve, or, as we shall say, a curve of zero order of which nothing is required. For instance, if we start with a sextic curve with three triple points, O_1, O_2, O_3, the special adjoints are the three fundamental lines $O_i O_j$. These are abolished by the quadratic transformation. The new curve is a cubic, and we are quite justified in saying that its special adjoints are of order 0 required to do nothing. There is no arithmetical contradiction in speaking of such a curve.

Consider a straight line. The search for a special adjoint of any index leads us to an arithmetical contradiction. Hence, if it be possible to carry a certain rational curve into a straight line by a factorable Cremona transformation, the search for a special adjoint of every index must lead to an arithmetical contradiction. This is a necessary condition for the transformation to be possible. Let us prove that it is also sufficient.

If the rational curve lacking all special adjoints of any index have but one singular point, this must be of order $n-1$. The order of the curve can be successively reduced by factorable De Jonquières transformations as explained in Ch. I of Book II. Suppose there are only two singular points of order $r_1, r_2, (r_1 \geqslant r_2)$. Let $n-r_1 = 2s$. The special adjoints of index s would consist in curves of order $n-3s$ with a multiple point of order $r_1-s = n-3s$. As $r_2-s \leqslant r_1-s$, we have no contradiction in setting up this curve which consists in concurrent straight lines, of which at least r_2-s are coincident. There is no contradiction in this requirement. We may show in the same way there is no contradiction if $n-r_1 = 2s+1$. Hence a curve where the requirement for a special adjoint of any index involves a contradiction must have at least three singular points if it have more than 1. As before, assume $n-r_1 = 2s$.

If none of the expressions $r_2-s, r_3-s, \ldots$ is positive, there is no incompatibility for the special adjoints of index s, hence a necessary condition for incompatibility is

$$r_1-s+r_2-s+r_3-s > n-3s$$

$$r_1+r_2+r_3 > n.$$

If the three points be distinct, they cannot be collinear, and the order of the curve can be reduced by a standard quadratic transformation. The same holds if only two be distinct, or if all three cluster on a set of osculating conics, the order of the curve can be reduced by a factorable quadratic Cremona transformation of the sort described in Book II, Ch. I. The only troublesome cases where we cannot run in such a transformation are those where O_2, O_3 are infinitely near to O_1 on two different branches, or all are on one branch, but that is not linear. In either case O_2, O_3 cannot be taken as fundamental points in a quadratic transformation but go into two distinct or adjacent points on the opposite side, but surely* $r_1 > r_2 + r_3$.

Now there is a further condition for incompatibility. Not only must we have $r_1 + r_2 + r_3 > n$, but also

$$(r_2 - s) + (r_3 - s) + \ldots + (r_l - s) > r_1 - s$$
$$r_2 + r_3 + \ldots + r_l > r_1,$$

so that the transforms of the points of multiplicity $> s$ cannot all lie on the opposite side of the triangle. It must, hence, be possible to find three points O_i, O_j, O_k such that $r_i + r_j + r_k > n$, yet which lie on a net of conics enabling us to transform our curve to one of lesser order. We may reason in the same way when $n - r_1 = 2s + 1$. If the conditions for each type of special adjoint be incompatible, the order of the curve can be reduced.

Theorem 4] *The necessary and sufficient condition that it be possible to transform a rational curve into a straight line by means of a factorable Cremona transformation is that the conditions for special adjoints of every index should be incompatible.*

The first rational curve that cannot be carried into a straight line is the sextic with ten nodes. A special adjoint of index 2 would be a curve of order 0 which was required to pass through no points, and we have seen that this does not count as an arithmetical contradiction.

Suppose that we have a rational curve uniquely determined by a normal base which includes all the singular points. We have

$$\frac{n(n+3)}{2} = \sum \frac{r_i(r_i+1)}{2} \qquad \frac{n(n-3)}{2} = \sum \frac{r_i(r_i-1)}{2} - 1$$
$$3n - 1 = \sum r_i$$
$$n(n - 3k) = \sum r_i(r_i - k) - (k+1).$$

* Cf. Franciosi, pp. 144 ff.

This shows that there cannot be a special adjoint of index k, as such an adjoint would intersect the base curve too often.

Theorem 5] *A rational curve completely determined by a normal base that includes all the singular points can be transformed into a straight line by a factorable Cremona transformation.*

§ 3. Reduction of singularities

Suppose that a curve has a set of special adjoints of index k which consists in the totality of curves of a given order. This system of curves has neither base points nor fundamental curves, so that there is the same number of the two; the special adjoints of index $k-1$ are merely required to pass simply through a certain number of points. If we make a series of quadratic transformations of the system, avoiding clustering singular points, the base points for the system of special adjoints, and the fundamental curves, are introduced *pari passu*. These new fundamental curves will be rational, each containing a number of base points making a normal base which determines it completely.

Suppose, conversely, a curve has the following properties:

1) The fundamental curves of the special adjoint system of index k are rational.

2) The base points on each of these fundamental curves and on the given curve form a complete base for the former, determining it completely.

3) The total number of base points on the given curve is equal to the number of these fixed curves.

4) Through each base point on the given curve will pass at least two fixed curves.

Usually such a system will have no base points not on the given curve, but it is conceivable that there might be such. We see by 5] that any chosen one of the fixed curves of the kth adjoint system may be reduced to a straight line; no new fundamental curve or base point has been introduced, and this line must have two base points on it, for it must contain a complete normal base. Through each base point on the line must pass at least one other fixed curve by 4). The two base points on the

line could not constitute a complete base for any other rational
curve of order $n > 1$, for

$$n(n+3) = r_1(r_1+1) + r_2(r_2+1)$$
$$n(n-3) = r_1(r_1-1) + r_2(r_2-1) - 2$$
$$3n = (r_1+r_2) + 1 \leqslant n+1,$$

which is absurd. Hence we may find a base point off the line.
Using this and the two points on the line as O_1, O_2, O_3, we make
a standard quadratic transformation which removes this fundamental line and introduces no other fundamental curve. Continuing thus, we may remove all the fixed curves of the adjoint
system of index k, and so, also, all the base points on the fixed
curve. Hence adjoints of index k are now merely required to
have a certain order, and those of index $k-1$ to pass simply
through a certain number of points.

Suppose that the system of special adjoints of index 1 have
these properties, then the given curve can be transformed into
one with no singular points. Conversely, if it have no singular
points, without being either a cubic, conic or a straight line, its
special adjoints of index 1 have these properties.

Theorem 6] *The necessary and sufficient conditions that a given
curve be transformable into one with no singularities by means of
a factorable Cremona transformation are that either there be no
special adjoints of any index, or those of index 1 fulfil the conditions* 1) *to* 4).

If we assume that these conditions hold for special adjoints
of index 2, we can transform to a curve where such special
adjoints are merely required to exist, and those of index 1 to
pass simply through certain points. We have therefore transformed to a curve with nothing worse than double points.

Suppose, conversely, that a curve has nothing worse than
double points and that there are no special adjoints of index 2
(including as existent a curve of order 0 of which nothing is
required). The order of the curve is 5 or less. A straight line,
conic or cubic has no singularity of order higher than 2. A
quartic with a triple point can be carried into a line by factorable
De Jonquières transformations, and the same is true of a quintic
with a quadruple point. A quintic with a triple point is a hyperelliptic curve of genus 3 with a special adjoint of index 1 but

none of index 2. It cannot be carried into a curve with nothing worse than double points, for we have exhausted the curves of that sort with no special adjoints of index 2, and none of them are equivalent to this curve in the present sense.

Again, if a curve have no special adjoints of index 1 or 2, and if it be capable of being carried into a curve with nothing worse than double points, this latter curve will be of order 5 or less, and so by the above will lack special adjoints of every index. If a curve can be carried into one with only double singular points and have special adjoints of index 1 but none of index 2, it can be carried into one where the adjoints of index 1 are lines or conics, so that all of index above 2 are lacking. And if all of index 2 or greater are lacking, the general adjoint of index 1 can be carried to a line or conic, so the given curve becomes one of order 4.

Theorem 7] *The necessary and sufficient conditions that it be possible to transform a curve by a factorable Cremona transformation into one with nothing worse than double points are that either all special adjoints of index 2 or greater are lacking, yet the curve is not hyperelliptic of genus 2, or else those of index 2 are present and obey conditions* 1) *to* 4).*

The important element in this theorem is to show that Clebsch's transformation theorem 14] of Book II, Ch. I, is untrue if we restrict ourselves to transformations which are birational, not merely for the curve, but for the whole plane, for we shall see subsequently that the word 'factorable' which we have applied to Cremona transformations is quite needless; all birational transformations of the plane turn out to be factorable. Note also that in theorem 7] we do not claim to reduce to a curve with only nodes; we allow cusps or tacnodes as well.

§ 4. Reduction to linear systems of minimum order

A great deal of attention has been given to the problem of reducing a linear system given by base points to one of minimum order. Part of the earlier work is vitiated by inadmissible assumptions, the more recent work is somewhat laborious.†
Certain theorems are, however, simple and evident.

---

* Cf. Coolidge[6] for this theorem and the last.
† For an elaborate bibliography see Franciosi.

Theorem 8] *If a curve have three singular points the sum of whose multiplicities exceeds the order of the curve, and if they be not infinitely near on a branch of order higher than* 1, *or two infinitely near a third on different branches, the order of the curve may be reduced by a factorable Cremona transformation.*

Suppose that we have a linear system of curves of order n given by base points $P_1, P_2,\dots$ of multiplicities $r_1, r_2,\dots$. Suppose, further, there is a fundamental curve of order ν with multiplicities $s_1, s_2,\dots$ at $P_1, P_2,\dots$, and that the conditions so imposed are independent,

$$\sum r_i s_i = n\nu \qquad \sum s_i(s_i+1) = \nu(\nu+3) \qquad \sum s_i(s_i-1) \leqslant (\nu-1)(\nu-2)$$
$$\sum s_i^2 \leqslant \nu^2+1 \qquad \sum s_i \geqslant 3\nu-1.$$

If our curves form a two-parameter system, a residual curve must intersect the fundamental curve:

$$\nu(n-\nu) > \sum s_i(r_i-s_i)$$
$$\sum s_i^2 > \nu^2.$$

Hence
$$\sum s_i^2 = \nu^2+1 \qquad \sum s_i = 3\nu-1.$$
$$\sum r_i s_i = (r_1+r_1+\dots+r_1)+(r_2+r_2+\dots+r_2)+\dots.$$

The number of terms here is $\sum s_i = 3\nu-1$. If, in every case, $r_i+r_j+r_k \leqslant n$, we should have $\nu-1$ triples, and one pair, with in each case a sum not greater than n, and in the case of the pair, if rightly chosen, less than n. Then the whole sum would be less than $n\nu$, contrary to what we have seen. This gives[*]

Theorem 9] *If a linear system of curves determined by base points depend on at least two parameters, and if there be a fundamental curve on which base points have imposed independent conditions, and if the base points be distinct, the order of the curves may be reduced by a standard quadratic transformation.*

Let us now see what will happen if [†]

$$r_1 \geqslant r_2 \geqslant r_3 \geqslant r_4 \dots \qquad r_1+r_2+r_3 < n.$$

Suppose that we have a factorable Cremona transformation where straight lines go into rational curves of order ν with fixed points of orders $s_1, s_2,\dots$.

$$\nu^2 - \sum s_i^2 = 1 \qquad \frac{\nu(\nu+3)}{2} - \sum \frac{s_i(s_i+1)}{2} = 2$$
$$3(\nu-1) = \sum s_i.$$

* Cf. Caporali[2], p. 147.   † Cf. Jung[2].

The order of the new curve is n' where

$$n'-n = n(v-1) - \sum r_i s_i$$
$$= n(v-1) - (r_1-r_3)s_1 - (r_2-r_3)s_2 - r_3(s_1+s_2+s_3) - r_4 s_4 \cdots$$
$$n'-n \geqslant n(v-1) - (r_1-r_3)s_1 - (r_2-r_3)s_2 - r_3 \sum s_i$$
$$s_1 \leqslant (v-1) \qquad s_2 \leqslant (v-1) \qquad \sum s_i = 3(v-1)$$
$$n'-n \geqslant [n-(r_1+r_2+r_3)](v-1).$$

Theorem 10] *If the sum of the three highest multiplicities of the singular points of an irreducible curve be less than the order of the curve, that order cannot be reduced by a factorable Cremona transformation.*

§ 5. Reduction of curves of low genus

We have already seen the necessary and sufficient conditions that it should be possible to carry a rational curve into a straight line by means of a factorable Cremona transformation. When we have given not one rational curve but a linear system, the matter is even simpler. Suppose the special adjoint system of index k is present.

$$n(n-3k) \geqslant \sum r_i(r_i-k) \qquad n(n-3)+2 = \sum r_i(r_i-1)$$
$$n(n+3) > \sum r_i(r_i+1)$$
$$3(n-1) > \sum r_i - 1$$
$$(k-1)[3n - \sum r_i] > (k-1)$$
$$n^2 - \sum r_i^2 = (3n - \sum r_i) - 2$$
$$n^2 - \sum r_i^2 - k[3n - \sum r_i] < -(k-1)$$
$$n(n-3k) \leqslant \sum r_i(r_i-k) - (k-1).$$

This is a contradiction, so, by 4], any one of our curves can be carried into a straight line. As long as in making this transformation we use three base points of the linear system, we reduce the orders of all the curves, and we can do this as long as there are three distinct base points properly placed. For instance, we have seen that if there be three base points which are singular, we can reduce the orders of all the curves. We could not have but two base points which were singular; it is easy to show that the genus of a curve with but two singular points is positive. If there be but one singular base point which is singular, we can reduce the order as long as the others are not infinitely near on different branches.

Theorem 11] *Every linear system of rational curves can be carried by a factorable Cremona transformation into a) the totality of conics in the plane, b) the totality of lines in the plane, c) the totality of lines through a point, d) the totality of curves of order n with a common point of order n−1 and with no other or one other distinct point in common, or e) any number up to n−1 of fixed tangents at the singular point.**

Let us next look at an elliptic curve. If it be possible to transform this to a cubic, there can be no special adjoint of index above 1, it being considered that a cubic has an adjoint of index 1 in the present sense. Suppose, conversely, all special adjoint systems after the first are non-existent. If there were but one singular point the curve could not be elliptic. If there were two or more we could repeat our previous reasoning, unless we had $s = 1$, and we have either $r_0 = n-2$ or $r_0 = n-3$.

In the first case we can take a double point, whether, or not, adjacent to the chief singularity, and a simple point, getting a net of conics which reduce the order of the curve. In the second case there are $4(n-3)$ double points, or the equivalent in doubles and triples. If there be only doubles we can get two of them not adjacent to the principal singularity on different branches; if there be a triple point, we use it and the principal singularity and a non-singular point; in either case we can reduce the order of the curve.

Theorem 12] *The necessary and sufficient condition that it be possible to change an elliptic curve into a cubic is that it should lack all special adjoints of index greater than 1.*

Suppose that we have a linear system of elliptic curves given by base points. Let us first suppose that the system depends on at least two parameters. The base is then normal. We have the last equations in slightly modified form:

$$n(n-3) = \sum r_i(r_i+1)$$
$$n(n+3) > \sum r_i(r_i+1)$$
$$3n - \sum r_i > 0$$
$$n^2 - \sum r_i^2 = 3n - \sum r_i$$
$$n^2 - \sum r_i^2 < k(3n - \sum r_i) \qquad k > 1$$
$$n(n-3k) < \sum r_i(r_i-k) \qquad k > 1.$$

* Cf. Enriques-Chisini, vol. iii, p. 194.

The conditions for a special adjoint of index greater than 1 are incompatible. Consequently the curves can all be reduced to cubics, provided there are as many as three base points.

If there be but one base point the curves cannot be elliptic unless they are cubics. Suppose there are two base points of orders r_1 and r_2. First let

$$r_1 + r_2 = n$$
$$n(n-3) - r_1(r_1-1) - (n-r_1)^2 + (n-r_1) = 0$$
$$nr_1 = r_1^2 + n$$
$$\left(r_1 - \frac{n}{2}\right)^2 = \frac{n^2 - 4n}{4}.$$

$n^2 - 4n$ must be a perfect square.

Let
$$n^2 - 4n = l^2$$
$$(n-2)^2 - l^2 = 4$$
$$(n-2-l)(n-2+l) = 4$$
$$l = 0 \qquad n = 4.$$

We have a quartic with two double points.

Let $\qquad\qquad r_1 + r_2 = n' < n.$

Maximum value for $\qquad r_1^2 + r_2^2$ is n'^2

Minimum value for $n(n-3) - (r_1^2 + r_2^2) + r_1 + r_2$
$$= (n-n')(n+n'+3) - 2n' > 0$$

It appears, then, that if the system depend on two or more parameters, it can always be reduced to a set of cubics, or of all quartics with two double points.

Suppose, now, we have a one-parameter system

$$n^2 = \sum r_i^2 \qquad 3n = \sum r_i.$$

As there is one special adjoint, a curve of the system through a point of that adjoint includes it entirely; the residue is a cubic through all the base points.

One of our curves is reducible, with a cubic factor, the residue being a special adjoint for all our curves. If this special adjoint have any irreducible factor other than the cubic, such a factor must be a rational curve, otherwise its special adjoint and the remaining factors of the original curve would make a new special adjoint to our pencil. Also it is a rational curve with no special adjoints of any index, and so can be reduced to a straight line by a series of quadratic transformations, none of which introduces a new fundamental curve into the given system of elliptic curves. One further quadratic transformation will abolish this fundamental straight line altogether. We may abolish other fundamental curves in the same way. We thus find a series of quadratic transformations, each carrying our fundamental cubic into a fundamental cubic, which carry our pencil of elliptic curves into such a pencil that the one special adjoint consists in a cubic counted $r_1 - 1$ times. Then all the bases of the pencil are points of multiplicity r_1 on this cubic, r in number:

$$rr_1^2 = (3r_1)^2$$

$$r = 9.$$

Theorem 13] *An infinite system of elliptic curves given by base points can be carried by a Cremona transformation into the system of all quartics with two double points, a linear system of cubic curves given by base points, or a pencil of curves of order $3r$ with nine common points of order r.* *

We might, if we chose, press the question of reduction a good deal further; the methods, however, become rather cumbersome.† It is to be noted that in handling a single elliptic curve, the principal property we were interested in was the absence of special adjoints of index greater than 1. We get in the same way

Theorem 14] *If a curve lack special adjoints of index greater than 1, it may be carried into a straight line if rational, a curve of order n with a point of multiplicity $n-2$ if elliptic or hyperelliptic, otherwise into one with a point of multiplicity $n-3$.*

Suppose that we have two curves each of which lacks every system of special adjoints of index greater than 1, which are birationally related. If one be rational, so is the other. Each may be carried by a factorable Cremona transformation into a straight line. If two straight lines be birationally related, this relation is a projective one, and is included in a projective transformation of the plane. Hence the relation between our two original curves is included in a factorable Cremona transformation of the plane.

Suppose, secondly, that neither curve is elliptic or hyper-

* Cf. Enriques-Chisini, vol. iii, p. 195.   † Cf. Feretti.

elliptic. If $p < 5$, i.e. $p - 3 < 2$, when we reduce one to a curve of order n with a multiple point of order $n-3$ and more than $2n-5$ double points, these could not all be adjacent to the point of order $n-3$ on different branches, i.e. we could find a quadratic transformation reducing the order of our curve. On the other hand, if we have $p - 3 \geqslant 2$, there is at least a two-parameter system of special adjoints through $p-3$ general points of the curve. These special adjoints can be carried into a system of straight lines, since they have no special adjoints, so that the curve will have as a pure adjoint system lines in the plane. The same will hold for a transform of the other curve. If the lines were concurrent, the canonical curves would be composite, and so the curve hyperelliptic, by theorem 21], Book IV, Ch. I, but this is against hypothesis. Hence the lines are not concurrent. We have thus two plane curves so related that collinear points on one correspond to collinear points on the other; the relation must be included in a collineation of the plane.

There remains the possibility that our birationally related curves are both elliptic or hyperelliptic. We can carry them by factorable Cremona transformations into curves whose special adjoints are sets of concurrent lines, i.e. into two curves of order n each with a singular point of order $n-1$. The lines through these two points will correspond projectively; we may make a linear transformation so that the corresponding lines have the same slope. We may write our two curves

$$\phi_1^{n-2}(x,y) + 2\chi_1^{n-1}(x,y) + \psi_1^n(x,y) = 0,$$
$$\phi_2^{n-2}(x,y) + 2\chi_2^{n-1}(x,y) + \psi_2^n(x,y) = 0.$$

Since lines through the origin correspond, and tangents from the origin to one curve will correspond to such tangents for the other, we have, if $y = \lambda x$,

$$\phi_1(\lambda) + 2x\chi_1(\lambda) + x^2\psi_1(\lambda) = 0 \qquad \phi_2(\lambda) + 2x\chi_2(\lambda) + x^2\psi_2(\lambda) = 0$$

$$\chi_1^2(\lambda) - \phi_1(\lambda)\psi_1(\lambda) = \chi_2^2(\lambda) - \phi_2(\lambda)\psi_2(\lambda) = \mu^2$$

$$x = \frac{-\chi_1(\lambda) + \mu}{\psi_1(\lambda)} \qquad y = \frac{-\lambda\chi_1(\lambda) + \lambda\mu}{\psi_1(\lambda)}$$

$$x = \frac{-\chi_2(\lambda) + \mu}{\psi_2(\lambda)} \qquad y = \frac{-\lambda\chi_2(\lambda) + \lambda\mu}{\psi_2(\lambda)}.$$

Each of the curves is carried by a Cremona transformation into the same curve

$$\chi^2(\lambda) - \phi(\lambda)\psi(\lambda) = \mu^2,$$

which, in turn, is carried by a Cremona transformation into the one or the other.

Theorem 15] *If two curves which lack special adjoints of all indices greater than* 1 *be birationally related, that relation is included in a Cremona transformation of the plane.*[*]

Suppose that we have a birational relation between two curves of the same order n, each of which has at least one adjoint of order $n-4$. The lines in the plane cut a special g_n^2. Let us show that there can be no other g_n^2. Let $P_1, P_2, ..., P_n$ be a group of such a series, which is special. Let $[R]$ be the residual group, while $P_1 P_2$ meets the base curve again in $Q_3, ..., Q_n$. Since $P_3, ..., P_n$ and $Q_3, ..., Q_n$ are co-residual, $P_1, P_2, Q_3, ..., Q_n$ is residual to R, a special group. But a special adjoint through $P_1, P_2, Q_3, ..., Q_n$ includes that line. Hence R is the intersection with an adjoint curve of order $n-4$. The g_n^2 cut by straight lines must be complete and all its groups residual to R. Hence the other g_n^2 of groups $P_1, ..., P_n$ must be identical therewith. If thus our two curves are birationally related, collinear points correspond to collinear points.

Theorem 16] *If two curves of the same order n, each of which has at least one special adjoint of order $n-4$, be birationally related, that relation is contained in a collineation of the plane.*[†]

Suppose that we have a linear system given by base points whose apparent dimension exceeds a number one less than the genus, the base being complete for singular points. Consider the special adjoint system of index k. Let r_i be the generic name for the multiplicity of a base point, when this multiplicity is as great as k, otherwise s_i. Let s be the superabundance, G the grade or order of the characteristic series, and N the order of the series which special adjoints of index k cut on the base curve.

$$r = \frac{n(n+3)}{2} - \sum \frac{r_i(r_i-1)}{2} - \sum \frac{s_i(s_i-1)}{2} + s;$$

* Cf. Merletta, p. 237.

† The special case of this where the curves are non-singular was proved by Snyder, q.v.

$$N = n(n-3k) - \sum r_i(r_i-k)$$

$$G = n^2 - \sum r_i^2 - \sum s_i^2$$

$$p-1 = \frac{n(n-3)}{2} - \sum \frac{r_i(r_i-1)}{2} - \sum \frac{s_i(s_i-1)}{2}$$

$$r-s-(p-1) = 3n - \sum r_i - \sum s_i$$

$$G-N = k[3n - \sum r_i] - \sum s_i^2 = k[(r-s)-(k-1)] + k \sum s_i - \sum s_i^2.$$

But $\qquad N \geqslant 0 \qquad k \geqslant s_i \qquad G+s = r+p-1,$

by Ch. I, theorem 15],

$$k \leqslant \frac{(r-s)+(p-1)}{(r-s)-(p-1)}.$$

Theorem 17] *If a linear system with apparent freedom* $r-s$, *given by a base which is complete for singular points, have an apparent dimension greater than* $p-1$, *there is no special adjoint of index greater than*

$$\frac{(r-s)+(p-1)}{(r-s)-(p-1)}.$$

CHAPTER III

LINEAR SYSTEMS—APOLARITY

§ 1. Linear systems and hyperspace

THE linear systems which we have studied so far have been those given by bases, and indeed those are much the most interesting ones. They are not, however, the most general, as we have already seen. Consider the linear system of conics

$$\sum_{ij} a_{ij} x_i x_j = 0 \qquad a_{ij} = a_{ji}$$
$$\sum_{ij} a_{ij} \beta_{ij} = 0 \qquad \beta_{ij} = \beta_{ji}.$$

It is not difficult to show that if $|\beta_{ij}| \neq 0$ we have the system of all conics circumscribed to triangles which are self-conjugate with regard to the fixed conic

$$\sum_{ij} \beta_{ij} u_i u_j = 0.$$

In our present study it is very desirable to handle simultaneously point-curves of a given order and envelopes of an equal class. A point curve is usually an envelope, and vice versa, but this is not always the case, so we retain the two terms. Consider the curves

$$f \equiv \sum \frac{n!}{k!\, l!\, m!} a_{klm} x_1^k x_2^l x_3^m \equiv a_x^n \equiv a_x'^n = 0 \qquad k+l+m=n \quad (1)$$

and the envelopes

$$\phi \equiv \sum \frac{n!}{\kappa!\, \lambda!\, \mu!} \alpha_{\kappa\lambda\mu} u_1^\kappa u_2^\lambda u_3^\mu \equiv u_\alpha^n \equiv u_{\alpha'}^n = 0 \qquad \kappa+\lambda+\mu=n. \quad (2)$$

We may make each curve correspond to a hyperplane in a space of $N = \dfrac{n(n+3)}{2}$ dimensions, and each envelope to a point in that same space, S_n. Certain envelopes will consist in points counted n times; such will be the case if

$$a_{\kappa\lambda\mu} \equiv y_1^\kappa y_2^\lambda y_3^\nu.$$

They will be represented in S_N by the points of a certain rational surface. The order of this surface will be the number of intersections with an S_{N-2}, and so the number of common solutions to the two equations $\qquad a_y^n = b_y^n = 0.$

This number is manifestly n^2. If our surface lay in a space of less than N dimensions, it would be impossible to find N of its points which determine one hyperplane, or N points in our original plane that determine just one curve of order n, but we know from theorem 13] of Book I, Ch. II, that it is perfectly easy to determine N such points.

Theorem 1] *If the totality of envelopes of class n be represented by the points of a space of* $N = \dfrac{n(n+3)}{2}$ *dimensions, and the totality of curves of order n by that of hyperplanes in this same space, then the totality of these envelopes which consist in a point counted n times will be represented by the points of a rational surface of order n^2 which does not lie in a flat space of lower dimension.*

Theorem 2] *The totality of curves of order n which consist in a straight line counted n times will be represented by the hyperplanes of a rational two-parameter system of class n^2 with no common point.*

Theorem 3] *The totality of curves or envelopes which are subjected to $r+1$ independent linear conditions will be linearly dependent on $N-r$ of their number.*

Since our surface in S_N does not, necessarily, meet a flat space of less than $N-2$ dimensions at all, but meets one of that dimensionality in n^2 points, we have

Theorem 4] *A linear system of curves of dimension greater than 1 is not, in general, determined by a base.*

§ 2. Apolarity

Consider the system of all curves of order n whose coefficients are limited by a single linear condition, not an identity. They will correspond to the hyperplanes of S_N through a chosen point. We can write the condition in the form

$$\sum \frac{n!}{k!\,l!\,m!} a_{klm}\alpha_{klm} = 0 \qquad k+l+m = 0. \tag{3}$$

It is worth while expressing this in covariant form, using at first non-symbolic coefficients.

$$f \equiv \sum \frac{n!}{k!\,l!\,m!} a_{klm}x_1^k x_2^l x_3^m = 0 \qquad k+l+m = n. \tag{1}$$

Consider the envelope

$$\phi \equiv \sum \frac{n!}{\kappa!\,\lambda!\,\mu!}\alpha_{\kappa\lambda\mu}u_1^\kappa u_2^\lambda u_3^\mu = 0 \qquad \kappa+\lambda+\mu = n \qquad (2)$$

$$F \equiv \phi f$$

$$\frac{1}{n^2}\left[\frac{\partial^2 F}{\partial u_1\partial x_1} + \frac{\partial^2 F}{\partial u_2\partial x_2} + \frac{\partial^2 F}{\partial u_3\partial x_3}\right]$$

$$= \sum \frac{(n-1)!}{k'!\,l'!\,m'!}\sum \frac{(n-1)!}{\kappa'!\,\lambda'!\,\mu'!}\,a_{klm}\alpha_{\kappa\lambda\mu}x_1^{k'}x_2^{l'}x_3^{m'}u_1^{\kappa'}u_2^{\lambda'}u_3^{\mu'}$$

$$(k'-k+1)(l'-l+1)(m'-m+1)$$

$$= (\kappa'-\kappa+1)(\lambda'-\lambda+1)(\mu'-\mu+1) = 0.$$

If we make a linear transformation

$$x_i' = \sum_j c_{ij}x_j \qquad u_i' = \sum_j C_{ij}u_j$$

$$\sum_i \frac{\partial^2 F}{\partial u_i\partial x_i} = \frac{1}{\Delta}\sum_{pqr} c_{pr}C_{qr}\frac{\partial^2 F'}{\partial u_q'\partial x_p'} = \sum_i \frac{\partial^2 F}{\partial u_i'\partial x_i'}.$$

Our equation (3) becomes

$$\left[\sum_i \frac{\partial^2(\phi f)}{\partial u_i\partial x_i}\right]^n = 0,$$

or better, $$a_\alpha^n \equiv a_{\alpha'}'^{\,n} = 0. \qquad (4)$$

A curve and envelope which have this relation are said to be 'apolar'. The reader will note the points of likeness and contrast to the binary apolarity discussed in a previous chapter.*

Theorem 5] *If an envelope consist in a point counted n times, it is apolar to every curve passing through that point; if a curve consist in a line counted n times, it is apolar to every envelope of the nth order tangent to that line.*

Suppose that the point (y) has exactly the multiplicity r for our curve (1), $$(ay)^{n-r+1}(ax)^{r-1} \equiv 0.$$

If $$(u\alpha)^n \equiv (uy)^{n-r+1}(u\beta)^{r-1}; \qquad (a\alpha)^n = 0.$$

Theorem 6] *The necessary and sufficient condition that a point should have exactly the multiplicity r for a curve of order n is that this curve should be apolar to every envelope of class n which includes as a part of itself the point counted n−r+1 times, but not to every envelope including it a lesser number of times.*

* Cf. especially Rosanes. The idea was foreshadowed by certain earlier writers as Battaglini, q.v., and De Paolis, q.v.

Theorem 7] *The totality of curves of order n apolar to R linearly independent envelopes of class n will be linearly dependent on $N-R+1$ of their number.*

Theorem 8] *A system of curves of order n linearly dependent on N of their number, which are linearly independent, will contain an infinite number of curves, each of which consists in a line counted n times. The envelope of these lines is the envelope apolar to all the curves of the system.*

Theorem 9] *A system of curves of order n linearly dependent on $N-1$ independent curves will, in general, contain n^2 curves, each of which consists in a line counted n times.*

§ 3. Apolarity between forms of different orders

Suppose that we have our curve (1) and an envelope of class $n' < n$,

$$(u\alpha)^{n'} = 0 \qquad n' < n. \tag{5}$$

The two are said to be 'apolar' if every envelope of class n which includes the given envelope as a factor is apolar to the curve, i.e.

$$(a\alpha)^{n'}(a\beta)^{n-n'} = 0. \tag{6}$$

Theorem 10] *The necessary and sufficient condition that a point should have exactly the multiplicity r for a curve of order n is that that point counted $n-r+1$ and no less times as an envelope should be apolar to the given curve.*

If our envelope (5) be given and the curve (1), we shall define the curve

$$(a\alpha)^{n'}a_x^{n-n'} = 0 \tag{7}$$

as the polar of the envelope with regard to the curve.*

Theorem 11] *The polar of an envelope of class n' with regard to a curve of order n is the locus of points which, counted $n-n'$ times, will make, with the given envelope, an envelope of class n apolar to the curve.*

Theorem 12] *The necessary and sufficient condition that an envelope of a certain class should be apolar to a curve whose order exceeds that class is that its polar with regard to that curve should become illusory.*

Theorem 13] *The polar of an envelope of class n with regard to a curve of order n is the locus of points whose polars with regard to the curve are apolar to the envelope.*

* This concept is due to Clifford[2].

Theorem 14] *Two envelopes taken together will be apolar to a curve whose order is the sum of their classes if each is apolar to the polar of the other.*

Theorem 15] *The polars of an s-parameter linear system of envelopes of the same class with regard to a given curve, or of a single envelope with regard to an s-parameter linear system of curves, will be an s-parameter linear system.*

Theorem 16] *n points looked upon as an envelope of class n are apolar to a given curve, if each lies on the polar of the other, looked upon as constituting an envelope of class n−1.*

The condition for this is

$$a_x a_y a_z \ldots = 0. \tag{8}$$

Definition. $n+1$ points are said to be 'a self-conjugate set' with regard to a curve of order n if each set of n of them is apolar with regard to the given curve.

Theorem 17] *If n+1 points be a self-conjugate set with regard to a curve of order n, the polar of each sub-set of n−1 will pass through the other two.*

Suppose we have an apolar set of $n−1$ points (y), (z),..., (t),

$$a_y a_z \ldots a_t a_x \equiv 0. \tag{9}$$

If one of the given points be singled out, the others are apolar to the first polar of that one. The polar of $n−2$ points is a conic, and the equation just written shows that each of our $n−1$ points is a double point for the conic polar of the $n−2$ others, i.e. this conic is two lines meeting in that point.

Theorem 18] *If n+1 points be apolar with regard to a curve of order n, the polar of each set of n−2 is two lines through the other point.*

Theorem 19] *A point on the Hessian counted n−2 times and the corresponding point on the Steinerian are apolar.*

If in equation (9) we look upon $n−3$ of our given points as fixed and the other two as variable, we see that they are apolar with regard to the cubic polar of the $n−3$.

Theorem 20] *If n−3 points be taken in general position, two others which are apolar to them with regard to a curve of order **n** are corresponding points on the Hessian of the cubic curve polar to the n−3.*

§ 4. Expression of a form as a sum of nth powers

N points $x^{(1)}, x^{(2)},..., x^{(\nu)}$ form a normal base for curves of order n if N be the rank of the matrix

$$\left\| \begin{matrix} (x_1^{(1)})^n & (x_1^{(1)})^{n-1}x_2^{(1)} & . & (x_1^{(1)})^p(x_2^{(1)})^q(x_3^{(1)})^r & . \\ . & . & . & . & . \\ . & . & . & . & . \\ (x_1^{(\nu)})^n & (x_1^{(\nu)})^{n-1}x_2^{(\nu)} & . & (x_1^{(\nu)})^p(x_2^{(\nu)})^q(x_3^{(\nu)})^r & . \end{matrix} \right\|$$

The various expressions in (u),

$$(ux^{(1)})^n, (ux^{(2)})^n,..., (ux^{(\nu)})^n,$$

are here linearly independent. Conversely, when these expressions are linearly independent, the points form a normal base. Suppose, now, we have an envelope of class n expressible in the form

$$\rho_1(ux^{(1)})^n + \rho_2(ux^{(2)})^n + ... + \rho_\nu(ux^{(\nu)})^n.$$

If $a_x^n = 0$ be a curve through all of these points, it is apolar to every such envelope. Conversely, if we have a linear system of curves determined by a normal base of non-singular points, the general envelope apolar to all the curves may be expressed as a linear combination of the given points each expressed n times as a polar.

Theorem 21] *A necessary and sufficient condition that it be possible to express an envelope (a curve) of class (order) n as the sum of ν nth powers of linear forms is that ν points (lines) can be found forming a normal base for all curves (envelopes) apolar to the given envelope (curve).*

The most obvious way to do this is to take any apolar envelope of class n, choose tangents forming a normal base, and express the given curve as a linear combination of the nth powers of the equations of these tangents. Here is a better method.* Take a self-conjugate set of $n+1$ points, no three collinear, $(x^{(1)}), (x^{(2)}),..., (x^{(n+1)})$. Consider the different envelopes

$$(ux^{(2)})(ux^{(3)}) ... (ux^{(n+1)}) = 0$$
$$(ux^{(1)})(ux^{(3)}) ... (ux^{(n+1)}) = 0 \tag{10}$$
$$. \quad . \quad . \quad . \quad . \quad . \quad . \quad . \quad .$$
$$(ux^{(1)})(ux^{(2)}) ... (ux^{(n)}) = 0.$$

If they were linearly dependent, a linear combination of all but one would include a factor which the last one lacks. They are

* Cf. Rosanes[3], p. 32.

all apolar to the curve $a_x^n = 0$ with regard to which the set of points is self-conjugate. If we write the nth power of the equation of the line connecting two of the points

$$|xx^{(p)}x^{(q)}|^n = 0, \qquad\qquad (11)$$

we get a curve which is easily seen to be apolar to all of the envelopes (10). If these curves (11) were not linearly independent, there would be at least $n-1$ linearly independent envelopes of class n apolar, that is to say, tangent, to all of these lines, and one at least would degenerate into a point in general position and an envelope of class $n-1$ to which n tangents could be drawn from each of our original points—an absurdity. We have, then, a system of $\dfrac{n(n+1)}{2}$ linearly independent curves apolar to our $n+1$ envelopes, and the general curve apolar to these envelopes can be expressed as a linear combination of them.

Theorem 22] *A curve of order n can be expressed as a linear combination of the nth powers of the lines connecting two by two the $n+1$ points of a self-conjugate set, no three being collinear.*

It is possible to express a curve in terms of a lesser number of perfect nth powers, but there seems no very symmetrical way to do so.

CHAPTER IV

SPECIAL CURVES IN A LINEAR SYSTEM

§ 1. The pencil

In the linear systems studied in the present book we have fixed our attention on the general curve of the system. Special curves have special properties which the general curve lacks; it is worth while looking at these.

Let us begin with a pencil of curves

$$\lambda f_1^{(n)} + \mu f_2^{(n)} = 0. \tag{1}$$

If there be a singular point (x) we must have

$$\lambda \frac{\partial f_1}{\partial x_i} + \mu \frac{\partial f_2}{\partial x_i} = 0.$$

We know by theorem 11] of Book I, Ch. I, that the resultant of these three equations is of degree $3(n-1)^2$ in $\lambda : \mu$, so that gives the number of double points. Or we may proceed as follows. The singular points are common to the three Jacobian curves

$$\frac{\partial(f_1, f_2)}{\partial(x_1, x_3)} = 0 \qquad \frac{\partial(f_1, f_2)}{\partial(x_2, x_3)} = 0 \qquad \frac{\partial(f_1, f_2)}{\partial(x_1, x_2)} = 0.$$

Every intersection of the first two is also on the third unless it be on

$$\frac{\partial f_1}{\partial x_3} = \frac{\partial f_2}{\partial x_3} = 0.$$

The first two Jacobians have $4(n-1)^2$ intersections, the number of intersections of the last two curves is $(n-1)^2$, leaving the number already found.

We say as a first approximation that the number of curves in a pencil which have singular points is $3(n-1)^2$. This number is quite incorrect if there be any singular points common to all curves of the pencil. Suppose that we subject our pencil to a standard quadratic transformation, the curves of the new pencil with additional singular points will come in part from those of the old pencil possessed of such points, in part from reducible new curves which have a side of the fundamental triangle as part of themselves. We learned, however, in theorem 3], Ch. II of the present book, that new base points and fundamental curves come in together. This gives

Theorem 1] *If a pencil of curves with distinct base points be carried into another such pencil by a factorable Cremona transformation, the difference between the number of base points and of reducible curves is the same.*

Suppose that we have two curves of order n with a common point of order r_1 at O_3. We write them

$$0 = f_1 \equiv x_3^{n-r_1}\phi_1^{r_1}(x_1, x_2) + x_3^{n-r_1-1}\psi_1^{r_1+1}(x_1, x_2) + \dots,$$

$$0 = f_2 \equiv x_3^{n-r_1}\phi_2^{r_1}(x_1, x_2) + x_3^{n-r_1-1}\psi_2^{r_1+1}(x_1, x_2) + \dots.$$

The polynomials ϕ_1, ϕ_2 have no common factor, as we assume the base points are distinct. Let us find how many intersections

$$\frac{\partial(f_1, f_2)}{\partial(x_1, x_3)} = \frac{\partial(f_1, f_2)}{\partial(x_2, x_3)} = 0$$

have at this point, and subtract from the $4(n-1)^2$ total intersections of the two curves. From this remainder we take the difference between the total number of intersections of

$$\frac{\partial f_1}{\partial x_3} = \frac{\partial f_2}{\partial x_3} = 0,$$

and the number of intersections at this point. We get

$$\frac{\partial(f_1, f_2)}{\partial(x_1, x_3)} = (n-r_1)x_3^{2(n-r_1)-1}\begin{vmatrix} \dfrac{\partial\phi_1}{\partial x_1} & \phi_1 \\ \dfrac{\partial\phi_2}{\partial x_1} & \phi_2 \end{vmatrix} + \dots.$$

But
$$x_1\frac{\partial\phi_1}{\partial x_1} + x_2\frac{\partial\phi_1}{\partial x_2} = r_1\phi_1.$$

Hence we have

$$\frac{\partial(f_1, f_2)}{\partial(x_1, x_3)} = \frac{n-r_1}{r_1}x_3^{2(n-r_1)-1}x_2\frac{\partial(\phi_1, \phi_2)}{\partial(x_1, x_2)} + \dots$$

$$\frac{\partial(f_1, f_2)}{\partial(x_2, x_3)} = -\frac{n-r_1}{r_1}x_3^{2(n-r_1)-1}x_1\frac{\partial(\phi_1, \phi_2)}{\partial(x_1, x_2)} + \dots.$$

Here are two curves with a common point of order $2r_1-1$ with $2(r_1-1)$ common tangents there. The number of intersections is at least
$$4r_1^2 - 2r_1 - 1.$$

If there were necessarily more intersections, that is to say, if two branches necessarily osculated one another, this would still be the case when the two curves were merely of the order r_1+1.

If we have two curves of order r_1+1 with a common point of order r_1, the curves of their pencil with additional singular points would be curves of order r_1 with singular points of order r_1-1 and lines from the singular point to other base points of the pencil. But if in this case the curves

$$\frac{\partial(f_1, f_2)}{\partial(x_1, x_3)} = \frac{\partial(f_1, f_2)}{\partial(x_2, x_3)} = 0$$

osculated, the number of other intersections of $f_1 = f_2 = 0$ would be less than $2r_1+1$, which is not the case. Hence, in general, the Jacobian curves do not osculate, or there are $4r_1^2 - 2r_1 - 1$ intersections at the point of order r_1. The curves

$$\frac{\partial f_1}{\partial x_3} = \frac{\partial f_2}{\partial x_3} = 0$$

have r_1^2 intersections at O_3. We get, finally,

$$4(n-1)^2 - \sum [4r_i^2 - 2r_i - 1] - [(n-1)^2 - \sum r_i^2]$$
$$= 3[(n-1)^2 - \sum r_i^2] + \sum [2r_i + 1].$$

Theorem 2] *If the base of a pencil of curves be a set of distinct points of multiplicities $r_1, r_2, \dots$, the number of curves with additional singularities is*

$$3(n-1)^2 - \sum (3r_i^2 - 2r_i - 1).$$

The invariant number, by 1], is the difference between this and $\sum 1$, and so is
$$3(n-1)^2 - \sum r_i(3r_i - 2).$$

But
$$n^2 = \sum r_i^2$$
$$2(p-1) = n(n-3) - \sum r_i(r_i - 1)$$
$$= \sum r_i - 3n$$
$$3(n-1)^2 - \sum r_i(3r_i - 2) = 4(p-1) + 3 = 4p - 1.$$

Theorem 3] *If a pencil of curves have distinct base points, the difference between the number of curves with additional singularities and the number of base points is one less than four times the genus of the general curve of the pencil.*

In this phrase of course the words 'number of curves' mean the order of the equation determining them.

Theorem 4] *If a pencil of rational curves have distinct base points, the number of these points exceeds by one the number of reducible curves.*

A pencil of conics gives a fine example of such a pencil.

Let us look for the locus of the inflexions of the curves of a pencil. We must form the Hessian of the general curve $\lambda f_1 + \mu f_2 = 0$.

$$\begin{vmatrix} \lambda \dfrac{\partial^2 f_1}{\partial x_1^2} + \mu \dfrac{\partial^2 f_2}{\partial x_1^2} & \cdots \cdots \\ \cdots \cdots \cdots \\ \cdots \cdots & \lambda \dfrac{\partial^2 f_1}{\partial x_3^2} + \mu \dfrac{\partial^2 f_2}{\partial x_3^2} \end{vmatrix} = 0.$$

Eliminating $\lambda : \mu$, we get

$$\begin{vmatrix} f_2 \dfrac{\partial^2 f_1}{\partial x_1^2} - f_1 \dfrac{\partial^2 f_2}{\partial x_1^2} & f_2 \dfrac{\partial^2 f_1}{\partial x_1 \partial x_2} - f_1 \dfrac{\partial^2 f_2}{\partial x_1 \partial x_2} & \cdots \cdots \\ \cdots \cdots \cdots \\ \cdots \cdots & f_2 \dfrac{\partial^2 f_1}{\partial x_3^2} - f_1 \dfrac{\partial^2 f_2}{\partial x_3^2} \end{vmatrix} = 0.$$

Let us define the 'tangential locus' of a point (y) with regard to the curves of the pencil as the locus of points of contact of tangents from (y). All singular points besides base points will be on it. The equation is

$$f_2 \left(y \frac{\partial f_1}{\partial x} \right) - f_1 \left(y \frac{\partial f_2}{\partial x} \right) = 0.$$

This locus will have a double point at (x) if

$$f_2 \sum_j y_j \frac{\partial^2 f_1}{\partial x_i \partial x_j} - f_1 \sum_j \frac{\partial^2 f_2}{\partial x_i \partial x_j} + \sum_j y_j \frac{\partial (f_2, f_1)}{\partial (x_i, x_j)} = 0,$$

$$\begin{vmatrix} f_2 \dfrac{\partial^2 f_1}{\partial x_1^2} - f_1 \dfrac{\partial^2 f_2}{\partial x_1^2} & f_2 \dfrac{\partial^2 f_1}{\partial x_1 \partial x_2} - f_1 \dfrac{\partial^2 f_2}{\partial x_1 \partial x_2} + \dfrac{\partial (f_1, f_2)}{\partial (x_1, x_2)} & \cdots \cdots \\ \cdots \cdots \cdots \\ \cdots \cdots & f_2 \dfrac{\partial^2 f_1}{\partial x_3^2} - f_1 \dfrac{\partial^2 f_2}{\partial x_3^2} \end{vmatrix} = 0.$$

This curve is of the same order as the tangential locus just written, but looks a little a little more complicated owing to the presence of the terms $\dfrac{\partial (f_1, f_2)}{\partial (x_i, x_j)}$.

Nevertheless, the two are identical. We prove this indirectly.

Let the curves be

$$0 = f_1 \equiv x_3^n + x_3^{n-1}[a_1 x_1 + a_2 x_2] + x_3^{n-2}[a_{11} x_1^2 + 2a_{12} x_1 x_2 + a_{22} x_2^2] + \ldots$$
$$0 = f_2 \equiv x_3^n + x_3^{n-1}[b_1 x_1 + b_2 x_2] + x_3^{n-2}[b_{11} x_1^2 + 2b_{12} x_1 x_2 + b_{22} x_2^2] + \ldots.$$

The tangential locus of $(0, 1, 0)$ is

$$0 = f_2 \frac{\partial f_1}{\partial x_2} - f_1 \frac{\partial f_2}{\partial x_2} \equiv x_3^{2n-1}(a_2 - b_2) +$$
$$+ x_3^{2(n-1)}\left[\left\{\begin{vmatrix} a_2 & a_1 \\ b_2 & b_1 \end{vmatrix} + 2|a_{12} - b_{12}|\right\} x_1 + (a_{22} - b_{22})x_2\right].$$

This will have a double point at $(0, 0, 1)$ if

$$a_2 - b_2 = \begin{vmatrix} a_2 & a_1 \\ b_2 & b_1 \end{vmatrix} + 2|a_{12} - b_{12}| = a_{22} - b_{22} = 0.$$

The equation of the curve of the system through $(0, 0, 1)$ is, under the present circumstances,

$$0 = (a_1 - b_1)x_3^{n-1} x_1 + x_3^{n-2}[(a_{11} - b_{11})x^2 + 2(a_{12} - b_{12})x_1 x_2] + \ldots.$$

The tangent is the line going to $(0, 1, 0)$ and has 3-point contact. The locus of the double points of tangential loci is, thus, a part of the locus of the inflexions, and, as the two are of the same order, they are identical. We thus get a pretty theorem due to Guccia.*

Theorem 5] *The locus of the inflexions of a pencil of curves of order n which contains no curve with a multiple factor or a linear factor is a curve of order $6(n-1)$. This curve is the Jacobian of the net of tangential curves of the various points of the plane. It passes through all singular points of curves of the pencil. The inflexional tangent is always the line joining the point of contact to that point whose tangential curve has a double point at that point of contact.*

Let us look for the class of the envelope of the inflexional tangents. If such a tangent go through (y), we have

$$\lambda f_1 + \mu f_2 = 0 \qquad \lambda\left(y \frac{\partial f_1}{\partial x}\right) + \mu\left(y \frac{\partial f_2}{\partial x}\right) = 0.$$

$$\begin{vmatrix} \lambda \dfrac{\partial^2 f_1}{\partial x_1^2} + \mu \dfrac{\partial^2 f_2}{\partial x_1^2} & \cdot & \cdot & \cdot & \cdot & \cdot \\ \cdot & \cdot & \cdot & \cdot & \cdot & \cdot \\ \cdot & \cdot & \cdot & \cdot & \lambda \dfrac{\partial^2 f_1}{\partial x_3^2} + \mu \dfrac{\partial^2 f_2}{\partial x_3^2} \end{vmatrix} = 0.$$

* Guccia[2]. The first writer to study this locus seems to have been Weyr, q.v.

The degree of the resultant in $\lambda : \mu$ is $3n(n-2)+6(n-1)^2$ by theorem 11] of Book I, Ch. I. At the singular points of curves of the pencil a curve and a corresponding first polar will have two intersections; it is a point of the Hessian. These must be deducted.

Theorem 6] *If a pencil of curves of order n have $3(n-1)^2$ members with double points, the class of the curve enveloped by the inflexional tangents is $3n(n-2)$.*

§ 2. Two-parameter nets

The simplest linear system after the pencil is the two-parameter net. We have studied this in considerable detail earlier in our work. We get at once from Book I, Ch. IX, theorem 25] ff.:

Theorem 7] *The Jacobian curve of a net is the locus of variable singular points of curves of the system, and of points where curves are tangent. It passes through all base points. The curves of the system through a non-singular point of the Jacobian are tangent to a line harmonically separated from the tangent to the Jacobian by the tangents to that curve which has a double point there.*

If we take the three curves

$$f_1 = 0 \qquad f_2 = 0 \qquad f_3 = 0$$

and make the transformation $x_i = x_j' x_k'$,

$$\frac{\partial(f_1, f_2, f_3)}{\partial(x_1, x_2, x_3)} = \begin{vmatrix} 0 & x_3' & x_2' \\ x_3' & 0 & x_1' \\ x_2' & x_1' & 0 \end{vmatrix} \frac{\partial(f_1, f_2, f_3)}{\partial(x_1, x_2, x_3)}.$$

It appears, thus, that the Jacobian is carried over covariantly by a standard quadratic transformation, except that sides of the fundamental triangle may be added thereto. This part, however, may be neglected, for a standard quadratic transformation is a contact transformation, and a locus of points where curves touch will go over into the corresponding locus.

We next notice that we may transform any net into one where all base points are distinct. If they have the multiplicities $r_1, r_2, \dots$, the order of the characteristic series, or grade as we have defined it, is

$$G = n^2 - \sum r_i^2,$$

the genus of the general curve is p where

$$2(p-1) = n(n-3) - \sum r_i(r_i - 1).$$

Let us see how the Jacobian behaves at a base point of order r_1, say $(0, 0, 1)$. Let

$$0 = f_i = x_3^{n-r_1}\phi_i^{r_1}(x_1, x_2) + x_3^{n-r_1-1}\psi_i^{r_1+1}(x_1, x_2) + \dots .$$

Since

$$\begin{vmatrix} \dfrac{\partial\phi_1}{\partial x_1} & \dfrac{\partial\phi_1}{\partial x_2} & \phi_1 \\[2mm] \dfrac{\partial\phi_2}{\partial x_1} & \dfrac{\partial\phi_2}{\partial x_2} & \phi_2 \\[2mm] \dfrac{\partial\phi_3}{\partial x_1} & \dfrac{\partial\phi_3}{\partial x_2} & \phi_3 \end{vmatrix} \equiv 0,$$

the lowest terms in the Jacobian in x_1, x_2 are

$$\begin{vmatrix} \dfrac{\partial\phi_1}{\partial x_1} & \dfrac{\partial\phi_1}{\partial x_2} & \psi_1 \\[2mm] \dfrac{\partial\phi_2}{\partial x_1} & \dfrac{\partial\phi_2}{\partial x_2} & \psi_2 \\[2mm] \dfrac{\partial\phi_3}{\partial x_1} & \dfrac{\partial\phi_3}{\partial x_2} & \psi_3 \end{vmatrix},$$

that is to say, of order $3r_1 - 1$. The number of variable intersections of a curve of the net with the Jacobian will be an invariant for Cremona transformations. That number is, in the present instance,

$$3n(n-1) - \sum r_i(3r_i - 1) = 3[n^2 - \sum r_i^2] + \sum r_i - 3n$$
$$= 2[p + G - 1].$$

Theorem 8] *The number of variable intersections of the curves of a linear net with the Jacobian is twice the number which is one less than the sum of the grade and the genus of the general curve.*

§ 3. The Laguerre net

Suppose that we have two curves of order n with $n-1$ collinear points in common. Let the curves be f_1, f_2, the line in question being $x_3 = 0$. Let f_1 meet the line again at O_1, while f_2 meets it again at O_2, then since $x_1 f_1$ passes through all the intersections of the line with f_2, we have

$$x_1 f_1 + x_2 f_2 + x_3 f_3 \equiv 0. \tag{2}$$

Consider, now, the net of curves called a Laguerre net:*

$$y_1 f_1 + y_2 f_2 + y_3 f_3 = 0. \tag{3}$$

* Laguerre[3], pp. 540 ff.

The curve which corresponds to each point (y) will pass through it. The curves f_1, f_2 have n^2 intersections. Of these $n-1$ are on $x_3 = 0$. The remaining n^2-n+1 are on $f_3 = 0$, and so are base points of the net. Take two curves of the net,

$$y_1f_1+y_2f_2+y_3f_3 = 0 \qquad z_1f_1+z_2f_2+z_3f_3 = 0,$$

then $$|xyz| = 0.$$

It appears, thus, that every intersection of two curves of the net which is not a base point is on the line connecting the points to which these curves correspond.

Theorem 9] *In a Laguerre net all intersections of two curves which are not base points are on the line connecting the two points to which the curves correspond.*

Theorem 10] *If a point trace a straight line, the curves to which it corresponds pass through $n-1$ fixed points on that line.*

Suppose that the base points of the net are simple. The order of the characteristic series is, then, $n-1$ and the genus of the general curve $\dfrac{(n-1)(n-2)}{2}$. We know by 8] that the number of variable intersections with the Jacobian is

$$n^2-n-2 = 3n(n-1)-2(n^2-n+1).$$

Theorem 11] *When the base points of a net are simple they are double points for the Jacobian.*

If we draw a tangent from a general point to the corresponding curve of a Laguerre net, we get $n-1$ collinear points of which two are adjacent. Hence the pencil of curves through them are tangent to one another.

Theorem 12] *If tangents be drawn from a general point to the corresponding curves of the Laguerre net, the points of contact lie on the Jacobian curve.*

CHAPTER V

NON-LINEAR SYSTEMS OF CURVES

§ 1. General formulation

ALL of the systems of curves which we have considered so far have been linear systems, whether given by base points, or by conditions of apolarity. It is time to consider more general systems. The theory of these is much less complete and much more difficult. We saw in the last book that the theory of non-linear series of point groups on a curve is more difficult and less satisfactory than the theory of linear series; the difficulty continues here. We see at the very start that Bertini's precious theorem that the general curve may not have a variable singular point is lacking.

How shall we indicate the general curve of a k-parameter algebraic system ? We first write the general curve of order n in the shape

$$\sum a_{qr}x^q y^r = 0 \qquad q+r \leqslant n.$$

These curves are in one-to-one correspondence with points of a projective space of $N = \dfrac{n(n+3)}{2}$ dimensions. A k-parameter system of curves will correspond to a k-dimensional algebraic variety therein, and this we may write

$$a_{qr} = a_{qr}(X_0, X_1,..., X_k) \qquad F(X_0, X_1,..., X_k) = 0,$$

The general form for a k-parameter system of curves becomes, in this way,*

$$f(x, y, X_0, X_1,..., X_k) = 0 \qquad F(X_0, X_1,..., X_k) = 0. \tag{1}$$

We shall, for the present, confine our attention to one-parameter systems, which we write

$$f(x, y, X, Y) = 0, \tag{2}$$

$$F(X, Y) = 0. \tag{3}$$

---

* I cannot find out that any previous writer has used this form for the general equation, even in the simple case of a one-parameter system, though Clebsch[4] uses it for conics and would, doubtless, have used it for other curves had he been interested in the problem.

If we use y' to indicate the total derivative of y with regard to x, we have

$$\frac{\partial f}{\partial x} + \frac{\partial f}{\partial y} y' = 0,$$

eliminating X and Y between this equation and the equations (2) and (3), we get

$$\chi(x, y, y') = 0.$$

The degree in y' which we have called N, the index of the system, gives the number of curves through an arbitrary point of the plane. Conversely, if we have an equation of this type, and if it have algebraic integrals, we have a one-parameter system of algebraic curves neatly expressed. Unfortunately the integrals are usually not algebraic; it is not easy to tell whether we have algebraic solutions or not, and the equation as it stands does not give a great deal of information about the curves any way.*

We return to equation (3), which we assume to be irreducible, while f is also assumed to be irreducible, and not representable by a reducible combination of f and F. The genus p of the general curve f in x and y, and the genus P of F, are two important invariants, the latter being called the 'genus' of the system. It will be unaltered by any birational transformation of the curve F, or of the (x, y) plane. It is worth noting that a given system of curves can be written in an infinite number of ways. We can replace X and Y by any pair obtained from them by a Cremona transformation of their plane, or we may replace equations (2) and (3) by

$$\bar{F}(X, Y)f(x, y, X, Y) + F(X, Y)\bar{f}(x, y, X, Y) = F(X, Y) = 0,$$

where $\bar{f}$ and $\bar{F}$ are arbitrary polynomials. A finite number of these curves may be different from any curve in the original system. The same phenomenon may appear when we write our system of curves in tangential coordinates:

$$\phi(u, v, U, V) = \Phi(U, V) = 0.$$

Here the curves corresponding to limiting values may be different from anything which we had before. For instance, a system of confocal conics can be written in two different ways:

$$(b^2+\lambda)x^2+(a^2+\lambda)y^2-(a^2+\lambda)(b^2+\lambda) = 0,$$
$$(a^2+\lambda)u^2+(b^2+\lambda)v^2-1 = 0.$$

The limiting curves in point coordinates are the two axes and the line at infinity; the limiting envelopes are the foci on the major axis, those on the minor axis, and the circular points at infinity. With this warning we shall drop tangential coordinates for the rest of this chapter.

If the genus of a one-parameter system be 0, we may express X and Y rationally in terms of a parameter z, substituting in (2) we get the simple form

$$f(x, y, z) = 0.$$

Theorem 1] *A rational one-parameter system of curves may always be obtained as the orthogonal projections on a fixed plane of sections of a surface by planes parallel to the first one.**

Let us try to generalize this theorem to a system of any genus. The general rotation of space about the origin may be expressed as a homogeneous linear ternary collineation where the coefficients have a common denominator which, like the numerators, is a homogeneous polynomial of the second degree in four independent homogeneous Eulerian parameters.† Let us express these parameters rationally in terms of X and Y. This amounts to finding a rotation of the (x, y, z) space which will carry the plane $z = 0$ and the cylinder (2) into

$$U(X, Y)x+V(X, Y)y+W(X, Y)z = 0 \qquad \psi(x, y, z, X, Y) = 0.$$

Eliminating X and Y, we get

$$\theta(x, y, z) = 0.$$

Our original curves are congruent to the sections cut from this surface by the planes

$$U(X, Y)x+V(X, Y)y+W(X, Y)z = 0 \qquad F(X, Y) = 0. \qquad (4)$$

These planes envelop a cone with the same genus as the system.

Theorem 2] *The curves of a one-parameter system are congruent*

---

* De Jonquières erroneously assumed that every one-parameter system could be obtained in this way. The error is corrected in De Jonquières[3], where it is simply stated that most of the results previously obtained are not to be taken as literally true.

† Cf. Study[2], p. 176.

to the curves cut from a surface by the tangent planes to a cone whose genus is that of the system.

We have once or twice referred to the 'index' of the system, the number of curves through an arbitrary point. This is at once seen to be as follows:

Theorem 3] *If a one-parameter system of curves be given by equations* (2) *and* (3), *its index will be the number of intersections of the curves* (2) *and* (3) *of the* (X, Y) *plane which depend on* x *and* y.

Let the order of f in X and Y be ν, while its order in x and y is n, and the order of F is ν', and if at the intersections which are fixed the multiplicities for f are $R_1, R_2,...$ and for F, $S_1, S_2,...$, the index N is given by

$$N = \nu\nu' - \sum R_i S_i. \tag{5}$$

§ 2. Singular points, and the envelope

The next Cremona invariant we shall seek is the 'grade' of the system, that is to say, the order of the characteristic series. If the curves f have fixed points of multiplicity $s_1, s_2,...$, the grade G is
$$G = n^2 - \sum s_i^2.$$

These fixed singular points do not by any means exhaust all that may appear. For a singular point we have the equations

$$\frac{\partial f}{\partial x} = \frac{\partial f}{\partial y} = \frac{\partial f}{\partial 1} = 0.$$

We find the resultant of these three. There are various possibilities:

A) It vanishes identically. Then every curve of the two-parameter system (2) has one or more singular points.

B) It contains F as a factor. Then every curve of our one-parameter system has at least one singular point. These points may be fixed or trace certain curves.

C) The resultant is a polynomial different from F. The general curve has no singular points, but some curves have.

D) For some curves f is reducible with a multiple factor. It is to be noted that, by assumption, the general curve f is not reducible.

In order to be as general as possible, let us assume that the

general curve f has, besides the fixed singularities of multiplicities $s, s_2, \ldots$, variable singularities of orders $r_1, r_2, \ldots$ and
cuspidal indices $\kappa_1, \kappa_2, \ldots$. The reduction in class produced by
one of these is

$$\lambda_i = r_i(r_i - 1) + \kappa_i. \tag{6}$$

Let us assume, finally, that certain curves have factors of
orders $\nu_1, \nu_2, \ldots$ counted $t_1, t_2, \ldots$ times respectively.

The genus of the curve, or the genera of the curves traced by
variable singularities, will be unaltered by a factorable Cremona
transformation of the plane, provided such a curve be not
abolished. Let us explain what we mean by this possibility.
Suppose that we have a series of quartic curves each with a
double point at the origin, each passing through each circular
point at infinity, and each with a variable double point on the
infinite line. Their inverses in a circle whose centre is the origin
would be a new net of quartics each with a tacnode at the
origin, but with a variable direction for the tangent. Perhaps
we may describe these poetically by saying that they have a
common fixed double point, and a variable infinitely near double
point which traces no locus. If we remember that the only
sort of curve that can be abolished by a factorable Cremona
transformation is one that can be carried into a straight line,
we have

Theorem 4] *The genus of every curve traced by a variable
singular point, unless that curve be rational with no special adjoints
of any index, is an invariant for a one-parameter family of algebraic curves under all factorable Cremona transformations.*

Let us next seek the envelope of our one-parameter family.
The classical method is to introduce an explicit parameter, say
t, writing

$$f[x, y, X(t), Y(t)] = 0 \qquad F[X(t), Y(t)] \equiv 0$$

$$\frac{\partial f}{\partial X} \frac{dX}{dt} + \frac{\partial f}{\partial Y} \frac{dY}{dt} = 0 \qquad \frac{\partial F}{\partial X} \frac{dX}{dt} + \frac{\partial F}{\partial Y} \frac{dY}{dt} = 0.$$

Eliminating $\dfrac{dX}{dt}, \dfrac{dY}{dt},$

$$\frac{\partial(f, F)}{\partial(X, Y)} = 0. \tag{7}$$

The envelope will be one factor of the result of eliminating

X and Y between (2), (3), and (7). If we use homogeneous variables X, Y, and Z, we write more neatly

$$\frac{\partial(f,F)}{\partial(Y,Z)} = \frac{\partial(f,F)}{\partial(Z,X)} = \frac{\partial(f,F)}{\partial(X,Y)} = 0. \tag{8}$$

The envelope will be a factor of the eliminant, the other factors, when not constants, giving curves traced by variable singular points. We see, in fact, that if we have such a curve, x and y will be functions of the auxiliary parameter t mentioned above, and we shall have

$$f[x(t), y(t), X(t), Y(t)] \equiv F[X(t), Y(t)] = 0$$

$$\frac{\partial f}{\partial x}\frac{dx}{dt} + \frac{\partial f}{\partial y}\frac{dy}{dt} + \frac{\partial f}{\partial X}\frac{dX}{dt} + \frac{\partial f}{\partial Y}\frac{dY}{dt} = 0 \qquad \frac{\partial F}{\partial X}\frac{dX}{dt} + \frac{\partial F}{\partial Y}\frac{dY}{dt} = 0.$$

But $\qquad \dfrac{\partial f}{\partial x} = \dfrac{\partial f}{\partial y} = 0.$ Hence $\dfrac{\partial(f,F)}{\partial(X,Y)} = 0.$

Let us see if we can determine the order of the resultant in x and y, and then the orders of the different factors and the powers to which they appear. To get the order of the resultant, we assume the axes to be in general position and so seek the number of intersections with $y = 0$. The question, then, is, for how many values of x will the three curves (2), (3), and (7) have a common point, or, what comes to the same thing, for what values of x, when $y = 0$, will the curves (2) and (3) in the XY plane touch one another, or (2) have a singular point on (3)? Let P be a point of F. There will correspond thereto n values of x. To each of these there will correspond N points on F of which one is P, the others P', so that to P will correspond $n(N-1)$ points P' and to P' as many points P. The value of the correspondence is n, so that the number of coincidences is

$$2n[N + P - 1].$$

We may assume that F has only ordinary singularities, so that these coincidences only arise from contact or when a wandering singularity of the curves (2) falls on F, equally acceptable for our present purposes. This is the order of the resultant. Let us now see what reduction must be made for the locus of the movable singular points. This will be the number of intersections that adjacent curves of our system have at such a point multiplied by the order of the curve of singularities. Let (x_0, y_0)

be a variable singular point of order r_i, such that a general first polar has λ_i intersections with the curve there, as shown in (6). Suppose, first, that but one curve has this singular point. x_0 and y_0 are algebraic functions of X and Y, so that

$$\theta_1(x_0, X, Y) = \theta_2(y_0, X, Y) = 0.$$

Since, when x_0 and y_0 are given there is but one curve, it must be possible to find X and Y as rational functions of x_0 and y_0 and write a new set of equations for our system of curves, namely,

$$\bar{f}(x, y, x_0, y_0) = \bar{F}(x_0, y_0) = 0. \tag{9}$$

Developing $\bar{f}$ in powers of $(x - x_0)$ and $(y - y_0)$,

$$\bar{f}_{r_0}[(x - x_0), (y - y_0)] + \bar{f}_{r_0+1}[(x - x_0), (y - y_0)] + \ldots = 0,$$

where $\bar{f}_s$ is a polynomial of degree s with coefficients which are polynomials in x_0, y_0. To find the envelope we must have

$$\frac{\partial(\bar{f}, \bar{F})}{\partial(x_0, y_0)} = 0.$$

We see that $\dfrac{\partial(\bar{f}, \bar{F})}{\partial(x_0, y_0)}$ acts at (x_0, y_0) like a general first polar, so that the number of intersections is λ_i. We could have established the same fact by differential considerations regardless of the number of curves sharing this singular point, hence, if there be l_i such curves, the reduction is $l_i\lambda_i$. The total amount to be taken from $2n[N+P-1]$ is $\sum n_i l_i \lambda_i$. If a curve of our system be reducible with multiplicity l_s, we write

$$f_s \equiv (\psi)^{l_s}; \qquad \left(y \frac{\partial f}{\partial x}\right) = \psi^{l_s-1}\left(y \frac{\partial \psi}{\partial x}\right).$$

The number of intersections with a general first polar is $\lambda_s = l_s(l_s - 1)$, so that these curves may be included in the singular loci of orders n_i.

Theorem 5] *If a one-parameter system of curves of order n and index N have genus P, and if there be curves of order $n_1, n_2, \ldots$, where $l_1, l_2, \ldots$ curves have points where a general first polar has $\lambda_1, \lambda_2, \ldots$ intersections, the order of the envelope is*

$$2n[N+P-1] - \sum n_i l_i \lambda_i.$$

This can be put in much better form. We see that our curves cut a general line in a correspondence with the indices $N(n-1)$ and, hence, with $2N(n-1)$ coincidences. These coincidences will come only from tangency and from intersections with curves of varying singular points, as defined above. If the number of curves tangent to the line, which we define as the 'class' of the system, be M, we shall have

$$M = 2N(n-1) - \sum n_i l_i \lambda_i. \qquad (10)$$

Eliminating $\sum n_i l_i \lambda_i$, we get the order of the envelope

$$M + 2N + 2n(P-1). \qquad (11)$$

Theorem 6] *If a one-parameter family of curves be given, the order of the envelope is the sum of the class plus twice the index plus twice the product of the order of the curves and a number one less than the genus of the system.*

There is another application of equations (9), and the subsequent reasoning which enables us to advance a little the problem of the existence of curves with given singularities which we discussed in Book I, Ch. VI, § 2.* Consider the system of all curves of a given order n with δ nodes and κ cusps, it being assumed that $n > 2$. If there be one such curve, there will be an 8-parameter system, for no curve of positive genus has an infinite number of projective transformations into itself. It is easy to see in fact that the only curves carried into themselves by an infinite number of projective transformations are straight lines and conics. If, therefore, there exist one curve with δ nodes and κ cusps, there will exist ∞^8 into which this is carried by projective transformations. We may calculate the actual freedom in the following fashion. If we have a geometric variety of any sort whose points depend on k independent variables $u_1, u_2, ..., u_k$, its dimensionality is k, which is one more than the dimensionality of the flat variety of tangents, as that depends on k homogeneous parameters $du_1, du_2, ..., du_k$. We thus get the dimensionality of the series cut on a curve of a system by the other curves, by adding 1 to the dimensionality of the linear series cut by the infinitely near curves. Now we have just seen that the number of intersections of two infinitely near curves at a singular point is the number of intersections the curve has with the general first polar, and so 2 for a node and 3 for a cusp, hence the order of the linear series cut by the infinitely near curves is

$$n^2 - 2\delta - 3\kappa = m + n.$$

* Cf. Severi-Löffler, pp. 307-10, and Segre, Beniamino².

The complete linear series will be that cut by all adjoints of order n which are tangent at the cusps, or, what amounts to the same thing, the sum of the series cut by all first polars, and that cut by all straight lines. The dimension of the system of curves being one greater than that of the linear system of point groups is

$$r+1 = m+n-p+i+1.$$

On the other hand, the apparent freedom is

$$\frac{n(n+3)}{2} - \delta - 2\kappa = 3n+p-1-\kappa$$
$$= m+n-p+1.$$

Theorem 7] *If there exist irreducible curves with δ nodes and κ cusps, the number of conditions which they impose is $\delta+2\kappa-i$, where i is the index of specialization of the series which is the sum of those cut by first polars and by straight lines.*

Reverting to the equation of the apparent freedom, we see that if $3n > \kappa$, the apparent freedom, and hence the real freedom, is greater than $p-1$, the dimension of the canonical series, so that $i = 0$.

Theorem 8] *If there exist a curve with a certain number of nodes and cusps, whose order exceeds one-third the number of cusps, then each node imposes one condition and each cusp two.*

This does not show that the curve exists; the conditions might cause it to become reducible.

§ 3. The inflexions

To find the inflexions of our general curve f, we must find its intersections with the Hessian, discarding those at the singular points, unless there be inflexions included there also, as in the case of a figure 8. We must eliminate X and Y between F, f, and its Hessian h. This Hessian

$$h(x, y, X, Y) = 0$$

is of order $3(n-2)$ in x and y, and 3ν in X and Y. It has the multiplicity $3R_i$ where f has the multiplicity R_i, and F the multiplicity S_i, hence the index of the system of Hessians is $3N$. To find the order of the eliminant amounts to finding how many points of a general line in the (x, y) plane are on f and the corresponding h. If a point P be taken on the line, there will correspond N points on F, and $3N(n-2)$ points P'. To each P' will correspond $3N$ points on F, and so $3Nn$ points P'. The degree of the eliminant is, thus, $6N(n-1)$. We have, by Plücker's equations,

$$n+\iota = 2m+2(p-1).$$

If there be a point of multiplicity r_i, cuspidal index κ_i, and λ_i intersections with the general first polar, we have

$$m = n(n-1)- \sum \lambda_i \qquad 2(p-1) = n(n-3)- \sum r_i(r_i-1)$$
$$\lambda_i = r_i(r_i-1)+\kappa_i \qquad \iota = 3n(n-2)-3\sum \lambda_i + \sum \kappa_i.$$

Hence our point absorbs $3\lambda_i-\kappa_i$ intersections with the Hessian. The degree of the locus of inflexions is thus,

$$6N(n-1)-3 \sum n_i l_i \lambda_i - \sum n_i l_i \kappa_i.$$

But from (10), $\qquad 3M = 6N(n-1)-3 \sum n_i l_i \lambda_i.$

Hence the order sought is

$$3M+ \sum n_i l_i \kappa_i.$$

Theorem 9] *If a one-parameter family of curves be given, no curve being reducible with a multiple factor, the locus of the points of inflexion is a curve of order $3M+ \sum n_i l_i \kappa_i$ where M is the class of the system, and variable singular points of cuspidal indices κ_i are shared by l_i curves, and trace curves of orders n_i.*

Theorem 10] *If a one-parameter system of curves have no variable singular point with a cuspidal index greater than 0, the order of the locus of the inflexions is three times the class of the system.*

It might seem as though this theorem went wrong in the case of a pencil of curves of the third order with nine common inflexions. However, the locus we seek is the twelve lines, each of which contains three inflexions, and it is easy to show by Chasles-Cayley-Brill that four of the curves touch a general line.

Let us examine whether theorem 5] of the last chapter applies to our more general systems. Let us write

$$F \equiv A_1 X+A_2 Y+A_{20}X^2+2A_{11}XY+A_{02}Y^2+\dots$$
$$f \equiv (a_1 x+a_2 y+a_{20}x^2+2a_{11}xy+a_{02}y^2+\dots)+$$
$$+(b_0+b_1 x+b_2 y+b_{20}x^2+2b_{11}xy+b_{02}y^2+\dots)X+$$
$$+(c_0+c_1 x+c_2 y+c_{20}x^2+2c_{11}xy+c_{02}y^2+\dots)Y+$$
$$+\quad . \quad . \quad . \quad . \quad . \quad . \quad . \quad . \quad . \quad . \quad . \quad .$$

$$x_1 \frac{\partial f}{\partial x} + y_1 \frac{\partial f}{\partial y} + \frac{\partial f}{\partial 1}$$

$$\equiv [a_1 x_1 + a_2 y_1 + \{(n-1)a_1 + 2a_{20}x_1 + 2a_{11}y_1\}x + $$
$$+ \{(n-1)a_2 + 2a_{11}x_1 + 2a_{02}y_1\}y + ...] + $$
$$+ [nb_0 + b_1 x_1 + b_2 y_1 + \{(n-1)b_1 + 2b_{20}x_1 + 2b_{11}y_1\}x + $$
$$+ \{(n-1)b_2 + 2b_{11}x_1 + 2b_{02}y_1\}y + ...]X + $$
$$+ [nc_0 + c_1 x_1 + c_2 y_1 + \{(n-1)c_1 + 2c_{20}x_1 + 2c_{11}y_1\}x + $$
$$+ \{(n-1)c_2 + 2c_{11}x_1 + 2c_{02}y_1\}y + ...]Y + $$
$$+ \quad . \quad . \quad . \quad . \quad . \quad . \quad . \quad . \quad . \quad . \quad . \quad . \quad . \quad . \quad . \quad . \quad . \quad .$$

If we solve the last two equations for X and Y, which, mercifully, we are not required to do, and substitute in F, we get the power-series development for the tangential curve of the point (x_1, y_1). The conditions for a double point at $x = y = 0$ will not involve X and Y above the first degree, and would be the same if all higher powers were everywhere lacking. But when they are lacking, we fall back upon a pencil of curves, and the theorem 5] of the last chapter; there will be a singular point of the tangential locus at $(0, 0)$ if it is singular for a curve of the system, or an inflexion.

Theorem 11] *If tangents be drawn to the curves of a one-parameter system from an arbitrary point, the locus of their points of contact will have singular points only at singular points or inflexions of curves of the system, and, conversely, every such variable inflexion or singular point is singular for the tangential locus.*

§ 4. Projective theorems

Our next task is to prove a number of simple projective theorems, some of which were given in an article by De Jonquières mentioned at the beginning of the present chapter, though his proofs were sketchy, to say the least. We rewrite our equations

$$f(x, y, X, Y) = 0, \tag{2}$$

$$F(X, Y) = 0, \tag{3}$$

$$x \frac{\partial f}{\partial x_1} + y \frac{\partial f}{\partial y_1} + \frac{\partial f}{\partial 1} = 0.$$

This also is of order ν in X and Y, and behaves at the singular points of F as f does for a general (x_1, y_1).

Theorem 12] *The index of a one-parameter family of curves is the class of the envelope of the line polars of a general point.*

Let us take an arbitrary point N in the plane and draw tangents thence to the curves of our system. The tangential locus which we have already discussed will have multiplicity N at the point whence the tangents were drawn; it will also cut a line through this point in the M points of contact with curves of the system.

Theorem 13] *If tangents be drawn to the curves of a one-parameter family from a general point, the order of the tangential locus is the sum of the index and class of the given system of curves.*

Let us now seek an answer to the interesting question: How many curves of our system are tangent to a given curve ? Let this be of order n_1, class m_1, genus p_1, with a cuspidal index κ_1; we assume that it passes through no base point of the system. If P be a point of this curve, there will pass through it N curves of the system meeting this curve in $N(nn_1-1)$ other points P', and to each P' will correspond as many points P. The correspondence has the value N, so that the number of coincidences is $2N(nn_1+p-1)$.

Let us lop off the coincidences which we do not desire. First there are those which come at points with a cuspidal component greater than 0. The number of this sort is independent of everything but the index of our system, as is clearly $N\kappa_1$. The number of coincidences remaining is

$$N[2(nn_1+p_1-1)-\kappa_1] = N[2n_1(n-1)+m_1].$$

We have other undesirable coincidences arising from intersections with the loci of movable singular points or with reducible curves with a multiple factor. The number of these is n_1 times the number of such coincidences in the case of a straight line, and so is $Nn_1[2(n-1)]-n_1M$.

Hence the number of contacts is m_1N+n_1M.

Chasles's Contact Theorem 14] *If a one-parameter family of curves have index N and class M, the number tangent to a curve of order n_1 and class m_1 in general position is*[*]

$$m_1N+n_1M. \tag{12}$$

The reader may have noticed how often the two numbers

* Chasles[3], p. 300 note. No proof is given, though several have been found since.

M and *N* appear in recent formulae. They are called 'characteristics' of the system, only the latter is a birational invariant, the former is projectively invariant merely. There is a very large number, in fact an infinite number, of other projectively invariant numbers derived from the Plücker characteristics of certain associated loci and envelopes. Zeuthen has given a list of forty of these, dual in pairs except for four which are self-dual, and has found twenty-eight equations connecting them.* In the case where there is no reducible curve with a multiple factor, most of the numbers of the system can be derived from those for a simple set of nodes and cusps. The restriction is significant; we have already used it in 10].

§ 5. Systems depending on more than one parameter

A general two-parameter family of curves can be written

$$f(x, y, X, Y, Z) = F(X, Y, Z) = 0; \qquad (13)$$

the singular points of the system appear in various ways. We first write

$$\frac{\partial f}{\partial x} = \frac{\partial f}{\partial y} = \frac{\partial f}{\partial 1} = 0.$$

We then eliminate x and y. There are various possibilities:

A) The eliminant vanishes identically, or contains F as a factor. Then every curve has a singular point, or singular points. These may be fixed, or trace curves, or cover the whole plane. In the second situation there will be for each point of such a curve or curves a one-parameter sub-set with a singularity there.

B) The eliminant does not vanish identically, nor contain F as a factor. Then there is a one-parameter family of curves in our system which contain singular points not common to all curves of the system. The locus of such points is obtained by eliminating X, Y, and Z from

$$\frac{\partial f}{\partial x} = \frac{\partial f}{\partial y} = \frac{\partial f}{\partial 1} = F = 0.$$

Singular points may also come from reducible curves with multiple factors. If there be a singly infinite set of such curves, every point of the plane will be singular for some curve; if there be only a finite number, we only get a singly infinite set of

---

* Zeuthen⁴. The Danish article is followed by a fairly full French synopsis.

singular points in this way. The conics through a given point having double contact with a given conic form a good example of the first case, each line through the point counted twice being a curve of the system.

A two-parameter system of curves has three important projective characteristics; they are:

(N^2) The index of the system, or number of curves through two general points.

(NM) The number through an arbitrary point, tangent to an arbitrary line..

(M^2) The number tangent to two arbitrary lines.

The reader will understand that these expressions are purely symbolic and do not have any relation to products or powers. There is one other useful characteristic sometimes written Θ: the number of curves which pass through an arbitrary point and touch an arbitrary line there. This is self-dual, for it is the number which touch an arbitrary line and have a given point of contact on that line. It might seem as though this were (N^2), for we merely require a curve to pass through two adjacent points. Such is not the case; on the contrary,

$$(N^2) = \Theta + K \qquad \Theta = (N^2) - K = (M^2) - I,$$

where K is the total cuspidal component of a general point, and I the total inflexional component of a general line, the number of curves with three-point contact. How many curves will osculate a curve of order n_1, class m_1, genus p_1, and cuspidal component κ_1 in general position ? If P be a point on this curve, the curves of our system through it are a one-parameter set of index (N^2) and class (NM). Hence, by (12), the number tangent to our curve is $m_1(N^2) + n_1(NM) - 2\Theta$, and this gives the number of points P'. Conversely, when P' is given, there are Θ tangent curves of our system each meeting the fixed curve in $nn_1 - 2$ other points. The value of the correspondence is 2Θ, so that the number of coincidences is

$$\Theta[n_1 n + 4(p_1 - 1)] + m_1(N^2) + n_1(NM).$$

From these we must deduct $\Theta \kappa_1$ coincidences at cuspidal points, and n_1 times the number of improper coincidences in the case our curve is a straight line, namely,

$$n_1[(NM) + \Theta(n - 4) - I].$$

There will thus remain

$$m_1(N^2)+n_1I+\Theta[4n_1+4(p_1-1)-\kappa_1] = m_1K+n_1I+\Theta[3m_1+\kappa_1].$$

Theorem 15] *If a two-parameter system of curves have a total cuspidal component K for an arbitrary point, and a total inflexion component I for an arbitrary line, and if Θ of the curves touch an arbitrary line at an arbitrary point, then the number which osculate a curve of order n_1, class m_1, and cuspidal index κ_1 is*

$$m_1K+n_1I+\Theta[3m_1+\kappa_1]. \tag{14}$$

This formula will give the correct number of inflexions of a curve if we put $I = -3$. This seems a bit arbitrary, to say that a straight line has -3 inflexions, but there is this justification for it, in that it follows from Plücker's equation

$$\iota-\kappa = 3(m-n).$$

The next problem is, obviously, to find how many curves of our two-parameter system will touch two given curves in general position. It is just as easy to generalize this to the problem of finding the number of curves of a k-parameter system tangent to k given curves. Let us, then, suppose that we have a k-parameter system given by such equations as (1) and mean by (N^sM^t), $s+t = k$ the number of curves through s points and tangent to t lines, in general position, i.e. this is the order of the equation which we come to when we try to find the curves through so many points and tangent to so many lines, after extraneous factors have been thrown out. We are going to demonstrate that if k curves be given whose orders are $n_1, n_2,...,$ n_k, and whose classes are $m_1, m_2,..., m_k$ in general position, the number of curves of our system tangent thereto is

$$\prod_{i=1}^{i=k} (m_iN+n_iM). \tag{15}$$

We have seen in Chasles's theorem 14] that this formula is correct when $k = 1$. Let us assume that it holds for any $(k-1)$-parameter system. Consider a k-parameter system. Let P be a point of a kth fixed curve of order n_k, class m_k, genus p_k, and cuspidal index κ_k. The variable curves through our point P form a $(k-1)$-parameter system whose indices are (N^k),

---

* First proved by Halphen[1], p. 475. He considers a system of curves given by a differential equation. Another proof was found by Zeuthen[6], pp. 302 and 304, by reasoning from degenerate cases in a very dangerous fashion.

$(N^{k-1}M),...,(NM^{k-1})$. The number tangent to $k-1$ curves is, by hypothesis, $N \prod\limits_{i=1}^{i=k-1} (m_iN+n_iM)$, so that to P will correspond $\prod(m_iN+n_iM)N(nn_k-1)$ points P': to P' will correspond as many points P, and the value of the correspondence is $\prod(m_iN+n_iM)N$, so that the number of coincidences is

$$2 \prod_{i=1}^{i=k-1} (m_iN+n_iM)N[nn_k+(p_k-1)].$$

From these we must deduct, in the first place,

$$\kappa_k\prod(m_iN+n_iM)N$$

coincidences at points with a cuspidal index above 0, and n_k times the number of improper coincidences when we apply this formula to a straight line, namely,

$$n_k\left\{ 2 \prod_{i=1}^{i=k-1} (m_iN+n_iM)N(n-1) - \prod_{i=1}^{i=k-1} (m_iN+n_iM)M \right\}$$

We have left

$$2 \prod_{i=1}^{i=k-1} (m_iN+n_iM)[N\{2n_k+2(p_k-1)\}-N\kappa_k+Mn_k]$$
$$= \prod_{i=1}^{i=k} (m_iN+n_iM). \qquad (15)$$

Theorem 16] *The number of curves of a k-parameter system tangent to k given curves of orders $n_1, n_2,..., n_k$ and classes $m_1, m_2,..., m_k$ in general position is $\prod\limits_{i=1}^{i=k} (m_iN+n_iM)$, where (N^sM^t) indicates the number of curves through s general points and tangent to t general lines.*

There are not a few enumerative problems whose answers take the form $\prod\limits_{i=1}^{i=k} (\alpha_iN+\beta_iM)$, where α_i, β_i are numbers independent of the system of curves.* In fact the literature dealing with similar problems, especially in the case of conics, is quite extensive.† It is also true that a good many mathematicians look askance at the methods employed, which frequently consist in finding the number of solutions to a problem in a limiting or special case, and reasoning back to the number of solutions in the general case. The initiator of the general proceeding was

---

* Zeuthen⁶, pp. 306 ff.   † Cf. Zeuthen⁵, Part III, ch. 3, pp. 290 ff.

Schubert.* It is certain that he and his followers have succeeded in solving a good many problems that have baffled
others, but a doubt often remains as to whether the reasoning
is legitimate and the answers correct. Geometers of the first
rank, such as Severi and Study, have held divergent opinions
on these questions.† A better foundation for the whole theory
has recently been developed by van der Waerden through a
study of the specialization of figures,‡ and through the consideration of topological indices first developed by Lefschetz.§

* See especially Schubert[2].
† See Severi[3] and Severi[4]—Study[3] and Study[4].
‡ van der Waerden[1].   § van der Waerden[2].

CHAPTER VI

THE GENERAL CREMONA TRANSFORMATION

§ 1. Fundamental properties

WE have had frequent occasion to discuss Cremona transformations in the course of our work, and found how useful they were in simplifying curves. The only transformations we have discussed have been linear ones, quadratic ones, and De Jonquières ones, all of which are factorable in the sense that they can be split into successions of collineations and standard quadratic transformations. The time has now come to take up the general Cremona transformation and examine it for its own sake. We shall see at once that we have here merely a question of studying certain very special types of linear nets.*

Suppose that we have a birational transformation from a point (x) in a plane π to a point (x') in a plane π'. We shall have equations

$$\rho'x_1' = \phi_1(x_1, x_2, x_3) \quad \rho'x_2' = \phi_2(x_1, x_2, x_3) \quad \rho'x_3' = \phi_3(x_1, x_2, x_3). \quad (1)$$

The polynomials ϕ_i are supposed to be irreducible and of order n. This number is called the 'degree' of the transformation. The curves
$$u_1'\phi_1 + u_2'\phi_2 + u_3'\phi_3 = 0,$$
which lie in the plane π, and which correspond to straight lines in the plane π', are called by the cacophonous name of 'homaloids'. Their totality is a 'homaloidal net'. In order that this transformation shall be birational, or a Cremona transformation, it is necessary and sufficient that two of them should have but one variable intersection. They must clearly be rational curves. Our curves must pass through certain points $P_1, P_2, \ldots$ with multiplicities $r_1, r_2, \ldots$. These points are called 'fundamental points' of the transformation in the plane π. If a variable point approach a fundamental point as a limiting position, its mate in the transformation will approach some definite limiting position, depending upon the method of approach. In the plane π' there will be a curve, all of whose points correspond to the

---

* An excellent bibliography will be found in 'Topics', which has been of the greatest use to me in writing these last three chapters. A very extensive work is that of Hudson. Cremona's first work is reprinted in Cremona[1].

fundamental point in π. Such a curve shall be said to be 'fundamental' in the plane. We shall presently see that it is a fundamental curve of the net in that plane in the sense of Ch. I.

Since two homaloids have but one non-fundamental intersection, we have
$$\sum_i r_i^2 = n^2 - 1.$$

Since they are rational, and a variable curve in a net cannot have a variable singular point by Bertini's theorem 10] of Book I, Ch. VII,
$$(n-1)(n-2) - \sum r_i(r_i-1) = 0.$$
From these equations we get
$$\sum r_i^2 = n_i^2 - 1 \qquad \sum r_i = 3(n-1) \tag{2}$$
$$\sum \frac{r_i(r_i+1)}{2} = \frac{n(n+3)}{2} - 2.$$

We learned in theorem 16] that the base of a net of rational curves has no superabundance; this last equation shows that no further conditions are imposed on the curves of a homaloidal net than those imposed by the base point.

Theorem 1] *The homaloids of a net are subjected to no restrictions other than those imposed by the fundamental points, and these are independent of one another.*

If we eliminate the multipliers ρ' from equations (1), we get
$$x_i' \phi_k(x_1,x_2,x_3) - x_k' \phi_i(x_1,x_2,x_3)$$
$$= x_j' \phi_k(x_1,x_2,x_3) - x_k' \phi_j(x_1,x_2,x_3) = 0.$$
These equations will have, *ex hypothesi*, but one solution dependent on (x'), so that we shall have
$$\rho x_1 = \phi_1'(x_1',x_2',x_3') \quad \rho x_2 = \phi_2'(x_1',x_2',x_3') \quad \rho x_3 = \phi_3'(x_1',x_2',x_3'). \tag{3}$$
Here is the inverse of our given transformation. The curves ϕ_i' are the homaloids of π'. If we take a line and a homaloid in π,
$$u_1 x_1 + u_2 x_2 + u_3 x_3 = 0 \qquad u_1' \phi_1 + u_2' \phi_2 + u_3' \phi_3 = 0,$$
the number of variable intersections is n, hence the corresponding curves
$$u_1 \phi_1' + u_2 \phi_2' + u_3 \phi_3' = 0 \qquad u_1' x_1' + u_2' x_2' + u_3' x_3' = 0$$
have n variable intersections.

Theorem 2] *A Cremona transformation of the plane and its inverse are, necessarily, of the same order.*

It is an interesting fact that this theorem is not true in spaces of more than two dimensions.

Let us look for a fundamental curve ψ' in π', that is to say, a curve all of whose points correspond to a single point (y). We shall have three equations:

$$y_j \phi_k' - y_k \phi_j' = \theta_i(x_1', x_2', x_3') \psi'(x_1', x_2', x_3').$$

These three equations give two linearly independent homaloids which include the fundamental curve ψ'. It will therefore form a part of a pencil of homaloids. The general homaloid cannot have a variable intersection with it, as then the general straight line in the other plane would go through (y). A homaloid which meets this fundamental curve at any but a fundamental point must include it all.

Theorem 3] *A fundamental curve of a Cremona transformation is a fundamental curve of the corresponding linear net in the sense defined in Ch. I. It forms a part of a pencil of homaloids, the variable parts corresponding to lines of a pencil through the corresponding fundamental point of the other plane.*

If our point (y) in the equation above lay on a pencil of homaloids, and not on other homaloids, then the curve ψ' would meet the lines of a pencil, and not other lines, which is absurd.

Theorem 4] *The only points which can correspond to curves are fundamental ones.*

Suppose, conversely, that we have a fundamental curve of a homaloidal net. Since it cannot share a non-fundamental point with a homaloid unless the latter include it, it must correspond to a point, not a curve, in the other plane, and so be a fundamental curve of the transformation.

Theorem 5] *The fundamental curves of a homaloidal net are fundamental for the corresponding Cremona transformation.*

What is the Jacobian of a homaloidal net ? It is the locus of additional singular points of curves of the net. But since the general curve is rational, the additional singularities can only come in when a homaloid becomes reducible. But a homaloid, reducible or no, with an additional singular point would seem to correspond to a straight line with a singular point, which is absurd. Hence one part of such a reducible homaloid must be fundamental, or the Jacobian is composed of fundamental curves. Conversely, if we take a point on a fundamental curve, all the homaloids but one through that point have the same tangent, and that one is reducible with a double point there, a property characteristic of points on the Jacobian only.

Theorem 6] *The Jacobian of a Cremona transformation is composed of fundamental curves, and every point on a fundamental curve lies on the Jacobian.*

We shall have to sharpen this theorem somewhat when there are infinitely close fundamental points, and multiply counting fundamental curves.

Lemma. *If the curves of a linear system do not have a common tangent at a base point, it is an ordinary singularity for the general curve that has a singularity there.*

We see, in fact, that the condition for any singularity other than ordinary is quadratic, unless all the curves have a common tangent.

Theorem 7] *If the fundamental points of a Cremona transformation be all distinct, they are ordinary singular or non-singular points for the general homaloid.*

Suppose that such a singular point is O_3 of order r_1. Our homaloids may be written

$$\rho' x_1' = x_3^{n-r_1} \theta_i^{r_1}(x_1, x_2, x_3) + \dots .$$

The three polynomials θ_i have no common factor not a constant, for if they did so, all homaloids would be tangent at that point, or we should have clustering fundamental points. If we put $x_3 = 1$, $x_2 = \lambda x_1$ and divide out $x_1^{r_1}$, we get

$$\rho' x_1' = \theta_i^{r_1}(1, \lambda) + x_1 \Phi.$$

If we allow x_1 to approach 0, then (x') will approach a definite limiting position on the rational fundamental curve

$$\rho' x_1' = \theta_i^{r_1}(1, \lambda).$$

Theorem 8] *A fundamental curve at a finite distance from all others will correspond to a rational fundamental curve whose order is the multiplicity of the point.*

The second of our equations (2) gives the sum of the orders

of the fundamental points, and we see that this is the order of the Jacobian.

Theorem 9] *If the fundamental points be all distinct, the order of each will be the order of the corresponding fundamental curve, which will appear but once as a factor of the Jacobian.*

It is to be noted that this method breaks down when we have clustering singular points, except for the leader of a cluster. Consider the quadratic transformation

$$\rho'x_1' = x_1^2 \qquad \rho'x_2' = x_1x_2 \qquad \rho'x_3' = x_2x_3.$$

The point O_3 in π is certainly fundamental. But if we put $x_3 = 1$, $x_2 = \lambda x_1$ and divide by x_1, we get, when $x_1 = 0$,

$$x_1' = 0 \qquad x_2' = 0 \qquad x_3' = \lambda,$$

which looks as though this fundamental point corresponded to a single point. To get the real facts we write the inverse transformation

$$\rho x_1 = x_1'x_2' \qquad \rho x_2 = x_2'^2 \qquad \rho x_3 = x_1'x_3'.$$

We see that the line $x_2' = 0$ corresponds to O_3. The Jacobian is

$$\begin{vmatrix} x_2' & x_1' & 0 \\ 0 & 2x_2' & 0 \\ x_3' & 0 & x_1' \end{vmatrix} \equiv 2x_1'x_2'^2,$$

so that the fundamental line mentioned appears twice as a factor.

§ 2. Nöther's factorization theorem

In theorem 11] of Ch. II of the present book we found that all infinite linear systems of rational curves could be reduced by a factorable Cremona transformation to one of a small number of types. When we limit ourselves to a two-parameter net of rational curves, we see that the only irreducible type is that of all straight lines of a plane. If, therefore, we have a Cremona transformation T, and if S be the factorable Cremona transformation that carries its homaloids into the totality of lines, then the transformation TS^{-1} carries lines into lines and is a collineation C, or

$$T = SC,$$

which shows that T is factorable. We thus get the magnificent result known as

Nöther's Factorization Theorem 10] *Every Cremona trans-*
formation can be factored into a product of collineations and
*standard quadratic transformations.**

The history of this theorem is curious. It stood unchallenged
for some thirty years till Segre[6] showed that the usual proof
was invalid for certain arrangements of the fundamental points
It is said that Nöther shed tears when he heard of this. There
was no need to do so. A valid proof was presently found by
Castelnuovo[7] using a De Jonquières transformation. One of the
best proofs is Alexander, q.v.

Suppose that we have two successive Cremona transformations:

$$\rho' x_i' = \phi_i(x_1, x_2, x_3)$$
$$\sigma'' x_i'' = \theta_i(x_1', x_2', x_3')$$
$$= \theta_i(\phi_1, \phi_2, \phi_3)$$
$$\frac{\partial(x_1'', x_2'', x_3'')}{\partial(x_1, x_2, x_3)} = K \frac{\partial(x_1'', x_2'', x_3'')}{\partial(x_1', x_2', x_3')} \frac{\partial(x_1', x_2', x_3')}{\partial(x_1, x_2, x_3)}. \quad (4)$$

The Jacobian of the product is made up of the Jacobians of
the two factors unless a part of the Jacobian of the first factor
is fundamental for the inverse of the second.

Theorem 11] *The fundamental curves of a Cremona trans-*
formation are composed of the transforms of the fundamental lines
of the factor quadratic transformations except in so far as a point
which is fundamental for one factor is also fundamental for the
inverse of the product of the preceding factors.

Theorem 12] *The irreducible fundamental curves of a Cremona*
transformation are rational curves, each determined by a normal
base.

In the quadratic transformation which we considered on
page 446 there are but two distinct fundamental points, with
a third nestling close to one. The fundamental curves of the
inverse transformation were two lines, of which one was counted
twice in the Jacobian. Here is another illustrative example:

$$\rho' x_1' = x_1(x_1 - x_2)x_3$$
$$\rho' x_2' = x_2(x_1 - x_2)x_3 \quad (5)$$
$$\rho' x_3' = \phi'^3(1, 1)\psi^2(x_1, x_2)x_3 - \psi^2(1, 1)\phi^3(x_1, x_2).$$

* Nöther[8], p. 167.

The homaloids are cubics with a node at O_3 and four simple fixed points, namely, $(1, 1, 1)$ and the intersections of

$$x_3 = 0 \qquad \phi^3(x_1, x_2) = 0.$$

The inverse transformation is

$$\rho x_1 = [\phi^3(1, 1)\psi^2(x_1', x_2') - x_3'(x_1' - x_2')]x_1'$$
$$\rho x_2 = [\phi^3(1, 1)\psi^2(x_1', x_2') - x_3'(x_1' - x_2')]x_2' \qquad (6)$$
$$\rho x_3 = \psi^2(1, 1)\phi^3(x_1', x_2').$$

The homaloids are cubics with a node at O_3 and a fixed tangent there, i.e. an infinitely near simple base point. If we form the Jacobian of the inverse transformation (5) it will be found to contain the factors $(x_1 - x_2)^2 x_3$, which correspond to O_3. We may say that the double point corresponds to the reducible conic $(x_1 - x_2)x_3 = 0$, and the infinitely near single point to the line $x_1 - x_2 = 0$. We shall develop this idea in more detail presently.

§ 3. Applications of the factorization theorem

If a point P be fundamental of order r_i and at a finite distance from all other fundamental points, or else the leader of a cluster, then a line through it meets a general homaloid $n - r_i$ times in variable points. Corresponding thereto we shall have the same number of variable intersections of a general line with so much of a reducible homaloid as does not correspond to the point P_i. This shows that the corresponding fundamental curve is of order r_i. A curve of order ν with the multiplicity s_i at P_i will have $n\nu - r_i s_i$ variable intersections with a general homaloid, and so will transform into a curve that is reducible and contains the curve of order r_i as a factor s_i times.

When the fundamental point P is included in the interior or end of a train we cannot, unfortunately, proceed so simply; the facts are, however, the same, as we shall proceed to show indirectly.

Consider two Cremona transformations S and T which come in that order. What of the product TS? What are the fundamental points? They are, I) fundamental points of S which are not carried into curves which are fundamental for T, II) the S^{-1} transforms of those of T which are not fundamental for S^{-1}.

The fundamental curves are, I) those of S which are not carried into points fundamental for T, and II) the S^{-1} transforms of those of T which are not fundamental for S^{-1}. Suppose, now, that S is a Cremona transformation which has the property that an irreducible fundamental curve of any order, say ν, with any permissible multiplicities $s_1, s_2, \ldots$ at the fundamental points, goes into a curve which is reducible, containing the fundamental curve of S^{-1} which corresponds to P exactly s_i times for P_i. Let T be a standard quadratic transformation. Consider TS. If we take a fundamental point of TS of type I), our fundamental point considered as a point of our given curve is carried by TS into the T transform of a certain curve counted s_i times. If it be a point of type II) looked on as a point of our given curve it will go into s_i times the corresponding line of the quadratic transformation T. Hence TS has the property assumed for S.

Theorem 13] *If a curve have any set of permissible multiplicities at the fundamental points of a Cremona transformation, it will be carried into a reducible curve which contains each fundamental curve of the other plane a number of times equal to the sum of the multiplicities of the corresponding fundamental points.*

Suppose that S is a transformation which has the property that each factor of the Jacobian appears to a degree equal to the sum of the multiplicities of the infinitely near fundamental points of the inverse transformation that correspond thereto. We wish to show that the same applies to TS. To be general, let us assume that each of the fundamental points of T is fundamental for S^{-1}. Then S may be written

$$x_1' = \psi_1 \theta_2 \theta_3 \qquad x_2' = \psi_2 \theta_3 \theta_1 \qquad x_3' = \psi_3 \theta_1 \theta_2, \qquad (7)$$

and, since T is a standard quadratic transformation, we write TS

$$x_1'' = \theta_1 \psi_2 \psi_3 \qquad x_2'' = \theta_2 \psi_3 \psi_1 \qquad x_3'' = \theta_3 \psi_1 \psi_2.$$

If we have three curves of the same order $\chi\phi_1$, $\chi\phi_2$, $\chi\phi_3$, we find by a skilful use of Euler's theorem, or the geometrical property of the Jacobian,

$$\frac{\partial(\chi\phi_1, \chi\phi_2, \chi\phi_3)}{\partial(x_1, x_2, x_3)} \equiv (\chi)^3 \frac{\partial(\phi_1, \phi_2, \phi_3)}{\partial(x_1, x_2, x_3)}.$$

Hence, since $\theta_1\theta_2\theta_3 x_i'' = x_j'x_k'$, we have

$$(\theta_1\theta_2\theta_3)^3 \frac{\partial(x_1'', x_2'', x_3'')}{\partial(x_1, x_2, x_3)} = \frac{\partial(x_2'x_3', x_3'x_1', x_1'x_2')}{\partial(x_1, x_2, x_3)}$$

$$\frac{\partial(x_2'x_3', x_3'x_1', x_1'x_2')}{\partial(x_1, x_2, x_3)} = 2\,x_1'x_2'x_3'\frac{\partial(x_1', x_2', x_3')}{\partial(x_1, x_2, x_3)}.$$

Now
$$x_i' = \theta_1\theta_2\theta_3\,\frac{\psi_i}{\theta_i}$$

$$\frac{\partial(x_1', x_2', x_3')}{\partial(x_1, x_2, x_3)} = \theta_1^3\theta_2^3\theta_3^3 \begin{vmatrix} \dfrac{\theta_1\dfrac{\partial\psi_1}{\partial x_1} - \psi_1\dfrac{\partial\theta_1}{\partial x_1}}{\theta_1^2} & \cdot & \cdot & \cdot \\ \cdot & \cdot & \cdot & \cdot \\ \cdot & \cdot & \cdot & \cdot \end{vmatrix}$$

$$\frac{\partial(x_1', x_2', x_3')}{\partial(x_1, x_2, x_3)} = \theta_1\theta_2\theta_3 \begin{vmatrix} \theta_1\dfrac{\partial\psi_1}{\partial x_1} - \psi_1\dfrac{\partial\theta_1}{\partial x_1} & \cdot & \cdot & \cdot \\ \cdot & \cdot & \cdot & \cdot \\ \cdot & \cdot & \cdot & \cdot \end{vmatrix}$$

$$\frac{\partial(x_1'', x_2'', x_3'')}{\partial(x_1, x_2, x_3)} = 2\psi_1\psi_2\psi_3 \begin{vmatrix} \theta_1\dfrac{\partial\psi_1}{\partial x_1} - \psi_1\dfrac{\partial\theta_1}{\partial x_1} & \cdot & \cdot & \cdot \\ \cdot & \cdot & \cdot & \cdot \\ \cdot & \cdot & \cdot & \cdot \end{vmatrix}. \qquad (8)$$

The determinant factor here is the same as in

$$\frac{\partial(x_1', x_2', x_3')}{\partial(x_1, x_2, x_3)}.$$

It gives the fundamental curves which do not correspond to O_1, O_2, O_3 as fundamental points of S^{-1}. The orders of the multiplicity of such fundamental points will not be altered. Hence, if the order of each factor of the determinant be the sum of the orders of the infinitely close fundamental points which correspond thereto for S, it will also be so for TS. The new factors ψ_1, ψ_2, ψ_3 correspond to O_1, O_2, O_3. But these three points are either at a finite distance from other fundamental points or are leaders of trains of clustering points, and we have seen that their orders are those of the corresponding curves.

Theorem 14] *Each fundamental point of a Cremona transformation will correspond to a fundamental curve whose order is the multiplicity of the point, and each factor of a fundamental curve will appear to a total multiplicity which is the sum of its multiplicities for the infinitely near fundamental points corresponding.*

We get at once from 13] and 14]

Theorem 15] *If a Cremona transformation of order n be given with fundamental points P_1, P_2,... of orders r_1, r_2,..., then, if a curve of order x_0 have at these points the multiplicities s_1, s_2,..., the non-fundamental part of the transformed curve will have the order $nx_0 - r_1s_1 - r_2s_2 - \ldots$.*

Let P be an isolated fundamental point or the leader of a train, its coordinates being (y). We have

$$\phi_j' y_i - \phi_i' y_j = \theta_k' \psi'.$$

Hence, in π' every curve which corresponds to (y) or a point infinitely near is a factor of ψ'.

Suppose that the transformation S has clustering singular points P_i, P_{ij},... following in that order, and that the fundamental curve corresponding to each P includes as a part of itself all factors corresponding to subsequent P's. Consider $S^{-1}T$ where T is a standard quadratic transformation. A T transform of a fundamental point whose corresponding curves have this clustering property will give a new fundamental point whose curves have the property, a fundamental point of T that is also fundamental for $S^{-1}T$ will either be distinct from other fundamental points or the leader of a train.

Theorem 16] *If a Cremona transformation have a cluster of following infinitely near singular points, the fundamental curve corresponding to any point c includes in itself those which correspond to all infinitely near following points.*

Let P_i be an isolated fundamental point, or the leader of a train, its multiplicity r_i, while it has the multiplicity α_{ij} for a curve of order r_j' which corresponds to the point P_j' of the other plane. Let the curve of order r_i which corresponds to P_i in π' have the multiplicity α_{ji}' at P_j'. A homaloid which includes the curve of order r_j' and which comes from a line through P_j' will have a variable part of order $n - r_j'$ with a multiplicity $r_i - \alpha_{ij}$ at P_i. It will meet a variable line through P in $n - r_i - r_j' + a_{ij}$ variable points, and these will correspond to $n - r_j' - r_i + a_{ji}'$ variable points in π where a line through P meets the non-fundamental part of a homaloid corresponding to a line through P. Hence $a_{ij} = a'_{ji}$.

Let S be a transformation that has the property that the order of a fundamental point for a fundamental curve is the same as the order of the point that corresponds to the curve, for the curve that corresponds to the point. This is certainly the case for a transformation with distinct fundamental points such as a standard quadratic one. Consider the transformation $S^{-1}T$. The T transforms of the fundamental points of S^{-1} which are fundamental for $S^{-1}T$ will retain the property mentioned above, the fundamental points of T are either distinct from other fundamental points, or leaders of trains.

Theorem 17] *The multiplicity of the fundamental point P_i for the curve corresponding to the fundamental point P'_j is equal to the multiplicity of P'_j for the curve corresponding to P_i.*

Suppose that we have a transformation of order n, and that a certain curve of order N has multiplicities $s_1, s_2,...$ at the fundamental points of orders $r_1, r_2,...,$ and $t_1, t_2,...$ at other points. Let the corresponding curve be of order N', its multiplicities at the fundamental points $r'_1, r'_2,...,$ and at other points $t'_1, t'_2,....$ Since the two systems of points have the same superabundance for the two curves, we have

$$N(N+3) - \sum s_i(s_i+1) - \sum t_i(t_i+1)$$
$$= N'(N'+3) - \sum s'_i(s'_i+1) - \sum t'_i(t'_i+1).$$

The two curves have the same genus, so that

$$N(N-3) - \sum s_i(s_i-1) - \sum t_i(t_i-1)$$
$$= N'(N'-3) - \sum s'_i(s'_i-1) - \sum t'_i(t'_i-1).$$

We get, hence,

$$3N - \sum s_i - \sum t_i = 3N' - \sum s'_i - \sum t'_i, \tag{9}$$

$$N^2 - \sum s_i^2 - \sum t_i^2 = N'^2 - \sum s'^2_i - \sum t'^2_i. \tag{10}$$

We shall presently prove that the number of fundamental points is the same in both systems, so that $\sum 1 = \sum' 1$.

$$3(N-3) - \sum (s_i-1) - \sum (t_i-1)$$
$$= 3(N'-3) - \sum (s'_i-1) - \sum (t'_i-1),$$

$$(N-3)^2 - \sum (s_i-1)^2 - \sum (t_i-1)^2$$
$$= (N'-3)^2 - \sum (s'_i-1)^2 - \sum (t'_i-1)^2.$$

This suggests that a special adjoint is carried into a special adjoint. We saw in the second section of Ch. II that under a standard quadratic transformation the special adjoint system of any index goes into a special adjoint system of the same index, if fundamental curves be counted properly. But we learned in Nöther's factorization theorem of the present chapter that all Cremona transformations are factorable. This gives

Theorem 18] *A Cremona transformation will carry the special adjoint system of any index of a curve into the special adjoint system of the same index. of the corresponding curve, if fundamental curves be counted with the correct multiplicity. The pure adjoint system will also go into the pure adjoint system when the genus exceeds 1.*

Returning to equations (9) and (10), we get

Montesano's Theorem 19] *If a Cremona transformation carry a curve of order N with multiplicities $s_1, s_2, \ldots$ at the fundamental points and $t_1, t_2, \ldots$ elsewhere into a curve of order N' with multiplicities $s'_1, s'_2, \ldots$ at the fundamental points and $t'_1, t'_2, \ldots$ elsewhere, then*[*]

$$3N - \sum s_i - \sum t_i = 3N' - \sum s'_i - \sum t'_i, \qquad (9)$$

$$N^2 - \sum s_i^2 - \sum t_i^2 = N'^2 - \sum s_i'^2 - \sum t_i'^2. \qquad (10)$$

§ 4. The identities of Clebsch[†]

We have encountered a number of important integers in our theory of Cremona transformations; it is important to establish a series of identical relations connecting them. The theorem of Montesano just established gave us a good start. We found at the beginning of the chapter

$$\sum_i r_i^2 = n^2 - 1 \qquad \sum_i r_i = 3(n-1). \qquad (2)$$

Applying Montesano's relations (9), (10) and (2) to a fundamental curve which comes by successive transformations from a straight line determined by two fundamental points, we have

$$\sum_i \alpha_{ij} = 3r'_j - 1 \qquad \sum_j \alpha_{ij} = 3r_i - 1, \qquad (11)$$

$$\sum_i \alpha_{ij}^2 = r_j'^2 + 1 \qquad \sum_j \alpha_{ij}^2 = r_i^2 + 1. \qquad (12)$$

* Montesano[1], p. 365.   † Cf. Clebsch[3], also Hudson, ch. 2.

Since a fundamental curve meets a homaloid only at fundamental points,

$$\sum_i r_i\alpha_{ij} = nr_j' \qquad \sum_j r_j'\alpha_{ij} = nr_i. \tag{13}$$

Two different fundamental curves can meet only at fundamental points:

$$\sum_i \alpha_{ij}\alpha_{ik} = r_j'r_k' \qquad \sum_j \alpha_{ji}\alpha_{ki} = r_jr_k. \tag{14}$$

We get from (11) and (2)

$$3\sum_i r_i - \sum 1 = \sum_{ij} \alpha_{ij} \qquad \sum 1 = 9(n-1) - \sum_{ij} \alpha_{ij}$$

$$3\sum_j r_j' - \sum 1' = \sum_{ij} \alpha_{ij} \qquad \sum 1' = 9(n-1) - \sum_{ij} \alpha_{ij}$$

$$\sum 1 = \sum 1'.$$

Theorem 20] *A Cremona transformation and its inverse have the same number of fundamental points.*

Let us next look at the determinant

$$\begin{vmatrix} \alpha_{11} & \alpha_{12} & \cdot & \cdot & \cdot & \alpha_{1n} \\ \alpha_{21} & \cdot & \cdot & \cdot & \cdot & \cdot \\ \cdot & \cdot & \cdot & \cdot & \cdot & \cdot \\ \alpha_{n1} & \cdot & \cdot & \cdot & \cdot & \alpha_{nn} \end{vmatrix} = \Delta. \tag{15}$$

Squaring and comparing with (12) and (14), we get

$$\begin{vmatrix} r_1'^2+1 & r_2'r_1' & \cdot & \cdot & r_n'r_1' \\ r_1'r_2' & r_2'^2+1 & \cdot & \cdot & \cdot \\ \cdot & \cdot & \cdot & \cdot & \cdot \\ r_1'r_n' & \cdot & \cdot & \cdot & r_n'^2+1 \end{vmatrix} = \begin{vmatrix} r_1^2+1 & r_1r_2 & \cdot & \cdot & r_1r_n \\ r_2r_1 & r_2^2+1 & \cdot & \cdot & r_2r_n \\ \cdot & \cdot & \cdot & \cdot & \cdot \\ r_nr_1 & r_nr_2 & \cdot & \cdot & r_n^2+1 \end{vmatrix} = \Delta^2.$$

Expanding in terms of the 1's in the principal diagonal,

$$1^n + 1^{n-1}\sum r_i^2 + \ldots = \Delta^2.$$

The coefficients of lower powers will come from determinants like

$$\begin{vmatrix} r_1^2 & r_1r_2 & \cdot & \cdot & \cdot & r_1r_\nu \\ r_2r_1 & \cdot & \cdot & \cdot & \cdot & \cdot \\ \cdot & \cdot & \cdot & \cdot & \cdot & \cdot \\ r_\nu r_1 & \cdot & \cdot & \cdot & \cdot & r_\nu^2 \end{vmatrix} = 0.$$

$$n^2 = \Delta^2$$

$$\Delta = \pm n. \tag{16}$$

We shall next proceed to arrange our determinant in a very special order. We remember that the only conditions imposed upon a homaloid are that it should have certain multiplicities at certain fundamental points. If we group together all of the fundamental points of one order, they must appear symmetrically with regard to the various fundamental curves. Let the first rows of (15) correspond to the complete set of fundamental points P_i of one first multiplicity, the second set to points of a second multiplicity, and so on. In the same way, the first set of columns shall correspond to points P' of one multiplicity, the second set to points of a second, and so on. We thus divide the matrix into rectangles, all the rows in one rectangle corresponding to points P_i of one multiplicity, all the columns to points P'_j of one multiplicity. In such a rectangle, if a set of numbers α_{ij} appear in one row, they will appear in every other, and every possible permutation of them will appear. A similar result will hold for the columns. Let the width of such a rectangle be k, and its depth k'. Let there be π different permutations of the numbers in one row, π' permutations of the numbers in one column

$$k' \geqslant \pi \qquad k \geqslant \pi'.$$

Now the number of permutations of a set of objects is greater than the number of objects, except in two cases, A) all are alike, B) one is different from the others. If all of the α_{ij}'s were alike in one row of a rectangle, they would be all alike in every other row, and the columns would all be alike, i.e. all the α_{ij}'s in the rectangle would be alike. But if all rectangles were of this sort, the value of the determinant would be 0 and not $\pm n$. Hence A) cannot occur in each rectangle. If all the α_{ij}'s but one were alike in a row, the same would be true of a column; we should have

$$k' \geqslant \pi = k \qquad k \geqslant \pi' = k' \qquad \pi = \pi',$$

which means that the rectangle is a square.

It is important to notice next that two such squares could not share a row or a column, as some of the fundamental points of a given order would appear asymmetrically to others of that order; hence we can place such squares so that their principal diagonals fall on the principal diagonal of the determinant. Also we can fill the whole principal diagonal this way, as otherwise two rows would be alike. We thus get

Clebsch's Cremona Transformation Theorem 21] *In a Cremona transformation and its inverse, the groups of fundamental points of like multiplicity are of the same size in pairs.*

Two equivalent groups of this sort in the two transformations are defined as 'concordant'. We may also speak of a group of points and of fundamental curves as concordant. Suppose that all of the α_{ij}'s but one in a row or column have the same value r and the odd one has the value r'. The other rectangles which share rows with this first square must be of the other kind where all members are alike, hence, if we take two rows, not only in the rectangle but right across the determinant, they differ only in this, that in two places one has multiplicity r, and the other the multiplicity r', and the number of intersections is rr' instead of r^2 and r'^2, as would be the case if they had the same multiplicities everywhere. Consider the total number of intersections of the curves of order r_k' which correspond to these two rows:

$$r_k'^2 = \sum_i \alpha_{ik}\alpha_{jk} = \sum_i \alpha_{ik}^2 - r^2 - r'^2 + 2rr'.$$

But
$$\sum_i \alpha_{ik}^2 = r_k'^2 + 1$$

$$(r'-r)^2 = 1. \tag{17}$$

Theorem 22] *If a group of fundamental points be coordinated to a group of fundamental curves, then at each of these points each of the curves has the same multiplicity except that at each point one different curve has a multiplicity one more or one less than the others.**

This can be pushed a bit further. Let Q_1, Q_2 be any two fundamental points of a group. We may coordinate Q_1 with Q_1' in the other plane, and Q_2 with Q_2' in the sense that the curve of order r_k' which corresponds to Q_1' has multiplicity r' at Q_1 and r at Q_2, while the curve of order r_k' corresponding to Q_2' has multiplicity r at Q_1 and r' at Q_2. The two curves will have the same multiplicity at the other fundamental points.

Let us next take a curve in the plane π which has multiplicity s_1 at Q_1 and s_2 at Q_2. These numbers are the same as the numbers of non-fundamental intersections of the transformed curve of order v' in π' with the curves of order r_k corresponding to Q_1 and Q_2. In one case there will be $r's_1'$ intersections at Q_1', rs_2' at Q_2' and N others; in the other case rs_1' at Q_1', $r's_2'$ at Q_2' and N others:

$$s_1 = v'r_k - r's_1' - rs_2' - N$$
$$s_2 = v'r_k - rs_1' - r's_2' - N$$
$$(s_1 - s_2) = (r - r')(s_1' - s_2').$$

Either $s_1 - s_1' = s_2 - s_2'$, or $s_1 + s_1' = s_2 + s_2'$.

* Bertini⁶, p. 445. The details of the proof are ascribed to Bianchi.

Theorem 23] *If two coordinated groups of points P_1, P_2,... and P'_1, P'_2,... be given, and if any two points of the first group be given, each may be coupled with one of two points in the coordinated group in such a way that either the sum or the difference of the multiplicities of any two corresponding curves at one couple of points is equal to the corresponding sum or difference for the other couple.*

Consider a curve of order r'_k corresponding to the point P'_k. We are to compare its multiplicities α_{ik} and α_{jk} at the fundamental points P_i and P_j of multiplicities r_i and r_j respectively. Let us assume that $r_i > r_j$. Suppose, also, that $\alpha_{ik} < \alpha_{jk}$, i.e. since we are dealing with integers, $\alpha_{ik} \leqslant \alpha_{jk}+1$. Let us see whether we can find a curve of order r'_k with multiplicity $\alpha_{ik}+1$ at P_i and $\alpha_{jk}-1$ at P_j. The increase in the number of conditions imposed on this curve as compared with the fundamental curve of order r'_k given by a complete base is

$$\frac{(\alpha_{ik}+1)(\alpha_{ik}+2)}{2} - \frac{\alpha_{ik}(\alpha_{ik}+1)}{2} + \frac{\alpha_{jk}(\alpha_{jk}-1)}{2} - \frac{\alpha_{jk}(\alpha_{jk}+1)}{2}$$

$$= \alpha_{ik}+1-\alpha_{jk} \leqslant 0.$$

We are not, therefore, imposing too many conditions on the supposed curve. It will be transformed into a curve whose order, by 15], is

$$nr'_k - \sum_l \alpha_{lk}r_l - r_i + r_j = -r_i + r_j < 0.$$

This absurd result leads to

Theorem 24] *If two fundamental points be of different orders, that of higher order cannot have a lower multiplicity for any fundamental curve.*

It is to be noted that this theorem holds even when the lower multiplicity is 0. A number of interesting corollaries follow immediately.

Theorem 25] *If a fundamental curve contain a fundamental point of any order, it contains all those of higher orders.*

Theorem 26] *If two fundamental curves pass through the same fundamental point, that of lower order cannot have higher multiplicity there.*

We could not have a fundamental point which lay on no fundamental curve, for there would correspond a fundamental

* Montesano[1], p. 365.

curve through no fundamental point, but a fundamental curve meets a homaloid nowhere else. A Cremona transformation where all of the fundamental points are of the same order is called a 'symmetric' Cremona transformation. We shall determine in the next chapter what symmetric transformations actually exist.

Theorem 27] *In an unsymmetric Cremona transformation, every fundamental curve of highest order goes through every fundamental point of order above the lowest, and through at least one of the latter points.*

Suppose that some fundamental curve, not of the lowest order, goes through a point of the lowest order, some other curve of this order goes through each point of lowest order. Hence, by 26], we get

Theorem 28] *If in an unsymmetric Cremona transformation a fundamental curve not of lowest order pass through any point of lowest order, then every fundamental curve of higher order goes through every fundamental point.*

We saw in the reasoning that led up to 10] of Ch. II of this book that, since a homaloidal net can be carried over into the system of all coplanar lines, the sum of the three highest orders for fundamental points must exceed n.

Theorem 29] *The sum of the three highest orders of the fundamental points, or three highest orders of the fundamental curves, of a Cremona transformation exceeds the order of the transformation.*

Suppose that one fundamental curve is a straight line. It will pass through a fundamental point of highest order, and at least one fundamental point of the same or next highest order. It could not contain any third fundamental point, for it would have to contain the third highest then, and the sum of the multiplicities of the three highest would, by 29], give too many intersections with a homaloid. On the other hand it could not meet a homaloid in any non-fundamental point.

Theorem 30] *If in a Cremona transformation a straight line be fundamental, it will connect a point of highest multiplicity with one of next highest; the sum of these two multiplicities will be the order of the transformation.*

Theorem 31] *Unless there be two or more fundamental points of order $n/2$, if there be any fundamental straight lines, they all radiate from one point of highest multiplicity.*

§ 4. Transformations in one plane

We have so far treated the planes π and π' as if they were totally distinct. For some purposes it is more interesting to look upon a Cremona transformation as a means of carrying a plane into itself. Here certain new questions arise.

Let S^{-1} be a Cremona transformation, and T a standard quadratic transformation. The fundamental points of $S^{-1}T^{-1}$ are those of T, and the T transforms of those of S^{-1}, and these are usually different from those of S which are fundamental for TS.

Theorem 32] *A Cremona transformation and its inverse have not, usually, the same fundamental points.*

Let us look for fixed points in a Cremona transformation. The coordinates of such a point will satisfy three equations of the form
$$x_i\,\phi_j(x_1,x_2,x_3)-x_j\,\phi_i(x_1,x_2,x_3) = 0.$$

It is better to replace these equations by some others obtained by a simple geometrical device. Take a fixed point (ξ). If the corresponding points (x) and (x') be collinear with this, we have
$$\begin{vmatrix} \xi_1 & \xi_2 & \xi_3 \\ x_1 & x_2 & x_3 \\ \phi_1 & \phi_2 & \phi_3 \end{vmatrix} = 0. \tag{18}$$

Such a locus of points (x) is called an 'isologue'.* There will correspond thereto the second isologue:
$$\begin{vmatrix} \xi_1 & \xi_2 & \xi_3 \\ x'_1 & x'_2 & x'_3 \\ \phi'_1 & \phi'_2 & \phi'_3 \end{vmatrix} = 0. \tag{19}$$

The point (ξ) is called the centre. It always lies on the curve. If the three expressions $x_i\,\phi_j-x_j\,\phi_i$ be not linearly dependent with constant coefficients, the transformation is called 'non-isologous', otherwise 'isologous'; corresponding points are collinear with a fixed point.

Theorem 33] *In a non-isologous Cremona transformation, the isologues form a Laguerre net of order one greater than the order of the transformation, each passing through the fundamental points and the fixed points of the transformation.*

* Cf. De Jonquières[1].

Our equation (18) is immediately transformed into

$$\begin{vmatrix} \xi_i & \xi_j & (u\xi) \\ x_i & x_j & (ux) \\ \phi_i & \phi_j & (u\phi) \end{vmatrix} = 0.$$

If
$$(u\xi) = (ux) = 0,$$

$$(\xi_i x_j - \xi_j x_i)(u\phi) = 0.$$

If $(u\phi) \neq 0$,
$$\xi_i = \rho x_i,$$

or (x) is identical with the centre. On the other hand, the intersections of

$$(ux) = 0 \qquad (u\phi) = 0$$

are independent of (ξ).

Theorem 34] *If a point trace a straight line, the corresponding pencil of isologues will have no other variable intersections with that line.*

This we saw previously when discussing the Laguerre net.

We see from (18) that at an isolated fundamental point, or one that is the leader of a train of infinitely near fundamental points, an isologue has the multiplicity of a homaloid. More generally, if O_3 be a fundamental point, the general homaloid

$$(u\phi) = 0$$

and the isologue $\qquad x_3(\xi_2 \phi_1 - \xi_1 \phi_2) = 0$

will have the same multiplicity at O_3 and for all clustering singularities. The general isologue and the general homaloid will not have more intersections at the clustering singularities than this particular isologue and the general homaloid; on the other hand they will not have less, for these two have the number that occurs in the general case where the fundamental points do not cluster. This gives

Theorem 35] *The general isologue behaves at a fundamental point as does the general homaloid.*

If we take two general isologues, we have to account for $(n+1)^2$ intersections. Of these, $\sum r_i^2 = n^2 - 1$ go to the fundamental points, and n are on the line connecting the centres. There remain $n+2$ each of which has the property that its mate lies in two different directions, i.e. coincides with the point itself. The reasoning is reversible.

Theorem 36] *In a non-isologous transformation of order n there are $n+2$ distinct or coalescing fixed points. When there are more the number is infinite, or there is a curve of fixed points.*

Suppose that there is a curve of fixed points. The order cannot be as high as $n+1$, for in that case a straight line would have that number of intersections with the corresponding homaloid which is of order n. The curve of fixed points will also be a part of every isologue. We shall have in fact three equations,

$$(x_i\phi_j-x_j\phi_i) = \theta_k\psi \qquad (x_i'\phi_j'-x_j'\phi_i') = \theta_k'\psi, \qquad (20)$$

so that ψ will appear once as a factor of an isologue. Suppose that the curve of fixed points is of order n, the order of the transformation. θ_i is linear. Since

$$|xx\phi| \equiv \psi(\theta x) \equiv 0,$$

$$(\theta x) \equiv 0$$

$$\theta_k \equiv a_{ki}x_i - a_{jk}x_j.$$

The three lines θ_i are concurrent or identical. In the latter case they would form a part of ψ which would be of order $n+1$, and that, we have seen, is inadmissible. Hence these three lines are concurrent. Suppose that they meet in O_3, we have

$$\theta_1 = a_{12}x_2 \qquad \theta_2 = -a_{12}x_1 \qquad \theta_3 \equiv 0$$

$$x_2\phi_3-x_3\phi_2 \equiv a_{12}x_2\psi_1 \quad x_3\phi_1-x_1\phi_3 \equiv -a_{12}x_1\psi \quad x_1\phi_2-x_2\phi_1 \equiv 0.$$

The transformation is isologous, corresponding points are collinear with O_3:

$$\phi_1 \equiv x_1\chi(x_1,x_2,x_3) \qquad \phi_2 \equiv x_2\chi(x_1,x_2,x_3) \qquad \phi_3 \equiv x_3\chi+a_{12}\psi.$$

The curve χ is fundamental of order $n-1$. Hence the inverse transformation is of the De Jonquières type with $2(n-1)$ simple fundamental points. Hence the given transformation is of the De Jonquières type by 31]. A line through O_3 is self-corresponding, and so forms a part of the corresponding homaloid, which can meet the general homaloid but once away from O_3. It appears that ψ is a curve of order n with multiplicity $n-2$ or $n-1$ at O_3.

If ψ have multiplicity $n-1$ at O_3, so has the fundamental curve χ, for ϕ_3 has the multiplicity $n-1$. The fundamental curve χ consists in $n-1$ lines running from O_3 to as many simple fundamental points. But this disagrees with (12) except in the case where $n = 2$. In all other cases, ψ must have multiplicity $n-2$ at O_3.

Theorem 37] *If a Cremona transformation have a curve of fixed points of the same order as the transformation, it is an isologous De Jonquières transformation. If the order exceed 2, the curve of fixed points has, at the singular fundamental point, a multiplicity two less than the order of the transformation.*

Suppose, conversely, we have an isologous transformation, corresponding points being collinear with O_3. We have, first of all,

$$\phi_1 = x_1 \chi \qquad \phi_2 = x_2 \chi.$$

All lines through O_3 are self-corresponding. Since they meet other lines but once, they meet homaloids but once, and so we have multiplicity $n-1$ at O_3 for all homaloids, and the transformation is of the De Jonquières type. It appears that if a point lie on the curve

$$\phi_3 - x_3 \chi = 0,$$

$$\phi_i = \rho x_i,$$

so that this is a curve of fixed points.

Theorem 38] *In an isologous transformation there is a curve of fixed points whose order is the order of the transformation.*

A very good example of the isologous transformation is the ordinary circular inversion

$$x_1' = x_1 x_3 \qquad x_2' = x_2 x_3 \qquad x_3' = x_3^2 + x_1^2 + x_2^2 - x_3^2.$$

The curve of fixed points

$$x_1^2 + x_2^2 - x_3^2 = 0$$

has multiplicity 0 at O_3. When $n = 2$ we can have a curve of the second order with multiplicity $n-1 = 1$ at the point of concurrence:

$$\phi_1 = x_1^2 \qquad \phi_2 = x_2 x_1 \qquad \phi_3 = -x_3 x_1 + x_2^2.$$

The homaloids are conics which osculate one another. All points of the conic $x_2^2 - x_1 x_3 = 0$ are self-corresponding.

Let us return to the non-isologous case, writing, as before,

$$x_i \phi_j - x_j \phi_i = \theta_k \psi. \tag{20}$$

Let us assume that the transformation and its inverse have different fundamental points. Let ψ have the order ν and the multiplicity s_i at P_i and s'_j at P'_j. As it must intersect a general homaloid as often as it intersects a straight line, we have

$$\sum_i r_i s_i = n\nu - \nu, \tag{21}$$

$$\sum_j r'_j s'_j = n\nu - \nu. \tag{22}$$

Let us look next for the intersections with the curve of order r_i which corresponds to P_i. If the self-corresponding curve go through P_i, then the curve which corresponds to P_i also goes through there, and has but a simple point, since it has the maximum number of singularities elsewhere. Hence we get

$$\sum_j r_{ij} s'_j = \nu r_i - s_i, \tag{23}$$

$$\sum_i r_{ij} s_i = \nu r'_j - s'_j. \tag{24}$$

To find isolated self-corresponding points we proceed as before, when we assumed there were no self-corresponding points, namely, we find the intersections of two isologues. The number will then be

$$(n+1-\nu)^2 - \sum_i (r_i - s_i)^2 - (n-\nu)$$

$$= (n+1-\nu)^2 - (n^2-1) + 2(n\nu-\nu) - \sum s_i^2 - (n-\nu)$$

$$= n + (\nu-1)(\nu-2) - \sum s_i^2$$

$$= n + (\nu-1)(\nu-2) - \sum s'^2_j.$$

Theorem 39] *If a non-isologous Cremona transformation of order n have different fundamental points from its inverse, and a curve of fixed points of order ν with multiplicities s_i and s'_j at the fundamental points P_i and P'_j, then the number of isolated fixed points is*

$$n + (\nu-1)(\nu-2) - \sum s_i^2 = n + (\nu-1)(\nu-2) - \sum s'^2_j,$$

$$\sum s_i^2 = \sum s'^2_j. \tag{25}$$

It is conceivable that in some cases the isolated points might lie on the curve of self-corresponding points.

If a transformation be involutory, each corresponding pair of points are coupled both in the transformation and its inverse, which is the same thing. In other cases there will, perhaps, be a finite number of pairs of points which correspond in both the transformation and its inverse, or a curve of such points. If a pair of points correspond in a non-involutory transformation and its inverse they are fixed points in the square of the transformation. Conversely, if a point be fixed for the square of a given non-involutory transformation, it is either fixed for the transformation, or has the same mate in the transformation and its inverse.

The square of a Cremona transformation of order n is, usually, of order n^2. The number of invariant points is n^2+2, of which $n+2$ are fixed for the transformation.

Theorem 40] *A non-isologous Cremona transformation of order n which has no curve of fixed points has, in general, $n(n-1)$ pairs of points which correspond to one another in the transformation and in its inverse. When there are more than this, there is a curve of such points, or else the transformation is involutory.*

Let us rewrite the equations of our specimen isologues

$$|\xi x\phi| = 0 \qquad |\xi x'\phi'| = 0.$$

The tangents at the centre have the equations

$$|x\xi\phi(\xi)| = 0 \qquad |x'\xi\phi'(\xi)| = 0.$$

Theorem 41] *The tangent to an isologue at its centre is the line thence to the mate of that centre in the given transformation.*[*]

There are one or two other curves associated with a Cremona transformation which are worth short consideration. If the two mates of (x) in the transformation and its inverse be collinear with (ξ), we have

$$|\xi\phi\phi'| = 0. \qquad (26)$$

This is sometimes called the M curve of (ξ). It is of order $2n$, when there is no curve of self-corresponding points. A curve of self-corresponding points will form a part of every M curve. It is not clear whether it should be counted multiply or not. That doubt can be removed as follows. Let P be a general point of ϕ_i. It will correspond to a single point on x_i, and so to a single point on $\phi' = 0$. The line from the latter to (ξ) will meet $\phi_i = 0$ in n points P'. Conversely, when P' is given, the line thence to (ξ) meets $\phi' = 0$ in n points, each of which corresponds to a point of $x_i = 0$, and so to a point P of $\phi_i = 0$. We have, thus, on our rational curve ϕ_i an n-to-n correspondence with $2n$ coincidences. They correspond to the points on $x_i = 0$ whose

[1] Cf. Guccia[3].

two mates are collinear with (ξ), i.e. to the intersections of $x_i = 0$ with this M-curve, and to the intersections with the curve of self-corresponding points, and these need not count multiply by Zeuthen's rule of Book I, Ch. VIII. The order of the curve of self-corresponding points is, thus, $2n-v$.

Theorem 42] *If a non-involutory transformation of order n be non-isologous and have different singular points from its inverse, but a curve of self-corresponding points of order v, the M-curve of a general point has the order $2n-v$ with multiplicity r_i-s_i at P_i and $r'_j-s'_j$ at P'_j.*

There is more interest attached to the related N-curve which is the locus of points collinear with their two mates. Its equation is
$$|x\phi\phi'| = 0.$$

Theorem 43] *If a non-isologous transformation of order n have different fundamental points from its inverse, its N-curve is the locus of*

a) points collinear with their two mates;

b) points which lie on the corresponding M-curves;

c) points where a line meets both corresponding homaloids;

d) points where the two isologues and the M-curve of one same point are concurrent;

e) points whose two isologues are tangent at that point.

It is clear that our curve of self-corresponding points must split off from the N-curve, but it is not clear how often it counts as a factor. Let us return for a moment to the case where there is no self-corresponding curve. The isologues whose centre is $(\xi)+\lambda(\eta)$ have the equations
$$|\xi x\phi|+\lambda|\eta x\phi| = 0 \qquad |\xi x\phi'|+\lambda|\eta x\phi'| = 0$$
as the centre traces the line from (ξ) to (η); these isologues trace two projective pencils of curves of order $n+1$; the locus of their intersections is found by eliminating λ:
$$|\xi x\phi|.|\eta x\phi'| - |\eta x\phi|.|\xi x\phi'| = 0.$$
But this may be greatly simplified by a simple device, for
$$\begin{vmatrix} \xi_1 & \xi_2 & \xi_3 & |\xi x\phi| \\ \eta_1 & \eta_2 & \eta_3 & |\eta x\phi| \\ \phi'_1 & \phi'_2 & \phi'_3 & |\phi' x\phi| \\ x_1 & x_2 & x_3 & |xx\phi| \end{vmatrix} \equiv 0 \qquad |xx\phi| \equiv 0,$$
$$-|\xi x\phi|.|\eta x\phi'| + |\eta x\phi|.|\xi x\phi'| \equiv -|\xi\eta x|.|x\phi\phi'|.$$

The locus is the N-curve, together with the line from (ξ) to (η). If all of the curves of one pencil be reducible with a common factor, that factor enters to the first degree into the locus; the same will hold for a common factor of the curves of the other pencil. Hence ψ will come out at least twice as a factor. But this is not all. If a point be coincident with both its mates, it is collinear with both, and the locus of such points must be a part of the locus remaining, so that ψ comes out three times as a factor. In certain cases it may come out more often, but not in general, as we may see by trying a special case.

Theorem 44] *If a non-isologous Cremona transformation of order n have different fundamental points from its inverse, but a curve of fixed points of order ν with multiplicities s_1, s_2,... at P_1, P_2,... and s_1', s_2',... at P_1', P_2',..., the N-curve will be of order $2n+1-3\nu$ with multiplicity r_i-3s_i at P and multiplicity $r_j'-3s_j'$ at P_j'.*[*]

We return to the self-corresponding points. These fall into two categories. In any analytic point-transformation of the plane there is a projective relation between corresponding directions at corresponding points. It might happen at a self-corresponding point that there are two distinct or coincident self-corresponding directions, in which case the point is said to be of the 'first sort', or all directions are self-corresponding, in which case it is said to be of the 'second sort'. If O_3 be self-corresponding, we may write our transformation

$$x_1' = x_3^{n-1}(a_{11}x_1+a_{12}x_2)+...$$
$$x_2' = x_3^{n-1}(a_{21}x_1+a_{22}x_2)+...$$
$$x_3' = x_3^n+(a_{31}x_1+a_{32}x_2)x_3^{n-1}+....$$

This will be of the second sort if

$$a_{11} = a_{22} \qquad a_{12} = a_{21} = 0.$$

The terms of lowest order in x_1, x_2 in the equation of the isologue of a general point are now

$$x_3^N(1-a_{11})(\xi_2 x_1-\xi_1 x_2)+....$$

It appears, then, that unless $a_{11} = 1$ so that all these isologues have a singular point there, the isologues of a general point

* Döhlemann[2].

touch the line from O_3 to that point at O_3. The reasoning is easily found to be reversible.

Theorem 45] *The necessary and sufficient condition that a self-corresponding point should be of the second sort is that the isologue of a general point should either have a singularity at the self-corresponding point, or else touch there the line to the general point.*

We get at once from Book I, Ch. IX, 25], that if two isologues touch, the point of contact is on the Jacobian of the net of isologues. There will be a pencil of tangent isologues, whose centres trace the common tangent, such being the property of any Laguerre net, as we saw at the end of Ch. IV. This gives

Theorem 46] *All fixed points of the second sort are on the Jacobian of the net of isologues.*

If a point have the same mate in a transformation and its inverse, we have
$$\phi_i = \rho\phi_i' \qquad |\xi\phi\phi'| = 0,$$
the point will, therefore, lie on every M-curve and on the N-curve.

Theorem 47] *If a transformation be not involutory nor isologous, and if there be a curve of points which have the same mates in this transformation and its inverse, that curve is a part of the N-curve, and of every M-curve.**

* Cf. Döhlemann[3].

CHAPTER VII

TYPES OF CREMONA TRANSFORMATIONS

§ 1. Types of lowest order

In the preceding chapter we found a large number of properties of the general Cremona transformation, laying great stress on the fact that it was factorable, but we did not say much about any particular type of Cremona transformation except perhaps the standard quadratic and the De Jonquières. It is our present task to discuss special types. But what do we mean by such a phrase ? Is the standard quadratic transformation of the same 'type' as an inversion in a circle ? The order is the same, so is the number and nature of the fundamental points, so that arithmetically the two are alike, geometrically they are in some ways quite different, as we know. For the purposes of the present chapter, or until further notice, two Cremona transformations are alike if they be of the same order, with the same multiplicities for the fundamental points. We seek at present for an arithmetical classification. We must have, in the first place, numbers n, r_1, r_2,... which satisfy the fundamental relations

$$\sum r_i = 3(n-1) \qquad \sum r_i^2 = n^2-1 \qquad \sum 1 = r, \qquad (1)$$

and, secondly, we must show that there actually exist Cremona transformations corresponding to these numbers. We shall find that this latter existence question will involve some further considerations.

If a Cremona transformation be of order 1, it is clearly a collineation. There are no fundamental points. If it be of order 2, there must be three simple fundamental points; the homaloids must be conics through three distinct points, or through two points with a fixed tangent at one, or all osculating at a fixed point. All of these types are easy to set up.

Suppose the order is three. Since the cubics are rational, they must have a fixed double point, so that the transformation is of the De Jonquières type. The situation is equally simple when we come to quartic transformations. We may either have three double fundamental points, or else the De Jonquières type with a triple point and six simple ones. The case becomes a bit more complicated when the order is 5. Here, first of all, we may have a De Jonquières transformation with a fundamental point of order 4, and eight simple ones. There could not be a transformation with two triple points, as the homaloids would be reducible. If there were one triple point, there would have to be three double points to make the homaloids rational, and three simple points. If there were no triple point, there would have to be six double and no single.

Next take $n = 6$. There is the De Jonquières type with one quintuple and ten simple points. If there were a quadruple point, there would have to be four doubles to make the homaloids rational, and then three simple points. The maximum number of permissible triple points would seem to be three. We get solutions of our equations by assuming three triple points, one double, and four simple. Or if there were but two triple points, we should have to assume four double and one simple point. If we assumed less than two triple points, we should have to assume such a large number of double points to make the homaloids rational that the sum of the orders of the fundamental points would come too high.

Take $n = 7$. There is the De Jonquières type with a sextuple and twelve simple points. If there were a quintuple point, there would have to be five double and three simple ones. If there were a quadruple point there could not be more than three triples; in that case we should have to have five simple points. Or we might have a quadruple and two triple points, when three double and two simple points would be needed. If there were a quadruple and one triple point, we should need six doubles to make the homaloids rational, but then the sum of the multiplicities would be too great, and the same would be true if we had less than four triple points. But we might have four triple points and three double ones; five triples would give us a conic with fifteen intersections.

When $n = 8$, the only transformations with less than nine fundamental points are:

a) Two quadruples, two triples, three doubles, and one simple.

b) One quadruple, five triples, and two simples.

c) Seven triples.

But how do we know that all of these exist ? Because we know that those of lowest order exist, and those of any order can be obtained from transformations of lower order by means of standard quadratic transformations.

Order.*	Fundamental points.	Order.	Fundamental points.
1	0	6	$3 \times 3 + 2 + 4 \times 1$
2	3×1	6	$2 \times 3 + 4 \times 2 + 1$
3	$2 + 4 \times 1$	7	$6 + 12 \times 1$
4	$3 + 6 \times 1$	7	$5 + 5 \times 2 + 3 \times 1$
4	$3 \times 2 + 3 \times 1 \cdot$	7	$4 + 3 \times 3 + 5 \times 1$
5	$4 + 8 \times 1$	7	$4 + 2 \times 3 + 3 \times 2 + 2 \times 1$
5	$3 + 3 \times 2 + 3 \times 1$	7	$4 \times 3 + 3 \times 2$
5	6×2	8	$2 \times 4 + 2 \times 3 + 3 \times 2 + 1$
6	$5 + 10 \times 1$	8	$4 + 5 \times 3 + 2 \times 1$
6	$4 + 4 \times 2 + 3 \times 1$	8	7×3

§ 2. Numerical relations

In order that a set of points $P_1, P_2, \dots$ be fundamental for a Cremona transformation of order n with multiplicities $r_1 \geqslant r_2 \geqslant r_3 \dots$ it is necessary that

$$\sum r_i = 3(n-1) \qquad \sum r_i^2 = n^2 - 1 \qquad \sum 1 = r, \qquad (1)$$

$$r_1 + r_2 \leqslant n \qquad r_1 + r_2 + \dots + r_5 \leqslant 2n \qquad r_1 + r_2 + \dots + r_9 \leqslant 3n. \qquad (2)$$

The last three equations result from the fact that a homaloid must not intersect a line, a conic, a cubic, etc., too often. We get from theorem 10] of Ch. II

$$r_1 + r_2 + r_3 > n. \qquad (3)$$

Theorem 1] *If the multiplicity of no fundamental point exceed 2, the order of a Cremona transformation cannot exceed 5.*

We have already defined a Cremona transformation as 'symmetric' when all the fundamental points are of the same order of multiplicity. Here we have

$$n^2 - 1 = r r_1^2 \qquad 3(n-1) = r r_1 \qquad (4)$$

$$\frac{n+1}{3} = r_1$$

$$9 - \frac{18}{n+1} = r.$$

---

* Cremona[1] determined all possible types up to $n = 10$. Hudson, p. 437, gives up to $n = 16$. In 'Topics', p. 84, it is stated that in 1924 Mlodziejowski determined all up to $n = 24$. This I have not been able to verify. It appears about as useful as calculating π up to 707 places of decimals.

It appears that 18 must be divisible by $n+1$. The possibilities, then, are

$$n = 1, \ r = 0; \qquad n = 2, \ r = 3, \ r_1 = 1; \qquad n = 5, \ r = 6, \ r_1 = 2;$$
$$n = 8, \ r = 7, \ r_1 = 3; \qquad n = 17, \ r = 8, \ r_1 = 6.$$

Only one of these is new to us, the last. Let us start with the transformation of order 8 and system of multiplicities $2 \times 4 + 2 \times 3 + 3 \times 2 + 1$ and take O_1, O_2, O_3 at points of multiplicity 2, 2, and 1. We get a transformation of this sort:

Order 11, fundamental points $2 \times 5 + 3 \times 4 + 2 \times 3 + 2$.

Continuing successively by taking O_1, O_2, O_3 at the three fundamental points of lowest multiplicity, we get the following:

Order 14, multiplicities $2 \times 6 + 3 \times 5 + 3 \times 4$.

Order 16, multiplicities $5 \times 6 + 3 \times 5$.

Order 17, multiplicities 8×6.

Theorem 2] *The only symmetric Cremona transformations are collineations, quadratic transformations, quintic transformations with six double points, octavic ones with seven triple points, and heptadekadic with eight sextuple points.*

We return to equations (1) and write a familiar identity from the theory of determinants*

$$\sum r_i^2 \sum 1 - (\sum r_i)^2 = (n-1)[(n+1)r - 9(n-1)] = \tfrac{1}{2} \sum_{ij} (r_i - r_j)^2. \quad (5)$$

The last expression is positive, except when it vanishes for a symmetric transformation.

Theorem 3] *A Cremona transformation which is symmetric has fewer fundamental points than any other of the same order.*

In the unsymmetric case

$$r > 9 \frac{(n-1)}{(n+1)}.$$

If $\qquad\qquad\qquad\qquad n \geqslant 8, \qquad r > 7.$

If $\qquad\qquad\qquad\qquad n \geqslant 17, \quad r > 8.$

Theorem 4] *If the order of a Cremona transformation exceed 7, there are more than seven fundamental points, if the order exceed 18, there are more than eight.*

It is now time to look for an upper limit to the number of fundamental points. If we consult our table we see that in the

* Cf. Kowalewski, p. 75.

case of a De Jonquières transformation $r = 2n-1$, in all other cases $r \leqslant n+2$. Let us prove that this is always the case. Suppose that we have proved this for every Cremona transformation, or every homaloidal net whose order does not exceed n. Take a transformation of order n which is not of the De Jonquières type and follow it by a standard quadratic transformation carrying the net into one of higher order:

$$n' = n + [n - (r_\alpha + r_\beta + r_\gamma)].$$

Since $n' > n$ $r_\alpha + r_\beta + r_\gamma < n$ $r \leqslant n+2$.

If three fundamental points be added,

$$r_\alpha = r_\beta = r_\gamma = 0   r' = r+3   n' = 2n$$
$$n' + 2 - r' = n + 2 - r + (n-3) \geqslant 0.$$

If two fundamental points be added,

$$r_\beta = r_\gamma = 0   r' = r+2   n' = n + (n - r_\alpha)$$
$$n' + 2 - r' = n + 2 - r + (n - 2 - r_\alpha).$$

Since the transformation is not De Jonquières,

$$r_\alpha \leqslant n-2   n' + 2 - r' \geqslant 0.$$

If one fundamental point be added,

$$r_\gamma = 0   r' = r+1   n' = n + (n - r_\alpha - r_\beta)$$
$$n' + 2 - r' = n + 2 - r + n - r_\alpha - r_\beta - 1.$$

But $r_\alpha + r_\beta < n$.

Hence $r_\alpha + r_\beta \leqslant n-1$ $n' + 2 - r' \geqslant 0$.

If no fundamental point be added,

$$r' = r   n' = n + [n - (r_\alpha + r_\beta + r_\gamma)]$$
$$n' + 2 - r' = n + 2 - r + [n - (r_\alpha + r_\beta + r_\gamma)].$$

Hence $n' + 2 - r' \geqslant 0$.

Suppose, secondly, the transformation of order n is of the De Jonquières type and the fundamental singular point is not included in the set O_1, O_2, O_3, but these include s simple fundamental points, we have

$$r' = r + 3 - s   n' = 2n - s   s(s-1)(s-2)(s-3) = 0$$
$$r' = 2n + 2 - s   n' + 2 - r' = 0.$$

If, however, we do include the singular fundamental point, we must not include any simple fundamental point, otherwise the order would not go up, so that

$$r' = r+2 = 2n+1 \qquad n' = n+1$$
$$r' - 2n' + 1 = 0.$$

Theorem 5] *If a Cremona transformation of order n be of the De Jonquières type, the number of fundamental points is $2n-1$, otherwise the number does not exceed $n+2$.*[*]

In a De Jonquières transformation, the highest multiplicity for any singular point is $n-1$. Suppose that we have a point of order $n-2$. The other fundamental points must be double and simple, namely, $n-2$ double points and three simple ones. We have seen that such transformations exist for the lower values of n, and it is easy to show that if there exist such a transformation of order $n-1$, there is one of order n.

Theorem 6] *The only transformations of order n with a fundamental point of order $n-2$ are those which have also $n-2$ double and three simple fundamental points. Such transformations exist for all values of $n > 2$.*

Theorem 7] *The highest multiplicity for any fundamental point lies in the limits $\dfrac{n+1}{3}$ and $n-1$.*

Suppose there are s points of equal highest multiplicity.

$$sr_1 \leqslant 3(n-1) \qquad 3r_1 > n$$
$$s \leqslant \frac{9(n-1)}{n} \qquad s < 9.$$

Theorem 8] *There cannot be more than eight points of equal highest multiplicity.*

We saw in theorem 4] that if the order of a transformation exceed 17, there must be more than eight fundamental points. It looks as though the minimum permissible number would go up with n, but that is not the case.

Consider a pencil of cubics with no reducible member. That means that no three centres are on a line, and no six are on a conic. Let O_1, O_2, O_3 be three of these. We may construct a homaloidal net of quintics with nodes at the other six centres.

[*] Cf. Montesano[2], p. 26.

Transform by a standard quadratic transformation. The net of quintics goes into a net of curves of order 10, with three quintuple points and six double points. The net of cubics goes into a net of cubics with no reducible member, hence no three of the nine fundamental points lie on a line. Take another standard quadratic transformation with three of the double points as O_1, O_2, O_3. We get a new net of order 14 with nine fundamental points, no three of which are collinear, for they are centres of a pencil of cubics with no degenerate member. We may keep on in this way indefinitely; no three fundamental points will be collinear, for no cubic will be factorable, and as the sum of the three lowest of nine fundamental points must be less than n, the order will be increased.

Theorem 9] *There exist Cremona transformations with orders greater than an assigned number, yet with only nine fundamental points.*

Suppose that the sum of the three highest multiplicities is $n+1$.

$$r_1+r_2+r_3 = n+1$$
$$r_3+r_4+...+r_r = 3(n-1)-(r_1+r_2)$$
$$r_3^2+r_4^2+...+r_r^2 = n^2-1-r_1^2-r_2^2$$
$$r_3(r_3+r_4+...+r_r) \geqslant r_3^2+r_4^2+...+r_r^2.$$

The sign of equality holds only when $r_3 = r_4 = ... = r_r = 1$.

$$3r_3(n-1)-r_1r_3-r_2r_3 \geqslant n^2-1-r_1^2-r_2^2$$
$$r_1^2+r_2^2+1-r_3(r_1+r_2+3) \geqslant n(n-3r_3).$$

If we put
$$r_1+r_2+r_3-1 = n,$$
$$(r_3-1)^2-(r_1-1)(r_2-1) \geqslant 0.$$

But
$$r_1 \geqslant r_2 \geqslant r_3.$$

Theorem 10] *The only transformations where the sum of the three highest multiplicities is one more than the order of the transformation are non-linear symmetric transformations and De Jonquières ones.*

§ 3. Transformations with a curve of fixed points

We saw in the last chapter that if, in a transformation of order n, we have more than $n+2$ fixed points, there is a whole curve of such. Suppose there is such a curve of order ν which has no singularity at a fundamental point but multiplicity s_i there, where this number is 1 or 0. As this will meet a straight line and a homaloid in the same number of non-fundamental points, we have

$$nv = \sum s_i r_i + v$$

$$v(n-1) = \sum s_i r_i. \qquad (6)$$

But $\qquad\qquad 3(n-1) = \sum r_i \qquad s_i \leqslant 1.$

Hence $\qquad\qquad v \leqslant 3,$

and the inequality holds only when $s_i = 1$ in every case.

Theorem 11] *If a transformation have a curve of fixed points which has no singularity at any fundamental point, the order of the curve is not greater than 3, and can only reach this latter number when it passes through every fundamental point.*

Definition. If $S, T,$ and S' be three Cremona transformations so related that $S' = T^{-1}ST$, then S and S' are said to be 'equivalent'.

It is clear that T^{-1} will carry a curve of fixed points for S into a curve of fixed points for S'. If a transformation have a curve of fixed points which has no special adjoint of any index greater than 1, it is equivalent to a Cremona transformation with a line of fixed points, say $x_3 = 0$. We may write this

$$x_1' = \theta x_1 + \psi_1 x_3 \qquad x_2' = \theta x_2 + \psi_2 x_3 \qquad x_3' = \psi_3 x_3,$$

$$x_1 = \theta' x_1' + \psi_1' x_3' \qquad x_2 = \theta' x_2' + \psi_2' x_3' \qquad x_3 = \psi_3' x_3'.$$

As x_3 must vanish with x_3', and x_3' with x_3, and we may assume that ψ_3 is not a factor of x_1' and x_2', we must have

$$x_3' = kx_3^n \qquad x_3 = lx_3'^n,$$

so that $n = 1$.

Theorem 12] *If a Cremona transformation have a curve of fixed points which lacks special adjoints of every index, it is equivalent to a collineation with a line of fixed points.*

Theorem 13] *If a Cremona transformation have a curve of fixed points which lacks all special adjoints of index greater than 1, but not all of that index, it is equivalent to a transformation where all points of a cubic are fixed. Such a cubic will pass through all the fundamental points.*

It is easy to set up such a transformation. Take a cubic curve, and a fixed point O thereon. A general point P will correspond to P', its harmonic conjugate with regard to the other two intersections of OP with the curve. The transformation is involutory, the general point of the cubic curve is fixed. If the fixed cubic be written

$$y^2 = f^3(x)$$

and we take the end of the Y-axis as O, the transformation is

$$yy' = f^3(x).$$

Suppose that there is a curve of fixed points of genus greater than 1. There will be at least a one-parameter system of special adjoints which is carried into itself. Moreover, each curve of the system is invariant, for two different special adjoints will not cut the same group of the canonical series. If these special adjoints be rational curves, we may get a one-parameter set of them which, by theorem 11] of Ch. II, can be carried into a pencil of lines. But a Cremona transformation with a pencil of invariant lines is isologous, and so, by theorems 37] and 38] of the last chapter, a De Jonquières transformation. If the special adjoints have genus 1, by theorem 13] of Ch. II they may be carried into a set of cubics each invariant. Such an invariant cubic must have two invariant points at least, belonging to the group it cuts of the canonical series of the curve of fixed points. We may assume that the tangent at A meets the curve again at A', which is different from B. The g_2^1 with AA as a pair will be carried into itself, so that the lines through A' are permuted, as are the three points of contact of tangents from A' to the curve. Now if the curve be not harmonic or equi-harmonic, the only permutation of three lines of a pencil which leaves invariant the cross ratio with a fourth is the identical transformation. But a projective transformation of the lines of a pencil which leaves invariant four members is the identical one, so that all lines through A' stay in place, or the transformation on this cubic is involutory or identical. If the cubic be harmonic or equi-harmonic, it may take the third, fourth, or sixth power of the given transformation to leave all points of the general cubic in place. But if all points of the general cubic of an infinite set lie in place, the transformation is the identity.

If the special adjoints of index 1 be of genus greater than 1, there will be an infinite number of special adjoints of index

2, each having at least two fixed intersections with the curve of fixed points, but varying from one adjoint to another, for if there were but one, the curve of fixed points would be rational, *contra hypothesem.* We may reason on these adjoints of index 2 as we did on those of index 1, and so on down. We thus reach an admirable theorem due to Castelnuovo:*

Theorem 14] *If, in a Cremona transformation, there be a curve of fixed points of genus greater than* 1, *the transformation is either equivalent to a De Jonquières transformation, or periodic with a period of two, three, four, or six.*

Suppose that a transformation is not involutory, but that there is a curve of points which are transformed in an involutory manner, and the genus of this is greater than 1. If the special adjoints be rational, we may proceed as before; the transformation is equivalent to one where the lines of a pencil are transformed in an involutory manner. The product of our transformation and an involutory projective transformation of the plane will leave all lines of a pencil in place and so be a De Jonquières transformation. On the other hand, if we have a De Jonquières transformation with the singular fundamental point at O_3, and follow it by an involutory projective transformation of the plane that permutes the lines through O_3, the result will still be a De Jonquières transformation. If the special adjoints of index greater than 1 in which we are interested be not rational, the square of our transformation is periodic, unless it be equivalent to a De Jonquières.

Theorem 15] *If a Cremona transformation be not involutory, but have a curve of points transformed in an involutory manner whose genus exceeds* 1, *then either the transformation is equivalent to a De Jonquières transformation, or it is periodic with a period two, three, four, six, eight, or twelve.*

Suppose that a curve of genus greater than 1 is carried into itself by a Cremona transformation. Let us assume that the curve is not hyperelliptic. As this cannot be carried into itself by an infinite number of birational transformations, by theorem 8] of Book III, Ch. IV, some power of our transformation will leave all points of the curve invariant. We may reason as we did before in the case of the last theorem.

* Castelnuovo[8], p. 50.

Theorem 16] *If a curve of genus greater than 1 be carried into itself by a Cremona transformation, that transformation is periodic, or equivalent to a De Jonquières transformation.*

§ 4. Involutory transformations

The most interesting of all Cremona transformations are involutory ones. We see at once that if

$$SS = 1 \qquad S' = T^{-1}ST, \qquad S'S' = 1.$$

Theorem 17] *A transformation equivalent to an involutory transformation is itself involutory.*

It is immediately evident that we can find a transformation equivalent to a given transformation, but of as high order as we please. Hence we cannot limit involutory transformations as we did symmetric ones. We can, however, prove that they are equivalent to transformations of a few well-defined types.

Let us first look for involutory symmetric transformations. We know well that there are involutory collineations, and involutory quadratic transformations, such as circular inversions. Moreover, the standard quadratic transformation is involutory. Next comes the transformation of the fifth order with six fundamental double points. We make an involutory transformation of this sort as follows. Let O be the centre of a unit circle, I the inversion in that circle, S a standard quadratic transformation where O_1, O_2, O_3 are on the circle. Consider

$$S' = SIS.$$

It appears that S' being equivalent to I is involutory. A straight line will be carried by S into a conic through O_1, O_2, O_3, then by I into a quartic with a double point at O and at each circular point, and passing simply through O_1, O_2, O_3, and then by S into a quintic with double points at O_1, O_2, O_3, and at the S-transforms of O and the circular points. This is symmetric, involutory of order 5.

An involutory transformation of order 8 with seven triple points is called a 'Geiser involution'* and is found in a very simple manner. Let us take seven points, no three on a straight line, and no six on a conic, and consider the net of cubics through them. If P be any point in the plane, the cubics of

---

* Geiser.

the net through it go through a ninth point P'. The relation of P to P' is one-to-one, algebraic and involutory, the seven chosen points are the only fundamental ones, and they appear symmetrically. Hence this is a symmetric transformation of order 8. Moreover, there is no other sort of symmetric involutory transformation of order 8. For if there were such a transformation, we could not have three fundamental points on a line, nor six on a conic; there would be too many intersections with a certain fundamental curve. The product of our transformation and a Geiser involution with the same fundamental points would leave invariant each cubic through six of the points with a singularity at the other one, and seven points on each cubic. But a birational transformation of a rational curve into itself must be a projective one on the corresponding straight line, and if more than two points be invariant, all are. Hence all points on each of seven cubics will be invariant. Every straight line in the plane would have twenty-one invariant points. But in the product transformation a straight line goes to a straight line. Hence the product is an identity, or the two transformations, which are involutory, are identical.

A symmetric transformation of order 17 with eight sextuple points is obtained in a similar but slightly more complicated fashion. Consider a pencil of cubics through nine given points, no three collinear, no six on a conic, one point being singled out and called O. If P be a general point of the plane it will determine one cubic of the pencil. Let the tangent at O to this cubic meet the curve again in Q, and let PQ meet that same cubic again in P'. The relation of P to P' is one-to-one, algebraic and symmetric, so that we have here an involutory Cremona transformation. The point O will correspond to itself, the other centres of the pencil of cubics will be fundamental points, the only ones, and they appear symmetrically.

Theorem 18] *There exist involutory Cremona transformations of all five symmetric types.*

Next, let us consider unsymmetric transformations, endeavouring to determine the general types to which they are equivalent. Let P_1 be a point of the highest multiplicity of all, say r_1. We know by theorems 24] to 27] of the last chapter that it is on every fundamental curve, and one of the points of highest multiplicity for that curve, and that its multiplicity is highest for a fundamental curve of highest order, so that we may assume α_{11} its highest multiplicity for any fundamental curve. Now let us consider a curve of order r_1 with the same multiplicities at the fundamental points as the one just mentioned, except that at P_1 it has multiplicity $\alpha_{11}-1$. As the fundamental points form a normal base for a fundamental curve, the amount of freedom for this new curve is

$$\frac{\alpha_{11}(\alpha_{11}+1)}{2} - \frac{\alpha_{11}(\alpha_{11}-1)}{2} = \alpha_{11}.$$

The number of non-fundamental intersections with the curve corresponding to P_1 is, by (12) of the last chapter;

$$r_1^2 - \sum \alpha_{i1}^2 + \alpha_{11} - 1 = \alpha_{11} - 1,$$

the number of non-fundamental intersections with the curve corresponding to P_j is, by (14) of the last chapter,

$$r_1 r_j - \sum \alpha_{1i}\alpha_{ji} + \alpha_{1j} = \alpha_{1j}.$$

These equations show that this system of curves is carried into itself by the given transformation. Their genus is

$$\frac{\alpha_{11}(\alpha_{11}-1)}{2} - \frac{(\alpha_{11}-1)(\alpha_{11}-2)}{2} = \alpha_{11} - 1.$$

If $\alpha_{11} = 1$, we have a one-parameter family of invariant curves of genus 0, our transformation is equivalent to one that leaves invariant a pencil of lines, and we have just seen that such a transformation as this latter must be of the De Jonquières type.

If $\alpha_{11} = 2$, we have a two-parameter family of elliptic curves, and we know, by theorem 13] of Ch. II, that this can be carried into a two-parameter family of cubics through seven fundamental points. These are all the fundamental points there are, for

$$3n - r_1 - r_2 - \ldots - r_7 = 3 \qquad 3(n-1) = \sum r_i.$$

But we have in our table all the Cremona transformations with just seven fundamental points; one a De Jonquières transformation, one a symmetric one. It is not hard to show that the others are reducible to transformations of lower order with an invariant net of cubics, unless the order be 2 already.

If, thirdly, the invariant system of curves have genus 2 or more, they have an infinite linear system of special adjoints, to which we may transfer our attention. We have linear systems of successively diminishing orders till we meet a rational or elliptic system. A rational system will contain an invariant pencil composed of a curve and its mate, and so, as above, give us a transformation equivalent to a De Jonquières transformation. If the invariant system be elliptic, there are only two cases to fear.

a) The elliptic system is equivalent to a set of all quartics with two given double points. But such a set could not be invariant under a Cremona transformation, as we see from the equations

$$4n = n + 2r_1 + 2r_2 \qquad 4n = n + 3 + \sum r_i.$$

b) The elliptic system is equivalent to a pencil of curves of order $3s_1$ with nine base points of multiplicity s_1. Their special adjoints of index $s_1 - 1$ are an invariant pencil of cubics, and reasoning as above we see that there are but nine fundamental points, and these are of the same order. But

$$9 \sum r_i^2 - (\sum r_i)^2 = \tfrac{1}{2} \sum (r_i - r_j)^2$$
$$9(n^2 - 1) - [3(n-1)]^2 = 0 \qquad 18(n-1) = 0.$$

which is absurd.

Theorem 19] *An involutory Cremona transformation is equivalent to a De Jonquières or a symmetric transformation.**

Incidentally we have proved

Theorem 20] *If a system of cubic curves given by base points be carried into itself, it passes through all the fundamental points.*

Suppose $\alpha_{1i} = r_1 - 1$, the system of curves which are carried into themselves are of order r_1 with a point of multiplicity $r_1 - 2$, and so are hyperelliptic. Their special adjoints are lines of a pencil.

Theorem 21] *If a fundamental point of an involutory transformation have for a fundamental curve a multiplicity one less than the order of that curve, the transformation is a De Jonquières one.*

Suppose that in an involutory transformation there is a certain number of simple fundamental points which are coordinated to themselves or to one another. Then by theorem 22] of the last chapter, either every one of the coordinated straight lines passes through just one of the coordinated points, and through every one of the fundamental points of higher order, or else

* Cf. Bertini[5].

every one of the straight lines omits but one of the simple points and there are no fundamental points of higher order. In the former case we have clearly a De Jonquières transformation, in the latter a quadratic one.

Theorem 22] *If, in an involutory transformation, there be simple fundamental points coordinated to their own set, then either the transformation is quadratic or of the De Jonquières type.*

The properties of involutory transformations which we have studied so far have been generally invariant for a Cremona transformation, properties which they shared with equivalent transformations. There are other properties, however, which are not invariant under the Cremona group, yet which are worth notice.

Definition. The number of pairs of corresponding points of a Cremona transformation on a general line shall be called the 'class' of the transformation. If a transformation of order n have a curve of self-corresponding points of order ν, the class is

$$m' = \tfrac{1}{2}[n-\nu].$$

The order of an isologue is

$$n+1-\nu = 2m'+1.$$

If an involutory transformation be of class 0, there is a curve of fixed points of order n, and we know by theorem 36] of the last chapter that the transformation is of the De Jonquières type. Conversely, suppose we have an involutory transformation of the De Jonquières type. If all lines through the singular fundamental point be fixed, the transformation is isologous, and we know from 38] of the last chapter that there is a curve of fixed points of order n. If the transformation be not isologous, there are two fixed lines through the singular point. All points may be fixed on both, or on one, or on neither, giving curves of fixed points of orders 2, 1, or 0.

Theorem 23] *An involutory transformation of class 0 is a De Jonquières transformation, and an involutory De Jonquières transformation is of class* $0, \dfrac{n-2}{2}, \dfrac{n-1}{2}$ *or* $\dfrac{n}{2}$.

Suppose we have an involutory transformation of class 1. The curve of fixed points is of order $n-2$, the isologues will be a two-parameter net of cubics, namely, a net through seven or fewer fundamental points, and we know by 20] there are no other fundamental points.

Theorem 24] *An involutory transformation of class* 1 *cannot have more than seven fundamental points.* *

§ 5. Cremona transformations, and integral collineations of higher space

Let us now return to the general Cremona transformation of order n with r fundamental points of orders $r_1, r_2, ..., r_r$. The multiplicities of the fundamental points of the inverse transformation shall be $r'_1, r'_2, ..., r'_r$. Suppose that we have a curve of order x_0 with multiplicity x_i at the fundamental point P_i, and x_j at the non-fundamental point Q_j. The corresponding numbers for the transformed curve shall be x'_i, x'_j. We get from 15] of the last chapter†

$$\begin{aligned}
x'_0 &= nx_0 - r_1 x_1 - ... - r_r x_r \\
x'_1 &= r'_1 x_0 - \alpha_{11} x_1 - ... - \alpha_{r1} x_r \\
&\quad \cdot \quad \cdot \quad \cdot \quad \cdot \quad \cdot \quad \cdot \quad \cdot \quad \cdot \\
x'_r &= r'_r x_0 - \alpha_{1r} x_1 - ... - \alpha_{rr} x_r \qquad (7) \\
x'_{r+1} &= x_{r+1} \\
&\quad \cdot \quad \cdot \quad \cdot \\
x'_\nu &= x_\nu.
\end{aligned}$$

We have, thus, associated with our Cremona transformation a collineation in a space of $\nu + 1 \geqslant r + 1$ dimensions. We shall shortly see that the determinant is not equal to 0. Of course, it is not a general transformation. The coefficients indicated are positive integers or 0. Moreover, we have from equations (9) and (10) of the last chapter

$$3x'_0 - x'_1 - ... - x'_r - ... - x'_\nu = 3x_0 - x_1 - ... - x_r - ... - x_\nu \qquad (8)$$

$$-x'^2_0 + x'^2_1 + ... + x'^2_r + ... + x'^2_\nu = -x^2_0 + x^2_1 + ... + x^2_r + ... + x^2_\nu. \qquad (9)$$

Thus, in our higher space, we have a collineation leaving in place the hyperplane

$$-3x_0 + x_1 + ... + x_\nu = 0, \qquad (10)$$

and the hyperquadric

$$-x^2_0 + x^2_1 + ... + x^2_\nu = 0. \qquad (11)$$

---

* The concept of class comes from Caporali[1]. For transformations of classes 2, 3, or 4 see 'Topics', p. 96.

† Cf. Kantor[3], p. 32.

If we change x_0 into ix_0 we see that we have an orthogonal substitution which leaves a certain linear form invariant. The relations connecting the coefficients of an orthogonal substitution are classical. However, it is probably better not to lose sight of the real domain, so we shall press this no further.

Suppose, conversely, that we have an affine integral collineation of our space which leaves invariant every hyperplane $x_{r+k} = 0$, and every point for which the first $r+1$ coordinates vanish. Let us further suppose that we limit ourselves to such an integral affine collineation that the indicated coefficients are positive integers or 0, and that the hyperplane

$$-3x_0 + x_1 + \ldots + x_\nu = 0, \tag{10}$$

and the hyperquadric

$$-x_0^2 + x_1^2 + \ldots + x_\nu^2 = 0, \tag{11}$$

are invariant. This may be written in the form (7). We find by direct substitution

$$\sum_i r_i' = 3(n-1) \qquad \sum_j \alpha_{ij} = 3r_i - 1 \qquad \sum_i r_i'^2 = n^2 - 1 \tag{12}$$

$$\sum_j \alpha_{ij} r_j' = nr_i \qquad \sum_j \alpha_{ij}^2 = r_i^2 + 1 \qquad \sum_j \alpha_{ij}\alpha_{kj} = r_i r_k. \tag{13}$$

Let us next take the transformation

$$x_0'' = nx_0' - r_1' x_1' - \ldots - r_r' x_r'$$

$$x_1'' = r_1 x_0' - \alpha_{11} x_1' - \ldots - \alpha_{1r} x_r'$$

$$\cdot \quad \cdot \quad \cdot \quad \cdot \quad \cdot \quad \cdot \quad \cdot \quad \cdot \quad \cdot \quad \cdot$$

$$x_r'' = r_r x_0' - \alpha_{r1} x_1' - \ldots - \alpha_{rr} x_r' \tag{14}$$

$$x_{r+1}'' = x_{r+1}'$$

$$\cdot \quad \cdot \quad \cdot$$

$$x_\nu'' = x_\nu'.$$

The product turns out to be the identity. Hence (14) is the inverse of (7). Owing to the invariance of (10) and (11),

$$\sum_j r_j = 3(n-1) \qquad \sum_i \alpha_{ij} = 3r_j' - 1 \qquad \sum_j r_j^2 = n^2 - 1 \tag{15}$$

$$\sum_i \alpha_{ij} r_i = nr_j' \qquad \sum_i \alpha_{ij}^2 = r_j'^2 + 1 \qquad \sum_i \alpha_{ji}\alpha_{jk} = r_i' r_k'. \tag{16}$$

Our equations (12), (13), (15), and (16) give us equations (2), (11), (12), and (13) of the last chapter, the characteristic linear

relations of a Cremona transformation. If D be determinant of
the transformation, we have

$$-D^2 = \begin{vmatrix} in & -ir_1 & . & . & . & -ir_r & 0 & 0 & . & . & . & 0 \\ r_1 & -\alpha_{11} & . & . & . & -\alpha_{r1} & 0 & 0 & . & . & . & 0 \\ . & . & . & . & . & . & . & . & . & . & . \\ r'_r & -\alpha_{1r} & . & . & . & -\alpha_{rr} & 0 & 0 & . & . & . & 0 \\ 0 & 0 & . & . & . & 0 & 1 & 0 & . & . & . & 0 \\ . & . & . & . & . & . & . & . & . & . & . \\ 0 & 0 & . & . & . & 0 & 0 & 0 & . & . & . & 1 \end{vmatrix}^2$$

$$= \begin{vmatrix} -1 & 0 & 0 & . & . & . & 0 \\ 0 & 1 & 0 & . & . & . & 0 \\ . & . & . & . & . & . \\ 0 & 0 & 0 & . & . & . & 1 \end{vmatrix}$$

$$D = \pm 1. \tag{17}$$

We get at once from equations (12) to (16)

$$(r_i-1)(r_i-2) = \sum_j \alpha_{ij}(\alpha_{ij}-1) \qquad (r'_j-1)(r'_j-2) = \sum_i \alpha_{ij}(\alpha_{ij}-1).$$

This shows that the quantities fulfil the conditions for the
singular points of rational curves of order r_i and r'_j.

It is now time to show that every integral solution of the
equations (7), subject to the conditions (12) to (16) will actually
correspond to a Cremona transformation. We do this by factor-
ing, much as we factor a Cremona transformation into collineations and standard quadratic transformations. Let us begin
with a collineation which consists in permuting x_i's except the
first, and the last, $\nu-r$. We get this sort of collineation in higher
space by a permutation among the points P_i, and this does not
correspond to a geometrical transformation at all. Another
collineation in higher space which fulfils all the conditions is

$$\begin{aligned} x'_0 &= 2x_0 - x_1 - x_2 - x_3 \\ x'_1 &= x_0 - x_2 - x_3 \\ x'_2 &= x_0 - x_1 - x_3 \\ x'_3 &= x_0 - x_1 - x_2 \\ x'_{3+s} &= x_{3+s}. \end{aligned} \tag{18}$$

This transformation corresponds to a standard quadratic
transformation.

Let us first suppose that our transformation (7) is preceded by such a permutation of subscripts that thereafter

$$r_1 \geqslant r_2 \geqslant r_3 \geqslant r_{3+k}$$

$$r_3 \sum_{k=1}^{k=r-3} r_{3+k} - \sum_{k=1}^{k=r-3} r_{3+k}^2 = r_3[3(n-1) - r_1 - r_2 - r_3] - [(n^2-1) - r_1^2 - r_2^2 - r_3^2].$$

The left-hand side is not less than 0, hence

$$r_1^2 + r_2^2 - r_3(r_1 + r_2) \geqslant (n-1)[n+1-3r_3].$$

Suppose $\quad\quad n \geqslant r_1 + r_2 + r_3,$

$$r_1^2 + r_2^2 - (r_1 + r_2)r_3 \geqslant (r_1 + r_2 + r_3 - 1)(r_1 + r_2 - 2r_3 + 1)$$

$$2(r_3^2 - r_1 r_2) + (1 - 3r_3) \geqslant 0.$$

This is only possible when $r_1 = r_2 = r_3 = \ldots = r_r = 0$ and the transformation is the identity in higher space, corresponding to a collineation of the plane. We may assume therefore that

$$r_1 + r_2 + r_3 > n.$$

Let us precede by a transformation of the type (18). The resulting transformation will be of the type

$$x_0' = (2n - r_1 - r_2 - r_3)x_0 - (n - r_2 - r_3)x_1 - (n - r_3 - r_1)x_2 - (n - r_1 - r_2)x_3 - r_4 x_4 - \ldots - r_r x_r$$

$$x_1' = (2r_1' - \alpha_{11} - \alpha_{21} - \alpha_{31})x_0 - (r_1' - \alpha_{21} - \alpha_{31})x_1 - (r_1' - \alpha_{31} - \alpha_{11})x_2 - (r_1' - \alpha_{11} - \alpha_{21})x_3 - \alpha_{41}x_4 - \ldots - \alpha_{r1}x_r$$

$$x_2' = (2r_2' - \alpha_{12} - \alpha_{22} - \alpha_{32})x_0 - (r_2' - \alpha_{22} - \alpha_{32})x_1 - (r_2' - \alpha_{32} - \alpha_{12})x_2 - (r_2' - \alpha_{12} - \alpha_{22})x_3 - \alpha_{42}x_4 - \ldots - \alpha_{r2}x_r$$

$$x_3' = (2r_3' - \alpha_{13} - \alpha_{23} - \alpha_{33})x_0 - (r_3' - \alpha_{23} - \alpha_{33})x_1 - (r_3' - \alpha_{33} - \alpha_{13})x_2 - (r_3' - \alpha_{13} - \alpha_{23})x_3 - \alpha_{43}x_4 - \ldots - \alpha_{r3}x_r$$

$$x_4' = r_4' x_0 - \alpha_{14}x_1 - \alpha_{24}x_2 - \alpha_{34}x_3 - \alpha_{44}x_4 - \ldots - \alpha_{r4}x_r$$

$$\cdot \quad \cdot \quad \cdot \quad \cdot \quad \cdot \quad \cdot \quad \cdot \quad \cdot \quad \cdot \quad \cdot \quad \cdot \quad \cdot \quad \cdot \quad \cdot \quad \cdot \quad \cdot \quad \cdot \quad \cdot$$

$$x_r' = r_r' x_0 - \alpha_{1r}x_1 - \alpha_{2r}x_2 - \alpha_{3r}x_3 - \alpha_{4r}x_4 - \ldots - \alpha_{rr}x_r$$

$$x_{r+s}' = x_{r+s}.$$

Since our integral collineations form a group, this is a new collineation of exactly the sort we want. The leading coefficient is

$$2n - (r_1 + r_2 + r_3) = n + [n - (r_1 + r_2 + r_3)] < n.$$

We are uncertain about the relative sizes of the numbers

$$(n - r_2 - r_3), \ (n - r_3 - r_1), \ (n - r_1 - r_2), \ r_4, \ r_5, \ldots, \ r_r,$$

but by a rearrangement of terms we may put them in order of magnitude, and a rearrangement corresponds to another collineation of our group. Keeping on in this way we see that our original collineation can be factored into collineations of the type (19) and rearrangements of the subscripts 1 to r. These may be made to correspond to standard quadratic transformations, collineations of the plane, and rearrangements of the points P_i. Hence there is a succession of such transformations which will produce a Cremona transformation of the plane whose corresponding collineation in higher space has exactly the coefficients given. This gives a beautiful result:

Kantor's Theorem 25] *A necessary and sufficient condition that a set of positive integers $n, r_1, r_2, r_3, ..., r_r$ which satisfy the relations*

$$3n - r_1 - r_2 - r_3 - ... - r_r = 3 \qquad n^2 - r_1^2 - r_2^2 - r_3^2 - ... - r_r^2 = 1$$

should correspond to an actual Cremona transformation is that there should exist such positive integers r_i and such positive or 0 integers α_{ij} that equations (12) *and* (13) *are satisfied.*[*]

Let us give the matrices of the collineations in higher space which correspond to certain simple Cremona transformations. A collineation in the plane appears in higher space as the identity. The standard quadratic transformation is (19). The matrix for the De Jonquières is

$$\begin{Vmatrix} n & -(n-1) & -1 & -1 & . & . & . & -1 \\ (n-1) & -(n-2) & -1 & -1 & . & . & . & -1 \\ 1 & -1 & -1 & 0 & . & . & . & 0 \\ 1 & -1 & 0 & -1 & . & . & . & 0 \\ . & . & . & . & . & . & . & . \\ 1 & -1 & 0 & 0 & . & . & . & -1 \end{Vmatrix} \qquad (19)$$

Symmetric quartic:

$$\begin{Vmatrix} 5 & -2 & -2 & -2 & -2 & -2 & -2 \\ 2 & 0 & -1 & -1 & -1 & -1 & -1 \\ 2 & -1 & 0 & -1 & -1 & -1 & -1 \\ 2 & -1 & -1 & 0 & -1 & -1 & -1 \\ 2 & -1 & -1 & -1 & 0 & -1 & -1 \\ 2 & -1 & -1 & -1 & -1 & 0 & -1 \\ 2 & -1 & -1 & -1 & -1 & -1 & 0 \end{Vmatrix} \qquad (20)$$

---

[*] Kantor[3], p. 35. The statement is not quite explicit, nor does the **writer** seem to appreciate the full value of his theorem.

Symmetric octavic or Geiser involution:

$$\begin{Vmatrix} 8 & -3 & -3 & . & . & . & -3 \\ 3 & -2 & -1 & . & . & . & -1 \\ 3 & -1 & -2 & . & . & . & . \\ . & . & . & . & . & . & . \\ 3 & -1 & -1 & . & . & . & -1 \end{Vmatrix}. \tag{21}$$

Symmetric heptadekadic:

$$\begin{Vmatrix} 17 & -6 & -6 & . & . & . & -6 \\ 6 & -3 & -2 & . & . & . & -2 \\ 6 & -2 & -3 & . & . & . & -2 \\ . & . & . & . & . & . & . \\ 6 & -2 & -2 & . & . & . & -3 \end{Vmatrix}. \tag{22}$$

The relation between Cremona transformations and collineations in higher space has been carried much further, and methods of higher analysis, such as the use of Θ functions, have been fruitfully employed.* It would lead us too far afield to pursue them further.

* Cf. Coble[2].

CHAPTER VIII

GROUPS OF CREMONA TRANSFORMATIONS

§ 1. Continuous groups

THE study of Cremona transformations which we have made up to this point has been concerned with general properties and with the peculiar characteristics of transformations of certain special types. The concept of a group of Cremona transformations has never been explicitly introduced, although it cannot have escaped the reader's notice that the totality of Cremona transformations in the plane is an infinite group. It is our purpose in this present last chapter to consider Cremona groups of certain special sorts.

Let us begin with a study of continuous groups, depending analytically on a certain number of parameters. Let us bear in mind that, by definition, a group shall contain the inverse of each of its transformations. If a point be fundamental for a Cremona transformation it is fundamental for the product of this and a succeeding transformation unless the first carry it into a curve which is fundamental for the second. As any transformation of the group can be split into two factors, one of which is arbitrary, we have

Theorem 1] *In any continuous group of Cremona transformations, those fundamental points of a particular transformation which are not fundamental for the general transformation are carried into curves fundamental for the general transformation.*

Let us take, as an example, the totality of circular transformations of the projective plane. The fundamental points for any one are the circular points at infinity, and the point of concurrence of those circles which go into straight lines. This point goes into the line at infinity, which is fundamental.

Consider, next, a continuous group, and a particular curve. It will be carried by the general transformation into a curve of fixed order which will never be exceeded, but may be diminished in special cases when extra fundamental points fall on the given curve. The totality of all curves in the plane of this order n make a linear system determined by base points (0 in number). The invariant system of curves of order n will lie in this, perhaps in a linear system of that order determined by base points within the general system of order n. It must, in any case, lie in one linear system of order n, determined by base points, which is of lowest possible dimension. This linear system must be invariant, for if it were not it would share with all the systems to which it is transformed a linear system determined by base points of lower dimension which included the invariant curve system. The essential thing is that our continuous group will carry into itself some linear system determined by base points.

Theorem 2] *A continuous group of Cremona transformations will carry into itself an infinite linear system of curves determined by base points.*

If the general curve of the linear system have genus greater than 2, we may fix our attention on the system of special adjoints. We have thus only to consider the case of an invariant system of elliptic or rational curves.

Consider first the transformation which carries into itself a set of elliptic curves. If this set of elliptic curves be transformable into a set of quartics with two common double points, in the transformed group isomorphic with the first, reducible quartics will go to reducible quartics. The reducible quartics are a seven-parameter system consisting of the line which connects the two points and a cubic through them, and a six-parameter system consisting in two conics through them. Hence our group is simply isomorphic with the group that carries into itself a set of conics through two points. If the points be distinct this is a six-parameter group simply isomorphic with that of circular transformations,* and also simply isomorphic with the six-parameter group of collineations in space that carry into itself a general quadric. When the two double points are adjacent, the group is simply isomorphic with the group in the plane that carries into itself all parabolas with a set of parallel axes, or the group of collineations of space that carries a quadric cone into itself. This is simply isomorphic with the seven-parameter group of Euclidean motions.

In the other cases where elliptic curves are carried into themselves, we may either consider the case of an infinite system of cubics or a pencil of elliptic curves of order $3r_1$ with nine points

* For groups of circular transformations see Coolidge[5], pp. 330 ff.

of order r_1 in common, and these nine lie on a cubic. Hence all the fundamental points of every transformation will lie on a system of cubics, or be the nine centres of the pencil. In a continuous group the fundamental points must be fixed or vary continuously. Hence, in this continuous group all transformations have the same fundamental points. Since the product of two transformations is still a transformation of order n, a homaloid of one transformation goes into a homaloid of another:

$$1 = n^2 - \sum r_i^2 = n.$$

This case is, hence, excluded.

There remains the possibility that our transformation carries into itself a linear system of rational curves. Such a system may be carried into:

a) the system of all lines;

b) a pencil of lines;

c) a system of curves of order n' with a common multiple point of order $n'-1$, and perhaps certain other common nonsingular points.

The system of all Cremona transformations which permute all the lines of the plane is that of collineations or a sub-group.

If the lines of a pencil are permuted, all transformations must be of the De Jonquières type, and of common order.

If an irreducible invariant system of curves consist in curves of order n' with a common point of order $n'-1$ and certain fixed simple points, the number of these will not exceed $n'-1$, so that the number of parameters of the system will be

$$\geqslant \frac{n'(n'+3)}{2} - \frac{n'(n'-1)}{2} - (n'-1) = n'+1,$$

hence some of the curves will consist in n' concurrent lines, of which one must be variable. Hence, as before, a pencil of lines is invariant, and we have a De Jonquières transformation group with a common singular point. If the product of two De Jonquières transformations is to be a third of that same order and multiple point, the two must share the same $n-1$ simple fundamental points, and these must be adjacent to the singular point, otherwise the group could be replaced by a similar one of lower order. We have a group where all homaloids have the same singular point of order $n-1$ and the same tangents there.

The sub-group where all lines through this singular point O_3 are invariant can be written

$$x_1' = a\theta^{n-1}(x_1, x_2)x_1 \qquad x_2' = a\theta^{n-1}(x_1, x_2)x_2$$
$$x_3' = b\theta^{n-1}(x_1, x_2)x_3 + \chi^n(x_1, x_2).$$

Here a and b and the coefficients of χ are arbitrary, $n+3$ in all. Hence the general transformation depends on $n+5$ parameters.

Enriques's Theorem 3] *Every continuous group of Cremona transformations is simply isomorphic with*

a) a group of collineations;

b) a group of motions and reflections in 3-space;

c) a group of circular transformations;

*d) an $(n+5)$-parameter group of De Jonquières transformations, where all homaloids have the same singular point, and the same tangents there.**

Our De Jonquières transformation may be put into another form. We write first

$$\rho X_1 = a_1 x_1^n + \theta^{n-1}(x_1, x_2)x_3$$
$$\rho X_2 = a_2 x_1^{n-1} x_2 + \theta^{n-1}(x_1, x_2)x_3$$
$$\cdots \cdots \cdots \cdots \cdots$$
$$\rho X_{n+1} = a_{n+1} x_2^n + \theta^{n-1}(x_1, x_2)x_3.$$

In a space of $n+1$ dimensions with homogeneous coordinates $X_0 : X_1 : \ldots : X_{n+1}$, these represent a conical surface of order n with vertex at $(1, 0, 0, \ldots, 0)$.

Theorem 4] *A continuous group of Cremona transformations is simply isomorphic with*

a) a group of collineations of the plane;

b) a group of collineations of three-dimensional space which keeps invariant a non-reducible quadric or conic;

c) a group of collineations of space of $n-1$ dimensions which leave in place a rational conical surface of order n.†

§ 2. Infinite discontinuous groups

It might seem at first that the study of continuous groups would furnish the methods necessary for that of infinite discontinuous ones. Such is not, however, the case. In a discontinuous group the order of a curve can change suddenly; we have much fewer

---

* Enriques, cit.

† Ibid., p. 473. Continuous groups of De Jonquières transformations are found on p. 532. See also Fano.

tools to work with than before, and must content ourselves with pointing out certain easily obtainable types.

The infinite discontinuous groups of collineations of the plane constitute a large field by themselves. The reader can easily find such groups by imagining the plane filled with equilateral triangles, regular hexagons or squares, and considering the motions which carry one of these into another. In the same way we find infinite groups of circular transformations by studying automorphic functions of the complex variable. If we fill our space with cubes we get infinite discontinuous groups of motions which give infinite discontinuous groups carrying sets of tangent conics into themselves, etc. There will be more novelty, however, in determining infinite discontinuous groups of De Jonquières transformations with O_3 as a common singular fundamental point. There will be a sub-group where all the lines through O_3 stay in place. Each individual line will be carried into itself by an infinite group of projective transformations. If all of these be parabolic, the locus of fixed points is either the point O_3 itself or a curve of order n with a singular point of multiplicity $n-1$ at O_3. The possibility that the locus should be O_3 we may discard, since it is fundamental for the transformation. If the transformations on the individual lines be not all parabolic, the locus of the fixed points is a curve of order n with multiplicity $n-2$ at O_3. Since the intersections of a straight line with this curve are invariant, it must be possible for a line to meet a homaloid just n times, so that the order of the transformation is $\geqslant n$. Let us seek a De Jonquières transformation of this order which keeps such a curve fixed. Let the equation of the curve be

$$\psi(x_1, x_2, x_3) \equiv f_0^{n-2}(x_1, x_2)x_3^2 + f_1^{n-1}(x_1, x_2)x_3 + f_2^n(x_1, x_2).$$

The equations of the De Jonquières transformation with all lines through O_3 fixed will be

$$x_1' = x_1\theta^{n-1}(x_1, x_2) \qquad x_2' = x_2\theta^{n-1}(x_1, x_2)$$
$$x_3' = x_3\theta^{n-1}(x_1, x_2) + \psi^n(x_1, x_2, x_3).$$

Since the curve $x_3^{n-1}\theta + \psi = 0$

has multiplicity $n-1$ at O_3,

$$\theta \equiv -x_3f_0^{n-2}(x_1, x_2) + \bar{f}_1(x_1, x_2)$$
$$x_1' = [-x_3f_0 + \bar{f}_1]x_1 \qquad x_2' = [-x_3f_0 + \bar{f}_1]x_2 \qquad x_3' = [f_1 + \bar{f}_1]x_3 + f_2.$$

If we write $$f_1+\bar{f}_1+\bar{\bar{f}}_1 \equiv 0,$$
our transformation may be written

$$x'_1 = x_1 \qquad x'_2 = x_2 \qquad x'_3 = \frac{-\bar{\bar{f}}_1 x_3 + f_2}{-f_0 x_3 + \bar{f}_1} \qquad (1)$$

$$x_1 = x'_1 \qquad x_2 = x'_2 \qquad x_3 = \frac{-\bar{f}_1 x'_3 + f_2}{-f_0 x'_3 + \bar{\bar{f}}_1}. \qquad (2)$$

The remaining $2(n-1)$ other fundamental points of either transformation are on the lines

$$f_1\bar{\bar{f}}_1 - f_0 f_2 = 0. \qquad (3)$$

The two fundamental curves corresponding to O_3 are

$$-f_0 x_3 + \bar{f}_1 = 0 \qquad -f'_0 x'_3 + \bar{\bar{f'}}_1 = 0. \qquad (4)$$

They have the same tangents at O_3 as $\psi = 0$. The reasoning throughout is reversible.

Theorem 5] *Given a curve of order n with a singular point O_3 of multiplicity $n-2$ and distinct tangents. Take a curve of order $n-1$ with the same singular point and tangents thereat. This will be the fundamental curve corresponding to O_3 in a De Jonquières transformation of order n which leaves all points of the given curve invariant. The fundamental curve for the inverse transformation will have the same singular point and tangents, and meet the curve of fixed points on the same radiating lines as the given fundamental curve does.*[*]

We see that when the curve of invariant points is determined, the transformation depends merely on the binary form $\bar{f}_1$.

Theorem 6] *The determination of a De Jonquières transformation of order n, which keeps invariant all points of a curve of order n, with a multiple point of order $n-2$ with distinct tangents, depends on n parameters.*

Let us take a second transformation:

$$x''_1 = x'_1 \qquad x''_2 = x'_2 \qquad x''_3 = \frac{-\bar{\bar{\phi}}_1 x'_3 + f_2}{-f_0 x'_3 + \bar{\phi}_1}. \qquad (5)$$

The product of (1) and (5) will be

$$x''_1 = x_1 \quad x''_2 = x_2 \qquad x''_3 = \frac{-(f_0 f_2 - \bar{\bar{\phi}}_1 \bar{\bar{f}}_1)x_3 + f_2(\bar{f}_1 - \bar{\bar{\phi}}_1)}{-f_0(\bar{\phi}_1 - \bar{\bar{f}}_1)x_3 + \bar{\phi}_1 \bar{f}_1 - f_0 f_2}$$

$$f_1 + \bar{f}_1 + \bar{\bar{f}}_1 \equiv f_1 + \bar{\phi}_1 + \bar{\bar{\phi}}_1 \equiv 0$$

$$\bar{f}_1 - \bar{\bar{\phi}}_1 \equiv \bar{\phi}_1 - \bar{\bar{f}}_1.$$

---

[*] For this theorem and the next see Kantor[2].

Hence we may write

$$x_1'' = x_1 \qquad x_2'' = x_2 \qquad x_3'' = \frac{\dfrac{-(f_0 f_2 - \bar{\bar{f}}_1 \bar{\bar{\phi}}_1)}{\bar{f}_1 - \bar{\bar{\phi}}_1} x_3 + f_2}{-f_0 x_3 + \dfrac{\bar{\bar{f}}_1 \bar{\phi}_1 - f_0 f_2}{\bar{f}_1 - \bar{\bar{\phi}}_1}}.$$

The sum of minus the coefficient of x_3 in the numerator and the denominator constant is

$$\frac{\bar{f}_1 \bar{\phi}_1 - \bar{\bar{f}}_1 \bar{\bar{\phi}}_1}{\bar{f}_1 - \bar{\bar{\phi}}_1} = -f_1,$$

as it should be.

This will be of order n if

$$(f_0 f_2 - \bar{\bar{f}}_1 \bar{\bar{\phi}}_1) \equiv 0 \bmod (\bar{f}_1 - \bar{\bar{\phi}}_1).$$

This is not usually the case, so the product of two such transformations of order n is a transformation of order $n' > n$.

Theorem 7] *There is an infinite discontinuous group of De Jonquières transformations keeping invariant all points of a curve of order n with a multiple point of order $n-2$.*

Suppose that we have a transformation of this sort of order $n' > n$ that keeps all points of $\psi = 0$ invariant. We may find a transformation of order n whose simple fundamental points are identical with some of those of the inverse of the transformation of higher order. The first transformation will carry a straight line into a curve of order n', which will be carried by the second into one of order

$$nn' - (n-1)(n'-1) - n = n' - 1,$$

so that the product is a De Jonquières transformation of the required form of order less than n'.

Theorem 8] *Every De Jonquières transformation which keeps invariant all points of a hyperelliptic curve of order n with a singular point of multiplicity $n-2$ with distinct tangents may be factored into De Jonquières transformations of order n.*

It is quite conceivable that there might be a transformation which carries the curve ψ into itself but permutes its points. The lines through the singular point are permuted, as are the tangents, so they go to make up the special adjoints. If the genus of the curve exceed 1, there cannot be an infinite number

of these. Suppose that the singular point is at the end of the
y-axis, so that the curve is written

$$\phi_0^{n-2}(x)y^2 + 2\phi_1^{n-1}(x)y + \phi_2^n(x) = 0. \tag{6}$$

Let $\quad x = x' \qquad y = \dfrac{y' - \phi_1(x')}{\phi_0(x')} \qquad y' = \phi_0(x)y + \phi_1(x)$

$$y'^2 = [\phi_1(x')]^2 - \phi_0(x')\phi_2(x'). \tag{7}$$

A birational transformation of (11) into itself must carry its
g_2^1 into itself and so take the form

$$x' = \frac{\alpha\bar{x}' + \beta}{\gamma\bar{x}' + \delta} \qquad \alpha\delta - \beta\gamma \neq 0.$$

If this permute the roots of

$$F(x') \equiv \phi_0(x')\phi_2(x') - [\phi_1(x')]^2 = 0,$$

$$F(x') = \frac{kF(\bar{x}')}{(\gamma\bar{x}' + \delta)^{2n-2}}.$$

If we write $\quad x' = \dfrac{\alpha\bar{x}' + \beta}{\gamma\bar{x}' + \delta} \qquad y' = \dfrac{\sqrt{k}\bar{y}'}{(\gamma\bar{x}' + \delta)^{n-1}}$

$$\bar{x}' = \frac{-\delta x' + \beta}{\gamma x' - \alpha} \qquad \bar{y}' = \frac{\sqrt{l}y'}{(\gamma x' - \alpha)^{n-1}},$$

we have a Cremona transformation of the (x', y') plane that
carries (11) into itself, and corresponds to a Cremona transformation of the (x, y) plane that carries (10) into itself.

Theorem 9] *Every birational transformation of a curve of order
n, with a multiple point of order $n-2$, into itself is contained in
a Cremona transformation of the plane.*

When $n > 3$, there are clearly only a finite number of these,
and the same applies when the invariant curve has a singular
point of multiplicity $n-1$.

§ 3. Finite groups

It is a curious fact that the approach to finite groups follows
the analogy of continuous groups much more closely than is the
case for infinite discontinuous ones. Suppose that we have a
finite group containing n transformations, say $T_1, T_2, ..., T_n$. Let
f be a curve through no fundamental point of any transformation, and let us write

$$F \equiv T_1(f)T_2(f) ... T_n(f).$$

This reducible curve is invariant for all transformations of the group.

If the order of f be sufficiently high we can get as many linearly independent invariant curves of the order of F as we want; the linear system of least dimension, given by base points, that holds all these will be invariant. We thus get the theorem which is fundamental here as the corresponding theorem was for continuous groups.*

Theorem 10] *In any finite group of Cremona transformations there will always be an infinite linear system of curves given by base points which is invariant for all transformations of the group.*

We may follow our previous reasoning step by step and show that there must be invariant an infinite linear system either of rational or of elliptic curves. If there be an invariant one-parameter system of rational curves, these may be carried into a pencil of lines, and the transformations are all of the De Jonquières variety. If all lines through the singular point be invariant, we fall back on essentially the problem of the last section. If they be permuted, we meet also the problem of finite groups of binary projective transformations. These groups are thoroughly well known since the classic work of Klein[2]. Such groups are simply isomorphic with cyclic groups of rotations about a fixed axis, a dihedral group consisting in a cyclic group and a reflection in a plane perpendicular to the axis, and the groups which carry into themselves the five regular solids.

If an invariant system of curves depend on two parameters it is equivalent to the system of all lines in the plane, and we meet the problem of finding finite groups of plane collineations. These were first classified by Jordan[2], the results being completed by Valentiner[2]. If the invariant system depend on more than two parameters, it can be carried into a set of curves of order n with a fixed point of multiplicity $n-1$ and perhaps other fixed points; we are thrown back on a problem of De Jonquières transformations.

Let us next suppose that we have an invariant system of elliptic curves. If these can be carried into quartics with two

---

* The most extended researches in the present topic are Kantor[3] and Kantor[4]. The works are crammed full of results, but obscurely written and not free from errors. A better presentation is that of Wiman.

fixed double points, we are once more back either on the problem of finite groups of circular transformations, i.e. binary linear transformations, automorphic groups, or finite groups of motions. The other cases with invariant systems of elliptic curves have been studied at a good deal of length in the works of Klein and Wiman recently quoted. In many cases there is much to be gained by reverting to the method of mapping the plane on an auxiliary cubic surface that we developed in Book II, Ch. I, to prove Clebsch's transformation theorem at the end of the chapter. The problem then becomes one of finding groups of collineations of a three-dimensional space which leave a certain cubic surface invariant.*

Theorem 11] *A finite group of Cremona transformations is simply isomorphic with*

a) a group of binary linear transformations;

b) a group of motions and reflections in three-dimensional space;

c) a group of De Jonquières transformations with a common singular point;

d) a group with an invariant system of curves of order $3r$ with nine common points of multiplicity r;

e) a group with an invariant system of cubic curves through $1, ..., 7$ common points.

And so the end. We have covered a large amount of territory in the course of our wanderings; there lies incomparably more beyond. May future students boldly enter in and occupy the ground. Whatever the mathematical fashion of any particular moment may suggest, algebraic methods and algebraic curves will never cease to be important in pure mathematics. If any reader find help in the preceding pages towards pursuing these beautiful studies, the labour and effort put into this book will not have been spent in vain.

* Cf. Wiman, p. 198.

INDEX OF AUTHORS QUOTED

Abel[1], 'Démonstration d'une propriété générale d'une certaine classe de fonctions transcendantes', *Œuvres Complètes*, vol. i, new ed., Christiania, 1881, 277.

Abel[2], 'Solution d'un problème général concernant la transformation des fonctions elliptiques', ibid., 367.

Alexander, 'On the Factorization of Cremona Plane Transformations', *Transactions American Math. Soc.*, vol. xvii, 1916, 447.

Allen, 'Su alcuni caratteri di una serie algebrica, e la formola di De Jonquières', *Rendiconti Cercolo Matematico di Palermo*, vol. xxxvii, 1914, 328.

Amodeo[1], 'Curve K-gonali', *Annali di matematica*, Series (2), vol. xxi, 1893, 308.

Amodeo[2], 'Contribuzione alla teoria delle serie irrazionali involutorie giacenti sulle varietà algebriche ad una dimensione', ibid., vol. xx, 1892, 325.

Appell et Goursat, 'Théorie des fonctions algébriques', Paris, 1895, 213, 270, 271, 276, 277, 331.

Baccharach, 'Ueber den Cayleyschen Schnittpunktsatz', *Math. Annalen*, vol. xxvi, 1886, 37.

Battaglini, 'Sulle forme ternarie di grado qualunque', *Rendiconti della R. Accademia delle Scienze di Napoli*, vol. vii, 1868, 712.

Bertini[1], 'Trasformazione di una curva algebrica in un ultra con soli punti doppi', *Math. Annalen*, vol. xliv, 1894, 212.

Bertini[2], 'Sopra alcuni teoremi fondamentali dell curve piane algebriche', *Rendiconti R. Istituto Lombardo*, Series (2), vol. xxi, 1888, 207.

Bertini[3], 'La geometria delle serie lineari sopra curva piana secondo il metodo algebrico', *Annali di Matematica*, Series (2), vol. xxii, 189, 251.

Bertini[4], 'Sui sistemi lineari', *Rendiconti del R. Istituto Lombardo*, Series (2), vol. xv, 1882.

Bertini[5], 'Ricerche sulle trasformazioni univoche involutorie nel piano', *Annali di Matematica*, Series (2), vol. viii, 1877, 481.

Bertini[6], 'Sulle trasformazioni univoche piane, ed in particulare sulle involutorie', *Rendiconti del R. Istituto Lombardo*, Series (2), vol. xiii, 1880, 456, 481.

Berzolari[1], 'Allgemeine Theorie der höheren ebenen algebraischen Kurven', *Enzyklopädie der Math. Wissenschaften*, vol. iii, Part 2[1], Leipzig, 1906, 99.

Berzolari[2], 'Sulla determinazione di una curva o di una superficie algebrica e su alcune questioni di postulazione', *Rendiconti del R. Instituto Lombardo*, Series (2), vol. xlvii, 1914, 24.

Bioche, 'Sur les singularités des courbes algébriques planes', *Bulletin de la société mathématique de France*, vol. xx, 1892, 101.

Bliss, 'The Reduction of singularities of Plane Curves by Cremona Transformations', *Bulletin American Math. Soc.*, vol. xxix, 1923, 212.

Bobek, 'Ueber hyperelliptische Curven', *Math. Annalen*, vol. xxix, 1887, 307.

Böcher, *Introduction to Higher Algebra*, New York, 1907, 2, 7, 12.

Bouwmann, 'Ueber den Ort der Berührungspunkte von Strahlenbüscheln und Curvenbüscheln, *Nieuw Archief vor Wiskunde*, Series (2), vol. iv, 1900, 159.

Brill[1], 'Ueber Entsprechen von Punktsystemen auf einer Curve', *Math. Annalen*, vol. vi, 1883, 129.

Brill[2], 'Ueber die Hessesche Curve', ibid., vol. xiii, 1878.

Brill[3], 'Ueber Singularitäten ebener algebraischer Curven und eine neue Curvenspecies', ibid., vol. xvi, 1880, 227.

Brill und Nother, 'Ueber die algebraischen Functionen und ihre Anwendung in der Geometrie', ibid., vol. vii, 1874, 30, 251, 263, 298.

Brusotti[1], 'Sulla generazione di curve piane algebriche reali, etc.', *Annali di Matematica*, Series (3), vol. xxii, 1914, 53, 55.

Brusotti[2], 'Curve generatrici e curve aggregati nella costruzione di curve piane, etc.', *Rendiconti Cercolo Matematico di Palermo*, vol. xlii, 1917, 57.

Burkhardt[1], 'Sur le principe de correspondance', *Comptes Rendus*, vol. cxxvi, 1898, 344.

Burkhardt[2], 'Elliptische Funktionen', 2nd ed., Berlin and Leipzig, 1906, 364, 366.

Caporali[1], 'Sulle trasformazioni univoche piane involutorie', *Rendiconti della R. Accademia delle Scienze di Napoli*, vol. xviii, 1879, 483.

Caporali[2], 'Sopra i sistemi lineari triplamente infiniti di curve algebriche piane', *Collectanea Mathematica*, Milan, 1851, 402.

Carnot, *Géométrie de position*, Paris, 1803, 190.

Castelnuovo[1], 'Ricerche di geometria sulle curve algebriche', *Atti dell. Accademia di Torino*, vol. xxiv, 1889, 309.

Castelnuovo[2], 'Sui multipli di una serie lineare di gruppi di punti, etc.', *Rendiconti del Cercolo Matematico di Palermo*, vol. vii, 1893, 295.

Castelnuovo[3], 'Il numero delle involuzioni razionali geicenti sopra una curva di dato genere', *Atti della R. Accademia dei Lincei*, Series (4), vol. v, part 2, 1889.

Montesano[2], 'I gruppi Cremoniani di numeri', *Atti della R. Accademia delle Scienze di Napoli*, Series (2), vol. 15, 1914, 473.

Morley, 'The Eliminant of a Net of Curves', *American Journal of Math.*, vol. xlvii, 1925, 10.

Nagy[1] 'Ueber die reelen Züge algebraischer ebener und Raum-Kurven', *Math. Annalen*, vol. lxxvii, 1916, 66.

Nagy[2], 'Ueber die charakteristischen Zahlen einer Kurve von maximal Klassenindex', ibid., vol. c, 1928, 66.

Nagy[3], 'Ueber Kurven von maximal Klassenindex', ibid., vol. lxxxix, 1923, 60.

Newton, *Opuscula Mathematica Philosophica et Philologica*, Lausanne and Geneva, 1744, 45, 189.

Nöther[1], 'Ueber einen Satz aus der Theorie der algebraischen Functionen', *Math. Annalen*, vol. vi, 1873, 29.

Nöther[2], 'Rationale Ausführung der Operationen in der Theorie der algebraischen Functionen', ibid., vol. xxiii, 1884, 233, 353.

Nöther[3], 'Ueber die singuläre Werthsysteme einer algebraischen Function', ibid., vol. ix, 1876, 201.

Nöther[4], 'Les combinaisons caractéristiques dans la transformation d'un point singulier', *Rendiconti Cercolo Matematico di Palermo*, vol. iv, 1890, 237.

Nöther[5], 'Ueber die algebraische Functionen einer und zweier Variablen', *Göttingische Nachrichten*, 1871, 207, 213.

Nöther[6], 'Ueber die Schnittpunktsysteme einer algebraischen Curve mit nichtadjungirten Curven', *Math. Annalen*, vol. xv, 1879.

Nöther[7], 'Ueber die reductiblen algebraischen Curven', *Acta Mathematica*, vol. viii, 1886, 312.

Nöther[8], 'Ueber Flächen welche Schaaren rationaler Curven besitzen', *Math. Annalen*, vol. iii, 1871, 447.

Osgood, *Lehrbuch der Funktionentheorie*, vol. i, 5th ed., Leipzig, 1928, 358, 359; vol. ii, 2nd ed., Leipzig, 1929, 277.

Pernot et Moisson, 'Étude des points à l'infini d'une courbe algébrique', *Nouvelles Annales de Math.*, Series (4), vol. vi, 1906, 41.

Picard, *Traité d'Analyse*, 1st ed., vol. ii, Paris, 1893, 270, 356, 363.

Pitarelli, 'Sul significato geometrico delle "Ueberschiebungen" nelle forme binarie', *Giornale di matematiche*, vol. xvii, 1879, 369.

Poincaré, 'Théorie des groupes fuchsiennes', *Œuvres*, vol. ii, Paris, 1916, 360.

Puiseux, 'Recherches sur les Fonctions Algébriques', *Liouville*, vol. xv, 1850, 207.

Ragsdale, 'On the Arrangement of the Real Branches of Plane Algebraic Curves', *American Journal of Math.*, vol. xxviii, 1906, 59.

mente infinito', *Annali di Matematica*, Series (2), vol. xxii, 1894, 13, 251, 257, 292.

Segre[5], 'Intorno ai punti di Weierstrass', *Atti della R. Accademia dei Lincei*, Series (5), vol. viii, 1899, 292.

Segre[6], 'Un osservazione relativa alla riducibilità delle trasformazioni Cremoniane, etc.', *Atti della R. Accademia delle Scienze di Torino*, vol. xxxvi, 1901, 447.

Segre, Beniamino[1], 'Sui moduli delle curve poligonali', *Math. Annalen*, vol. c., 1928, 309.

Segre, Beniamino[2], 'Esistenza e dimensione di sistemi continui di curve piane', *Rendiconti della R. Accademia dei Lincei*, Series (6), vol. x, 1929, 432.

Severi[1], *Lezioni di geometria algebrica*, Padova, 1908, 129.

Severi[2], 'Le corrispondenze fra i punti di una curva algebrica, etc.', *Memorie della R. Accademia delle Scienze di Torino*, Series (2), vol. liv, 1904, 335.

Severi[3], 'Sul principio della conservazione del numero, *Rendiconti Cercolo Matematico di Palermo*, vol. xxxiii, 1912, 441.

Severi[4], 'Sui fondamenti della geometria numerativa e sulla teoria delle caratteristiche', *Atti del R. Istituto Veneto*, vol. lxxv, part 2^2, 1916.

Severi[5], 'Trattato di geometria algebrica', vol. i, Part 1, Bologna, 1926, 136.

Severi[6], 'Sul teorema di esistenza di Riemann, *Rendiconti Cercolo matematico di Palermo*, vol. xlvi, 1922.

Severi-Löffler, *Vorlesungen ueber algebraische Geometrie*, Leipzig, 1921, 100, 105, 259, 276, 277, 278, 282, 294, 298, 306, 320, 346, 432.

Siebeck, 'Ueber eine neue analytische Behandlungsweise der Brennpunkte', *Crelle*, vol. lxiv, 1865, 173.

Sisam, 'On Some Loci associated with Plane Curves', *American Journal of Math.*, vol. xxx, 1908, 164.

Snyder, 'On Birational Transformations of Curves of High Genus', ibid., same vol., 408.

Steiner, 'Systematische Entwicklung der Abhängigkeit geometrischer Gestalten von einander', *Werke*, vol i, Berlin, 1881, 201.

Stolz, 'Allgemeine Theorie der Asymptoten der algebraischen Curven', *Math. Annalen*, vol. xi, 1877, 41.

Study[1], 'Ueber Schnittpunktfiguren ebener algebraischer Curven', ibid., vol. xxxvi, 1890, 34, 37.

Study[2], *Die Geometrie der Dynamen*, Leipzig, 1903, 427.

Study[3], 'Ueber das sogenannte Prinzip der Erhaltung der Anzahl', *Grunerts Archiv der Mathematik und Physik*, Series (3), vol. viii, 1905, 441.

Transformationen in der Ebene', *Math. Annalen*, vol. xlviii, 1896, 497, 498.

Wölfling, 'Das Verhalten der Steinerschen, Cayleyschen und anderer Covarianter-curves in singulären Punkten der Grundcurve', *Zeitschrift für Mathematik und Physik*, vol. xl, 1895, 157.

Wright, 'The Ovals of a Plane Sextic Curve', *American Journal of Math.*, vol. xxix, 1907, 65.

Zeuthen[1], 'Nouvelle démonstration des théorèmes sur les séries de points correspondants sur deux courbes', *Math. Annalen*, vol. iii, 1871, 136.

Zeuthen[2], 'Note sur le principe de correspondance', *Bulletin des Sciences Mathématiques*, vol. v, 1873, 131, 164.

Zeuthen[3], 'Note sur un problème de Steiner', ibid., vol. xxii, 1887.

Zeuthen[4], 'Almindelige Egenskaber ved Systemer af plane Kurver', *Mémoires de la Société Danoise des Sciences et Lettres*, Series (5), vol. x, 1873, 437.

Zeuthen[5], 'Abzählende Methoden', *Enzyklopädie der Mathematischen Wissenschaften*, vol. iii, part 2^1, Leipzig, 1906, 440.

Zeuthen[6], *Lehrbuch der abzählenden Methoden in der Geometrie*, Leipzig, 1914, 288, 439, 440.

SUBJECT INDEX

DICTIONARY OF CONFORMAL REPRESENTATIONS
by H. Kober

Developed for the British Admiralty during World War II, this unique book enables its users to solve Laplace's Equation in Two Dimensions for many boundary conditions. It contains scores of geometrical forms and their transformations for use in checking against specific problems.

Kober's DICTIONARY OF CONFORMAL REPRESENTATIONS is especially helpful in hydrodynamics, gas dynamics, free streamline theory, heat flow, magnetic field problems, soil mechanics, electrostatics, map projection, etc. It contains the following specific features for workers in different fields: Linear and bilinear transformations for electrical engineers — Joukowski aerofoil for aerodynamists — Transcendental functions for physicists and engineers — Schwartz-Christophel transformations for hydrodynamicists and electrical engineers — Borda's mouthpiece for researchers in hydraulics and jet propulsion. The book is classified according to the analytic functions describing the transformations; it gives instant access to time-saving set-ups and eliminates much of the work involved in deriving a particular configuration.

"Of great value to workers in such fields as electricity, hydrodynamics, aerodynamics and heat flow," BRITISH JOURNAL OF APPLIED PHYSICS. "Useful to engineers and physicists as well as to mathematicians," JOURNAL OF ROYAL NAVAL SCIENTIFIC SERVICE. "May well remain the standard work for many years," MATHEMATICAL GAZETTE.

Bibliography. Glossary. Topological index. 447 diagrams. xvi + 208pp. 6⅛ x 9¼.

PARTIAL DIFFERENTIAL EQUATIONS OF MATHEMATICAL PHYSICS

by A. G. Webster

Still one of the most important treatises on partial differential equations in any language, this comprehensive work by one of America's greatest mathematical physicists covers the basic method, theory and application of partial differential equations. There are clear and full chapters on

Fourier series
integral equations
elliptic equations
spherical, cylindrical, ellipsoidal harmonics
Cauchy's method
boundary problems
method of Riemann-Volterra
and many other topics

This is a book complete in itself, developing fully the needed theory and application of every important field.

vibration
elasticity
potential theory
theory of sound
wave propagation
heat conduction
and others

Professor Webster's work is a keystone book in the library of every mature physicist, mathematical physicist, mathematician, and research engineer. It can also serve as an introduction and supplementary text for the student.

Edited by Samuel J. Plimpton. Second corrected edition. 97 illustrations. vii + 440pp. 5⅜ x 8.

S263 Paperbound $2.00

DOVER BOOKS ON SCIENCE
BOOKS THAT EXPLAIN SCIENCE

CONCERNING THE NATURE OF THINGS, Sir William Bragg. Christmas lectures delivered at the Royal Society by Nobel laureate. Why a spinning ball travels in a curved track; how uranium is transmuted to lead, etc. Partial contents: atoms, gases, liquids, crystals, metals etc. No scientific background needed; wonderful for intelligent high school student. 32pp. of photos, 57 figures. xii + 232pp. 5⅜ x 8.   T31 Paperbound **$1.35**

THE NATURE OF LIGHT AND COLOUR IN THE OPEN AIR, M. Minnaert. Why is falling snow sometimes black? What causes mirages, the fata morgana, multiple suns and moons in the sky; how are shadows formed? Prof. Minnaert of the University of Utrecht answers these and similar questions in optics, light, colour, for non-specialists. Particularly valuable to nature, science students, painters, photographers. Translated by H. M. Kremer-Priest, K. Jay. 202 illustrations, including 42 photos. xvi + 362pp. 5⅜ x 8.   T196 Paperbound **$1.95**

THE RESTLESS UNIVERSE, Max Born. New enlarged version of this remarkably readable account by a Noble laureate. Moving from subatomic particles to universe, the author explains in very simple terms the latest theories of wave mechanics. Partial contents: air and its relatives, electrons & ions, waves & particles, electronic structure of the atom, nuclear physics. Nearly 600 illustrations, including 7 animated sequences. 325pp. 6 x 9.   T412 Paperbound **$2.00**

MATTER & LIGHT, THE NEW PHYSICS, L. de Broglie. Non-technical papers by a Nobel laureate explain electromagnetic theory, relativity, matter, light and radiation, wave mechanics, quantum physics, philosophy of science. Einstein, Planck, Bohr, others explained so easily that no mathematical training is needed for all but 2 of the 21 chapters. Unabridged. Index. 300pp. 5⅜ x 9.   T35 Paperbound **$1.75**

THE COMMON SENSE OF THE EXACT SCIENCES, W. K. Clifford. Introduction by James Newman, edited by Karl Pearson. For 70 years this has been a guide to classical scientific and mathematical thought. Explains with unusual clarity basic concepts, such as extension of meaning of symbols, characteristics of surface boundaries, properties of plane figures, vectors, Cartesian method of determining position, etc. Long preface by Bertrand Russell. Bibliography of Clifford. Corrected, 130 diagrams redrawn. 249pp. 5⅜ x 8.   T61 Paperbound **$1.60**

THE EVOLUTION OF SCIENTIFIC THOUGHT FROM NEWTON TO EINSTEIN, A. d'Abro. Einstein's special and general theories of relativity, with their historical implications, are analyzed in non-technical terms. Excellent accounts of the contributions of Newton, Riemann, Weyl, Planck, Eddington, Maxwell, Lorentz and others are treated in terms of space and time, equations of electromagnetics, finiteness of the universe, methodology of science. 21 diagrams. 482pp. 5⅜ x 8.   T2 Paperbound **$2.00**

WHAT IS SCIENCE, Norman Campbell. This excellent introduction explains scientific method, role of mathematics, types of scientific laws. Contents: 2 aspects of science, science & nature, laws of science, discovery of laws, explanation of laws, measurement & numerical laws, applications of science. 192pp. 5⅜ x 8.   S43 Paperbound **$1.25**

THE RISE OF THE NEW PHYSICS, A. d'Abro. A half-million word exposition, formerly titled THE DECLINE OF MECHANISM, for readers not versed in higher mathematics. The only thorough explanation, in everyday language, of the central core of modern mathematical physical theory, treating both classical and modern theoretical physics, and presenting in terms almost anyone can understand the equivalent of 5 years of study of mathematical physics. Scientifically impeccable coverage of mathematical-physical thought from the Newtonian system up through the electronic theories of Dirac and Heisenberg and Fermi's statistics. Combines both history and exposition; provides a broad yet unified and detailed view, with constant comparison of classical and modern views on phenomena and theories. "A must for anyone doing serious study in the physical sciences," JOURNAL OF THE FRANKLIN INSTITUTE. "Extraordinary faculty . . . to explain ideas and theories of theoretical physics in the language of daily life," ISIS. Indexed. 97 illustrations. ix + 982pp. 5⅜ x 8.
T3 Volume 1, Paperbound **$2.00**
T4 Volume 2, Paperbound **$2.00**

A HISTORY OF ASTRONOMY FROM THALES TO KEPLER, J. L. E. Dreyer. (Formerly A HISTORY OF PLANETARY SYSTEMS FROM THALES TO KEPLER.) This is the only work in English to give the complete history of man's cosmological views from prehistoric times to Kepler and Newton. Partial contents: Near Eastern astronomical systems, Early Greeks. Homocentric spheres of Eudoxus, Epicycles. Ptolemaic system, medieval cosmology. Copernicus. Kepler, etc. Revised, foreword by W. H. Stahl. New bibliography. xvii + 430pp. 5⅜ x 8.   S79 Paperbound **$1.98**

THE PSYCHOLOGY OF INVENTION IN THE MATHEMATICAL FIELD, J. Hadamard. Where do ideas come from? What role does the unconscious play? Are ideas best developed by mathematical reasoning, word reasoning, visualization? What are the methods used by Einstein, Poincaré, Galton, Riemann. How can these techniques be applied by others? Hadamard, one of the world's leading mathematicians, discusses these and other questions. xiii + 145pp. 5⅜ x 8.   T107 Paperbound **$1.25**

SPINNING TOPS AND GYROSCOPIC MOTION, John Perry. Well-known classic of science still unsurpassed for lucid, accurate, delightful exposition. How quasi-rigidity is induced in flexible and fluid bodies by rapid motion; why gyrostat falls, top rises; nature and effect on climatic conditions of earth's precessional movement; effect of internal fluidity on rotating bodies, etc. Appendixes describe practical uses to which gyroscopes have been put in ships, compasses, monorail transportation. 62 figures. 128pp. 5⅜ x 8.   T416 Paperbound **$1.00**

A CONCISE HISTORY OF MATHEMATICS, D. Struik. Lucid study of development of mathematical ideas, techniques, from Ancient Near East, Greece, Islamic science, Middle Ages, Renaissance, modern times. Important mathematicians are described in detail. Treatment is not anecdotal, but analytical development of ideas. "Rich in content, thoughtful in interpretation" U. S. QUARTERLY BOOKLIST. Non-technical; no mathematical training needed. Index. 60 illustrations, including Egyptian papyri, Greek mss., portraits of 31 eminent mathematicians. Bibliography. 2nd edition. xix + 299pp. 5⅜ x 8.   S255 Paperbound **$1.75**

FOUNDATIONS OF GEOMETRY, Bertrand Russell. Analyzing basic problems in the overlap area between mathematics and philosophy, Nobel laureate Russell examines the nature of geometrical knowledge, the nature of geometry, and the application of geometry to space. It covers the history of non-Euclidean geometry, philosophic interpretations of geometry—especially Kant—projective and metrical geometry. This is most interesting as the solution offered in 1897 by a great mind to a problem still current. New introduction by Prof. Morris Kline of N. Y. University. xii + 201pp. 5⅜ x 8.
S232 Clothbound **$3.25**
S233 Paperbound **$1.60**

THE NATURE OF PHYSICAL THEORY, P. W. Bridgman. Here is how modern physics looks to a highly unorthodox physicist—a Nobel laureate. Pointing out many absurdities of science, and demonstrating the inadequacies of various physical theories, Dr. Bridgman weighs and analyzes the contributions of Einstein, Bohr, Newton, Heisenberg, and many others. This is a non-technical consideration of the correlation of science and reality. Index. xi + 138pp. 5⅜ x 8.
S33 Paperbound **$1.25**

EXPERIMENT AND THEORY IN PHYSICS, Max Born. A Nobel laureate examines the nature and value of the counterclaims of experiment and theory in physics. Synthetic versus analytical scientific advances are analyzed in the work of Einstein, Bohr, Heisenberg, Planck, Eddington, Milne, and others by a fellow participant. 44pp. 5⅜ x 8.   S308 Paperbound **60c**

THE STUDY OF THE HISTORY OF MATHEMATICS & THE STUDY OF THE HISTORY OF SCIENCE, George Sarton. Scientific method & philosophy in 2 scholarly fields. Defines duty of historian of math provides especially useful bibliography with best available biographies of modern mathematicians, editions of their collected works, correspondence. Shows that combination of history & science will aid scholar in understanding science today. Bibliography includes best known treatises on historical methods. 200-item critically evaluated bibliography. Index. 10 illustrations. 2 volumes bound as one. 113pp. + 75pp. 5⅜ x 8.   T240 Paperbound **$1.25**

SCIENCE AND METHOD, Henri Poincaré. Procedure of scientific discovery, methodology, experiment, idea-germination—the intellectual processes by which discoveries come into being. Most significant and most interesting aspects of development, application of ideas. Chapters cover selection of facts, chance, mathematical reasoning, mathematics and logic; Whitehead, Russell, Cantor; the new mechanics, etc. 288pp. 5⅜ x 8.   S222 Paperbound **$1.25**

SCIENCE AND HYPOTHESIS, Henri Poincaré. Creative psychology in science. How such concepts as number, magnitude, space, force, classical mechanics were developed, and how the modern scientist uses them in his thought. Hypothesis in physics, theories of modern physics. Introduction by Sir James Larmor. "Few mathematicians have had the breadth of vision of Poincaré, and none is his superior in the gift of clear exposition," E. T. Bell. Index. 272pp. 5⅜ x 8.
S221 Paperbound **$1.25**

FOUNDATIONS OF PHYSICS, R. B. Lindsay & H. Margenau. Excellent bridge between semi-popular works & technical treatises. A discussion of methods of physical description, construction of theory; valuable for physicist with elementary calculus who is interested in ideas that give meaning to data, tools of modern physics. Contents include symbolism, mathematical equations; space & time; foundations of mechanics; probability; physics & continua; electron theory; special & general relativity; quantum mechanics; causality. "Thorough and yet not overdetailed. Unreservedly recommended," NATURE (London). Unabridged, corrected edition. List of recommended readings. 35 illustrations. xi + 537pp. 5⅜ x 8.   S377 Paperbound **$2.45**

CLASSICS OF SCIENCE

THE THIRTEEN BOOKS OF EUCLID'S ELEMENTS, edited by **Sir Thomas Heath.** Definitive edition of one of the very greatest classics of Western world. Complete English translation of Heiberg text, together with spurious Book XIV. Detailed 150-page introduction discussing aspects of Greek and medieval mathematics. Euclid, texts, commentators, etc. Paralleling the text is an elaborate critical apparatus analyzing each definition, proposition, postulate, covering textual matters, mathematical analysis, commentators of all times, refutations, supports, extrapolations, etc. This is the full EUCLID. Unabridged reproduction of Cambridge U. 2nd edition. 3 volumes. Total of 995 figures, 1426pp. 5⅜ x 8.   S88,89,90 3 volume set, paperbound **$6.00**

OPTICKS, Sir Isaac Newton. In its discussions of light, reflection, color, refraction, theories of wave and corpuscular theories of light, this work is packed with scores of insights and discoveries. In its precise and practical discussion of construction of optical apparatus, contemporary understandings of phenomena it is truly fascinating to modern physicists, astronomers, mathematicians. Foreword by Albert Einstein. Preface by I. B. Cohen of Harvard University. 7 pages of portraits, facsimile pages, letters, etc. cxvi + 414pp. 5⅜ x 8.   S205 Paperbound **$2.00**

THE PRINCIPLE OF RELATIVITY, A. Einstein, H. Lorentz, M. Minkowski, H. Weyl. These are the 11 basic papers that founded the general and special theories of relativity, all translated into English. Two papers by Lorentz on the Michelson experiment, electromagnetic phenomena. Minkowski's SPACE & TIME, and Weyl's GRAVITATION & ELECTRICITY. 7 epoch-making papers by Einstein: ELECTROMAGNETICS OF MOVING BODIES, INFLUENCE OF GRAVITATION IN PROPAGATION OF LIGHT, COSMOLOGICAL CONSIDERATIONS, GENERAL THEORY, and 3 others. 7 diagrams. Special notes by A. Sommerfeld. 224pp. 5⅜ x 8.   S81 Paperbound **$1.75**

THE ANALYTICAL THEORY OF HEAT, Joseph Fourier. This book, which revolutionized mathematical physics, is listed in the Great Books program, and many other listings of great books. It has been used with profit by generations of mathematicians and physicists who are interested in either heat or in the application of the Fourier integral. Covers cause and reflections of rays of heat, radiant heating, heating of closed spaces, use of trigonometric series in the theory of heat, Fourier integral, etc. Translated by Alexander Freeman. 20 figures. xxii + 466pp. 5⅜ x 8. S93 Paperbound **$2.00**

THE WORKS OF ARCHIMEDES, edited by **T. L. Heath.** All the known works of the great Greek mathematician are contained in this one volume, including the recently discovered Method of Archimedes. Contains: On Sphere & Cylinder, Measurement of a Circle, Spirals, Concids, Spheroids, etc. This is the definitive edition of the greatest mathematical intellect of the ancient world. 186-page study by Heath discusses Archimides and the history of Greek mathematics. Bibliography. 563pp. 5⅜ x 8. S9 Paperbound **$2.00**

A PHILOSOPHICAL ESSAY ON PROBABILITIES, Marquis de Laplace. This famous essay explains without recourse to mathematics the principle of probability, and the application of probability to games of chance, natural philosophy, astronomy, many other fields. Translated from the 6th French edition by F. W. Truscott, F. L. Emory, with new introduction for this edition by E. T. Bell. 204pp. 5⅜ x 8. S166 Paperbound **$1.25**

INVESTIGATIONS ON THE THEORY OF THE BROWNIAN MOVEMENT, Albert Einstein. Reprints from rare European journals. 5 basic papers, including the Elementary Theory of the Brownian Movement, written at the request of Lorentz to provide a simple explanation. Translated by A. D. Cowper. Annotated, edited by R. Fürth. 33pp. of notes elucidate, give history of previous investigations. Author, subject indexes. 62 footnotes. 124pp. 5⅜ x 8.
S304 Paperbound **$1.25**

THE GEOMETRY OF RENÉ DESCARTES. With this book Descartes founded analytical geometry. Original French text, with Descartes' own diagrams, and excellent Smith-Latham translation. Contains Problems the Construction of Which Requires Only Straight Lines and Circles; On the Nature of Curved Lines; On the Construction of Solid or Supersolid Problems. Notes. Diagrams. 258pp. 5⅜ x 8. S68 Paperbound **$1.50**

DIALOGUES CONCERNING TWO NEW SCIENCES, Galileo Galilei. This classic of experimental science, mechanics, engineering, is as enjoyable as it is important. Based on 30 years' experimentation and characterized by its author as ''superior to everything else of mine,'' it offers a lively exposition of dynamics, elasticity, sound, ballistics, strength of materials, and the scientific method. Translated by H. Grew and A. de Salvio. 126 diagrams. Index. xxi + 288pp. 5⅜ x 8. S99 Paperbound **$1.65**

TREATISE ON ELECTRICITY AND MAGNETISM, James Clerk Maxwell. For more than 80 years a seemingly inexhaustible source of leads for physicists, mathematicians, engineers. Total of 1082pp. on such topics as Measurement of Quantities, Electrostatics, Elementary Mathematical Theory of Electricity, Electrical Work and Energy in a System of Conductors, General Theorems, Theory of Electrical Images, Electrolysis, Conduction, Polarization, Dielectrics, Resistance, etc. ''The greatest mathematical physicist since Newton,'' Sir James Jeans. 3rd edition. 107 figures, 21 plates. 1082pp. 5⅜ x 8. S186 Clothbound **$4.95**

PRINCIPLES OF PHYSICAL OPTICS, Ernst Mach. This classical examination of the propagation of light, color, polarization etc. offers a historical and philosophical treatment that has never been surpassed for breadth and easy readability. Contents: Rectilinear propagation of light. Reflection, refraction. Early knowledge of vision. Dioptrics. Composition of light. Theory of color and dispersion. Periodicity. Theory of interference. Polarization. Mathematical representation of properties of light. Propagation of waves, etc. 279 illustrations, 10 portraits. Appendix. Indexes. 324pp. 5⅜ x 8. S178 Paperbound **$1.75**

THEORY OF ELECTRONS AND ITS APPLICATION TO THE PHENOMENA OF LIGHT AND RADIANT HEAT, H. Lorentz. Lectures delivered at Columbia University by Nobel laureate Lorentz. Unabridged, they form a historical coverage of the theory of free electrons, motion, absorption of heat, Zeeman effect, propagation of light in molecular bodies, inverse Zeeman effect, optical phenomena in moving bodies, etc. 109 pages of notes explain the more advanced sections. Index. 9 figures. 352pp. 5⅜ x 8. S173 Paperbound **$1.85**

MATTER & MOTION, James Clerk Maxwell. This excellent exposition begins with simple particles and proceeds gradually to physical systems beyond complete analysis: motion, force, properties of centre of mass of material system, work, energy, gravitation, etc. Written with all Maxwell's original insights and clarity! Notes by E. Larmor. 17 diagrams. 178pp. 5⅜ x 8.
S188 Paperbound **$1.25**

AN INTRODUCTION TO THE STUDY OF EXPERIMENTAL MEDICINE, Claude Bernard. 90-year-old classic of medical science, only major work of Bernard available in English, records his efforts to transform physiology into exact science. Principles of scientific research illustrated by specific case histories from his work; roles of chance, error, preliminary false conclusions, in leading eventually to scientific truth; use of hypothesis. Much of modern application of mathematics to biology rests on the foundation set down here. New foreword by Professor I. B. Cohen, Harvard Univ. xxv + 266pp. 5⅜ x 8. T400 Paperbound **$1.50**

PRINCIPLES OF MECHANICS, Heinrich Hertz. This last work by the great 19th century physicist is not only a classic, but of great interest in the logic of science. Creating a new system of mechanics based upon space, time, and mass, it returns to axiomatic analysis, to understanding of the formal or structural aspects of science, taking into account logic, observation, and a priori elements. Of great historical importance to Poincaré, Carnap, Einstein, Milne. A 20-page introduction by R. S. Cohen, Wesleyan University, analyzes the implications of Hertz's thought and the logic of science. Bibliography. 13-page introduction of Helmholtz. xiii + 274pp. 5⅜ x 8.

S316 Clothbound **$3.50**
S317 Paperbound **$1.75**

ANIMALS IN MOTION, Eadweard Muybridge. Largest, most comprehensive selection of Muybridge's famous action photos of animals, from his ANIMAL LOCOMOTION. 3919 high-speed shots of 34 different animals and birds in 123 different types of action: horses, mules, oxen, pigs, goats, camels, elephants, dogs, cats, guanacos, sloths, lions, tigers, jaguars, raccoons, baboons, deer, elk, gnus, kangaroos, many others, in different actions—walking, running, flying, leaping. Horse alone shown in more than 40 different ways. Photos taken against ruled backgrounds; most actions taken from 3 angles at once: 90°, 60°, rear. Most plates original size. Of considerable interest to scientists as a classic of biology, as a record of actual facts of natural history and physiology. "A really marvellous series of plates," NATURE (London). "A monumental work," Waldemar Kaempffert. Photographed by E. Muybridge. Edited by L. S. Brown, American Museum of Natural History. 74-page introduction on mechanics of motion. 340 pages of plates, 3919 photographs. 416pp. Deluxe binding, paper. (Weight 4½ lbs.) 7⅞ x 10⅝.

T203 Clothbound **$10.00**

THE HUMAN FIGURE IN MOTION, Eadweard Muybridge. This new edition of a great classic in the history of science and photography is the largest selection ever made from the original Muybridge photos of human action: 4789 photographs, illustrating 163 types of motion: walking, running, lifting, etc. in time-exposure sequence photos at speeds up to 1/6000th of a second. Men, women, children, mostly undraped, showing bone and muscle positions against ruled backgrounds, mostly taken at 3 angles at once. Not only was this a great work of photography, acclaimed by contemporary critics as a work of genius, it was also a great 19th century landmark in biological research. Historical introduction by Prof. Robert Taft, U. of Kansas. Plates original size, full detail. Over 500 action strips. 407pp. 7¾ x 10⅝.

T204 Clothbound **$10.00**

ON THE SENSATIONS OF TONE, Hermann Helmholtz. This is an unmatched coordination of such fields as acoustical physics, physiology, experiment, history of music. It covers the entire gamut of musical tone. Partial contents: relation of vibration, resonance, analysis of tones by sympathetic resonance, beats, chords, tonality, consonant chords, discords, progression of parts, etc. 33 appendixes discuss various aspects of sound, physics, acoustics, music, etc. Translated by A. J. Ellis. New introduction by Prof. Henry Margenau of Yale. 68 figures. 43 musical passages analyzed. Over 100 tables. Index. xix + 576pp. 6⅛ x 9¼.

S114 Clothbound **$4.95**

COLLECTED WORKS OF BERNHARD RIEMANN. This important source book is the first to contain the complete text of both 1892 Werke and the 1902 supplement, unabridged. It contains 31 monographs, 3 complete lecture courses, 15 miscellaneous papers, which have been of enormous importance in relativity, topology, theory of complex variables, and other areas of mathematics. Edited by R. Dedekind, H. Weber, M. Noether, W. Wirtinger. German text. English introduction by Hans Lewy. 690pp. 5⅜ x 8.

S226 Paperbound **$2.85**

CONTRIBUTIONS TO THE FOUNDING OF THE THEORY OF TRANSFINITE NUMBERS, Georg Cantor. These papers founded a new branch of mathematics. The famous articles of 1895-7 are translated with an 82-page introduction by P. E. B. Jourdain dealing with Cantor, the background of his discoveries, their results, future possibilities. Bibliography. Index. Notes. ix + 211pp. 5⅜ x 8.

S45 Paperbound **$1.25**

PRINCIPLES OF PSYCHOLOGY, William James. This is the complete "Long Course," which is not to be confused with abridged editions. It contains all the wonderful descriptions, deep insights that have caused it to be a permanent work in all psychological libraries. Partial contents: functions of the brain, automation theories, mind-stuff theories, relation of mind to other things, consciousness, times, space, thing perception, will, emotions, hypnotism, and dozens of other areas in descriptive psychology. "A permanent classic like Locke's ESSAYS, Hume's TREATISE," John Dewey. "The preeminence of James in American psychology is unquestioned," PERSONALIST. "The American classic in psychology—unequaled in breadth and scope in the entire psychological literature," PSYCHOANALYTICAL QUARTERLY. Index. 94 figures. 2 volumes bound as one. Total of 1408pp.

T381 Vol. 1. Paperbound **$2.00**
T382 Vol. 2. Paperbound **$2.00**

RECREATIONS

SEVEN SCIENCE FICTION NOVELS OF H. G. WELLS. This is the complete text, unabridged, of seven of Wells's greatest novels: War of the Worlds, The Invisible Man, The Island of Dr. Moreau, The Food of the Gods, The First Men in the Moon, In the Days of the Comet, The Time Machine. Still considered by many experts to be the best science-fiction ever written, they will offer amusement and instruction to the scientific-minded reader. 1015pp. 5⅜ x 8.

T264 Clothbound **$3.95**

28 SCIENCE FICTION STORIES OF H. G. WELLS. Unabridged! This enormous omnibus contains 2 full-length novels—Men Like Gods, Star Begotten—plus 26 short stories of space, time, invention, biology, etc. The Crystal Egg, The Country of the Blind, Empire of the Ants, The Man Who Could Work Miracles, Aepyornis Island, A Story of the Days to Come, and 22 others! 915pp. 5⅜ x 8.　　　　　　　　　　　　　　　　　　　　　T265 Clothbound **$3.95**

FLATLAND, E. A. Abbott. This is a perennially popular science-fiction classic about life in a two-dimensional world, and the impingement of higher dimensions. Political, satiric, humorous, moral overtones. Relativity, the fourth dimension, and other aspects of modern science are explained more clearly than in most texts. 7th edition. New introduction by Banesh Hoffmann. 128pp. 5⅜ x 8.　　　　　　　　　　　　　　　　　　　　　　　　T1 Paperbound **$1.00**

CRYPTANALYSIS, Helen F. Gaines. (Formerly ELEMENTARY CRYPTANALYSIS.) A standard elementary and intermediate text for serious students. It does not confine itself to old material, but contains much that is not generally known except to experts. Concealment, Transposition, Substitution ciphers; Vigenere, Kasiski, Playfair, multafid, dozens of other techniques. Appendix with sequence charts, letter frequencies in English, 5 other languages, English word frequencies. Bibliography. 167 codes. New to this edition: solutions to codes. vi + 230pp. 5⅜ x 8⅜.
T97 Paperbound **$1.95**

FADS AND FALLACIES IN THE NAME OF SCIENCE, Martin Gardner. Examines various cults, quack systems, frauds, delusions which at various times have masqueraded as science. Accounts of hollow-earth fanatics like Symmes; Velikovsky and wandering planets; Hoerbiger; Bellamy and the theory of multiple moons; Charles Fort, dowsing, pseudoscientific methods for finding water, ores, oil. Sections on naturopathy, iridiagnosis, zone therapy, food fads, etc. Analytical accounts of Wilhelm Reich and orgone sex energy; L. Ron Hubbard and Dianetics; A. Korzybski and General Semantics; many others. Brought up to date to include Bridey Murphy, others. Not just a collection of anecdotes, but a fair, reasoned appraisal of eccentric theory. Formerly titled IN THE NAME OF SCIENCE. Preface. Index. x + 384pp. 5⅜ x 8.
T394 Paperbound **$1.50**

REINFELD ON THE END GAME IN CHESS, Fred Reinfeld. Analyzes 62 end games by Alekhine, Flohr, Tarrasch, Morphy, Bogolyubov, Capablanca, Vidmar, Rubinstein, Lasker, Reshevsky, other masters. Only first-rate book with extensive coverage of error; of immense aid in pointing out errors you might have made. Centers around transitions from middle play to various types of end play. King & pawn endings, minor piece endings, queen endings, bad bishops, blockage, weak pawns, passed pawns, etc. Formerly titled PRACTICAL END PLAY. 62 figures. vi + 177pp. 5⅜ x 8.　　　　　　　　　　　　　　　　　　　　　　　　T417 Paperbound **$1.25**

PUZZLE QUIZ AND STUNT FUN, Jerome Meyer. 238 high-priority puzzles, stunts, and tricks—mathematical puzzles like The Clever Carpenter, Atom Bomb, Please Help Alice; mysteries and deductions like The Bridge of Sighs, Dog Logic, Secret Code; observation puzzlers like The American Flag, Playing Cards, Telephone Dial; more than 200 others involving magic squares, tongue twisters, puns, anagrams, word design. Answers included. Revised, enlarged edition of FUN-TO-DO. Over 100 illustrations. 238 puzzles, stunts, tricks. 256pp. 5⅜ x 8.
T337 Paperbound **$1.00**

THE BOOK OF MODERN PUZZLES, G. L. Kaufman. More than 150 word puzzles, logic puzzles. No warmed-over fare but all new material based on same appeals that make crosswords and deduction puzzles popular, but with different principles, techniques. Two-minute teasers, involved word-labyrinths, design and pattern puzzles, puzzles calling for logic and observation, puzzles testing ability to apply general knowledge to peculiar situations, many others. Answers to all problems. 116 illustrations. 192pp. 5⅜ x 8.　　　　　T143 Paperbound **$1.00**

101 PUZZLES IN THOUGHT AND LOGIC by C. R. Wylie, Jr. Designed for readers who enjoy the challenge and stimulation of logical puzzles without specialized mathematical or scientific knowledge. These problems are entirely new and range from relatively easy, to brainteasers that will afford hours of subtle entertainment. Detective problems, how to find the lying fisherman, how a blindman can identify color by logic, and many more. Easy-to-understand introduction to the logic of puzzle solving and general scientific method. 128pp. 5⅜ x 8.
T367 Paperbound **$1.00**

MATHEMAGIC, MAGIC PUZZLES, AND GAMES WITH NUMBERS, Royal V. Heath. Over 60 new puzzles and stunts based on properties of numbers. Demonstrates easy techniques for multiplying large numbers mentally, identifying unknown numbers, determining date of any day in any year, dozens of similar useful, entertaining applications of mathematics. Entertainments like The Lost Digit, 3 Acrobats, Psychic Bridge, magic squares, triangles, cubes, circles, other material not easily found elsewhere. Edited by J. S. Meyer. 76 illustrations. 128pp. 5⅜ x 8.
T110 Paperbound **$1.00**

LEARN CHESS FROM THE MASTERS, Fred Reinfeld. Improve your chess, rate your improvement, by playing against Marshall, Znosko-Borovsky, Bronstein, Najdorf, others. Formerly titled CHESS BY YOURSELF, this book contains 10 games in which you move against masters, and grade your moves by an easy system. Games selected for interest, clarity, easy principles; illustrate common openings, both classical and modern. Ratings for 114 extra playing situations that might have arisen. Full annotations. 91 diagrams. viii + 144pp. 5⅜ x 8.
T362 Paperbound **$1.00**

THE COMPLETE NONSENSE OF EDWARD LEAR. Original text & illustrations of all Lear's nonsense books: A BOOK OF NONSENSE, NONSENSE SONGS, MORE NONSENSE SONGS, LAUGHABLE LYRICS, NONSENSE SONGS AND STORIES. Only complete edition available at popular price. Old favorites such as The Dong With a Luminous Nose, hundreds of other delightful bits of nonsense for children & adults. 214 different limericks, each illustrated by Lear; 3 different sets of Nonsense Botany; 5 Nonsense Alphabets; many others. 546 illustrations. 320pp. 5⅜ x 8.
T167 Paperbound **$1.00**

CRYPTOGRAPHY, D. Smith. Excellent elementary introduction to enciphering, deciphering secret writing. Explains transposition, substitution ciphers; codes; solutions. Geometrical patterns, route transcription, columnar transposition, other methods. Mixed cipher systems; single-alphabet, polyalphabetical substitution; mechanical devices; Vigenere system, etc. Enciphering Japanese; explanation of Baconian Biliteral cipher frequency tables. More than 150 problems provide practical application. Bibliography. Index. 164pp. 5⅜ x 8.
T247 Paperbound **$1.00**

MATHEMATICAL EXCURSIONS, Helen A. Merrill. Fun, recreation, insights into elementary problem-solving. A mathematical expert guides you along by-paths not generally travelled in elementary math courses—how to divide by inspection, Russian peasant system of multiplication; memory systems for pi; building odd and even magic squares; dyadic systems; facts about 37; square roots by geometry; Tchebichev's machine; drawing five-sided figures; dozens more. Solutions to more difficult ones. 50 illustrations. 145pp. 5⅜ x 8.
T350 Paperbound **$1.00**

MATHEMATICAL RECREATIONS, M. Kraitchik. Some 250 puzzles, problems, demonstrations of recreational mathematics for beginners & advanced mathematicians. Unusual historical problems from Greek, Medieval, Arabic, Hindu sources; modern problems based on "mathematics without numbers," geometry, topology, arithmetic, etc. Pastimes derived from figurative numbers, Mersenne numbers, Fermat numbers; fairy chess, latruncles, reversi, many other topics. Full solutions. Excellent for insights into special fields of math. 181 illustrations. 330pp. 5⅜ x 8.
T163 Paperbound **$1.75**

MATHEMATICAL PUZZLES FOR BEGINNERS AND ENTHUSIASTS, G. Mott-Smith. 188 mathematical puzzles to test mental agility. Inference, interpretation, algebra, dissection of plane figures, geometry, properties of numbers, decimation, permutations, probability, all enter these delightful problems. Puzzles like the Odic Force, How to Draw an Ellipse, Spider's Cousin, more than 180 others. Detailed solutions. Appendix with square roots, triangular numbers, primes, etc. 135 illustrations. 2nd revised edition. 248pp. 5⅜ x 8.
T198 Paperbound **$1.00**

NEW WORD PUZZLES, Gerald L. Kaufman. Contains 100 brand new challenging puzzles based on words and their combinations, never published before in any form. Most are new types invented by the author—for beginners or experts. Chess word puzzles, addle letter anagrams, double word squares, double horizontals, alphagram puzzles, dual acrostigrams, linkogram lapwords—plus 8 other brand new types, all with solutions included. 196 figures. 100 brand new puzzles. vi + 122pp. 5⅜ x 8.
T344 Paperbound **$1.00**

MATHEMATICS, MAGIC AND MYSTERY, Martin Gardner. Card tricks, feats of mental mathematics, stage mind-reading, other "magic" explained as applications of probability, sets, theory of numbers, topology, various branches of mathematics. Creative examination of laws and their application, with sources of new tricks and insights. 115 sections discuss tricks with cards, dice, coins; geometrical vanishing tricks, dozens of others. No sleight of hand needed; mathematics guarantees success. 115 illustrations. xii + 174pp. 5⅜ x 8.
T335 Paperbound **$1.00**

MATHEMATICS ELEMENTARY TO INTERMEDIATE

HOW TO CALCULATE QUICKLY, Henry Sticker. This handy volume offers a tried and true method for helping you in the basic mathematics of daily life—addition, subtraction, multiplication, division, fractions, etc. It is designed to awaken your "number sense" or the ability to see relationships between numbers as whole quantities. It is not a collection of tricks working only on special numbers, but a serious course of over 9,000 problems and their solutions, teaching special techniques not taught in schools: left-to-right multiplication, new fast ways of division, etc. 5 or 10 minutes daily use will double or triple your calculation speed. Excellent for the scientific worker who is at home in higher math, but is not satisfied with his speed and accuracy in lower mathematics. 256pp. 5 x 7¼.
T295 Paperbound **$1.00**

FAMOUS PROBLEMS OF ELEMENTARY GEOMETRY, Felix Klein. Expanded version of the 1894 Easter lectures at Göttingen. 3 problems of classical geometry: squaring circle, trisecting angle, doubling cube, considered with full modern implications: transcendental numbers, pi, etc. Notes by R. Archibald. 16 figures. xi + 92pp. 5⅜ x 8.
T348 Clothbound **$1.50**
T298 Paperbound **$1.00**

HIGHER MATHEMATICS FOR STUDENTS OF CHEMISTRY AND PHYSICS, J. W. Mellor. Not abstract, but practical, building its problems out of familiar laboratory material, this covers differential calculus, coordinate, analytical geometry, functions, integral calculus, infinite series, numerical equations, differential equations, Fourier's theorem, probability, theory of errors, calculus of variations, determinants. "If the reader is not familiar with this book, it will repay him to examine it," CHEM. & ENGINEERING NEWS. 800 problems, 189 figures. Bibliography. xxi + 641pp. 5⅜ x 8.
S193 Paperbound **$2.00**

TRIGONOMETRY REFRESHER FOR TECHNICAL MEN, A. Albert Klaf. 913 detailed questions and answers cover the most important aspects of plane and spherical trigonometry. They will help you to brush up or to clear up difficulties in special areas.—The first portion of this book covers plane trigonometry, including angles, quadrants, trigonometrical functions, graphical representation, interpolation, equations, logarithms, solution of triangle, use of the slide rule and similar topics–188 pages then discuss application of plane trigonometry to special problems in navigation, surveying, elasticity, architecture, and various fields of engineering. Small angles, periodic functions, vectors, polar coordinates, De Moivre's theorem are fully examined—The third section of the book then discusses spherical trigonometry and the solution of spherical triangles, with their applications to terrestrial and astronomical problems. Methods of saving time with numerical calculations, simplification of principal functions of angle, much practical information make this a most useful book—913 questions answered. 1738 problems, answers to odd numbers. 494 figures. 24 pages of useful formulae, functions. Index. x + 629pp. 5⅜ x 8.
T371 Paperbound **$2.00**

CALCULUS REFRESHER FOR TECHNICAL MEN, A. Albert Klaf. This book is unique in English as a refresher for engineers, technicians, students who either wish to brush up their calculus or to clear up uncertainties. It is not an ordinary text, but an examination of most important aspects of integral and differential calculus in terms of the 756 questions most likely to occur to the technical reader. The first part of this book covers simple differential calculus, with constants, variables, functions, increments, derivatives, differentiation, logarithms, curvature of curves, and similar topics—The second part covers fundamental ideas of integration, inspection, substitution, transformation, reduction, areas and volumes, mean value, successive and partial integration, double and triple integration. Practical aspects are stressed rather than theoretical. A 50-page section illustrates the application of calculus to specific problems of civil and nautical engineering, electricity, stress and strain, elasticity, industrial engineering, and similar fields.— 756 questions answered. 566 problems, mostly answered. 36 pages of useful constants, formulae for ready reference. Index. v + 431pp. 5⅜ x 8.
T370 Paperbound **$2.00**

MONOGRAPHS ON TOPICS OF MODERN MATHEMATICS, edited by J. W. A. Young. Advanced mathematics for persons who haven't gone beyond or have forgotten high school algebra. 9 monographs on foundation of geometry, modern pure geometry, non-Euclidean geometry, fundamental propositions of algebra, algebraic equations, functions, calculus, theory of numbers, etc. Each monograph gives proofs of important results, and descriptions of leading methods, to provide wide coverage. New introduction by Prof. M. Kline, N. Y. University. 100 diagrams. xvi + 416pp. 6⅛ x 9¼.
S289 Paperbound **$2.00**

MATHEMATICS: INTERMEDIATE TO ADVANCED

INTRODUCTION TO THE THEORY OF FOURIER'S SERIES AND INTEGRALS, H. S. Carslaw. 3rd revised edition. This excellent introduction is an outgrowth of the author's courses at Cambridge. Historical introduction, rational and irrational numbers, infinite sequences and series, functions of a single variable, definite integral, Fourier series, Fourier integrals, and similar topics. Appendixes discuss practical harmonic analysis, periodogram analysis, Lebesgues theory. Indexes. 84 examples, bibliography. xiii + 368 pp. 5⅜ x 8.
S48 Paperbound **$2.00**

INTRODUCTION TO THE THEORY OF NUMBERS, L. E. Dickson. Thorough, comprehensive approach with adequate coverage of classical literature, an introductory volume beginners can follow. Chapters on divisibility, congruences, quadratic residues & reciprocity, Diophantine equations, etc. Full treatment of binary quadratic forms without usual restriction to integral coefficients. Covers infinitude of primes, least residues, Fermat's theorem, Euler's phi function, Legendre's symbol, Gauss's lemma, automorphs, reduced forms, recent theorems of Thue & Siegel, many more. Much material not readily available elsewhere. 239 problems. Index. 1 figure. viii + 183pp. 5⅜ x 8.
S342 Paperbound **$1.65**

MECHANICS VIA THE CALCULUS, P. W. Norris, W. S. Legge. Covers almost everything from linear motion to vector analysis: equations determining motion, linear methods, compounding of simple harmonic motions, Newton's laws of motion, Hooke's law, the simple pendulum, motion of a particle in 1 plane, centers of gravity, virtual work, friction, kinetic energy of rotating bodies, equilibrium of strings, hydrostatics, sheering stresses, elasticity, etc. 550 problems. 3rd revised edition. xii + 367pp.
S207 Clothbound **$3.95**

NON-EUCLIDEAN GEOMETRY, Roberto Bonola. The standard coverage of non-Euclidean geometry. It examines from both a historical and mathematical point of view the geometries which have arisen from a study of Euclid's 5th postulate upon parallel lines. Also included are complete texts, translated, of Bolyai's THEORY OF ABSOLUTE SPACE, Lobachevsky's THEORY OF PARALLELS. 180 diagrams. 431pp. 5⅜ x 8.
S27 Paperbound **$1.95**

ELEMENTS OF THE THEORY OF REAL FUNCTIONS, J. E. Littlewood. Based on lectures given at Trinity College, Cambridge, this book has proved to be extremely successful in introducing graduate students to the modern theory of functions. It offers a full and concise coverage of classes and cardinal numbers, well-ordered series, other types of series, and elements of the theory of sets of points. 3rd revised edition. vii + 71pp. 5⅜ x 8.
S171 Clothbound **$2.85**
S172 Paperbound **$1.25**

THE CONTINUUM AND OTHER TYPES OF SERIAL ORDER, E. V. Huntington. This famous book gives a systematic elementary account of the modern history of the continuum as a type of serial order. Based on the Cantor-Dedekind ordinal theory, which requires no technical knowledge of higher mathematics, it offers an easily followed analysis of ordered classes, discrete and dense series, continuous series, Cantor's transfinite numbers. 2nd edition. Index. viii + 82pp. 5⅜ x 8.
S129 Clothbound **$2.75**
S130 Paperbound **$1.00**

GEOMETRY OF FOUR DIMENSIONS, H. P. Manning. Unique in English as a clear, concise introduction. Treatment is synthetic, and mostly Euclidean, although in hyperplanes and hyperspheres at infinity, non-Euclidean geometry is used. Historical introduction. Foundations of 4-dimensional geometry. Perpendicularity, simple angles. Angles of planes, higher order. Symmetry, order, motion; hyperpyramids, hypercones, hyperspheres; figures with parallel elements; volume, hypervolume in space; regular polyhedroids. Glossary. 78 figures. ix + 348pp. 5⅜ x 8.
S181 Clothbound **$3.95**
S182 Paperbound **$1.95**

VECTOR AND TENSOR ANALYSIS, G. E. Hay. One of the clearest introductions to this increasingly important subject. Start with simple definitions, finish the book with a sure mastery of oriented Cartesian vectors, Christoffel symbols, solenoidal tensors, and their applications. Complete breakdown of plane, solid, analytical, differential geometry. Separate chapters on application. All fundamental formulae listed & demonstrated. 195 problems, 66 figures. viii + 193pp. 5⅜ x 8.
S109 Paperbound **$1.75**

INTRODUCTION TO THE DIFFERENTIAL EQUATIONS OF PHYSICS, L. Hopf. Especially valuable to the engineer with no math beyond elementary calculus. Emphasizing intuitive rather than formal aspects of concepts, the author covers an extensive territory. Partial contents: Law of causality, energy theorem, damped oscillations, coupling by friction, cylindrical and spherical coordinates, heat source, etc. Index. 48 figures. 160pp. 5⅜ x 8.
S120 Paperbound **$1.25**

INTRODUCTION TO THE THEORY OF GROUPS OF FINITE ORDER, R. Carmichael. Examines fundamental theorems and their application. Beginning with sets, systems, permutations, etc., it progresses in easy stages through important types of groups: Abelian, prime power, permutation, etc. Except 1 chapter where matrices are desirable, no higher math needed. 783 exercises, problems. Index. xvi + 447pp. 5⅜ x 8.
S299 Clothbound **$3.95**
S300 Paperbound **$2.00**

THEORY OF GROUPS OF FINITE ORDER, W. Burnside. First published some 40 years ago, this is still one of the clearest introductory texts. Partial contents: permutations, groups independent of representation, composition series of a group, isomorphism of a group with itself, Abelian groups, prime power groups, permutation groups, invariants of groups of linear substitution, graphical representation, etc. 45pp. of notes. Indexes. xxiv + 512pp. 5⅜ x 8.
S38 Paperbound **$2.45**

INFINITE SEQUENCES AND SERIES, Konrad Knopp. First publication in any language! Excellent introduction to 2 topics of modern mathematics, designed to give the student background to penetrate farther by himself. Sequences & sets, real & complex numbers, etc. Functions of a real & complex variable. Sequences & series. Infinite series. Convergent power series. Expansion of elementary functions. Numerical evaluation of series. Bibliography. v + 186pp. 5⅜ x 8.
S152 Clothbound **$3.50**
S153 Paperbound **$1.75**

THEORY OF SETS, E. Kamke. Clearest, amplest introduction in English, well suited for independent study. Subdivisions of main theory, such as theory of sets of points, are discussed, but emphasis is on general theory. Partial contents: rudiments of set theory, arbitrary sets and their cardinal numbers, ordered sets and their order types, well-ordered sets and their ordinal numbers. Bibliography. Key to symbols. Index. vii + 144pp. 5⅜ x 8.
S141 Paperbound **$1.35**

ELEMENTS OF NUMBER THEORY, I. M. Vinogradov. Detailed 1st course for persons without advanced mathematics; 95% of this book can be understood by readers who have gone no farther than high school algebra. Partial contents: divisibility theory, important number theoretical functions, congruences, primitive roots and indices, etc. Solutions to both problems and exercises. Tables of primes, indices, etc. Covers almost every essential formula in elementary number theory! 233 problems, 104 exercises. viii + 227pp. 5⅜ x 8.
S259 Paperbound **$1.60**

FIVE VOLUME "THEORY OF FUNCTIONS" SET BY KONRAD KNOPP. This five-volume set, prepared by Konrad Knopp, provides a complete and readily followed account of theory of functions. Proofs are given concisely, yet without sacrifice of completeness or rigor. These volumes are used as texts by such universities as M.I.T., University of Chicago, N. Y. City College, and many others. "Excellent introduction . . . remarkably readable, concise, clear, rigorous," JOURNAL OF THE AMERICAN STATISTICAL ASSOCIATION.

ELEMENTS OF THE THEORY OF FUNCTIONS, Konrad Knopp. This book provides the student with background for further volumes in this set, or texts on a similar level. Partial contents: Foundations, system of complex numbers and the Gaussian plane of numbers, Riemann sphere of numbers, mapping by linear functions, normal forms, the logarithm, the cyclometric functions and binomial series. "Not only for the young student, but also for the student who knows all about what is in it," MATHEMATICAL JOURNAL. Bibliography. Index. 140pp. 5⅜ x 8. S154 Paperbound **$1.35**

THEORY OF FUNCTIONS, PART I., Konrad Knopp. With volume II, this book provides coverage of basic concepts and theorems. Partial contents: numbers and points, functions of a complex variable, integral of a continuous function, Cauchy's integral theorem, Cauchy's integral formulae, series with variable terms, expansion of analytic functions in power series, analytic continuation and complete definition of analytic functions, entire transcendental functions, Laurent expansion, types of singularities. Bibliography. Index. vii + 146pp. 5⅜ x 8.   S156 Paperbound **$1.35**

THEORY OF FUNCTIONS, PART II., Konrad Knopp. Application and further development of general theory, special topics. Single valued functions: entire, Weierstrass. Meromorphic functions: Mittag-Leffler. Periodic functions. Multiple-valued functions. Riemann surfaces. Algebraic functions. Analytical configuration, Riemann surface. Bibliography. Index. x + 150pp. 5⅜ x 8.   S157 Paperbound **$1.35**

PROBLEM BOOK IN THE THEORY OF FUNCTIONS, VOLUME 1., Konrad Knopp. Problems in elementary theory, for use with Knopp's THEORY OF FUNCTIONS, or any other text, arranged according to increasing difficulty. Fundamental concepts, sequences of numbers and infinite series, complex variable, integral theorems, development in series, conformal mapping. Answers. viii + 126pp. 5⅜ x 8.   S158 Paperbound **$1.35**

PROBLEM BOOK IN THE THEORY OF FUNCTIONS, VOLUME 2, Konrad Knopp. Advanced theory of functions, to be used either with Knopp's THEORY OF FUNCTIONS, or any other comparable text. Singularities, entire & meromorphic functions, periodic, analytic, continuation, multiple-valued functions, Riemann surfaces, conformal mapping. Includes a section of additional elementary problems. "The difficult task of selecting from the immense material of the modern theory of functions the problems just within the reach of the beginner is here masterfully accomplished," AM. MATH. SOC. Answers. 138pp. 5⅜ x 8.   S159 Paperbound **$1.35**

SYMBOLIC LOGIC

AN INTRODUCTION TO SYMBOLIC LOGIC, Susanne K. Langer. Probably the clearest book ever written on symbolic logic for the philosopher, general scientist and layman. It will be particularly appreciated by those who have been rebuffed by other introductory works because of insufficient mathematical training. No special knowledge of mathematics is required. Starting with the simplest symbols and conventions, you are led to a remarkable grasp of the Boole-Schroeder and Russell-Whitehead systems clearly and quickly. PARTIAL CONTENTS: Study of forms, Essentials of logical structure, Generalization, Classes, The deductive system of classes, The algebra of logic, Abstraction of interpretation, Calculus of propositions, Assumptions of PRINCIPIA MATHEMATICA, Logistics, Logic of the syllogism, Proofs of theorems. "One of the clearest and simplest introductions to a subject which is very much alive. The style is easy, symbolism is introduced gradually, and the intelligent non-mathematician should have no difficulty in following argument," MATHEMATICS GAZETTE. Revised, expanded second edition. Truth-value tables. 368pp. 5⅜ x 8.
S164 Paperbound **$1.75**

THE ELEMENTS OF MATHEMATICAL LOGIC, Paul Rosenbloom. FIRST PUBLICATION IN ANY LANGUAGE. This book is intended for readers who are mature mathematically, but have no previous training in symbolic logic. It does not limit itself to a single system, but covers the field as a whole. It is a development of lectures given at Lund University, Sweden in 1948. Partial contents: Logic of classes, fundamental theorems, Boolean algebra, logic of propositions, logic of propositional functions, expressive languages, combinatory logics, development of mathematics within an object language, paradoxes, theorems of Post and Goedel, Church's theorem, and similar topics. iv + 214pp. 5⅜ x 8.   S277 Paperbound **$1.45**

THE LAWS OF THOUGHT, George Boole. This book founded symbolic logic some hundred years ago. It is the 1st significant attempt to apply logic to all aspects of human endeavour. Partial contents: derivation of laws, signs & laws, interpretations, eliminations, conditions of a perfect method, analysis, Aristotelian logic, probability, and similar topics. xviii + 424pp. 5⅜ x 8.
S28 Paperbound **$2.00**

ELEMENTARY MATHEMATICS FROM AN
ADVANCED STANDPOINT, Felix Klein.

This classic text is an outgrowth of Klein's famous integration and survey course at Göttingen. Using one field of mathematics to interpret, adjust, illuminate another, it covers basic topics in each area, illustrating its discussion with extensive analysis. It is especially valuable in considering areas of modern mathematics. "Makes the reader feel the inspiration of . . . a great mathematician, inspiring teacher . . . with deep insight into the foundations and interrelations," BULLETIN, AMERICAN MATHEMATICAL SOCIETY.

Vol. 1. ARITHMETIC, ALGEBRA, ANALYSIS. Introducing the concept of function immediately, it enlivens abstract discussion with graphical and geometrically perceptual methods. Partial contents: natural numbers, extension of the notion of number, special properties, complex numbers. Real equations with real unknowns, complex quantities. Logarithmic, exponential functions, goniometric functions, infinitesimal calculus. Transcendence of e and pi, theory of assemblages. Index. 125 figures. ix + 247pp. 5⅜ x 8.   S150 Paperbound **$1.75**

Vol. 2. GEOMETRY. A comprehensive view which accompanies the space perception inherent in geometry with analytic formulas which facilitate precise formulation. Partial contents: Simplest geometric manifolds: line segment, Grassmann determinant principles, classification of configurations of space, derivative manifolds. Geometric transformations: affine transformations, projective, higher point transformations, theory of the imaginary. Systematic discussion of geometry and its foundations. Indexes. 141 illustrations. ix + 214pp. 5⅜ x 8.   S151 Paperbound **$1.75**

MATHEMATICS: ADVANCED

ALMOST PERIODIC FUNCTIONS, A. S. Besicovitch. This unique and important summary by a well-known mathematician covers in detail the two stages of development in Bohr's theory of almost periodic functions: (1) as a generalization of pure periodicity, with results and proofs; (2) the work done by Stepanoff, Wiener, Weyl, and Bohr in generalizing the theory. Bibliography. xi + 180pp. 5⅜ x 8. **S17 Clothbound $3.50**
S18 Paperbound $1.75

LECTURES ON THE ICOSAHEDRON AND THE SOLUTION OF EQUATIONS OF THE FIFTH DEGREE, Felix Klein. The solution of quintics in terms of rotations of a regular icosahedron around its axes of symmetry. A classic & indispensable source for those interested in higher algebra, geometry, crystallography. Considerable explanatory material included. 230 footnotes, mostly bibliographic. 2nd edition, xvi + 289pp. 5⅜ x 8. **S314 Paperbound $1.85**

LINEAR INTEGRAL EQUATIONS, W. V. Lovitt. Systematic survey of general theory, with some application to differential equations, calculus of variations problems of math, physics. Partial contents: integral equations of 2nd kind by successive substitutions; Fredholm's equation as ratio of 2 integral series in lambda, applications of the Fredholm theory, Hilbert-Schmidt theory of symmetric integral kernels, application, etc. Neumann, Dirichlet, vibratory problems. Index. ix + 253pp. 5⅜ x 8. **S175 Clothbound $3.50**
S176 Paperbound $1.60

MATHEMATICAL FOUNDATIONS OF STATISTICAL MECHANICS, A. I. Khinchin. Offering a precise and rigorous formulation of problems, this book supplies a thorough and up-to-date exposition. It provides analytical tools needed to replace cumbersome concepts, and furnishes for the first time a logical step-by-step introduction to the subject. Partial contents: geometry & kinematics of the phase space, ergodic problem, reduction to theory of probability, application of central limit problem, ideal monatomic gas, foundation of thermodynamics, dispersion and distributions of sum functions. Key to notations. Index. xiii + 179pp. 5⅜ x 8. **S146 Clothbound $2.95**
S147 Paperbound $1.35

ORDINARY DIFFERENTIAL EQUATIONS, E. L. Ince. A most compendious analysis in real and complex domains. Existence and nature of solutions, continuous transformation groups, solutions in an infinite form, definite integrals, algebraic theory, Sturmian theory, boundary problems, existence theorems, 1st order, higher order, etc. "Deserves the highest praise, a notable addition to mathematical literature," BULLETIN, AM. MATH. SOC. Historical appendix. Bibliography. 18 figures. viii + 558pp. 5⅜ x 8. **S349 Paperbound $2.55**

TRIGONOMETRICAL SERIES, Antoni Zygmund. Unique in any language on modern advanced level. Contains carefully organized analyses of trigonometric, orthogonal, Fourier systems of functions, with clear adequate descriptions of summability of Fourier series, proximation theory, conjugate series, convergence, divergence of Fourier series. Especially valuable for Russian, Eastern European coverage. Bibliography. 329pp. 5⅜ x 8. **S290 Paperbound $1.50**

FOUNDATIONS OF POTENTIAL THEORY, O. D. Kellogg. Based on courses given at Harvard this is suitable for both advanced and beginning mathematicians. Proofs are rigorous, and much material not generally available elsewhere is included. Partial contents: forces of gravity, fields of force, divergence theorem, properties of Newtonian potentials at points of free space, potentials as solutions of Laplace's equations, harmonic functions, electrostatics, electric images, logarithmic potential, etc. ix + 384pp. 5⅜ x 8. **S144 Paperbound $1.98**

LECTURES ON CAUCHY'S PROBLEMS, J. Hadamard. Based on lectures given at Columbia and Rome, this discusses work of Riemann, Kirchhoff, Volterra, and the author's own research on the hyperbolic case in linear partial differential equations. It extends spherical and cylindrical waves to apply to all (normal) hyperbolic equations. Partial contents: Cauchy's problem, fundamental formula, equations with odd number, with even number of independent variables; method of descent. 32 figures. Index. iii + 361pp. 5⅜ x 8. **S105 Paperbound $1.75**

MATHEMATICAL PHYSICS, STATISTICS

THE MATHEMATICAL THEORY OF ELASTICITY, A. E. H. Love. A wealth of practical illustration combined with thorough discussion of fundamentals—theory, application, special problems and solutions. Partial contents: Analysis of Strain & Stress, Elasticity of Solid Bodies, Isotropic Elastic Solids, Equilibrium of Aeolotropic Elastic Solids, Elasticity of Crystals, Vibration of Spheres, Cylinders, Propagation of Waves in Elastic Solid Media, Torsion, Theory of Continuous Beams, Plates. Rigorous treatment of Volterra's theory of dislocations, 2-dimensional elastic systems, other topics of modern interest. "For years the standard treatise on elasticity," AMERICAN MATHEMATICAL MONTHLY. 4th revised edition. Index. 76 figures. xviii + 643pp. 6⅛ x 9¼. **S174 Paperbound $2.95**

TABLES OF FUNCTIONS WITH FORMULAE AND CURVES, E. Jahnke & F. Emde. The world's most comprehensive 1-volume English-text collection of tables, formulae, curves of transcendent functions. 4th corrected edition, new 76-page section giving tables, formulae for elementary functions—not in other English editions. Partial contents: sine, cosine, logarithmic integral; factorial function; error integral; theta functions; elliptic integrals, functions; Legendre, Bessel, Riemann, Mathieu, hypergeometric functions, etc. Supplementary books. Bibliography. Indexed. "Out of the way functions for which we know no other source," SCIENTIFIC COMPUTING SERVICE, Ltd. 212 figures. 400pp. 5⅜ x 8. **S133 Paperbound $2.00**

PRACTICAL ANALYSIS, GRAPHICAL AND NUMERICAL METHODS, F. A. Willers. Translated by R. T. Beyer. Immensely practical handbook for engineers, showing how to interpolate, use various methods of numerical differentiation and integration, determine the roots of a single algebraic equation, system of linear equations, use empirical formulas, integrate differential equations, etc. Hundreds of shortcuts for arriving at numerical solutions. Special section on American calculating machines, by T. W. Simpson. 132 illustrations. 422pp. 5⅜ x 8. S273 Paperbound **$2.00**

DICTIONARY OF CONFORMAL REPRESENTATIONS, H. Kober. Laplace's equation in 2 dimensions solved in this unique book developed by the British Admiralty. Scores of geometrical forms & their transformations for electrical engineers, Joukowski aerofoil for aerodynamists, Schwartz-Christoffel transformations for hydrodynamics, transcendental functions. Contents classified according to analytical functions describing transformation. Twin diagrams show curves of most transformations with corresponding regions. Glossary. Topological index. 447 diagrams. 244pp. 6⅛ x 9¼. S160 Paperbound **$2.00**

FREQUENCY CURVES AND CORRELATION, W. P. Elderton. 4th revised edition of a standard work covering classical statistics. It is practical in approach, and one of the books most frequently referred to for clear presentation of basic material. Partial contents. Frequency distributions. Method of moment. Pearson's frequency curves. Correlation. Theoretical distributions, spurious correlation. Correlation of characters not quantitatively measurable. Standard errors. Test of goodness of fit. The correlation ratio—contingency. Partial correlation. Corrections for moments, beta and gamma functions, etc. Key to terms, symbols. Bibliography. 25 examples in text. 40 useful tables. 16 figures. xi + 272pp. 5½ x 8½. Clothbound **$1.49**

HYDRODYNAMICS, H. Dryden, F. Murnaghan, Harry Bateman. Published by the National Research Council in 1932 this enormous volume offers a complete coverage of classical hydrodynamics. Encyclopedic in quality. Partial contents: physics of fluids, motion, turbulent flow, compressible fluids, motion in 1, 2, 3 dimensions; viscous fluids rotating, laminar motion, resistance of motion through viscous fluid, eddy viscosity, hydraulic flow in channels of various shapes, discharge of gases, flow past obstacles, etc. Bibliography of over 2,900 items. Indexes. 23 figures. 634pp. 5⅜ x 8. S303 Paperbound **$2.75**

HYDRODYNAMICS, A STUDY OF LOGIC, FACT, AND SIMILITUDE, Garrett Birkhoff. A stimulating application of pure mathematics to an applied problem. Emphasis is placed upon correlation of theory and deduction with experiment. It examines carefully recently discovered paradoxes, theory of modelling and dimensional analysis, paradox & error in flows and free boundary theory. The author derives the classical theory of virtual mass from homogeneous spaces, and applies group theory to fluid mechanics. Index. Bibliography. 20 figures, 3 plates. xiii + 186pp. 5⅜ x 8.
S21 Clothbound **$3.50**
S22 Paperbound **$1.85**

HYDRODYNAMICS, Horace Lamb. Internationally famous complete coverage of standard reference work on dynamics of liquids & gases. Fundamental theorems, equations, methods, solutions, background, for classical hydrodynamics. Chapters include Equations of Motion, Integration of Equations in Special Gases, Irrotational Motion, Motion of Liquid in 2 Dimensions, Motion of Solids through Liquid—Dynamical Theory, Vortex Motion, Tidal Waves, Surface Waves, Waves of Expansion, Viscosity, Rotating Masses of Liquids. Excellently planned, arranged; clear, lucid presentation. 6th enlarged, revised edition. Index. Over 900 footnotes, mostly bibliographical. 119 figures. xv + 738pp. 6⅛ x 9¼. S256 Paperbound **$2.95**

INTRODUCTION TO RELAXATION METHODS, F. S. Shaw. Fluid mechanics, design of electrical networks, forces in structural frameworks, stress distribution, buckling, etc. Solve linear simultaneous equations, linear ordinary differential equations, partial differential equations, Eigenvalue problems by relaxation methods. Detailed examples throughout. Special tables for dealing with awkwardly-shaped boundaries. Indexes. 253 diagrams. 72 tables. 400pp. 5⅜ x 8.
S244 Paperbound **$2.45**

PARTIAL DIFFERENTIAL EQUATIONS OF MATHEMATICAL PHYSICS, A. G. Webster. A keystone work in the library of every mature physicist, engineer, researcher. Valuable sections on elasticity, compression theory, potential theory, theory of sound, heat conduction, wave propagation, vibration theory. Contents include: deduction of differential equations, vibrations, normal functions, Fourier's series, Cauchy's method, boundary problems, method of Riemann-Volterra. Spherical, cylindrical, ellipsoidal harmonics, applications, etc. 97 figures. vii + 440pp. 5⅜ x 8.
S263 Paperbound **$1.98**

THE THEORY OF GROUPS AND QUANTUM MECHANICS, H. Weyl. Discussions of Schroedinger's wave equation, de Broglie's waves of a particle, Jordon-Hoelder theorem, Lie's continuous groups of transformations, Pauli exclusion principle, quantization of Maxwell-Dirac field equations, etc. symmetry permutation group, algebra of symmetric transformation, etc. 2nd revised edition. Unitary geometry, quantum theory, groups, application of groups to quantum mechanics, symmetry permutation group, algebra of symmetric transformation, etc. 2nd revised edition. Bibliography. Index. xxii + 422pp. 5⅜ x 8. S268 Clothbound **$4.50**
S269 Paperbound **$1.95**

PARTIAL DIFFERENTIAL EQUATIONS OF MATHEMATICAL PHYSICS, Harry Bateman. Solution of boundary value problems by means of definite analytical expressions, with wide range of representative problems, full reference to contemporary literature, and new material by the author. Partial contents: classical equations, integral theorems of Green, Stokes; 2-dimensional problems; conformal representation; equations in 3 variables; polar coordinates; cylindrical, ellipsoidal, paraboloid, toroidal coordinates; non-linear equations, etc. ''Must be in the hands of everyone interested in boundary value problems,'' BULLETIN, AM. MATH. SOC. Indexes. 450 bibliographic footnotes. 175 examples. 29 illustrations. xxii + 552pp. 6 x 9. S15 Clothbound **$4.95**

NUMERICAL SOLUTIONS OF DIFFERENTIAL EQUATIONS, H. Levy & E. A. Baggott. Comprehensive collection of methods for solving ordinary differential equations of first and higher order. All must pass 2 requirements: easy to grasp and practical, more rapid than school methods. Partial contents: graphical integration of differential equations, graphical methods for detailed solution. Numerical solution. Simultaneous equations and equations of 2nd and higher orders. "Should be in the hands of all in research in applied mathematics, teaching," NATURE. 21 figures. viii + 238pp. 5⅜ x 8.
S168 Paperbound **$1.75**

ASYMPTOTIC EXPANSIONS, A. Erdélyi. The only modern work available in English, this is an unabridged reproduction of a monograph prepared for the Office of Naval Research. It discusses various procedures for asymptotic evaluation of integrals containing a large parameter and solutions of ordinary linear differential equations. Bibliography of 71 items. vi + 108pp. 5⅜ x 8.
S318 Paperbound **$1.35**

THE FOURIER INTEGRAL AND CERTAIN OF ITS APPLICATIONS, Norbert Wiener. The only booklength study of the Fourier integral as link between pure and applied math. An expansion of lectures given at Cambridge. Partial contents: Plancherel's theorem, general Tauberian theorem, special Tauberian theorms, generalized harmonic analysis. Bibliography. viii + 201pp. 5⅜ x 8.
S272 Clothbound **$3.95**

THE THEORY OF SOUND, Lord Rayleigh. Most vibrating systems likely to be encountered in practice can be tackled successfully by the methods set forth by the great Nóble laureate, Lord Rayleigh. Complete coverage of experimental, mathematical aspects of sound theory. Partial contents: Harmonic motions, vibrating systems in general, lateral vibrations of bars, curved plates or shells, applications of Laplace's functions to acoustical problems, fluid friction, plane vortex-sheet, vibrations of solid bodies, etc. This is the first inexpensive edition of this great reference and study work. Bibliography. Historical introduction by R. B. Lindsay. Total of 1040pp. 97 figures. 5⅜ x 8.
S292, S293, Two volume set, paperbound **$4.00**

ANALYSIS & DESIGN OF EXPERIMENTS, H. B. Mann. Offers a method for grasping the analysis of variance and variance design within a short time. Partial contents: Chi-square distribution and analysis of variance distribution, matrices, quadratic forms, likelihood ratio tests and tests of linear hypotheses, power of analysis, Galois fields, non-orthogonal data, interblock estimates, etc. 15pp. of useful tables. x + 195pp. 5 x 7⅜.
S180 Paperbound **$1.45**

MATHEMATICAL ANALYSIS OF ELECTRICAL AND OPTICAL WAVE-MOTION, Harry Bateman. Written by one of this century's most distinguished mathematical physicists, this is a practical introduction to those developments of Maxwell's electromagnetic theory which are directly connected with the solution of the partial differential equation of wave motion. Methods of solving wave-equations, polar-cylindrical coordinates, diffraction, transformation of coordinates, homogeneous solutions, electromagnetic fields with moving singularities, etc. Index. 168pp. 5⅜ x 8.
S14 Paperbound **$1.60**

PHYSICAL PRINCIPLES OF THE QUANTUM THEORY, Werner Heisenberg. A Nobel laureate discusses quantum theory; Heisenberg's own work, Compton, Schroedinger, Wilson, Einstein, many others. Written for physicists, chemists who are not specialists in quantum theory, only elementary formulae are considered in the text; there is a mathematical appendix for specialists. Profound without sacrifice of clarity. Translated by C. Eckart, F. Hoyt. 18 figures. 192pp. 5⅜ x 8.
S113 Paperbound **$1.25**

FOUNDATIONS OF NUCLEAR PHYSICS, edited by R. T. Beyer. 13 of the most important papers on nuclear physics reproduced in facsimile in the original languages of their authors: the papers most often cited in footnotes, bibliographies. Anderson, Curie, Joliot, Chadwick, Fermi, Lawrence, Cockcroft, Hahn, Yukawa. Unparalleled Bibliography: 122 double-columned pages, over 4,000 articles, books, classified. 57 figures. 288pp. 6⅛ x 9¼.
S19 Paperbound **$1.75**

SELECTED PAPERS ON NOISE AND STOCHASTIC PROCESS, edited by Prof. Nelson Wax, U. of Illinois. 6 basic papers for newcomers in the field, for those whose work involves noise characteristics. Chandrasekhar, Uhlenbeck & Ornstein, Uhlenbeck & Ming, Rice, Doob. Included is Kac's Chauvenet-Prize winning Random Walk. Extensive bibliography lists 200 articles; up through 1953. 21 figures. 337pp. 6⅛ x 9¼.
S262 Paperbound **$2.25**

THERMODYNAMICS, Enrico Fermi. Unabridged reproduction of 1937 edition. Elementary in treatment; remarkable for clarity, organization. Requires no knowledge of advanced math beyond calculus, only familiarity with fundamentals of thermometry, calorimetry. Partial Contents: Thermodynamic systems; First & Second laws of thermodynamics; Entropy; Thermodynamic potentials: phase rule, reversible electric cell; Gaseous reactions: Van't Hoff reaction box, principle of LeChatelier; Thermodynamics of dilute solutions:: osmotic & vapor pressure, boiling & freezing points; Entropy constant. Index. 25 problems. 24 illustrations. x + 160pp. 5⅜ x 8.
S361 Paperbound **$1.75**

AN INTRODUCTION TO THE STUDY OF STELLAR STRUCTURE, Subrahmanyan Chandrasekhar. Outstanding treatise on stellar dynamics by one of world's greatest astrophysicists. Uses classical & modern math methods to examine relationship between loss of energy, the mass, and radius of stars in a steady state. Discusses thermodynamic laws from Caratheodory's axiomatic standpoint; adiabatic, polytropic laws; work of Ritter, Emden, Kelvin, others; Stroemgren envelopes as starter for theory of gaseous stars; Gibbs statistical mechanics (quantum); degenerate stellar configurations & theory of white dwarfs, etc. "Highest level of scientific merit," BULLETIN, AMER. MATH. SOC. Bibliography. Appendixes. Index. 33 figures. 509pp. 5⅜ x 8.
S413 Paperbound **$2.75**

APPLIED OPTICS AND OPTICAL DESIGN, A. E. Conrady. Thorough, systematic presentation of physical & mathematical aspects, limited mostly to "real optics." Stresses practical problem of maximum aberration permissible without affecting performance. All ordinary ray tracing methods; complete theory primary aberrations, enough higher aberration to design telescopes, low-powered microscopes, photographic equipment. Covers fundamental equations, extra-axial image points, transverse chromatic aberration, angular magnification, aplanatic optical systems, bending of lenses, oblique pencils, tolerances, secondary spectrum, spherical aberration (angular, longitudinal, transverse, zonal), thin lenses, dozens of similar topics. Index. Tables of functions of N. Over 150 diagrams. x + 518pp. 6⅛ x 9¼.
S366 Paperbound **$2.95**

SPACE-TIME-MATTER, Hermann Weyl. "The standard treatise on the general theory of relativity," (Nature), written by a world-renowned scientists, provides a deep clear discussion of the logical coherence of the general theory, with introduction to all the mathematical tools needed: Maxwell, analytical geometry, non-Euclidean geometry, tensor calculus, etc. Basis is classical space-time, before absorption of relativity. Partial contents: Euclidean space, mathematical form, metrical continuum, relativity of time and space, general theory. 15 diagrams. Bibliography. New preface for this edition. xviii + 330pp. 5⅜ x 8.
S267 Paperbound **$1.75**

RAYLEIGH'S PRINCIPLE AND ITS APPLICATION TO ENGINEERING, G. Temple & W. Bickley. Rayleigh's principle developed to provide upper and lower estimates of true value of fundamental period of a vibrating system, or condition of stability of elastic systems. Illustrative examples; rigorous proofs in special chapters. Partial contents: Energy method of discussing vibrations, stability. Perturbation theory, whirling of uniform shafts. Criteria of elastic stability. Application of energy method. Vibrating system. Proof, accuracy, successive approximations, application of Rayleigh's principle. Synthetic theorems. Numerical, graphical methods. Equilibrium configurations, Ritz's method. Bibliography. Index. 22 figures. ix + 156pp. 5⅜ x8.
S307 Paperbound **$1.50**

PHYSICS, ENGINEERING

THEORY OF VIBRATIONS, N. W. McLachlan. Based on an exceptionally successful graduate course given at Brown University, this discusses linear systems having 1 degree of freedom, forced vibrations of simple linear systems, vibration of flexible strings, transverse vibrations of bars and tubes, transverse vibration of circular plate, sound waves of finite amplitude, etc. Index. 99 diagrams. 160pp. 5⅜ x 8.
S190 Paperbound **$1.35**

WAVE PROPAGATION IN PERIODIC STRUCTURES, L. Brillouin. A general method and application to different problems: pure physics, such as scattering of X-rays of crystals, thermal vibration in crystal lattices, electronic motion in metals; and also problems of electrical engineering. Partial contents: elastic waves in 1-dimensional lattices of point masses. Propagation of waves along 1-dimensional lattices. Energy flow. 2 dimensional, 3 dimensional lattices. Mathieu's equation. Matrices and propagation of waves along an electric line. Continuous electric lines. 131 illustrations. Bibliography. Index. xii + 253pp. 5⅜ x 8.
S34 Paperbound **$1.85**

THE ELECTROMAGNETIC FIELD, Max Mason & Warren Weaver. Used constantly by graduate engineers. Vector methods exclusively: detailed treatment of electrostatics, expansion methods, with tables converting any quantity into absolute electromagnetic, absolute electrostatic, practical units. Discrete charges, ponderable bodies, Maxwell field equations, etc. Introduction. Indexes. 416pp. 5⅜ x 8.
S185 Paperbound **$2.00**

APPLIED HYDRO- AND AEROMECHANICS by L. Prandtl and O. G. Tietjens. Presents, for the most part, methods which will be valuable to engineers. Covers flow in pipes, boundary layers, airfoil theory, entry conditions, turbulent flow in pipes and the boundary layer, determining drag from measurements of pressure and velocity, etc. "Will be welcomed by all students of aerodynamics," NATURE. Unabridged, unaltered. Index. 226 figures. 28 photographic plates illustrating flow patterns. xvi + 311pp. 5⅜ x 8.
S375 Paperbound **$1.85**

FUNDAMENTALS OF HYDRO- AND AEROMECHANICS by L. Prandtl and O. G. Tietjens. The well-known standard work based upon Prandtl's unique insights and including original contributions of Tietjens. Wherever possible, hydrodynamic theory is referred to practical considerations in hydraulics with the view of unifying theory and experience through fundamental laws. Presentation is exceedingly clear and, though primarily physical, proofs are rigorous and use vector analysis to a considerable extent. Translated by L. Rosenhead. 186 figures. Index. xvi + 270pp. 5⅜ x 8.
S374 Paperbound **$1.85**

DYNAMICS OF A SYSTEM OF RIGID BODIES (Advanced Section), E. J. Routh. Revised 6th edition of a classic reference aid. Much of its material remains unique. Partial contents: moving axes, relative motion, oscillations about equilibrium, motion. Motion of a body under no forces, any forces. Nature of motion given by linear equations and conditions of stability. Free, forced vibrations, constants of integration, calculus of finite differences, variations, procession and nutation, motion of the moon, motion of string, chain, membranes. 64 figures. 498pp. 5⅜ x 8.
S229 Paperbound **$2.35**

MECHANICS OF THE GYROSCOPE, THE DYNAMICS OF ROTATION, R. F. Deimel, Professor of Mechanical Engineering at Stevens Institute of Technology. Elementary general treatment of dynamics of rotation, with special application of gyroscopic phenomena. No knowledge of vectors needed. Velocity of a moving curve, acceleration to a point, general equations of motion, gyroscopic horizon, free gyro, motion of discs, the dammed gyro, 103 similar topics. Exercises. 75 figures. 208pp. 5⅜ x 8.
S66 Paperbound **$1.65**

TABLES FOR THE DESIGN OF FACTORIAL EXPERIMENTS, Tosio Kitagawa and Michiwo Mitome. An invaluable aid for all applied mathematicians, physicists, chemists and biologists, this book contains tables for the design of factorial experiments. It covers Latin squares and cubes, factorial design, fractional replication in factorial design, factorial designs with split-plot confounding, factorial designs confounded in quasi-Latin squares, lattice designs, balanced incomplete block designs, and Youden's squares. New revised corrected edition, with explanatory notes. vii + 253pp. 7 1/8 x 10. S437 Clothbound **$8.00**

NUMERICAL INTEGRATION OF DIFFERENTIAL EQUATIONS, Bennett, Milne & Bateman. Unabridged republication of original monograph prepared for National Research Council. New methods of integration of differential equations developed by 3 leading mathematicians: THE INTERPOLATIONAL POLYNOMIAL and SUCCESSIVE APPROXIMATIONS by A. A. Bennett; STEP-BY-STEP METHODS OF INTEGRATION by W. W. Milne; METHODS FOR PARTIAL DIFFERENTIAL EQUATIONS by H. Bateman. Methods for partial differential equations, transition from difference equations to differential equations, solution of differential equations to non-integral values of a parameter will interest mathematicians and physicists. 288 footnotes, mostly bibliographic; 235-item classified bibliography. 108pp. 5 3/8 x 8. S305 Paperbound **$1.35**

DESIGN AND USE OF INSTRUMENTS AND ACCURATE MECHANISM, T. N. Whitehead. For the instrument designer, engineer; how to combine necessary mathematical abstractions with independent observation of actual facts. Partial contents: instruments & their parts, theory of errors, systematic errors, probability, short period errors, erratic errors, design precision, kinematic semi-kinematic design, stiffness, planning of an instrument, human factor, etc. Index. 85 photos, diagrams. xii + 288pp. 5 3/8 x 8. S270 Paperbound **$1.95**

CHEMISTRY AND PHYSICAL CHEMISTRY

KINETIC THEORY OF LIQUIDS, J. Frenkel. Regarding the kinetic theory of liquids as a generalization and extension of the theory of solid bodies, this volume covers all types of arrangements of solids, thermal displacements of atoms, interstitial atoms and ions, orientational and rotational motion of molecules, and transition between states of matter. Mathematical theory is developed close to the physical subject matter. 216 bibliographical footnotes. 55 figures. xi + 485pp. 5 3/8 x 8. S94 Clothbound **$3.95**
S95 Paperbound **$2.45**

THE PHASE RULE AND ITS APPLICATION, Alexander Findlay. Covering chemical phenomena of 1, 2, 3, 4, and multiple component systems, this "standard work on the subject" (NATURE, London), has been completely revised and brought up to date by A. N. Campbell and N. O. Smith. Brand new material has been added on such matters as binary, tertiary liquid equilibria, solid solutions in ternary systems, quinary systems of salts and water. Completely revised to triangular coordinates in ternary systems, clarified graphic representation, solid models, etc. 9th revised edition. Author, subject indexes. 236 figures. 506 footnotes, mostly bibliographic. xii + 494pp. 5 3/8 x 8. S92 Paperbound **$2.45**

DYNAMICAL THEORY OF GASES, James Jeans. Divided into mathematical and physical chapters for the convenience of those not expert in mathematics, this volume discusses the mathematical theory of gas in a steady state, thermodynamics, Boltzmann and Maxwell, kinetic theory, quantum theory, exponentials, etc. 4th enlarged edition, with new material on quantum theory, quantum dynamics, etc. Indexes. 28 figures. 444pp. 6 1/8 x 9 1/4. S136 Paperbound **$2.45**

POLAR MOLECULES, Pieter Debye. This work by Nobel laureate Debye offers a complete guide to fundamental electrostatic field relations, polarizability, molecular structure. Partial contents: electric intensity, displacement and force, polarization by orientation, molar polarization | and molar refraction, halogen-hydrides, polar liquids, ionic saturation, dielectric constant, etc. Special chapter considers quantum theory. Indexed. 172pp. 5 3/8 x 8. S63 Clothbound **$3.50**
S64 Paperbound **$1.50**

TREATISE ON THERMODYNAMICS, Max Planck. Based on Planck's original papers this offers a uniform point of view for the entire field and has been used as an introduction for students who have studied elementary chemistry, physics, and calculus. Rejecting the earlier approaches of Helmholtz and Maxwell, the author makes no assumptions regarding the nature of heat, but begins with a few empirical facts, and from these deduces new physical and chemical laws. 3rd English edition of this standard text by a Nobel laureate. xvi + 297pp. 5 3/8 x 8. S219 Paperbound **$1.75**

ATOMIC SPECTRA AND ATOMIC STRUCTURE, G. Herzberg. Excellent general survey for chemists, physicists specializing in other fields. Partial contents: simplest line spectra and elements of atomic theory, multiple structure of line spectra and electron spin, building-up principle and periodic system of elements, finer details of atomic spectra, hyperfine structure of spectral lines, some experimental results and applications. Bibliography of 159 items. 80 figures. 20 tables. Index. xiii + 257pp. 5 3/8 x 8. S115 Paperbound **$1.95**

EARTH SCIENCES

THE EVOLUTION OF THE IGNEOUS ROCKS, N. L. Bowen. Invaluable serious introduction applies techniques of physics and chemistry to explain igneous rocks diversity in terms of chemical composition and fractional crystallization. Discusses liquid immiscibility in silicate magmas, crystal sorting, liquid lines of descent, fractional resorption of complex minerals, petrogenesis, etc. Of prime importance to geologists & mining engineers, also to physicists, chemists working with high temperatures and pressures. "Most important," TIMES, London. 3 indexes. 263 bibliographic notes. 82 figures. xviii + 334pp. 5 3/8 x 8. S311 Paperbound **$1.85**

GEOGRAPHICAL ESSAYS, William Morris Davis. Modern geography & geomorphology rests on the fundamental work of this scientist. 26 famous essays presenting most important theories, field researches. Partial contents: Geographical Cycle, Plains of Marine and Subaerial Denudation, The Peneplain, Rivers and Valleys of Pennsylvania, Outline of Cape Cod, Sculpture of Mountains by Glaciers, etc. "Long the leader and guide," ECONOMIC GEOGRAPHY. "Part of the very texture of geography . . . models of clear thought," GEOGRAPHIC REVIEW. Index. 130 figures. vi + 777pp. 5⅜ x 8. S383 Paperbound **$2.95**

INTERNAL CONSTITUTION OF THE EARTH, edited by **Beno Gutenberg.** Completely revised, brought up-to-date, reset. Prepared for the National Research Council this is a complete & thorough coverage of such topics as earth origins, continent formation, nature & behavior of the earth's core, petrology of the crust, cooling forces in the core, seismic & earthquake material, gravity, elastic constants, strain characteristics and similar topics. "One is filled with admiration . . . a high standard . . . there is no reader who will not learn something from this book," London, Edinburgh, Dublin, Philosophic Magazine. Largest bibliography in print: 1127 classified items. Indexes. Tables of constants. 43 diagrams. 439pp. 6⅛ x 9¼. S414 Paperbound **$2.45**

THE BIRTH AND DEVELOPMENT OF THE GEOLOGICAL SCIENCES, F. D. Adams. Most thorough history of the earth sciences ever written. Geological thought from earliest times to the end of the 19th century, covering over 300 early thinkers & systems: fossils & their explanation, vulcanists vs. neptunists, figured stones & paleontology, generation of stones, dozens of similar topics. 91 illustrations, including medieval, renaissance woodcuts, etc. Index. 632 footnotes, mostly bibliographical. 511pp. 5⅜ x 8. T5 Paperbound **$2.00**

HYDROLOGY, edited by Oscar E. Meinzer. Prepared for the National Research Council. Detailed complete reference library on precipitation, evaporation, snow, snow surveying, glaciers, lakes, infiltration, soil moisture, ground water, runoff, drought, physical changes produced by water, hydrology of limestone terranes, etc. Practical in application, especially valuable for engineers. 24 experts have created "the most up-to-date, most complete treatment of the subject," AM. ASSOC. OF PETROLEUM GEOLOGISTS. Bibliography. Index. 165 illustrations. xi + 712pp. 6⅛ x 9¼. S191 Paperbound **$2.95**

DE RE METALLICA, Georgius Agricola. 400-year old classic translated, annotated by former President Herbert Hoover. The first scientific study of mineralogy and mining, for over 200 years after its appearance in 1556, it was the standard treatise. 12 books, exhaustively annotated, discuss the history of mining, selection of sites, types of deposits, making pits, shafts, ventilating, pumps, crushing machinery; assaying, smelting, refining metals; also salt, alum, nitre, glass making. Definitive edition, with all 289 16th century woodcuts of the original. Bibliographical, historical introductions, bibliography, survey of ancient authors. Indexes. A fascinating book for anyone interested in art, history of science, geology, etc. DELUXE EDITION. 289 illustrations. 672pp. 6¾ x 10¾. Library cloth. S6 Clothbound **$10.00**

URANIUM PROSPECTING, H. L. Barnes. For immediate practical use, professional geologists considers uranium ores, geological occurrences, field conditions, all aspects of highly profitable occupation. Index. Bibliography. x +117pp. 5⅜ x 8. T309 Paperbound **$1.00**

BIOLOGICAL SCIENCES

THE BIOLOGY OF THE AMPHIBIA, G. K. Noble, Late Curator of Herpetology at the Am. Mus. of Nat. Hist. Probably the most used text on amphibia, unmatched in comprehensiveness, clarity, detail. 19 chapters plus 85-page supplement cover development; heredity; life history; adaptation; sex, integument, respiratory, circulatory, digestive, muscular, nervous systems; instinct, intelligence habits environment economic value, relationships, classification, etc. "Nothing comparable to it," C. H. Pope, Curator of Amphibia, Chicago Mus. of Nat. Hist. 1047 bibliographic references. 174 illustrations. 600pp. 5⅜ x 8. S206 Paperbound **$2.98**

THE BIOLOGY OF THE LABORATORY MOUSE, edited by G. D. Snell. 1st prepared in 1941 by the staff of the Roscoe B. Jackson Memorial laboratory, this is still the standard treatise on the mouse, assembling an enormous amount of material for which otherwise you would spend hours of research. Embryology, reproduction, histology, spontaneous neoplasms, gene & chromosomes mutations, genetics of spontaneous tumor formation, genetics of tumor formation, inbred, hybrid animals, parasites, infectious diseases, care & recording. Classified bibliography of 1122 items. 172 figures, including 128 photos. ix + 497pp. 6⅛ x 9¼. S248 Clothbound **$6.00**

BEHAVIOR AND SOCIAL LIFE OF THE HONEYBEE, Ronald Ribbands. Oustanding scientific study; a compendium of practically everything known about social life of the honeybee. Stresses behavior of individual bees in field, hive. Extends von Frisch's experiments on communication among bees. Covers perception of temperature, gravity, distance, vibration; sound production; glands; structural differences; wax production, temperature regulation; recognition communication; drifting, mating behavior, other highly interesting topics. Bibliography of 690 references. Indexes. 127 diagrams, graphs, sections of bee anatomy, fine photographs. 352pp. S410 Clothbound **$4.50**

ELEMENTS OF MATHEMATICAL BIOLOGY, A. J. Lotka. A pioneer classic, the first major attempt to apply modern mathematical techniques on a large scale to phenomena of biology, biochemistry, psychology, ecology, similar life sciences. Partial Contents: Statistical meaning of irreversibility; Evolution as redistribution; Equations of kinetics of evolving systems; Chemical, interspecies equilibrium; parameters of state; Energy transformers of nature, etc. Can be read with profit even by those having no advanced math; unsurpassed as study-reference. Formerly titled ELEMENTS OF PHYSICAL BIOLOGY. 72 figures. xxx + 460pp. 5⅜ x 8. S346 Paperbound **$2.45**

THE ORIGIN OF LIFE, A. I. Oparin. A classic of biology. This is the first modern statement of the theory of gradual evolution of life from nitrocarbon compounds. A brand-new evaluation of Oparin's theory in light of later research, by Dr. S. Margulis, University of Nebraska. xxv + 270pp. 5⅜ x 8. S213 Paperbound **$1.75**

THE TRAVELS OF WILLIAM BARTRAM, edited by **Mark Van Doren.** This famous source-book of American anthropology, natural history, geography is the record kept by Bartram in the 1770's, on travels through the wilderness of Florida, Georgia, the Carolinas. Containing accurate and beautiful descriptions of Indians, settlers, fauna, flora, it is one of the finest pieces of Americana ever written. Introduction by Mark Van Doren. 13 original illustrations. Index. 448pp. 5⅜ x 8. T13 Paperbound **$2.00**

A SHORT HISTORY OF ANATOMY AND PHYSIOLOGY FROM THE GREEKS TO HARVEY, Charles Singer. Corrected edition of THE EVOLUTION OF ANATOMY, classic work tracing evolution of anatomy and physiology from prescientific times through Greek & Roman periods, Dark Ages, Renaissance, to age of Harvey and beginning of modern concepts. Centered on individuals, movements, periods that definitely advanced anatomical knowledge: Plato, Diocles, Aristotle, Theophrastus, Herophilus, Erasistratus, the Alexandrians, Galen, Mondino, da Vinci, Linacre, Harvey, others. Special section on Vesalius; Vesalian atlas of nudes, skeletons, muscle tabulae. Index of names. 20 plates, 270 extremely interesting illustrations of ancient, medieval, renaissance, oriental origin. xii + 209pp. 5⅜ x 8. T389 Paperbound **$1.75**

NEW BOOKS

LES METHODES NOUVELLES DE LA MÉCANIQUE CÉLESTE by H. Poincaré. Complete text (in French) of one of Poincaré's most important works. Revolutionized celestial mechanics: first use of integral invariants, first major application of linear differential equations, study of periodic orbits, lunar motion and Jupiter's satellites, three body problem, and many other important topics. "Started a new era . . . so extremely modern that even today few have mastered his weapons," E. T. Bell. Three volumes; 1282pp. 6⅛ x 9¼.

Vol. 1. S401 Paperbound **$2.75**
Vol. 2. S402 Paperbound **$2.75**
Vol. 3. S403 Paperbound **$2.75**

APPLICATIONS OF TENSOR ANALYSIS by A. J. McConnell. (Formerly, APPLICATIONS OF THE ABSOLUTE DIFFERENTIAL CALCULUS). An excellent text for understanding the application of tensor methods to familiar subjects such as: dynamics, electricity, elasticity, and hydrodynamics. It explains the fundamental ideas and notation of tensor theory, the geometrical treatment of tensor algebra, the theory of differentiation of tensors, and includes a wealth of practice material. Bibliography. Index. 43 illustrations. 685 problems. xii + 381pp. S373 Paperbound **$1.85**

BRIDGES AND THEIR BUILDERS, David B. Steinman and Sara Ruth Watson. Engineers, historians, and everyone who has ever been fascinated by great spans will find this book an endless source of information and interest. Dr. Steinman, the recent recipient of the Louis Levy Medal, is one of the great bridge architects and engineers of all time, and his analysis of the great bridges of all history is both authoritative and easily followed. Greek and Roman bridges, medieval bridges, oriental bridges, modern works such as the Brooklyn Bridge and the Golden Gate Bridge (and many others) are described in terms of history, constructional principles, artistry, and function. All in all this book is the most comprehensive and accurate semipopular history of bridges in print in English. New greatly revised enlarged edition. 23 photographs, 26 line drawings. Index. xvii + 401pp. 5⅜ x 8. T431 Paperbound **$1.95**

MATHEMATICS IN ACTION, O. G. Sutton. Excellent middle-level exposition of application of advanced mathematics to the study of the universe. The author demonstrates how mathematics is applied in ballistics, theory of computing machines, waves and wavelike phenomena, theory of fluid flow, meterological problems, statistics, flight, and similar phenomena. No knowledge of advanced mathematics is necessary to follow the author's presentation. Differential equations, Fourier series, group concepts, eigen functions, Planck's constant, airfoil theory and similar topics are explained so clearly in everyday language that almost anyone can derive benefit from reading this book. 2nd edition. Index. 88 figures. viii + 236pp. 5⅜ x 8.

T450 Clothbound **$3.50**

MATHEMATICAL FOUNDATIONS OF INFORMATION THEORY by A. I. Khinchin. For the first time, mathematicians, statisticians, physicists, cyberneticists and communications engineers are offered a complete and exact introduction to this relatively young field. Entropy as a measure of a finite "scheme," applications to coding theory, study of sources, channels and codes, detailed proofs of both Shannon theorems for any ergodic source and any stationary channel with finite memory, and much more is covered. Bibliography. vii + 120pp. 5⅜ x 8.

S434 Paperbound **$1.35**

Write for free catalogues!

Indicate your field of interest. Dover publishes books on physics, earth sciences, mathematics, engineering, chemistry, astronomy, anthropology, biology, psychology, philosophy, religion history, literature, mathematical recreations, languages, crafts, gardening, art, graphic arts, etc.

Available at your dealer or write Dover Publications, Inc., 920 Broadway, Department TF1, New York 10, New York.

1174